Please remember that this is a library book,
and that it belongs only temporarily to each
person who uses it. Be considerate. Do
not write in this, or any, library book.

MORPHOLOGY OF PLANTS

MORPHOLOGY

of Plants

BY HAROLD C. BOLD

Professor of Botany, The University of Texas

HARPER & ROW, PUBLISHERS

New York, Evanston, and London

Library of Congress catalog card number: 57–8055

Dedicated to

THE LATE PROFESSORS C. C. CURTIS,

R. A. HARPER, T. E. HAZEN, AND B. F. LUTMAN,

Great Teachers of Plant Science

CONTENTS

vii

PREFACE

TO THE TEACHER

As a result of the widespread practice in our colleges in recent years of revising the curriculum with increasing emphasis on "general education," the full-year course in introductory botany has suffered one of several fates. It is sometimes condensed and incorporated in a year course of so-called general biology, either as a minor unit or in scattered segments, or it occupies a still less prominent part of a "survey course" in the sciences. The most usual result of these arrangements is that students who elect further work in plant science enter it poorly grounded in the fundamental aspects of the science in the field of morphology and in other areas. Thus they find themselves inadequately prepared to read the more advanced text and reference books in the field, and the treatment of groups other than the flowering plants in introductory texts is in most cases rather limited, of necessity. On the other hand, the more advanced treatises deal with only a limited number of plant groups rather than with a complete range of morphological types.

The present text has been prepared as a possible solution to these difficulties. It is designed to present a discussion of the morphology and reproduction of the more important plant types. The "type method" has been employed and the text is designed for a year's course, with parallel, integrated study of the types presented. Wherever feasible, every effort has been made to select types readily available or obtainable in most localities. Information regarding where these materials may be obtained and how they may be maintained is included in the appendix. Appropriate substitutions and amplifications will suggest themselves to the teacher.

The author cannot emphasize sufficiently the indispensability of providing the students with living laboratory materials whenever possible. It is true that the collection and maintenance of such a variety of living plants are taxing and time-consuming, but the reward in student interest will amply repay the teacher's effort in this connection.

One who attempts the task of summarizing the structure and reproduction of representatives of the entire plant kingdom within the covers of a single volume is faced constantly with the problems of scope and degree of coverage. He must satisfy certain minima, but at the same time avoid overwhelming the student with detail. He also is liable to criticism from his colleagues for what may seem to them drastically abbreviated presentations. The phycologist and mycologist, for example, will deplore the omission of certain organisms which they deem important, and the bryologist and phanerogamic botanist will condemn the treatment of the algae and fungi as too exhaustive. The writer can only protest that the present text is designed to serve as an introduction on the basis of which more specialized treatments of the several groups may become more intelligible.

The author has been decidedly polyphyletic in the classification of the representative types at the divisional level. He is convinced that this is a conservative point of view. Should the classification he has suggested not meet with approval, he can only cite the subjective nature of the higher categories and add, in his defense, that he has minimized the formal classification of the representative types in view of our inability to come to final conclusions in this connection.

Discussion Questions are included at the end of each chapter to summarize the important data and to prepare the student for oral and/or written exercises on the subject matter presented. References are listed for those who may wish to explore certain aspects of a subject more intensively.

A high percentage of the illustrations is original and based on living material and fresh preparations. Acknowledgment of the source of figures which are not original is made on pp. xix–xxiii; the author is grateful for permission to use them. He appreciates especially the care and accuracy with which several of the habit drawings have been prepared by his colleague, Professor James J. Friauf.

A number of friends and colleagues have read portions of the manuscript and have made valuable suggestions for its improvement. The author wishes to thank especially Professors E. B. Matzke, Elsie Quarterman, and Richard C. Starr in this connection. He is particularly indebted to Dr. Harold W. Rickett for stimulating discussion and criticism of a number of points. He also wishes to thank Mr. Neal Buffaloe and Mr. Francis R. Trainor for their assistance in reading proof. The author is grateful to his wife, Mary Douthit Bold, for her aid in reading proof and preparing the index. He also acknowledges herewith his indebtedness to the Natural Science Fund of Vanderbilt University for financial aid in preparing the manuscript. The author alone, of course, accepts complete responsibility for the text which follows.

TO THE STUDENT

Many years ago, your author happened to glance at the preface of a textbook of elementary botany which he was studying at the time. He was somewhat mystified and disturbed when he read the following statements there: "The text is designed for the student beginning the subject. We trust that a study of it will bring him to the classroom prepared for a discussion of the topics and *we also trust that this work of preparation will tax him to the full measure of his intellectual capacity.* The author is old fashioned in his ideas of education. *Work that simply entertains or imparts information . . . can be of little permanent value or make for any considerable development.*"[1]

From a cursory perusal of these lines, it might appear that their author was implying in his preface that he had deliberately made his presentation difficult in order to tax the students' ability to interpret his meaning and that he smugly hoped he had succeeded. These lines have recurred frequently to the present writer, and his interpretation of them now is based upon years of experience which have convinced him of their truth. Facts easily memorized or crammed from textbooks, notes, or outlines to meet the immediate threat of an impending examination make little permanent addition to one's fund of knowledge, and they fail to supply material for reflection and to effect real understanding. The latter is achieved only as a result of active effort on the student's part. Superficial knowledge is of little value in the long run. Mediocrity of effort is rewarded only by mediocrity of achievement, and information crammed just before an examination is rarely retained after it is over.

The student should not regard this or any other textbook as a sort of bible in which the sum total of knowledge has been summarized for his convenience. He should consider it rather as a guide to his thinking, reading, and laboratory study of the plants themselves. It should supply many but not all of the facts for classroom discussion under the teacher's leadership. In this connection, the value of careful and critical laboratory study cannot be overemphasized. Many students look upon the laboratory

---

[1] C. C. Curtis. *Nature and Development of Plants;* Henry Holt and Company, Inc., 1918. (Italics added.)

as a penance or a drudgery devised by science instructors for unaccountable reasons. The true purpose of the laboratory is to afford the student an opportunity to obtain real understanding by verifying the knowledge gained from the text and classroom discussions, to add to it, and to explore unknown fields. The student's reading, class discussion, and laboratory work are mutually indispensable. Together they form an integrated whole, and slighting any one of them, by student or instructor, will jeopardize their potential values. As a final suggestion, the writer would enjoin the student to develop, by practice, the habit of applying his knowledge to plants in the field. The principles learned in connection with the type plants studied in classroom and laboratory should enable him to recognize and understand related plants which he sees outdoors.

The Discussion Questions at the conclusion of each chapter are included with the purpose of affording the student a readily available means of testing his retention and understanding of the material studied. They may be used as a basis for interstudent and classroom discussions. Relevant works by other authors are cited at the end of certain chapters for those who wish to read more widely.

HAROLD C. BOLD

June, 1957

ACKNOWLEDGMENTS

Sources of figures used in this book and permission to reproduce them are as follows:

Fig. 4–6: From Gilbert M. Smith, *Marine Algae of the Monterey Peninsula*, p. 465. Reprinted by permission of the publishers, Stanford University Press. Copyright, 1944, by the Board of Trustees of Leland Stanford Junior University.

Fig. 4–9: From T. Kanda, "On the Gametophytes of Some Japanese Species of Laminariales," *Scientific Papers*, Institute Algological Research, Hokkaido Imp. Univ., Vol. 1, No. 2, pp. 221–260.

Fig. 4–15B: From W. Nienburg, "Die Entwicklung der Keimlinge von *Fucus vesiculosus* und ihre Bedeutung für die Phylogenie der Phaeophyceen," *Wiss. Meeresuntersuchungen*, 1931, Vol. 21, p. 51.

Fig. 7–5C: From W. J. Koch, "A Study of the Motile Cells of Vaucheria," *Journal of the Elisha Mitchell Scientific Society*, 1951, Vol. 67, Plate 5, Fig. 18.

Fig. 7–6A: From G. M. Smith, *Cryptogamic Botany*, Vol. I, Fig. 61B. Copyright, 1955, McGraw-Hill Book Company, Inc. Reprinted by permission of the publishers.

Fig. 7–6B: From G. M. Smith, *Freshwater Algae of the United States*, Fig. 314. Copyright, 1950, McGraw-Hill Book Company, Inc. Reprinted by permission of the publishers.

Fig. 7–9A: From G. M. Smith, *Freshwater Algae of the United States*, Fig. 336B. Copyright, 1950, McGraw-Hill Book Company, Inc. Reprinted by permission of the publishers.

Fig. 7–12: From R. Subrahmanyan, "On Somatic Division, Reduction Division, Auxospore Formation and Sex Differentiation in *Navicula halophila* (Grunow) Cleve," *Journal of the Indian Botanical Society*, The M.O.P. Iyengar Commemoration Volume, 1946, pp. 239–266.

Fig. 9–4: From C. E. Clifton, *Introduction to the Bacteria*, Fig. 3–1. Copyright, 1950, McGraw-Hill Book Company, Inc. Reprinted by permission of the publishers.

Fig. 9–5: From W. B. Sarles, W. C. Frazier, J. B. Wilson, and S. G. Knight, *Microbiology: General and Applied*, 2nd ed., Harper & Brothers, 1956, p. 13. Reprinted by permission of W. D. Frost.

Fig. 9–7: From W. B. Sarles, W. C. Frazier, J. B. Wilson, and S. G. Knight,

Microbiology: General and Applied, 2nd ed., Harper & Brothers, 1956, p. 59. Reprinted by permission of S. A. Waksman.

Fig. 10–7: From R. A. Harper, "Morphogenesis in *Dictyostelium," Bulletin of the Torrey Botanical Club,* 1926, Vol. 53, Plate 7, Fig. 1.

Fig. 11–12A: From D. B. Swingle, "Formation of Spores in the Sporangia of *Rhizopus nigricans* and of *Phycomyces nitens," Bureau of Plant Industry Bulletin 37,* U.S. Department of Agriculture, 1903.

Fig. 12–13: From H. C. I. Gwynne-Vaughn and H. S. Williamson, "Contributions to the Study of *Pyronema confluens," Annals of Botany,* 1931, Vol. 45, Fig. 22.

Fig. 13–13: From C. J. Alexopoulos, *Introductory Mycology,* p. 314. Copyright, 1952, John Wiley & Sons, Inc. Reprinted by permission of the publishers.

Fig. 16–24: From D. H. Campbell, *Mosses and Ferns,* The Macmillan Company, 1928, Fig. 106A.

Fig. 17–7: From D. W. Bierhorst, "Structure and Development of the Gametophyte of *Psilotum nudum, American Journal of Botany,* 1953, Vol. 40, Figs. 5, 6, 7.

Figs. 18–10A, 18–13, 18–14: From H. Bruchmann, "Die Keimung der Sporen und die Entwicklung der Prothallien von *Lycopodium clavatum, L. annotinum* und *L. Selago," Flora,* 1910, Vol. 101, pp. 262, 263.

Fig. 18–32: From H. Bruchmann, "Vom Prothallien des grossen Sporen und von der Keimesentwicklung einiger *Selaginella*-Arten," *Flora,* 1909, Vol. 99, p. 15.

Fig. 18–39A: From J. Liebig, "Ergänzungen zur Entwicklungsgeschichte von *Isoetes lacustris* L.," *Flora,* 1931, Vol. 125, p. 343.

Fig. 18–39B, C: From C. LaMotte, "Morphology of the Megagametophyte and the Embryo Sporophyte of *Isoetes lithophila," American Journal of Botany,* 1933, Vol. 20, Figs. 3, 10.

Fig. 20–8: From H. Bruchmann, "Ueber das Prothallium und die Keimpflanze von *Ophioglossum vulgatum* L.," *Botanisches Zeitung,* 1904, Vol. 62, Figs. 35, 36.

Fig. 20–9: From R. von Wettstein, *Handbuch der Systematischen Botanik,* Franz Deuticke Co., 1933–1935, Abb. 266/1.

Fig. 20–11: From A. G. Stokey, "Gametophytes of *Marattia sambucina* and *Macroglossum Smithii," Botanical Gazette,* 1942, Vol. 103, University of Chicago Press, Fig. 3.

Fig. 21–2A, B: From C. E. Waters, *Ferns,* Henry Holt and Company, 1908, pp. 304, 308.

Fig. 21–11: From D. H. Campbell, "On the Prothallium and Embryo of *Osmunda claytoniana* L., and *O. cinnamomea* L.," *Annals of Botany,* 1892, Vol. 6, Figs. 81, 98.

Fig. 21–30: From A. Haupt, *Plant Morphology,* Fig. 247D. Copyright, 1953, McGraw-Hill Book Company, Inc. Reprinted by permission of the publishers.

Fig. 22–6: From A. Eames, *Morphology of Vascular Plants,* Fig. 133B. Copyright, 1936, McGraw-Hill Book Company, Inc. Reprinted by permission of the publishers.

Fig. 22–9A: From L. W. Sharp, "Spermatogenesis in *Marsilia,*" *Botanical Gazette,* 1914, Vol. 58, University of Chicago Press, Plate 33, Figs. 7, 8.

Fig. 22–12A: From D. H. Campbell, *Mosses and Ferns,* The Macmillan Company, 1928, Fig. 250A.

Fig. 22–18: Courtesy of Chicago Natural History Museum.

Fig. 24–11: From F. Grace Smith, "Development of the ovulate strobilus and young ovule of *Zamia floridana,*" *Botanical Gazette,* 1910, Vol. 50, University of Chicago Press, Figs. 9, 105.

Figs. 24–12, 24–14: From H. J. Webber, "Spermatogenesis and Fecundation of *Zamia,*" *Bureau of Plant Industry Bulletin 2,* U.S. Department of Agriculture, 1901.

Fig. 24–19: From G. S. Bryan, "The Cellular Proembryo of *Zamia* and Its Cap Cells," *American Journal of Botany,* 1952, Vol. 39, Fig. 5.

Fig. 25–12: From C. J. Chamberlain, *Gymnosperms,* University of Chicago Press, Fig. 223G. Copyright, 1935, by the University of Chicago.

Fig. 26–23: From J. T. Buchholz, "Suspensor and Early Embryo of *Pinus,*" *Botanical Gazette,* 1918, Vol. 66, University of Chicago Press, Plate VIII, Fig. 40.

Fig. 27–12: From W. J. G. Land, "Fertilization and Embryogeny in *Ephedra trifurca,*" *Botanical Gazette,* 1907, Vol. 44, University of Chicago Press, Figs. 17, 21.

Fig. 30–1: From C. R. Longwell and R. F. Flint, *Introduction to Physical Geology,* p. 55. Copyright, 1955, John Wiley & Sons, Inc. Reprinted by permission of the publishers.

Fig. 30–2: From S. A. Tyler and E. S. Barghoorn, "Occurrence of Structurally Preserved Plants in Pre-Cambrian Rocks of the Canadian Shield," *Science,* Vol. 119, Fig. 1.

Fig. 30–3: From R. E. Peck, "The North American Trocholiscids, Paleozoic Charophyta," *Journal of Paleontology,* 1934, Vol. 8, Plate 10, Figs. 16–18.

Fig. 30–4: From A. Mann, "The Economic Importance of the Diatoms," *Smithsonian Report for 1916,* Smithsonian Institution Pub. 2965, Plate 1.

Fig. 30–5: From J. W. Gruner, "The Origin of Sedimentary Iron Formations: The Biwabik Formation of the Mesabi Range," *Economic Geology,* 1922, Vol. 17, Plate VII, Fig. D.

Fig. 30–6: From R. Kidston and W. H. Lang, "On Old Red Sandstone Plants Showing Structure from the Rhynie Chert Bed, Aberdeenshire," *Transactions of the Royal Society of Edinburgh,* 1917–1921, Vols. 51, 52, Plate I, Fig. 4; Plate III, Fig. 34.

Fig. 30–7: From T. G. B. Osborn, "The Lateral Roots of *Amyelon radicans,* Will., and Their Mycorhiza," *Annals of Botany,* 1909, Vol. 23, Plate 47, Fig. 5.

Fig. 30–8: From J. Walton, "Carboniferous Bryophyta; I. Hepaticae," *Annals of Botany,* 1925, Vol. 39, Plate 13, Fig. 1.

Fig. 30–9: From W. C. Steere, "Cenozoic and Mesozoic Bryophytes," *The American Midland Naturalist,* 1946, Vol. 36, Plate 2.

Fig. 30–12: Courtesy of Chicago Natural History Museum.

Fig. 30–15: From R. Kidston and W. H. Lang, "On Old Red Sandstone Plants Showing Structure from the Rhynie Chert Bed, Aberdeenshire," *Transactions of the Royal Society of Edinburgh,* 1917–1921, Plate I, Fig. 4; Plate III, Fig. 34.

Figs. 30–16, 30–18: From R. Krausel and H. Weyland, "Pflanzenreste aus den Devon," *Senckenbergiana,* 1932, Vol. 14, Figs. 11, 14.

Fig. 30–19: Courtesy of Chicago Natural History Museum.

Fig. 30–22: Crown copyright reserved. Geological Survey Photograph, reprinted by permission of the Controller H.M. Stationery Office.

Fig. 30–23: From M. Hirmer "Paläophytologische Notizen: I. Rekonstruction von *Pleuromeia sternbergi* Corda, nebst. Bemerkungen zur Morphologie der Lycopodiales," *Palaeontographica,* 1933, Vol. 78, p. 48.

Fig. 30–24: From R. Krausel and H. Weyland, "Beiträge zur Kenntnis der Devon-flora II," *Abh. Senckenbergische Naturforsch. Gesellschaft,* 1926, Vol. 40, Fig. 24.

Figs. 30–25, 30–27: From M. Hirmer, *Handbuch der Paläobotanik,* R. Oldenbourg, 1927, Figs. 442, 418.

Fig. 30–28: Courtesy of Chicago Natural History Museum.

Fig. 30–29: From M. Hirmer, *Handbuch der Paläobotanik,* R. Oldenbourg, 1927, Fig. 483.

Fig. 30–31: From R. Krausel and H. Weyland, "Beiträge zur Kenntnis der Devon-flora II," *Abh. Senckenbergische Naturforsch. Gesellschaft,* 1926, Vol. 40, Fig. 27.

Fig. 30–33: Courtesy of Chicago Natural History Museum.

Fig. 30–35: From C. A. Arnold, *An Introduction to Paleobotany,* Fig. 102. Copyright, 1947, McGraw-Hill Book Company, Inc. Reprinted by permission of the publishers.

Fig. 30–38: From G. R. Wieland, *American Fossil Cycads,* Carnegie Institution of Washington Publication No. 34, Vol. I: Structure, 1906, Fig. 1.

Fig. 30–39A, B: From G. R. Wieland, *American Fossil Cycads,* Carnegie Institution of Washington Publication No. 34, Vol. II: Taxonomy, 1916, Figs. 87, 88.

Fig. 30–39C: Courtesy of Chicago Natural History Museum.

Fig. 30–44A, B, C, D: From E. W. Berry, "Professional Paper 91," *U.S. Geological Survey*, 1916, Plate LI, Figs. 9–11; Plate CI, Fig. 2; Plate CVI, Fig. 4.

Fig. 30–45: From I. W. Bailey and B. G. L. Swamy, "The Conduplicate Carpel of Dicotyledons and Its Initial Trends of Specialization," *American Journal of Botany*, Vol. 38, Figs. 2, 3.

MORPHOLOGY OF PLANTS

CHAPTER 1

Introduction

CLASSIFICATION OF PLANT SCIENCES

If each of us were to attempt to summarize the content of the course in introductory botany he took, we would agree probably that we devoted the greater part of it to studying the structure and functions of what is often spoken of as the "higher plant" or "flowering plant." In some cases, this may have been supplemented by a brief and rapid survey of other representatives of the plant kingdom from among the "lower plants," and possibly, in addition, by consideration of such important topics as organic evolution and inheritance. In such a course, in other words, consciously or in more or less complete oblivion, we would have made brief excursions into several fields of plant science, namely, morphology, ecology, genetics, and others.

These brief excursions, perhaps, have given us some insight into the nature and significance of these disciplines, but further discussion may afford us perspective as we begin a somewhat more intensive study of one of them, morphology. At the outset we must realize that these various divisions of plant science are not separate or mutually exclusive, but that most of the fundamental advances in our knowledge have been attained by correlation and synthesis of the contributions of the several fields. Furthermore, no one of them is intelligible without reference to the others. The physiologist, for example, would be hard-pressed to achieve real understanding of transpiration if he did not understand the structure of the leaf. Conversely, the leaf structure described by the morphologist lacks significance until one considers the functions of that organ, the genetic factors involved in its differentiation, and the variations a leaf may undergo under different environmental conditions.

1

The classification of plant science into major and minor subdivisions depends in some measure on the vocation and botanical interests of the classifier. Probably no one classification could be devised which would be acceptable to all botanists. However, it is possible to distinguish between the various fields of technological, economic, or applied botany, on the one hand, and those of pure botany, the basic science. Among the former may be listed such major divisions as **agriculture, horticulture, floriculture, plant breeding, forestry,** and **plant pathology.** The scope of each of these is well known or may be ascertained from the dictionary, encyclopedia, and other sources. In a sense these comprise the anthropocentric aspects of plant science—plants in their relation to man. Pure or basic botany is the study of plant life without exclusive interest in and reference to its relations to man. It includes such major divisions as **taxonomy, morphology, physiology, ecology, phytogeography,** and **genetics,** among others. In reality, it is often impossible to distinguish absolutely between pure and applied botany. The results of the researches in pure science achieved today often become the basis of applied science tomorrow. The field of antibiotics, for example, well illustrates this statement.

Taxonomy is probably the oldest division of plant science, inasmuch as primitive man, in order to survive, learned early to distinguish between edible or other useful plants and poisonous or otherwise noxious species. Taxonomy or systematic botany, as it is often called, deals with the identification, naming, and classification of the diverse types of plants which populate the earth. Its goal, in the eyes of most modern taxonomists, is the achievement of a "natural classification," which implies that the groupings indicate actual relationship by descent, based on the concept of organic evolution. **Physiology** is concerned with the fundamental nature of life itself, with vital activities and the mechanisms by which the living plant maintains itself. **Ecology** deals with the interrelation of the plant and its environment and with the mutual effects involved. **Phytogeography** is the study of the distribution of plants on the earth. The mechanisms and laws governing the transmission of structural and functional attributes of individual plants to their offspring form the subject matter of **genetics.**

It is relatively easy for a morphologist to summarize or define the scope of the other divisions of plant science, but more difficult for him to describe the nature of **plant morphology.** As understood by many botanists, modern morphology represents a study of the form and structure of plants, and, by implication, an attempt to interpret these on the basis of similarity of plan and/or origin. The minute structural details of the individual cell constitute the subject matter of **cytology**, and the study of aggregations of cells in groups or tissues and in organs comprises the fields of **histology** and **plant anatomy**. These categories represent subdivisions of morphology. All of them have contributed to our knowledge of the structure of plants. The morphologist also is preoccupied with a study of the life cycle and reproduction in plants, as these afford clues to understanding origin, development, and possible relationship. Furthermore, he has come to realize that the real significance of plants of the present must be sought, in part, in plants of the past which have been preserved as fossils. **Paleobotany**, therefore, is an important adjunct to plant morphology. In addition to the areas just cited as comprising plant morphology, a somewhat different concept of its scope has been developed by certain botanists. To them, morphology is more dynamic and experimental and they emphasize the development of the organism and the interplay of factors involved in its morphogenesis. In this area, especially, the morphologist has begun to use the methods of the biophysicist and biochemist.

On the basis of the facts derived from these several component disciplines, the morphologist often augments the methods of direct observation and perception and becomes a philosopher. At this stage he speculates and constructs hypotheses regarding the pattern of relationships among plants and their component structures and attempts to construct a **phylogeny** or history of extant plants in the light of the past. The student must be certain to distinguish such hypotheses from conclusions based on perceptual methods. Both, of course, are important in the progress of the science.

The various divisions of plant science described above are based on the several aspects of plant life which comprise the subject matter of each. There have developed also a number of other fields, each of which applies the methods already noted to a particular group of plants. This practice has given rise to such divisions as **bacteriology, phycology, mycology,** and **bryology,** among others, and to such vocations as bacteriologist, phycologist, mycologist, bryologist, and others.

One should not conclude from the foregoing discussion that modern botany is composed of categories or subdivisions which are sharply delimited and segregated like the cubicles in a warehouse. The cooperative investigations and methods of various specialists in plant science, together with those from other natural sciences, have resulted in the great advances of our knowledge of plant life. The student of plant science, no matter of what phase, is (or should be) first of all a botanist; secondarily he may become a specialist in one or more of the several subdivisions of the science.

THE ORIGIN AND DEVELOPMENT OF LIVING THINGS

Man always has been interested in the question of the origin of living things, although historically, and for obvious reasons, he has been most interested in the origin of the human species. Inasmuch as the method of origin of the *first* living things on this earth no longer is subject to experimental verification, no solution based exclusively on observation is possible. As a result, there have emerged a number of hypotheses and speculations regarding both the origin and the course of development of life upon the earth. However, recent experiments in the production of amino acids in inorganic systems indicate that experimentation has an important role in the problem of the origin of life.

Hypotheses which have been offered in solution to these questions may be grouped into two categories, namely, **creationism** and **evolution.** To many these categories seem to be in violent contradiction, whereas others do not find them mutually exclusive. Most creationist hypotheses postulate that living organisms arose first by an act of intervention on the part of a force extraneous to the earth itself and therefore supernatural. Some of them imply, furthermore, that the present species of animals and plants in all their diversity were called into existence in their present form at approximately the same time and that they have persisted in essentially that form until the present. By further implication it would seem that the possibility is entirely excluded that new types of living things are appearing now or that they may appear in the future. These last points of view, perhaps, represent extremes in creationist theories.

Evolutionist theories, on the contrary, emphasize the changes which seem to have modified species of living organisms over long periods of time. According to them, the population of living things on the earth at a given instant represents the more or less modified descendants of organisms which existed earlier. These processes of change and modification of extant species are continuing in the world today, according to evolutionists. Species are not fixed and immutable but are plastic and changing.

Space does not permit an extensive treatment of the evidence on which these theories are founded, and students beginning their study of this book will probably already have achieved some familiarity with the data. While there no longer can be doubt that living species are changing constantly, as evidenced by the recorded spontaneous and induced appearance of perceptible morphological and physiological mutations, the observation of such changes does not invalidate creationism with respect to ultimate origin.

The fundamental difficulty experienced by many students in considering evolutionist theories is occasioned by the stated or implied mechanistic philosophy of most of them. Mechanistic evolutionists state or imply that the changing manifestations of life have occurred by chance, or at least without supernatural intervention. They hold a similar view of the origin of life. To them, all life and living things do not differ fundamentally from inorganic phenomena except in details of physical and chemical structure and reactions. These physical and chemical attributes, they believe, ultimately will be completely understood as science progresses. Physical and chemical phenomena alone explain life sufficiently. Mechanistic biologists neither require nor postulate final or supernatural causes. The immediate has become final for them. It is quite possible, and not unreasonable, however, to subscribe to the theory that the organic does not differ from the inorganic in chemical and physical attributes, and at the same time to deviate from mechanism to the extent of postulating the existence of causes other than physical and chemical which affect living things. This is the viewpoint of modern vitalism.

In any event, we are confronted with a great diversity of living organisms which populate the earth, notwithstanding our speculations regarding their origin and history. It is the purpose of the present volume to survey this diversity and to attempt to reduce the *apparent* chaos to some semblance of order.

THE CLASSIFICATION OF PLANTS

When one considers that more than 350,000 species of plants have been described, it is manifestly impossible for a single individual to familiarize himself with all of them. As a beginning, therefore, one is driven to the expedient of selecting representatives or types which illustrate fundamental attributes of larger groups of organisms. The more diversified the group of plants under consideration, the more representatives will it be necessary to study. However, in attempting to include a survey of the morphology of representatives from the entire plant kingdom in one volume, it is obvious that rigorous selection of some types and exclusion of others are necessary. It is hoped that familiarity with the chosen representatives of the diverse plant groups will form a sound foundation and perhaps kindle the student's interest in a more extensive study of one or several of them. The vineyard is large and the laborers few!

Classification of plants is subjective in large measure. It is small wonder, therefore, that few students of plant science have reached unified conclusions regarding the proper classification of members of the plant kingdom. Furthermore, classifications are constantly altered by the discovery of new facts; they are fluid and dynamic, not static.

In spite of the subjective nature of classification, anarchy is no more desirable in the grouping of plants than it is elsewhere. If his efforts are to be recognized, the classifier is bound to make his taxonomic categories, called taxa, conform to the legislation of the International Botanical Congress,[1] which has stated that "every individual plant belongs to a species, every species to a genus, every genus to a family, every family to an order, every order to a class and every class to a division." In addition to this *prescription* regarding the hierarchy of taxonomic categories which is binding, there are *recommendations* regarding the endings of the names of the higher taxa (divisions and classes, among others) which have been followed in the present volume. The classification and arrangement of the plant types to be described here deviate to some degree from those in many other current texts. Table 1 in Chapter 31 summarizes the present and other systems of classification in comparative fashion.

While the relative merits of various systems of classification might be discussed at this point, profitable consideration of this subject presupposes considerable knowledge of the plants to be classified, knowledge which becomes available only after study of the plants themselves. For this reason a system of classification is introduced at this point with minimum comment, and extended discussion is deferred to the final chapter.

In classifying plants and animals, it is possible to set up the categories in several different ways, depending on the purpose of the classifier. In the first place, artificial systems can be devised, the primary purpose of which is ease and convenience of grouping and segregation, other considerations being minor. The classification of vascular plants into trees,

---

[1] International Code of Botanical Nomenclature; adopted by the Seventh International Botanical Congress, Stockholm, 1950. *Regnum Vegetabile 3*, Chronica Botanica Co.

shrubs, and herbs, and into annuals, biennials, and perennials exemplifies artificial systems. Phylogenetic systems of classification, on the other hand, endeavor to arrange plants in a fashion which indicates real relationship based upon evolutionary development. The closeness of the supposed relationships is implied by the proximity of the taxa to each other in the system. The system itself, of course, is (or should be) based on data available from paleobotany, comparative morphology, genetics, and other lines of evidence.

The system of classification[2] here presented will serve also as a sort of table of contents, for the illustrative genera will be discussed approximately in the order in which the higher categories to which they belong are arranged in the following summary.

PLANT KINGDOM

Division 1. Cyanophyta
   Class 1. Myxophyceae (Blue-green algae)
Division 2. Chlorophyta
   Class 1. Chlorophyceae (Green algae)
Division 3. Charophyta
   Class 1. Charophyceae (Stoneworts)
Division 4. Euglenophyta
   Class 1. Euglenophyceae (Euglenoids)
Division 5. Pyrrophyta
   Class 1. Cryptophyceae (Cryptomonads)
   Class 2. Dinophyceae (Dinoflagellates)
Division 6. Chrysophyta
   Class 1. Xanthophyceae (Yellow-green algae)
   Class 2. Chrysophyceae (Golden-brown algae)
   Class 3. Bacillariophyceae (Diatoms)
Division 7. Phaeophyta
   Class 1. Phaeophyceae (Brown algae)
Division 8. Rhodophyta
   Class 1. Rhodophyceae (Red algae)
Division 9. Schizomycota
   Class 1. Schizomycetes (Bacteria)
Division 10. Myxomycota
   Class 1. Myxomycetes (Slime molds)
Division 11. Phycomycota
   Class 1. Phycomycetes (Alga-like fungi)
Division 12. Ascomycota
   Class 1. Ascomycetes (Sac fungi)

[2] Only taxa with extant members are listed at this point.

Division 13. Basidiomycota
  Class 1. Basidiomycetes (Club fungi)
Division 14. Hepatophyta
  Class 1. Hepatopsida (Liverworts)
  Class 2. Anthoceropsida (Horned liverworts)
Division 15. Bryophyta
  Class 1. Sphagnopsida (Peat mosses)
  Class 2. Andreaeopsida (Rock mosses)
  Class 3. Mnionopsida (True or common mosses)
Division 16. Psilophyta
  Class 1. Psilopsida (Whisk ferns)
Division 17. Microphyllophyta
  Class 1. Aglossopsida (Eligulate lycopods)
  Class 2. Glossopsida (Ligulate lycopods)
Division 18. Arthrophyta
  Class 1. Arthropsida (Horsetails)
Division 19. Pterophyta
  Class 1. Eusporangiopsida (Eusporangiate ferns)
  Class 2. Leptosporangiopsida (Leptosporangiate ferns)
Division 20. Cycadophyta
  Class 1. Cycadopsida (Cycads)
Division 21. Ginkgophyta
  Class 1. Ginkgopsida (*Ginkgo*)
Division 22. Coniferophyta
  Class 1. Coniferopsida (Conifers)
Division 23. Gnetophyta
  Class 1. Gnetopsida (*Ephedra*)
Division 24. Anthophyta (Flowering plants)

To those familiar with older systems of classification (Table 1, Chapter 31) in which the plant kingdom was divided into four divisions—Thallophyta (including the algae and fungi), Bryophyta (liverworts and mosses), Pteridophyta (ferns and their "allies"), and Spermatophyta (seed plants)—the classification summarized above will seem longer and more complicated. At first glance there is merit in this complaint, for the four divisions have been replaced by twenty-four.

The student may well wonder on what criteria the divisions of the plant kingdom are defined. To some extent, the criteria vary with the classifier; but, in general, most botanists seem to agree that the division is the largest phylogenetic taxon in which should be grouped organisms which seem to be related because they possess common basic attributes. This definition itself probably will not satisfy all botanists. When one examines the old division Thallophyta in the light of this concept of the division, serious difficulties become apparent. For example, the division Thallophyta, usually defined as a group of organisms lacking stems and leaves, nonetheless included such brown algae as the kelps, in some of which leaf-like, stem-like, and root-like organs are developed. Furthermore, grouping the algae and fungi together in the same division is an indication that they are closely related groups. Modern study of these plants has not provided strong support for this view. In addition, there is good evidence that the several groups of algae, in the past included in a formal category under that name (Algae), are themselves diverse and fundamentally different from each other. Similarly, a great deal of evidence indicates that the vascular plants, those possessing xylem and phloem tissues which function in conduction, are more diverse than is indicated by their separation into only the two divisions Pteridophyta and Spermatophyta.

The division Bryophyta, which in other systems includes both liverworts and mosses, here is conceived in a more restricted sense. For reasons to be discussed in a later chapter, the writer is of the opinion that the liverworts and mosses are not such close "allies" as was implied by earlier views of the scope of the division Bryophyta. Therefore he has segregated the liverworts in the division Hepatophyta and retains the division Bryophyta for the mosses alone.

It will be recalled that the old division Pteridophyta included the ferns and their "allies." That these supposed alliances are as nebulous and untrustworthy as certain political groupings seems clear from a comparison of the morphology of the plants themselves. Divisions 16 through 19 have been proposed, therefore, in place of the old division Pteridophyta.

Probably no two botanists would agree regarding the disposition of the higher taxa of plants which formerly comprised the division Spermatophyta, the seed plants. In many current textbooks they are included in the same division with the ferns. For reasons which can be presented profitably only after the student has become familiar with the groups involved, the present author has divided the old division Spermatophyta into the five divisions listed as 20–24. A more detailed presentation of the evidence on which the present system of classification is based is included in the discussion of the several groups and in the summary chapters throughout the text.

Finally, before leaving the subject of classification for the present, the writer cannot emphasize too strongly the futility of attempting to memorize the system of classification at this point. The several divisions, together with their component classes and illustrative genera, will be learned more readily in connection with the discussion of their morphology.

DISCUSSION QUESTIONS

1. How might one define or explain the term "science"? What aspects of its method distinguish it from that in other fields of knowledge? Are all phenomena subject to analysis by the methods of science?

2. Is a distinction between pure botany and applied botany always possible? Do you have reasons for believing that the study of one is more valuable than the study of the other? Can you cite examples which indicate that researches in pure botany have led directly to important applications?

3. How may one distinguish the several divisions of plant science? Are they mutually exclusive? Explain.

4. What is meant by "Creationism"? "Evolution"? "Mechanism"? "Vitalism"?

5. Do you think that the various taxonomic categories or taxa like species, genus, etc., exist in nature? Explain.

6. What is meant by the "type method" of studying plant morphology? What are its disadvantages?

7. Should generic names and specific names of plants always be capitalized? Explain. Do the names of plants have meaning? Where can one find their meaning?

8. What syllables usually end the name of the plant family? The order? Are these endings subject to change by individual botanists?

9. Where can one find a printed copy of the International Rules of Botanical Nomenclature?

CHAPTER 2

Division Cyanophyta

GENERAL FEATURES

The division **Cyanophyta** (Gr. *kyanos*, blue + Gr. *phyton*, plant) contains only a single class, the **Myxophyceae** (Gr. *myxa*, mucus + Gr. *phykos*, seaweed), commonly known as **blue-green algae.** Some authors prefer the class name Cyanophyceae, whereas others use Schizophyceae (Gr. *schizo*, cleave + Gr. *phykos*).

Myxophyceae are ubiquitous in distribution, occurring in aerial, terrestrial, and aquatic habitats. Approximately 150 genera with 2500 species have been described. Myxophyceae frequently form extensive strata on moist, shaded bare soil and may appear as gelatinous incrustations on moist rocks and plants or inanimate objects. Aquatic species inhabit both salt and fresh water, either attached to submerged objects or free-floating. Blue-green algae often represent an important component of the **plankton** (Gr. *planktos*, wandering), the ecological term for organisms suspended in water. As such, they are important, along with other planktonic algae and minute animals, as the direct or

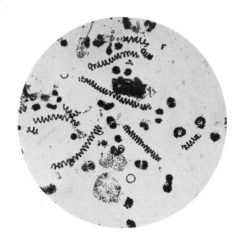

Fig. 2–1. Sample of a water bloom, living condition, as it appears under low magnification; the dominant organism is the spiral *Anabaena flos-aquae* B. and F.; occasional colonies of *Polycystis aeruginosa* Kütz. are present, one of them at the center of the field. X 60.

11

ultimate source of food for more complex aquatic animals. Under certain conditions, components of the plankton may increase tremendously in number to form "water blooms" (Fig. 2–1). A few genera of Myxophyceae are **endophytes** (Gr. *endon*, within + Gr. *phyton*) living within cavities in other plants. Species of *Nostoc*, for example, occur within the plant bodies of such liverworts as *Blasia* and *Anthoceros*, and a species of *Anabaena* grows within the water fern, *Azolla*, and in the roots of cycads. Species of some genera, like *Calothrix* and *Chamaesiphon*, live as **epiphytes** (Gr. *epi*, upon + Gr. *phyton*) on other algae. Members of the Myxophyceae may serve as the algal components of lichens; these are discussed in Chapter 14. A number of blue-green algae grow in waters of hot springs, where they deposit rock-like strata. Some of these are present in water which attains a temperature of 85° C.

Color alone is insufficient to distinguish Myxophyceae from other algae, for their color, especially *en masse*, may be black, dark purple, brown, or even red. This range in color is occasioned by the presence of varying proportions of several pigments. These are chlorophyll *a* and carotenoid pigments, as well as two proteinaceous pigments, **c-phycocyanin** (Gr. *phykos*, seaweed + Gr. *kyanos*, blue) and **c-phycoerythrin** (Gr. *phykos*, + Gr. *erythros*, red).[1] Species of Myxophyceae which are reddish contain a large proportion of phycoerythrin, while dark-colored species contain a preponderance of phycocyanin. Both the phycoerythrin and phycocyanin are water-soluble. They readily diffuse out of plants killed by boiling, leaving the unmasked chlorophyll behind. The relation of this pigment complex to the course of photosynthesis is being investigated currently in Myxophyceae grown in pure culture. These studies have demonstrated that a number of genera of Myxophyceae are autotrophic (Gr. *autos*, self + Gr. *trophe*, food), for they are able to grow and reproduce in culture media containing only inorganic compounds. There is good evidence, educed through the use of isotope techniques, that several species of *Nostoc* and *Calothrix* can grow in the absence of combined nitrogen, provided that atmospheric nitrogen is present. These species, therefore, carry on nitrogen fixation, as do certain bacteria. Unlike all other chlorophyllous plants, the pigments of blue-green algae are not localized in special regions of the cytoplasm, namely, in plastids or chromatophores. Instead, they are diffused throughout the peripheral portions

---

[1] The "c" is used to distinguish these pigments from those with similar names that are isolated from red algae.

of the cytoplasm which are not sharply delimited from the central, color-less region (Fig. 2–2). The excess photosynthate is said to be stored in the form of a glycogen-like substance, sometimes called "cyanophycean starch," the chemistry of which is imperfectly known.

The protoplast of myxophycean cells is surrounded by a delicate wall, probably composed of cellulose, through which it frequently secretes a layer of slimy material of varying thickness and consistency (Figs. 2–2, 2–3). The presence or absence of this sheath may be demonstrated read-ily by immersing the organisms in diluted India ink or by staining them with dilute methylene blue. Masses of blue-green algae often are slimy to the touch because of the copious ensheathing substance, and this char-acteristic has suggested the group name Myxophyceae.

Cytological investigation of the cells of blue-green algae indicates that the nuclear material, frequently called chromatin, is not present in the form in which one encounters it in other algae and in cells of higher plants. It occurs, instead, as granules or rods, or as a reticulum in the central portion of the cells (Figs. 2–10, 2–13B). The division of these bodies apparently differs from the process of mitosis as it occurs in most other organisms. However, application of the Feulgen technique, a test for desoxyribose nucleic acid, reveals that this substance is present in blue-green algal cells as it is in the more highly organized nuclei of other organisms. Finally, unlike most other plant cells, those of Myxophyceae normally lack prominent aqueous vacuoles, so that the cell lumina are filled with dense cytoplasm.

ILLUSTRATIVE TYPES

Three types of plant body structure occur in the Myxophyceae, namely, unicellular, colonial, and filamentous. In unicellular genera the plant is a single cell, either free-living or attached (Figs. 2–2, 2–4, 2–5). As a result of more or less temporary adherence of several generations of recently divided cells, incipient colonial forms may arise. Permanently colonial genera are those in which a number of cells grow together within a common sheath which is augmented by the secretions of the individual cells (Figs. 2–6, 2–8). The cells of filamentous genera are joined in un-branched (Fig. 2–11) or branched (Fig. 2–20) chains. Unbranched fila-ments arise as a result of restriction of cell division to one direction. The unicellular and colonial types usually are considered to be more primitive than the filamentous ones.

Unicellular Genera: *Chroococcus, Gloeocapsa,* and *Chamaesiphon*

Chroococcus (Gr. *chroa,* color + Gr. *kokkos,* berry), *Gloeocapsa* (Gr. *gloia,* glue + L. *capsa,* a box) and *Chamaesiphon* (Gr. *chamai,* on the ground + Gr. *siphon,* a tube) will be described as representatives of the more simple unicellular types. *Chroococcus* (Figs. 2–2, 2–3) fre-

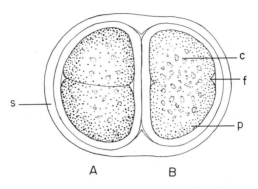

A   B

Fig. 2–2. *Chroococcus turgidus* (Kütz.) Näg. A, Dividing cell, surface view. B, Dividing cell, median optical section: c, colorless central region; f, incipient cleavage furrow; p, pigmented peripheral cytoplasm; s, sheath. X 1700.

quently occurs sparingly intermingled with other algae in the sludge at the bottom of quiet bodies of water; *Gloeocapsa* (Fig. 2–4), along with *Chroococcus,* is frequently encountered on moist rocks or on flower pots in greenhouses. *Chamaesiphon* (Fig. 2–5), on the other hand, is epiphytic on other algae and aquatic flowering plants.

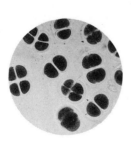

Fig. 2–3. *Chroococcus turgidus* (Kütz.) Näg. Living cells from a culture. X 270.

It is difficult sometimes to find single, isolated cells of *Chroococcus* and *Gloeocapsa* in a particular sample, because of the frequency of cell division and the tendency of the daughter cells to cohere at its conclusion. Cell division in both these genera is accomplished by the centripetal growth of a surface furrow which ultimately divides the cell (Fig. 2–2). New walls are then secreted by the daughter protoplasts within the persistent wall of the mother cell, which becomes distended as the division products increase in size. The nuclear material apparently is passively divided into two equal portions at cytokinesis. Thus, as in most unicellular organisms, cell division effects **reproduction** or multiplication of the individual. Subsequent growth of the division products results in their achieving the size characteristic of the species.

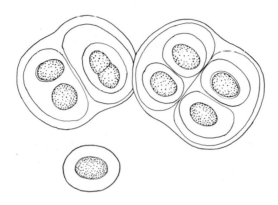

Fig. 2–4. *Gloeocapsa* sp. X 1700.

The sheaths of *Gloeocapsa* are colored in the living cells and usually thicker and more prominent than in *Chroococcus;* the incipient colonies of *Gloeocapsa* generally are composed of more individual cells than in *Chroococcus.* Careful microscopic study of such aggregations of *Gloeocapsa* cells usually reveals that each cell secretes an individual sheath (which may be lamellated) at the conclusion of cell division. The sheaths of the parent cells stretch and persist (Fig. 2–4). That these colonies do not represent multicellular plant bodies is evident from the ease with which they fragment; furthermore, even the unicellular fragments may continue to grow and divide.

The epiphytic cells of *Chamaesiphon* (Fig. 2–5) are attached to their host by somewhat disc-like holdfasts. The cells are enlarged distally from a tapering base. Cell division of one cell into two equal daughter cells does not occur in *Chamaesiphon*. Instead,

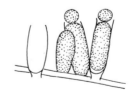

Fig. 2–5. *Chamaesiphon* sp., epiphytic on the green alga *Rhizoclonium,* showing endospore formation. X 1700.

a series of small, walled **spores** is delimited from the distal portion of the individual (Fig. 2–5), and these are gradually discharged through a terminal opening in the cell wall. These small cells are called **endospores** (Gr. *endon,* within + Gr. *spora,* seed or spore) and presumably float to suitable substrata, where they germinate into new individuals.

Colonial Genera: *Polycystis* and *Merismopedia*

Polycystis (Gr. *polys,* many + Gr. *kystis,* bladder, hence cell) and *Merismopedia* (Gr. *merismos,* dividing + Gr. *pedion,* a plain) illustrate the colonial type of plant body among Myxophyceae. In both these genera the cells are surrounded by a common envelope. In *Polycystis* the densely cellular colonies vary in shape from spherical to irregular (Figs.

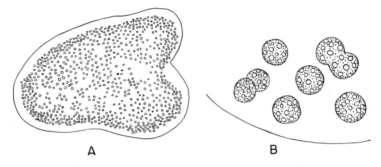

A   B

Fig. 2–6. *Polycystis aeruginosa* Kütz. A, Single colony. X 110. B, Portion of colony enlarged; note pseudovacuoles. X 1700.

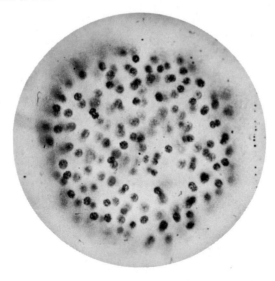

Fig. 2–7. *Polycystis aeruginosa* Kütz. Surface view of small, living colony. X 540.

2–1, 2–6, 2–7), whereas in *Merismopedia* the colony is a flattened or slightly curved plate (Fig. 2–8). *Polycystis aeruginosa* Kütz. frequently is a component of water blooms (Fig. 2–1). The individual cells are minute and spherical and usually contain refractive **pseudovacuoles** which are filled with gas; their exact nature is not understood. The ellipsoidal cells of *Merismopedia* are arranged in flat colonies in which the individual cells occur in rows (Fig. 2–8). This regularity of arrangement is occasioned by the limitation of cell division to two directions. Numerous dividing cells often are visible within the colony. In these colonial genera, in contrast to strictly unicellular organisms, cell

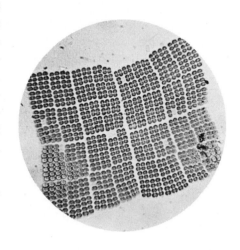

Fig. 2–8. *Merismopedia* sp. Living colony. X 250.

division results in increase in colony size rather than in multiplication of the individual. The latter is accomplished by fragmentation of larger colonies, the fragments continuing to increase in size by cell division. The individual cells of these colonies are independent units, often at some distance from each other.

Filamentous Genera: *Oscillatoria,* *Lyngbya,* *Anabaena,* *Nostoc,* *Scytonema,* *Rivularia,* *Gloeotrichia,* *Calothrix,* and *Hapalosiphon*

The coherence of the cells after the completion of cell division results in the production of another type of plant body, the **trichome** (Figs. 2–9, 2–10). Where cell division is entirely restricted to a single direction, an unbranched trichome results, as, for example, in *Oscillatoria* (L. *oscillare*, to swing) and *Lyngbya* (in honor of Lyngbye, a Danish phycologist). *Oscillatoria* (Figs. 2–9, 2–10), which occurs floating in aquatic habitats or on damp soil, is a genus containing many species. In some of them the cells are broader than long, whereas in others the reverse is true. In *Oscillatoria* and *Lyngbya* there is no differentiation among the component cells of a trichome, except that the apical cell may differ in shape from the other vegetative cells. Each cell shows characteristic myxophycean structure (Figs. 2–9, 2–10). Sheaths usually are not demonstrable around the trichomes of *Oscillatoria*. When they are observed in aqueous media, a number of the trichomes frequently exhibit an oscillating motion, as well as rotation and forward and backward movement along their long axes. The mechanism of these movements is not understood completely. *Lyngbya* (Fig. 2–11), which occurs in both fresh and salt water, differs from *Oscillatoria* in that the trichomes are surrounded by rather firm, clearly visible sheaths. A trichome and its surrounding sheath are usually designated as a **filament**. In both *Oscillatoria* and *Lyngbya*, cell division is generalized, all the cells of the trichomes being capable of division. Cell division here, as in colonial genera, results in increase in the size of the individual. Multiplication of the filaments takes place by a type of fragmentation called **hormogonium** (Gr. *hormos,* chain + Gr. *goneia,* generation) **formation.** In this process, either because of the death of one or more cells in the trichome (Fig. 2–9, 2–11) or because of weakness at one point, the chains of cells break up into multicellular fragments, the **hormogonia.** These usually are motile and are capable of forming new trichomes.

Anabaena (Gr. *anabaino,* arise) and *Nostoc* (name used by Paracelsus), although unbranched like *Oscillatoria* and *Lyngbya*, possess several attributes not present in the latter. *Anabaena* (Figs. 2–1, 2–12, 2–13), a genus which contains both planktonic species and some which form coatings on other aquatic vegetation, is widespread in bodies of fresh and salt water. *Nostoc* (Fig. 2–14, 2–15) includes a number of terrestrial or rock-inhabiting species in which the tortuous, bead-like filaments are grouped together in matrices of macroscopically recognizable form. The plant mass may be spherical, ovoidal, or sheet-like. Cell division is generalized also in *Anabaena* and *Nostoc*, but two manifestations of differentiation occur. Certain cells, the **heterocysts** (Gr. *heteros,* different + Gr. *kystis,* bladder), develop from some of the **vegetative cells.** In this process, the cell destined to be a heterocyst becomes op-

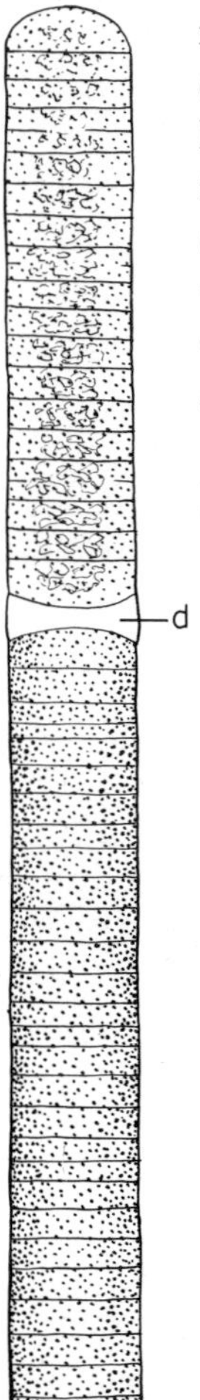

Fig. 2–9. *Oscillatoria limosa* Ag. ex Gom. Single trichome; lower portion in surface view, upper in median optical section: *d,* dead cell. X 700.

tically homogeneous. Its wall thickens uniformly, except in the region of contact with an adjacent cell. Here the thickening is deposited as a polar nodule (Figs. 2–12, 2–13, 2–15B). The formation of the heterocyst in *Anabaena* and *Nostoc* results in a weakness in the chain of cells, perhaps by destroying intercellular protoplasmic continuity, and the filaments break up readily into hormogonia. In some species, heterocysts have been

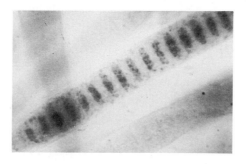

Fig. 2–10. *Oscillatoria* sp. Portion of trichome stained with aceto-carmine; chromatin visible in each cell. X 590.

observed to germinate into filaments. Other vegetative cells become transformed into **akinetes** (Gr. *akinesia*, absence of motility). An akinete (Figs. 2–12B, 2–13A, 2–18) is a thick-walled spore which, when set free from the parent plant, can germinate to form a new individual. As the akinete differentiates from the vegetative cell, certain changes take place. Refractive food granules increase in number and the cell may enlarge. While these changes are occurring, an additional wall layer is secreted between the original cellulose wall of the vegetative cell and its protoplast. Akinetes are highly resistant to environmental adversities and have been germinated after seventy years in air-dry storage.

Scytonema (Gr. *skytos*, hide or skin + Gr. *nema*, thread), a genus widely distributed on moist, shady rocks, where it forms dark, blackish, felty coatings, is of interest in two respects. Its sheaths are thick, firm, sometimes lamellated, and yellow-brown in color in older parts of the plant body (Fig. 2–16). Furthermore, there is a strong tendency for cell division to be restricted to cells near the apices of the filaments. However, heterocyst formation and renewal of cell division in intercalary vegetative cells between heterocysts often result in disturbances in the trichome. Inasmuch as the heterocysts are firmly attached to the sheath, pressure generated by intercalary cell division results in the rupture of the sheath and the emergence of pairs of trichomes (Fig. 2–16). In this way, although cell division is limited to one direction as in all the preceding filamentous genera, **false branching** takes place.

Rivularia (L. *rivulus,* a small brook) (Fig. 2–17) and *Gloeotrichia* (Gr. *gloios,* gelatinous + Gr. *thrix,* hair) (Fig. 2–18) also possess falsely branched filaments but differ from *Scytonema* in that their filaments are united in spherical attached colonies and their filaments taper from base to apex. The apices are composed of long, almost colorless, hair-like cells. The basal vegetative cell of each filament becomes transformed into a heterocyst (Figs. 2–17, 2–18). In *Gloeotrichia,* one or more enlarged akinetes usually are developed from the vegetative cells in the vicinity of the heterocyst; akinetes are lacking in *Rivularia* (Fig. 2–17). In both these genera the sheaths of the individual filaments are partially confluent, this contributing to the common matrix, but remnants of the individual sheaths are usually apparent at the base of the plants. The related genus *Calothrix* (Gr. *kalos,* beautiful + Gr. *thrix*) (Fig. 2–19) is abundant in and on soil and is frequently encountered as an epiphyte on aquatic plants or on rocks and pilings exposed to sea water and spray.

True branching, resulting from the division of certain cells of a trichome in a direction different from that of the majority, characterizes the genus *Hapalosiphon* (Gr. *hapalos,* gentle + Gr. *siphon,* tube) (Fig. 2–20). Species of *Hapalosiphon* often form extensive coatings on aquatic vegetation.

SUMMARY AND CLASSIFICATION

In summary, it should be emphasized that the blue-green algae, the Myxophyceae, represent a large but somewhat anomalous group among the algae. Their cell structure is more nearly like that of the bacteria (Chapter 9) than any other group of algae. Distinctive myxophycean attributes in-

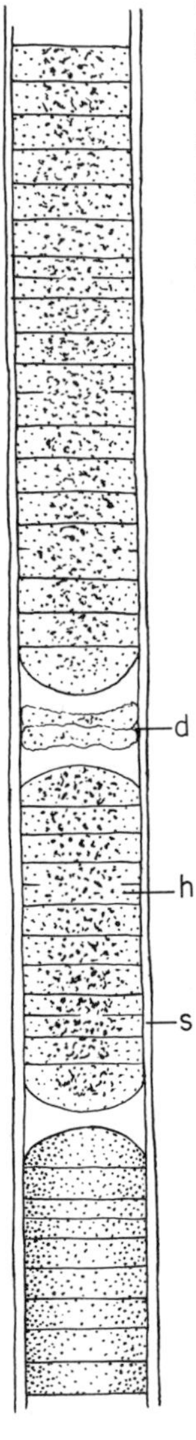

Fig. 2–11. *Lyngbya* sp. Portion of a filament; the lowermost portion of trichome in surface view, the remainder in median optical section: *d,* dead cells; *h,* hormogonium; *s,* sheath. X 700.

clude the absence from the cells of definitely delimited plastids, of highly organized nuclei, and of aqueous vacuoles, and the presence of c-phycocyanin and c-phycoerythrin in addition to chlorophyll and carotenoid pigments. Heterocysts do not occur in plants other than Myxophyceae. Their photosynthate, called "cyanophycean starch," a term which emphasizes our ignorance of its exact chemical nature, is unique among the al-

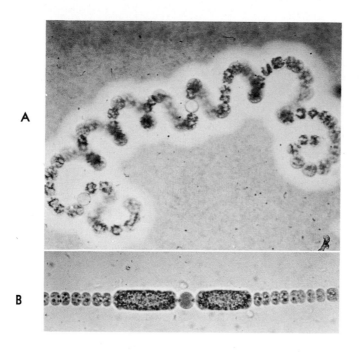

Fig. 2–12. A, Anabaena flos-aquae B. and F. A, Enlarged view of single filament showing vegetative cells and heterocysts. X 540. B, Anabaena sp. Note vegetative cells and heterocyst between two akinetes. X 540.

gae. Myxophyceae are of biological interest in their complete lack of sexuality. Reproduction is entirely asexual and is accomplished by cell division in unicellular genera and by various types of fragmentation in colonial and filamentous representatives. In the latter, the filamentous fragments are known as hormogonia. Two special types of reproductive cells, namely, heterocysts and akinetes, are developed by many of the filamentous genera. With few exceptions, cell division in multicel-

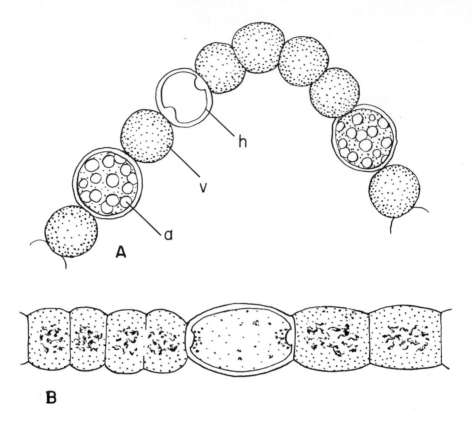

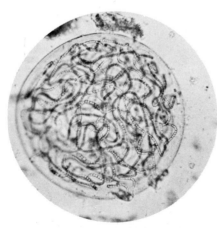

A

B

Fig. 2–13. *Anabaena circinalis* B. and F. A, Segment of a filament: *a*, akinete; *v*, vegetative cell; *h*, heterocyst. B, *Anabaena* sp. Segment of aceto-carmine-stained filament; note chromatin and dividing cells. X 1700.

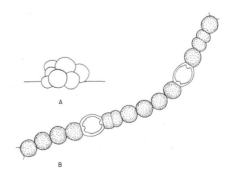

Fig. 2–14. *Nostoc microscopicum* B. and F. Small colony as it appears under low magnification. X 135.

Fig. 2–15. *Nostoc* sp. A, Colonies on moist rock. X 2. B, Single trichome. X 850.

lular types is generalized, not localized. *Scytonema, Rivularia,* and
Gloeotrichia differ from other filamentous genera in this respect. Growth
in *Scytonema* is largely apical, whereas in *Rivularia* and *Gloeotrichia*
it is basal. Although many Myxophyceae lead a terrestrial existence on
damp soil, students of plant evolution do not look upon them with in-

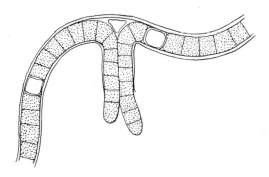

Fig. 2–16. *Scytonema myochrous* (Dillw.) Ag. Portion of filament with false branching. X 230.

terest as possible progenitors of higher forms of plant life because of
the anomalous attributes listed above, in all of which they differ markedly from other algae as well as from the higher plants. They have no
clear kinship with other living organisms, unless it be a distant one with
the bacteria, a suggestion made almost one hundred years ago.

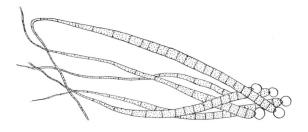

Fig. 2–17. *Rivularia* sp. Several trichomes. X 230.

The classification of Myxophyceae is relatively uncontroversial. The orders and families, of which representative genera have been chosen for
this chapter, may be classified as follows:

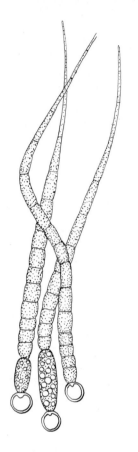

Division: Cyanophyta
  Class 1. Myxophyceae
    Order 1. Chroococcales
      Family 1. Chroococcaceae
        Genera: *Chroococcus, Gloeo-*
          capsa, Polycystis, Meris-
          mopedia
    Order 2. Chamaesiphonales
      Family 1. Chamaesiphonaceae
        Genus: *Chamaesiphon*
    Order 3. Oscillatoriales
      Suborder 1. Oscillatorineae
        Family 1. Oscillatoriaceae
          Genera: *Oscillatoria, Lyngbya*
      Suborder 2. Nostochineae
        Family 1. Nostocaceae
          Genera: *Anabaena, Nostoc*
        Family 2. Scytonemataceae
          Genus: *Scytonema*
        Family 3. Stigonemataceae
          Genus: *Hapalosiphon*
        Family 4. Rivulariaceae
          Genera: *Rivularia, Gloeo-*
          trichia, Calothrix

The orders are readily distinguishable from each other. The Chamaesiphonales alone produce endospores. The remaining unicellular and colonial Myxophyceae are members of the Chroococcales; the filamentous genera belong to the Oscillatoriales.

Fig. 2–18. *Gloeotrichia* sp. Three trichomes, two with akinetes. X 700.

Two series are distinguishable in the order Oscillatoriales based on lack (suborder Oscillatorineae) or possession (suborder Nostochineae) of heterocysts. The families of the latter are recognizable by the possession of the following unique attributes: The Nostocaceae are unbranched, with trichomes of uniform diameter; false branching occurs in the Scytonemataceae, which also have trichomes of uniform diameter. True branching characterizes the Stigonemataceae, while the trichomes of the Rivulariaceae are tapered.

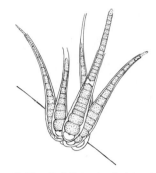

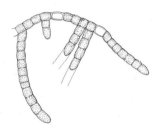

Fig. 2–19. *Calothrix fasciculata* Ag. on *Enteromorpha* sp. Group of epiphytic filaments. X 385.

Fig. 2–20. *Hapalosiphon* sp. Portion of branching filament. X 205.

DISCUSSION QUESTIONS

1. What organisms usually are included in the group Thallophyta?
2. What attributes distinguish Myxophyceae from other algae?
3. For what reasons is the cell structure of Myxophyceae said to be "anomalous"?
4. What possible functions can you see for the copious sheaths of certain Myxophyceae?
5. What is meant by the terms growth, reproduction, vegetative, vegetative reproduction, asexual reproduction, sexual reproduction, cytokinesis?
6. What types of growth can you distinguish on the basis of their location in the plant body?
7. Explain how cell division is related to the form of the plant body of Myxophyceae, mentioning illustrative genera.
8. Define or explain the following terms: heterocyst, spore, akinete, vegetative cell, hormogonium.
9. Do you consider colonies like *Polycystis* and *Merismopedia* multicellular organisms? Give reasons for your answer.
10. Where would you look for Myxophyceae in the field?

REFERENCE WORKS ON ALGAE[2]

Bold, H. C. The Cultivation of Algae, *Bot. Rev.*, 8:69–138, 1942.

Burlew, J. S. (ed.). *Algal Culture from Laboratory to Pilot Plant,* Publication 600, Carnegie Inst. Washington, 1953.

Chapman, V. J. *Seaweeds and Their Uses,* Methuen and Co., Ltd., 1950.

---

[2] These references should be consulted in connection with Chapters 2 through 8.

Chase, F. M. *Useful Algae,* Smithsonian Publication 3667, Smithsonian Institution, 1941.

Conger, P. S. Significance of Shell Structure in Diatoms, *Smithsonian Report,* 1936, pp. 325–344.

Davidson, B. Now—Bread from the Sea, *Colliers,* April 16, 1954.

Dawson, E. Y. *How to Know the Seaweeds,* Wm. C. Brown Company, 1956.

Fritsch, F. E. *Structure and Reproduction of the Algae,* Cambridge Univ. Press, vols. 1 and 2, 1935 and 1945.

Milner, H. W. Algae as Food, *Scientific American,* 189:31–35, 1953.

Newton, L. *Seaweed Utilization,* Sampson Low, 1951.

Prescott, G. W. *Algae of the Western Great Lakes Area,* Bulletin 31, Cranbrook Institute of Science Press, 1951.

Prescott, G. W. *How to Know the Fresh-Water Algae,* Wm. C. Brown Company, 1954.

Pringsheim, E. G. *Pure Cultures of Algae, Their Preparation and Maintenance,* Cambridge Univ. Press, 1946.

Setchell, W. A., and Gardner, N. L. *The Marine Algae of the Pacific Coast of North America,* Univ. California Publication in Botany 8: I. Myxophyceae, 1919; II. Chlorophyceae, 1920; III. Melanophyceae, 1925.

Smith, G. M. *Marine Algae of the Monterey Peninsula,* Stanford Univ. Press, 1944.

Smith, G. M. *Freshwater Algae of the United States,* McGraw-Hill Book Co., 1950.

Smith, G. M. *Cryptogamic Botany,* McGraw-Hill Book Co., vol 1, 1955.

Smith, G. M., *et al. Manual of Phycology,* Chronica Botanica Co., 1951.

Taylor, W. R. *Marine Algae of Florida with Special Reference to the Dry Tortugas,* Papers from the Tortugas Laboratory, Publication 379, Carnegie Inst. Washington, 1928.

Taylor, W. R. *Marine Algae of the Northeastern Coast of North America,* Univ. of Michigan Press, 1937.

Tiffany, L. H. *Algae, the Grass of Many Waters,* Charles C. Thomas, 1938.

Tiffany, L. H., and Britton, M. E. *The Algae of Illinois,* Univ. of Chicago Press, 1952.

Tilden, J. E. *The Algae and Their Life Relations,* Univ. of Minnesota Press, 1935.

Wardlaw, C. W. *Embryogenesis in Plants,* John Wiley and Sons, Inc., 1955.

CHAPTER 3

Division Chlorophyta

GENERAL FEATURES

The division **Chlorophyta** (Gr. *chloros,* green + Gr. *phyton,* plant) includes a single class of algae, the **Chlorophyceae.** The Chlorophyceae contain all plants usually denominated as **"green algae,"** with the exception of the stoneworts, *Chara, Nitella,* and related genera, which in this text are grouped in a separate division, the Charophyta.

Like the Myxophyceae, chlorophycean algae are widespread in distribution, occurring in both fresh and salt water, on moist rocks, on wood, and on the surface of and within the soil. More than 360 genera and 5700 species of Chlorophyta have been described. The green algae are well represented in both the **plankton** and **benthos** (Gr. *benthos,* depth of the sea) in bodies of water which range in size from small, temporary pools to oceans. Their role in the soil is not clear. Assertions that some soil species are able to fix free nitrogen require additional critical investigation. A number of species are epiphytic on other algae, aquatic flowering plants, and animals, and still others are endophytic within the cells of certain protozoa, coelenterates, and sponges. Marine species frequently are attached to rocks, pilings, or larger algae or may grow on the sandy bottoms of quiet estuaries. Planktonic species occasionally form water blooms in both fresh and salt water.

The Chlorophyceae (Gr. *chloros,* green + Gr. *phykos,* alga) are usually grass-green during their vegetative stages, except for a few species whose vacuolar pigments, in part, mask the green color. The cells contain both chlorophylls a and b as well as alpha and beta carotenes and certain xanthophylls. The predominance of the chlorophyll pigments accounts for the typical green color of the members of the class. Unlike the pigments of Myxophyceae, those of the Chlorophyceae usually are restricted to localized regions of the cytoplasm called **chloroplasts** or **chromatophores.** These exhibit a great range of form, varying from large urn-like structures to plane or twisted ribbons or minute discoidal lens-shaped bodies (Figs. 3–1, 3–9, 3–15, 3–29, 3–31). **Pyrenoids** (Gr. *pyren*, fruit stone) occur in the chloroplasts of a majority of genera (Fig. 3–1, *py*). They appear to be centers about which starch formation occurs, but their exact role in the process remains obscure. Of all the algae, the Chlorophyceae are most like the higher plants in that their excess photosynthate is stored in the cells as starch. The nuclei of Chlorophyceae appear to be similar in organization to those of plants other than blue-green algae and bacteria (Chapter 9) in their possession of nuclear membranes and one or more nucleoli in addition to so-called chromatin and nuclear sap. Mitotic nuclear division has been observed in many species. The nuclei (Fig. 3–1A, 3–15) are embedded in colorless cytoplasm which is internal to the chloroplasts. The cell walls are of cellulose, and in many cases are surrounded by colloidal sheaths. A few unicellular genera and the motile reproductive cells of others may lack cell walls entirely and are animal-like in this respect. Large **central vacuoles** occur in the cells of many Chlorophyceae, and small **contractile vacuoles** are present almost universally in their motile cells. The Chlorophyceae exhibit a range and complexity of structure and reproduction which surpass those described for the Myxophyceae. The details of these will be discussed in connection with the several illustrative genera. The latter will be considered as representing four types of plant bodies, namely, **the motile unicellular and colonial type; the nonmotile unicellular and colonial types; the filamentous and membranous type; the tubular (siphonaceous) type.**

ILLUSTRATIVE TYPES

Motile Unicellular and Colonial Genera

UNICELLULAR TYPE: CHLAMYDOMONAS

The simplest members of the Chlorophyceae appear to be unicellular organisms which are motile during their vegetative existence as well as during reproductive phases. *Chlamydomonas* (Gr. *chlamys*, mantle + Gr. *monas*, unit) is widespread in soil and aquatic habitats. The structure and reproduction of this genus will be described in considerable detail for a number of reasons: It is readily available in pure cultures for laboratory study, many of its attributes are shared by other genera of Chlorophyceae, and finally, it is currently the experimental organism in a number of biological investigations.

The cells of most species of *Chlamydomonas* do not exceed 25 microns in length (Fig. 3–1). The single-celled plant bodies are surrounded by a

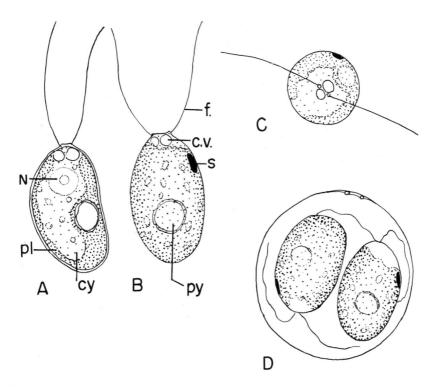

Fig. 3–1. *Chlamydomonas eugametos* Moewus. A-C, Motile individuals; A, in median optical section, B, in surface view, C, in anterior polar view. D, Asexual reproduction by endogenous bipartition: cy, colorless cytoplasm; c.v., contractile vacuole; f, flagellum; n, nucleus; pl, chloroplast; py, pyrenoid; s, stigma. X 2550.

cellulose wall through which two extensions of the protoplasm, the **flagella** (L. *flagellum*, small whip), protrude anteriorly. Motility is effected by the lashing movements of these organelles. Each cell contains a single massive chloroplast which may be urn-, cup-, band- or H-shaped. The chloroplast may contain one or more **pyrenoids,** as well as a red pigment body often called the **eyespot** or **stigma** (Gr. *stigma,* brand mark). With high magnification, one can frequently observe that there is an area of clear cytoplasm subtended by the concave stigma. It has been suggested that this functions as a primitive lens, and experiments with re-

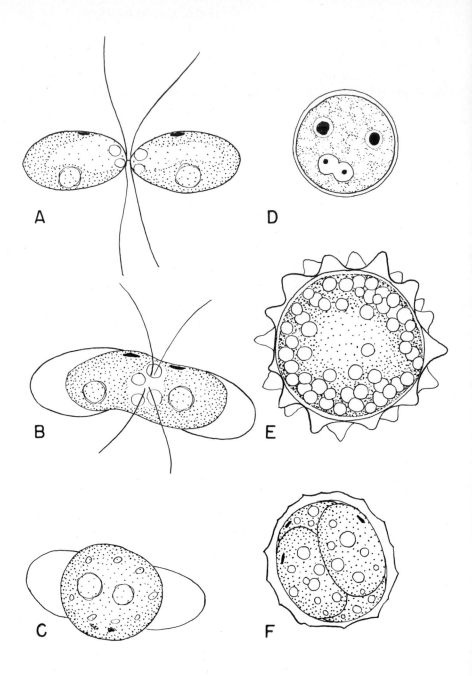

Fig. 3–2. *Chlamydomonas*. Sexual reproduction. A, Pair of isogametes recently departed from clump; B,C, Stages in plasmogamy; D, karyogamy; E, dormant zygospore; F, zygospore germination. (All except D from *C. eugametos*; D from *C. chlamydogama* Bold.) X 2550.

lated organisms containing stigmata indicate that the stigma is indeed a site of light perception.[1] The single **nucleus** lies in the colorless cytoplasm within the chloroplast and often is obscured by the latter in living cells, but it may be demonstrated readily by staining. Two or more **contractile vacuoles** are present near the anterior pole of each cell (Fig. 3–1). There is some evidence that they play a role in the elimination of waste materials and excess fluids from the cells.

Multiplication of the plant is accomplished by cell division which involves nuclear and cytoplasmic division. The process is illustrated, in part, in Fig. 3–1D. Two or more daughter cells may arise within a single mother cell by repeated bipartition. The flagella of the parent cell are withdrawn at the beginning of division. The daughter cells emerge, after becoming motile within the mother cell, by the deliquescence of the mother cell wall. The liberated individuals gradually grow to the size characteristic of the species.

Under environmental and protoplasmic conditions not yet completely understood, certain individuals undergo **sexual reproduction.** This process is made manifest in many species by the rapid aggregation of a number of individuals in groups or **clumps** (Fig. 3–3A). Careful study reveals that the individuals in a clump become paired and that they emerge from the clump in pairs (Figs. 3–2, 3–3B). In some species, such pairs seem to be held together by a delicate protoplasmic thread which connects them at the base of their flagella (Fig. 3–2A); the latter are not entangled, except momentarily, after the cells have paired. Ultimately the cellulose walls of each member of the pair are dissolved at the anterior poles, and the protoplasts emerge, gradually uniting to form a single unit (Figs. 3–2B, 3–3B,C) into which the four flagella are withdrawn. The discarded cell walls persist for some time in the vicinity of the fusion cell but finally disintegrate. Stained preparations of the uniting cells reveal that the two nuclei, which are thus brought together in one protoplast, finally unite to form one larger nucleus (Fig. 3–2D).

The process just described represents the sexual reproduction of *Chlamydomonas.* It is characterized by the union of two cells, the union of their nuclei, and the association within the fusion nucleus of the chromosome complements (and genes) of the two uniting cells. Each of the cells which undergoes union is called a **gamete** (Gr. *gamos,* marriage) or sex cell. The product of the sexual union is a **zygote** (Gr. *zygon,* yoke).

---

[1] That cells of *Chlamydomonas* with stigmata react with greater rapidity to the stimulus of light than those which lack them has recently been demonstrated.

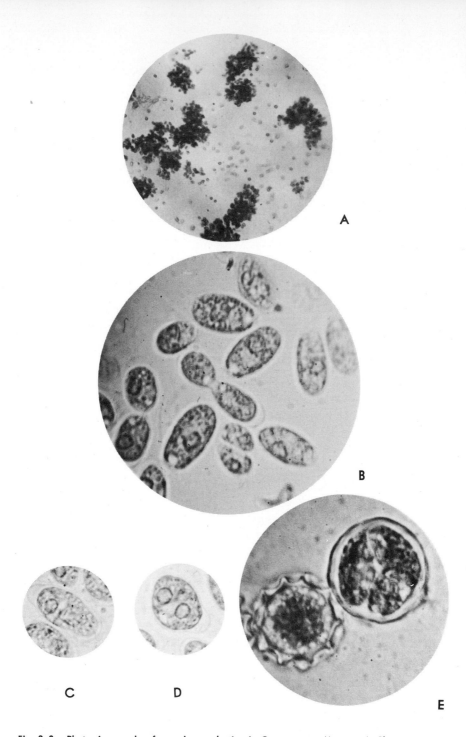

Fig. 3–3. Photomicrographs of sexual reproduction in C. *eugametos* Moewus. *A,* Clump or group formation, 1 minute after mixing compatible mating types. X 125. *B,* Vegetative cells, gametes in plasmogamy and asexual reproduction. X 1260. *C, D,* Zygotes 24 hours old. X 1260. *E,* Zygospore germination after 8 months' dormancy; three of four daughter cells visible in one. X 1260.

In *Chlamydomonas* and many other algae and fungi, the zygote secretes a thick wall and enters a period of dormancy. Such thick-walled zygotes are called **zygospores** (Fig. 3–2E).

The phenomenon of sexual reproduction is so uniform in its essentials in all living organisms that it seems imperative at this point to consider certain of its significant features and implications. Cytological investigation has demonstrated that the process always involves the union of two cells and their nuclei; genetic experiments indicate that an association of parental genes occurs. Whenever these three phenomena take place, the total process is known as sexual reproduction. Although the fusion of the cells, **plasmogamy** (Gr. *plasma,* formed substance + Gr. *gamos,* marriage), may precede nuclear fusion, **karyogamy** (Gr. *karyon,* nut + Gr. *gamos*), and chromosome association, **synapsis** (Gr. *syn,* together + Gr. *hapto,* unite), by a considerable interval, these three essential phases always are involved in true sexual reproduction in diverse organisms. Primitive organisms like *Chlamydomonas* have recently received intensive consideration with regard to their sexual reproduction, inasmuch as the phenomenon in such plants is not obscured by secondary morphological features.

Although the origin of sexual reproduction remains unknown, it seems clear that in primitive organisms of this type the process is not as indispensable to the maintenance of the species as it is in higher plants and especially in animals. It has been demonstrated recently that sexual reproduction is favored by low nitrogen availability in *Chlamydomonas.* In **clonal**[2] cultures of *Chlamydomonas* the cells may multiply indefinitely by cell division without intervening sexuality.

Figs. 3–2A, B and 3–3B illustrate pairs of cells observed in *Chlamydomonas eugametos* Moewus. In this and many other species the uniting gametes are morphologically similar and are therefore called **isogametes** (Gr. *isos,* equal + Gr. *gamos,* marriage). Their production and union are known as **isogamy.** In another species of *Chlamydomonas,* although the gametes are morphologically isogamous, the flagella of only one of the gametes functions in propelling the uniting pair. In still other species of the same genus, the uniting gametes are markedly different in size. Such gametes are known as **heterogametes** (Gr. *heteros,* different + Gr. *gamos*) or **anisogametes** (Gr. *anisos,* unequal + Gr. *gamos*); their production is called **heterogamy** or **anisogamy.** Probably on the basis of analogy with

---

[2] Clonal cultures are those in which all the organisms present have arisen from a single individual.

sexual reproduction in animals, the smaller gamete in such cases is referred to as **male** and the larger as **female**. Finally, in another species of *Chlamydomonas* it has been shown that the gametes display still further dimorphism. One is large and nonmotile at the time of union and represents a single parent cell. The other type is smaller and motile and is produced in larger numbers from one cell. Such pronounced heterogamy is known as **oogamy** (Gr. *ōon,* egg + Gr. *gamos*). In this case, the larger, female gamete is spoken of as the **egg** and the male gamete as the **sperm** or **antherozoid.**

Studies of *Chlamydomonas* have demonstrated that in isogamous species the individual gametes are of different mating type, although morphologically indistinguishable; they may be referred to as "plus" and "minus." It has also been shown that in some species clonal cultures never undergo sexual reproduction unless they are mixed with others of opposite mating type. Such species are said to be **heterothallic** (Gr. *heteros,* different + Gr. *thallos,* a young shoot, plant body). In other species sexual reproduction occurs readily in clonal cultures. These are said to be **homothallic** (Gr. *homos,* same + Gr. *thallos*).

No matter what the origin of the zygote, whether from the union of isogametes or heterogametes, an understanding of its further development is of fundamental importance. It is obvious that the zygote, a product of the union of two cells, will contain associated in its nucleus two sets of chromosomes. The chromatin material has been doubled and the genes of two cells have become associated in the same nucleus. It is well known that when the chromosomes of two parents become associated together in a single nucleus or its descendants, a phase follows sooner or later in which the parental chromosomes are redistributed. This phase is called **meiosis** (Gr. *meioō,* to make smaller). This process involves not only a quantitative reduction in the chromosome number but a qualitative segregation of genes as well. That meiosis has taken place often may be inferred indirectly from the occurrence of two rapidly successive nuclear divisions and cytokineses in which four daughter cells are produced from a single mother cell (Figs. 3–2*F,* 3–3*E*). Cytological and genetic study of *Chlamydomonas* indicates that meiosis takes place at the time of zygospore germination. Meiosis therefore is said to be **zygotic** with reference to its site of occurrence in the life cycle of *Chlamydomonas.* The germinating zygospore gives rise to four (or more) motile cells (Figs. 3–2*F,* 3–3*E*) which are liberated by the swelling and dissolution of the zygospore wall.

The foregoing account of sexuality in *Chlamydomonas* has been some-what detailed, not only because it is designed to present specific informa-tion about a single alga, but also because the principles and terminology involved are of general application to other groups of plants and animals.

COLONIAL GENERA: PANDORINA AND VOLVOX

Pandorina (mythology, reproduction like opening of *Pandora's* box) and *Volvox* (L. *volvere*, to roll) (Figs. 3–4, 3–6) are two widely dis-

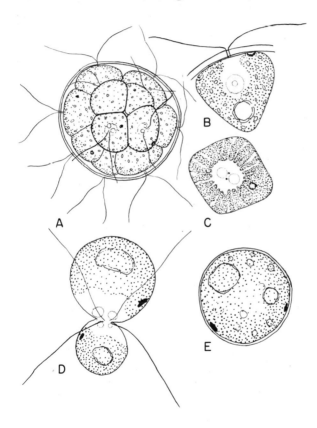

Fig. 3–4. *Pandorina* sp. A, Mature colony, surface view. B, Vegetative cell, median optical section, vertical plane. C, Vegetative cell, anterior polar view. D, Sexual reproduction. E, Zygote. A, X 700; B–E, X 1700.

tributed genera which illustrate the motile colonial type of plant body. The individual cells, which are included in a common matrix, show many morphological features reminiscent of *Chlamydomonas,* such as massive chloroplasts, stigmata, and contractile vacuoles. Multiplication in all these genera is effected by repeated division of cells of the parent colony to form miniature daughter colonies which are liberated ultimately by dissolution of the matrix of the mother colony (Fig. 3–5). The young colonies increase in cell size, but not in cell number, until the dimensions characteristic of the species have been attained.

Fig. 3–5. *Pandorina* sp. Photomicrograph of colony (flattened) with 16 daughter colonies. X 250.

The mature colonies of *Pandorina* (Fig. 3–4A) consist of sixteen cells arranged in an almost solid colony. Each cell is somewhat truncate at the anterior pole and narrowed posteriorly (Fig. 3–4B). The chloroplast is massive and contains a prominent stigma and basal pyrenoid. In anterior polar view (Fig. 3–4C), two alternately pulsating contractile vacuoles are visible in the opening of the plastid at the base of the two flagella. The single nucleus lies in the central, colorless cytoplasm. After attaining the maximum size characteristic of the species,

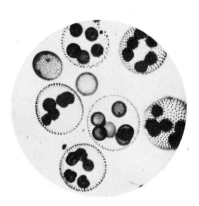

Fig. 3–6. *Volvox aureus* Ehr. Vegetative colonies of various ages; note stages in formation and eversion of daughter colonies. X 40.

the colonies sink to the bottom of the pond or culture vessel, withdraw their flagella and initiate daughter colony formation (Fig. 3–5). Each of the component cells undergoes repeated nuclear and cell division until miniature sixteen-celled colonies are produced. The minute cells of these colonies then develop flagella and begin to move slowly within the parent colony until liberated. Under certain conditions colonies of *Pandorina morum* Bory exhibit heterothallic, heterogamous sexual reproduction (Fig. 3–4D,E). Meiosis is probably zygotic.

Volvox is perhaps the most spectacular of the motile colonial Chlorophyceae, for its colonies may contain thousands of cells arranged over the periphery of a colloidal sphere (Fig. 3–6). The plant is readily visible to the unaided eye and has been known for several hundred years. In a number of species of *Volvox*, the protoplasts of the individual cells are connected to their walls by delicate protoplasmic extensions. Those of contiguous cells appear to be continuous through the cell walls (Fig. 3–7*A,B*). In the ontogeny of the colony, the cells are entirely similar to each other during the early stages. However, a dimorphism soon becomes apparent, in that certain cells enlarge and become slightly depressed beneath the surface. As the colonies move, it becomes evident that these

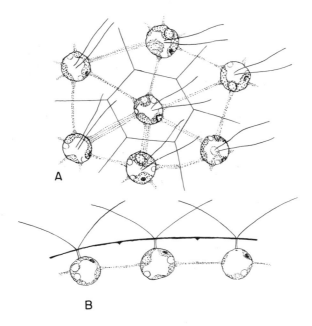

Fig. 3–7. *Volvox aureus.* Vegetative cells. A, Surface view; B, vertical section. X 700.

larger cells lie in the posterior hemisphere. These enlarged cells alone are capable of dividing to form daughter colonies (Fig. 3–6); the remainder are purely vegetative and disintegrate when the adult colony liberates its daughters. Special enlarged cells also give rise to gametes when the colonies become sexually mature. Sexual reproduction in *Volvox* is oogamous, and both homothallic and heterothallic species are known. The male gametes, sperms, are borne in disc-like or spherical colonies each of which may contain as many as 512 male cells (Fig. 3–8*C*). The sperm groups are liberated from the parent colony, and in heterothallic species are probably attracted chemically to the female colonies. There the individual sperms are set free and penetrate to the eggs (Fig. 3–8A,B). The eggs, which have the appearance of young asexual reproductive cells, differ in their pyriform shape. They are fertilized within the parent colony. The zygotes develop thick walls after fertilization (Fig. 3–8D,E), undergo a period of dormancy after they are liberated by disintegration of the parent colony, and undergo meiosis during germination.

In both *Pandorina* and *Volvox*, the number of cells in the colony is fixed before liberation of the daughter colonies from the parent, and it is

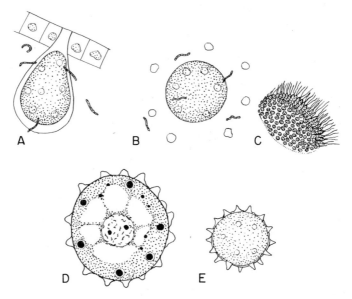

Fig. 3–8. *Volvox globator* L. Sexual reproduction. A, Vertical section, and B, polar views of egg surrounded by sperm cells. C, Platelet of sperm. D, Stained section of zygospore soon after union of gamete nuclei. E, Mature zygospore. A,B, and C, X 700; D, X 770; E, X 315.

not augmented by cell division later, even though one or more of the component cells is injured or destroyed. Such colonies, in which the cell number is fixed throughout development, are known as **coenobia.**

Nonmotile Unicellular and Colonial Genera

UNICELLULAR GENERA: CHLOROCOCCUM AND CHLORELLA

Nonmotility, usually considered a plant-like attribute, characterizes numerous unicellular and colonial Chlorophyceae as well as the filamentous, membranous, and tubular types. That these nonmotile organisms may have sprung from a motile ancestry is suggested by the frequency with which they revert to motility in both their asexual and sexual reproductive cells.

Two genera, namely, *Chlorococcum* and *Chlorella*, are chosen as representative of the unicelluar Chlorophyceae in which the vegetative phase is nonmotile. In the first, however, the reproductive cells are flagellate, whereas in the latter, motility is entirely absent.

Chlorococcum (Gr. *chloros*, green + Gr. *kokkos*, berry) (Fig. 3–9) is widely distributed in fresh water and especially in soil, but it is difficult

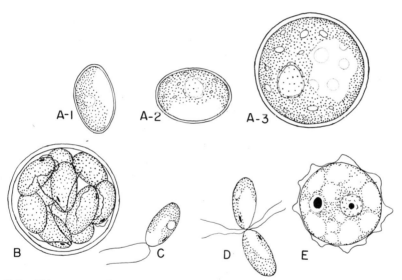

Fig. 3–9. *Chlorococcum echinozygotum* Starr. A, 1–3, Vegetative cells of increasing age. B, Zoospore formation. C, Single zoospore. D, Isogametes. E, Stained section of zygospore. X 1700.

to distinguish it from other nonmotile spherical unicellular Chlorophyceae, unless one cultivates it in unialgal[3] cultures. In agar media, the organism grows as a green stratum over the surface, while in liquid cultures it occurs as a surface film and as a positively phototactic ring. The individual cells are spherical (Fig. 3–9A3), unless they have become polyhedral by mutual compression. Each has a cellulose wall and a protoplast containing a hollow spherical chloroplast, usually with one

---

[3] A unialgal culture is one that contains individuals which belong to only one species of algae.

aperture. A single pyrenoid often is embedded in the plastid opposite the region of the opening. Both uninucleate and multinucleate species of *Chlorococcum* are known. Simple division of one cell into two, a process which occurs so widely in unicellular organisms, normally is absent in *Chlorococcum*. Instead, at the time of reproduction the protoplast of the vegetative cell becomes divided into eight to sixteen or more uninucleate portions, each of which contains a portion of the chloroplast and often a fragment of the original pyrenoid (Fig. 3–9B). These minute protoplasts secrete delicate walls and develop two minute contractile vacuoles and two flagella each, while still enclosed within the parent cell wall (Fig. 3–9B). Upon liberation, it may be seen clearly that each of the motile cells possesses the attributes of a small *Chlamydomonas* individual, with which it might be confused were its origin and subsequent development unknown. These motile cells are called **zoospores** or **swarmspores** because of their motility. A cell which produces zoospores is called a **zoosporangium**. After a period of activity, the duration of which is influenced by such environmental factors as light, temperature, composition of the culture medium and its concentration, the zoospores gather in the most brightly illuminated portion of the culture vessel, withdraw their flagella, and grow into new vegetative individuals by cell enlargement (Fig. 3–9C,A1,A3). During this process the stigma disappears, but the contractile vacuoles may persist for some time. In *Chlorococcum* and other algae, zoospores usually are interpreted as reversions to a primitive motile condition. In some species of *Chlorococcum*—*C. echinozygotum* Starr, for example—some of the zoospores function as isogamous gametes (Fig. 3–9D,E) and unite to form spiny-walled zygospores. These germinate, forming four zoospores which grow into vegetative cells. Meiosis is thought to be zygotic. When cultivated on agar, and presumably in nature as well, vegetative cells may undergo zoosporogenesis but fail to liberate zoospores. The latter remain nonmotile and initiate their development into a new generation of vegetative cells within the parent cell wall, which is finally ruptured by their increasing size. Such reproductive cells are called **aplanospores**. The capacity of the juvenile motile cells of *Chlorococcum* and *Chlamydomonas* to function either asexually or sexually often is interpreted as evidence of a primitive grade of development, in contrast with the higher algae in which gametes and zoospores may differ morphologically.

Chlorella (Gr. *chloros*, green + L. *ella*, diminutive) (Fig. 3–10) is widespread in fresh and salt water and also in soil. It appears often with surprising rapidity in laboratory vessels in which distilled water or inorganic salt solutions are stored. Like *Chlorococcum*, it is most successfully studied in unialgal cultures. The cells of most species of *Chlorella* are minute green spheres (Fig. 3–10A) in which the details of cell structure are seen best under high magnification. The protoplast is composed of a cuplike chloroplast which may or may not contain a pyrenoid, and colorless central cytoplasm in which the minute nucleus is embedded. As in *Chlorococcum*, the capacity for division of one cell into two daughter cells has been lost. Instead, a series of bipartitions occurs, so that four or eight protoplasts are formed endogenously. These develop delicate cell walls, and after they have begun to enlarge they are liberated by rupture of the mother cell wall (Fig. 3–10B). Such

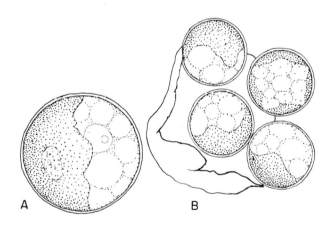

Fig. 3–10. *Chlorella* sp. A, Vegetative cell; B, autospore liberation. X 1700.

asexual reproductive cells are known as **autospores**, because they resemble, in miniature, the mother cells which produce them. They are, in fact, similar to aplanospores, except that *Chlorella* produces no motile reproductive cells. Sexual reproduction also is absent. A number of species of *Chlorella* have been grown in pure culture and have formed the basis for experimental studies of photosynthesis.

COLONIAL GENERA: PEDIASTRUM, HYDRODICTYON, AND SCENEDESMUS

Pediastrum (Gr. *pedion*, plane + Gr. *astron*, star), *Hydrodictyon* (Gr. *hydor*, water + Gr. *dictyon*, net), and *Scenedesmus* (Gr. *scene*, tent + Gr. *desmos*, bond) are examples of Chlorophyceae with nonmotile colonial plant bodies. Colonies of *Pediastrum* (Fig. 3–11) grow on the bottom of quiet pools and ponds as well as in the plankton. *Hydrodictyon reticulatum* (L.) Lagerh., commonly known as the "water net," often appears in great abundance in late summer in pools and lakes. The mature colonies are composed of large cylindrical cells joined together in polygonal configurations, the whole colony being cylindrical in shape. The young cells (Fig. 3–12A) are uninucleate and delicate green in color. They ultimately enlarge many times, and develop many nuclei and large central vacuoles which force the cytoplasm into a peripheral position.

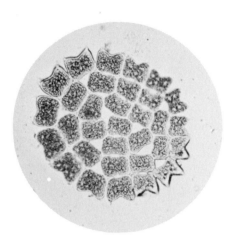

Fig. 3–11. *Pediastrum* sp. Photomicrograph of mature coenobium. X 250.

In asexual reproduction, the mature cylindrical cell segments of a net undergo an autonomous plasmolysis and their protoplasts withdraw from the wall. There follows a process of cytokinesis, known as **progressive cleavage,** in which the multinucleate mass of protoplasm is gradually segmented into smaller and smaller portions until uninucleate segments result (Fig. 3–12B). Each of these functions as a zoospore (Fig. 3–13A) which is actively motile in a restricted orbit. As motility abates, the zoospores are arranged in a rod-like mass in groups of four to nine, typically six. After the flagella have been withdrawn, the cells begin to enlarge and to assume a cylindrical form (Fig. 3–12C). By continuous increase in cell size, nets more than twelve inches in length may develop.

Sexual reproduction is isogamous. Unlike the zoospores which they resemble morphologically, the gametes are liberated from the parent cells. Meiosis is zygotic and the germinating zygotes develop four zoospores which grow into nonmotile polyhedral cells known as **polyeders** (Fig. 3–13B). These enlarge, undergo cleavage and zoosporogenesis, and liberate a number of actively swimming zoospores within a gelatinous vesicle. These zoospores arrange themselves as a flat plate, withdraw their flagella, and grow into cylindrical cells typical of the adult plant. This juvenile colony is flattened, not cylindrical as in the adult (Fig.

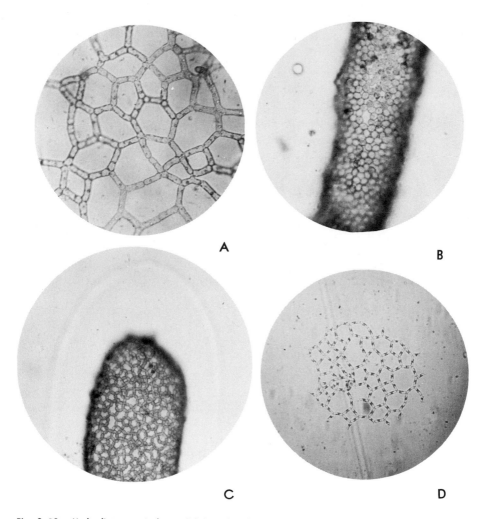

Fig. 3–12. *Hydrodictyon reticulatum* (L.) Lagerh. Photomicrographs. *A*, Portion of young net. *B*, Zoospores just before initiation of motility within parent cell. *C*, End of parent cell that contains young net, 18 hours after zoospores became nonmotile. *D*, Juvenile circular net, from polyeder. *A,D*, X 135; *B*, X 250; *C*, X 125.

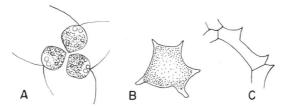

Fig. 3–13. *Hydrodictyon reticulatum. A*, Three motile zoospores. *B*, Polyeder. *C*, Marginal cell of juvenile net; note *Pediastrum*-like protuberances. *A*, X 770; *B*, X 315; *C*, X 700.

3–12*D*), although its component cells are cylindrical. Of great interest is the fact that its marginal cells bear two *Pediastrum*-like protuberances each (Fig. 3–13*C*). These phenomena often are interpreted as evidence of a common ancestry for *Hydrodictyon* and *Pediastrum*. In this connection, it is of interest that two other species of *Hydrodictyon* possess adult colonies which are flattened rather than cylindrical, possibly because they lack asexual reproduction.

Scenedesmus stands in relation to *Pediastrum* and *Hydrodictyon* as *Chlorella* does to *Chlorococcum*. As in *Chlorella*, motile cells are not produced in *Scenedesmus*. This alga is ubiquitous, occurring abundantly in almost every fresh-water habitat. It consists of a colony composed of four or more component cells united laterally (Fig. 3–14). In

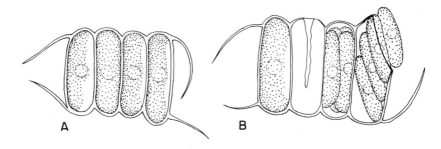

Fig. 3–14. *Scenedesmus* sp. A, Immature vegetative colony. B, Autocolony formation and liberation. X 770.

some species the terminal cells have spine-like processes. Reproduction, which is entirely asexual, is by the formation of **autocolonies** within each cell of the adult (Fig. 3–14*B*). These are liberated by the rupture of the parent cell wall and gradually achieve the size and ornamentation characteristic of the species.

Filamentous and Membranous Genera

As in the Myxophyceae, restriction of cell division to one plane and adherence of the products of division have produced Chlorophyceae with filamentous plant bodies. Initiation of cell division in a direction other than transverse (at right angles to the long axis) by certain cells of the filament results in a branching plant body. Finally, equally abundant division in two directions produces a membranous plant body which may be one or more layers thick. Representatives of all these types are included in the following discussion. The genera to be described may be

grouped into two categories. In the first, all produce flagellate reproductive cells. The genera *Ulothrix, Stigeoclonium, Ulva, Cladophora* and
Oedogonium belong to this group. To the second belong *Spirogyra* and
Zygnema, in which flagellate reproductive cells are absent. In addition,
the desmids are classified with this second group.

ZOOSPORE-PRODUCING TYPES: ULOTHRIX, STIGEOCLONIUM, CLADOPHORA,
ULVA, AND OEDOGONIUM

The unbranched filaments of *Ulothrix* (Fig. 3–15A) grow attached to
stones, other submerged objects, and vegetation in cold-water streams
and lakes; several species are marine. In *Ulothrix* (Gr. *oulos,* wooly +
Gr. *thrix,* hair), the cells of each filament are as similar to each other as
are those of *Oscillatoria,* except
that the basal cell is modified
as an attaching organ, the **holdfast** (Fig. 3–15A). The cells
contain partial or complete
band-shaped chloroplasts (Fig.
3–15C) and are uninucleate.
After a period of vegetative
growth by cell division and
elongation, asexual reproduction by zoospores may occur
(Fig. 3–16). Zoospores may be
produced singly (Figs. 3–16,
3–18) or in multiples of two
from each vegetative cell. The
liberated zoospores exhibit such
attributes of motile cells as

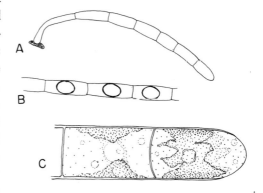

Fig. 3–15. *Ulothrix* sp. A, Outline drawing of young
plant attached by holdfast to a particle of debris.
B, Portion of filament containing hypnospores. C,
Cell structure at apex of filament; apical cell in
surface view, second cell in median section. A and ?
X 215; C, X 770.

stigmata, contractile vacuoles, and four flagella (Figs. 3–16, 3–17). After
a period of activity, the zoospores settle on submerged objects with their
flagellate poles foremost (Fig. 3–17B), lose their flagella, secrete a wall,
and attach themselves. Elongation and division of the original zoospore
(Fig. 3–17C,D) produce a vegetative filament. Sexual reproduction by
union of biflagellate isogametes (Fig. 3–17E,F) also occurs. There is evidence that the sexual filaments are heterothallic in some species. Meiosis
occurs, as in all other genera so far considered, just prior to germination
of the zygospore. The latter gives rise to four zoospores each of which
grows into a new filament.

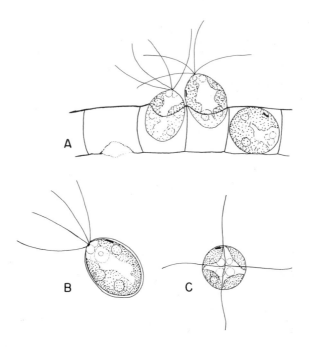

Fig. 3–16. *Ulothrix* sp. *A,* Zoospore formation and liberation. *B,* Single zoospore stained with I₂–KI₂. *C,* Living zoospore in polar view. X 770.

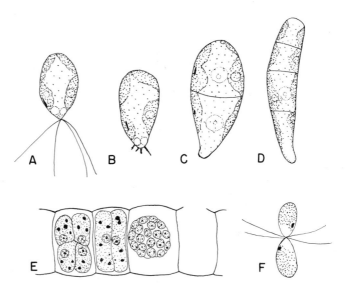

Fig. 3–17. *Ulothrix* sp. *A-D,* Development of zoospore into young filament. *E,* Gametogenesis in *U. zonata* (Weber and Mohr) Kütz. *F,* Union of isogametes. *A-C* and *F,* X 770; *D, E,* X 315.

Occasional cell division in a second direction produces a branching, filamentous plant body in *Stigeoclonium* and *Cladophora*. *Stigeoclonium* (L. *stigens*, sharp-pointed + Gr. *klonion*, branch) is a plant widely distributed in cold lakes and streams, where it grows attached to stones and vegetation. The plant consists of two portions (Figs. 3–19, 3–20). A prostrate, and probably perennial, system of irregular branched filaments is attached to the substratum. From this, elongate branching filaments grow out into the water. These are attenuated and end in hairlike branches. Because they have two branch sys-

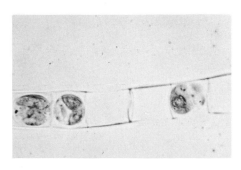

Fig. 3–18. *Ulothrix* sp. Photomicrograph of segment of a filament during zoospore formation and liberation. X 590.

tems, the plants are said to be **heterotrichous**. The cells of *Stigeoclonium* are uninucleate and contain peripheral chloroplasts with one or several pyrenoids. In asexual reproduction, quadriflagellate zoospores are liberated singly from the cells of the plant body. After a period of activity, these become attached to the substratum by the formerly flagellate pole,

Fig. 3–19. *Stigeoclonium* sp. Erect system. X 30.

secrete a wall, and develop into new plant bodies. Union of biflagellate gametes has been described for some species; in others the gametes are quadriflagellate. There is good evidence that meiosis is zygotic in most species of *Stigeoclonium*. As in *Ulothrix*, the zygospore germinates to form four zoospores which ultimately grow into new plants.

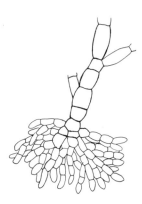

Fig. 3–20. *Stigeoclonium sp.* Prostrate system. X 315.

Cladophora (Gr. *klados*, branch + Gr. *phores*, bearer) (Fig. 3–21A) differs from *Stigeoclonium* in a number of respects, among them, larger size, multinucleate cells, and especially life cycle. Species of *Cladophora* are widespread in both fresh and salt water, where they grow attached to rocks or vegetation. The plants are anchored to the substratum by rhizoidal branches. The latter are perennial and persist through adverse conditions. Growth of the branching filaments is localized near the apices of the filaments, in contrast with the generalized

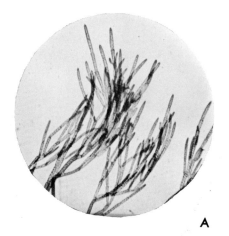

A   B

Fig. 3–21. *Cladophora sp.* A, Fresh-water species, vegetative condition. B, Marine species undergoing zoospore liberation. X 30.

growth of *Ulothrix*. The branches arise as eversions from the upper portions of the lateral walls of relatively young cells (Fig. 3–21A). When they have achieved a certain length, they are delimited from the parent cell by annular ingrowth of the wall.

The cylindrical cells of *Cladophora* are much larger than those of *Stigeoclonium*, and their cell walls are thicker and stratified (Fig. 3–22A).

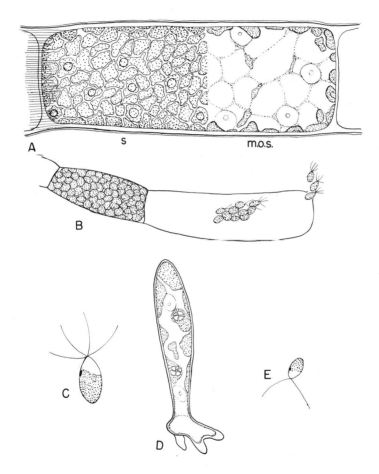

Fig. 3–22. *Cladophora* sp. A, Cell structure; surface view at s, median optical section at m.o.s. B, Zoospore formation and liberation in marine species. C, Zoospore. D, Germling from zoospore. E, Gamete. A, C, and E, X 770; B, X 315; D, X 410.

The structure of the chloroplast varies with the age of the cell. In younger cells it is a continuous reticulum, but in older ones it is largely peripheral and composed of irregular segments in some of which pyrenoids are embedded (Fig. 3–22A). Segments of the plastid may extend toward the center of the cell. An alveolar reticulum of cytoplasm fills the lumen. Numerous nuclei (Fig. 3–22A) are suspended in its meshes. Nuclear division is mitotic. Mitosis and cytokinesis are independent processes in *Cladophora,* in contrast with their rather close relationship in most plants and animals with uninucleate cells.

Asexual reproduction is accomplished by uninucleate, quadriflagellate zoospores (Fig. 3–22B,C). These arise by cleavage of the protoplasts of terminal and near-terminal cells into uninucleate segments. Each segment develops four flagella, and the mature zoospores are liberated through a pore in the zoosporangial wall (Fig. 3–21B, 3–22B). After a period of motility the zoospores grow into new plants (Fig. 3–22D). The young germlings are uninucleate, but the **coenocytic** (multinucleate) condition is soon initiated by the continuation of mitosis without ensuing cytokinesis. *Cladophora* plants also produce biflagellate, isogamous gametes (Fig. 3–22E) in sexual reproduction. These also are formed in the terminal and near-terminal cells. The zygotes germinate without a period of dormancy and grow directly into new plants.

Cytological studies of plants in culture indicate that two types of life cycle may occur in the genus *Cladophora*. In a fresh-water species, *C. glomerata* (L.) Kütz., it has been reported that zygotic meiosis does not take place but that the zygote develops into a diploid adult plant. Zoospores produced by such plants also are diploid. However, prior to gamete formation, the nuclei of the cells that are to form gametes undergo two successive divisions, during which meiosis is accomplished. The gametes therefore are haploid. In all the genera of Chlorophyceae discussed up to this point, the plant body is haploid; the zygote, which becomes a dormant zygospore, alone is diploid (Type I, p. 51). But in *C. glomerata* the reverse is true, for the plant body is diploid and the gametes alone are haploid. Meiosis in *C. glomerata,* as in most animals, is **gametic** rather than zygotic (Type II, p. 51).

Another type of life cycle has been reported to occur in several marine species of *Cladophora*. In *C. suhriana* Kütz., for example, it has been shown that two types of plant occur in nature. These are morphologically indistinguishable but differ in chromosome complement and nature of their reproductive cells. One type of plant is diploid and produces only zoospores from cells in which meiosis precedes the cleavage into zoospores. These develop into haploid plants, morphologically similar to the diploid ones. However, the haploid plants produce only biflagellate gametes at maturity. The gametes unite in pairs to form zygotes, which develop without meiosis into diploid filaments. Meiosis in *C. suhriana,* therefore, is **sporic** rather than gametic or zygotic (Type III, below).

The three types of life cycle described in the preceding pages may be summarized comparatively as shown below. The numbers and letters in parentheses indicate the chromosome constitution. Where this change from $2n$ to n is in succeeding stages, meiosis has occurred. Where the chromosome constitution changes from n to $2n$, sexual union has intervened. For emphasis, $2n$ phases are doubly underscored, n phases singly.

Until relatively recently it was thought that meiosis was zygotic in all Chlorophyceae and that the plant body was always haploid (Type I). Intensive investigation in the last decade has revealed the types of life cycle of the *Cladophora* species just described (Types II and III), as well as their counterparts in other genera.

Organisms in which two distinct, free-living plants occur in the life cycle are said to be **diplobiontic** (Gr. *diplos,* double + Gr. *bioo,* to

Three Types of Life Cycle

Type I

Type II

Type III

live); *Cladophora suhriana,* therefore, is diplobiontic. Other genera, in which only one free-living organism occurs in the life cycle, are **haplobiontic** (Gr. *haploos,* single + Gr. *bioo*). Diplobiontic life cycles illustrate but one manifestation of the larger phenomenon of **alternation of generations**. They are a specialized example in which the alternants occur as free-living individuals. In contrast, alternation of generations of another type, in which the alternants are physically connected, occurs in the liverworts, mosses, and some vascular plants.

Haplobiontic life cycles may be thought of as possessing only cytological alternation, one alternant, either the zygote or the gamete, consisting merely of a single cell and not of a free-living plant. This condition occurs in *Chlamydomonas* and *Spirogyra,* among others (Type I). In these genera the entire life cycle consists of haploid individuals, with the exception of the diploid zygospores. It should be noted that the terms **haploid** and **diploid** are used with reference to chromosome constitution. Haploid organisms possess a single basic complement of chromosomes in their nuclei; diploid individuals have nuclei with two such sets.

A reverse type of haplobiontic life cycle (Type II) is present in *Cladophora glomerata* and *Bryopsis* (p. 65). In these, the diploid plant body is dominant and the haploid phase is represented only by the gametes.

Diplobiontic life cycles often are said to exhibit **morphological** (as well as cytological) **alternation of generations,** for in this type both the diploid and haploid phases occur as morphologically recognizable plants. The alternants may be equal in stature and fundamentally similar, as in *Cladophora suhriana.* In this case, alternation is said to be **isomorphic.** When the alternating phases are dissimilar morphologically (as in *Laminaria,* a brown alga, p. 74, and in the land plants) the alternation is called **heteromorphic.**

One can compare the two alternating generations of the marine *Cladophora* species with the sporophyte and gametophyte phases of the land plants, for in origin, function, and position in the life cycle they seem to be fundamentally similar. The significance of these facts has not been appreciated as widely as it should have been by those interested in the problems of evolution and phylogeny of plants. While an alternation of generations like that described as Type III has long been known in the land plants, few students of these groups, in speculating about their origin, have considered the significance of the occurrence of a similar type of life cycle in the Chlorophyceae. This problem will be discussed again in our consideration of the land plants.

In addition to the unbranched (*Ulothrix*) and branched (*Stigeoclonium, Cladophora*) zoospore-producing Chlorophyceae, there remain the membranous, blade-like forms; these will now be described. A plant body of the *Ulva* (L. *ulva,* marsh plant) (Fig. 3–23) type arises by abundant

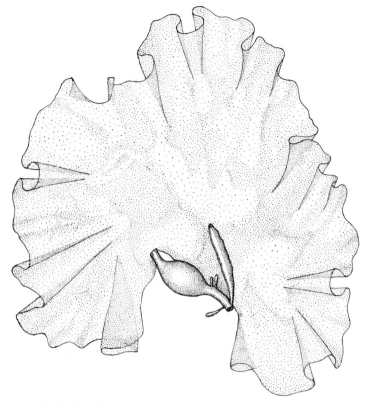

Fig. 3–23.   *Ulva lactuca* L., growing on *Ascophyllum,* a brown alga. X 1.

and continued cell division in two directions. A single series of divisions in a third direction results in a two-layered stratum (Fig. 3–24A). *Ulva,* the sea lettuce, is a familiar alga of marine and brackish waters. It is a widely distributed perennial alga which grows attached to rocks, wood-work, and larger marine algae in quiet estuaries. In *Ulva lactuca* L., the plant body is blade-like, often lobed and undulate; in some varieties it may exceed three feet in length. Each plant is anchored to the substratum by a small multicellular holdfast composed of cells with rhizoidal pro-tuberances. The cell walls of *Ulva* (Fig. 3–24B) are rather thick, a prob-able correlative of the fact that the plants can withstand some desiccation when exposed at low tide. Each cell (Fig. 3–24B) contains a single laminate chloroplast with one or more pyrenoids. The cells of the blade are uninucleate, but those of the holdfast may have several nuclei in their rhizoidal processes. Growth of the plant is generalized.

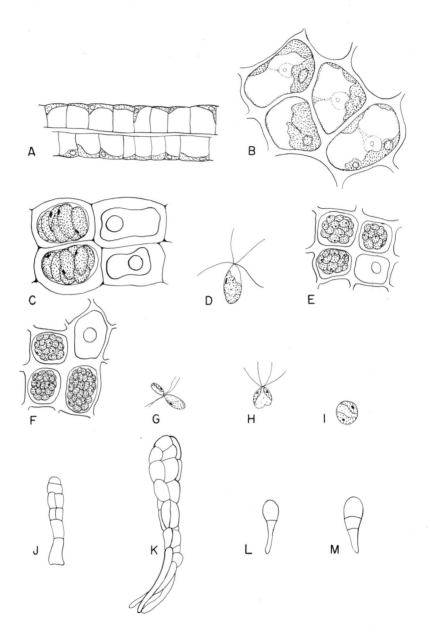

Fig. 3–24. *Ulva lactuca.* A, Transverse section. B, Cell structure, surface view. C, Zoospore formation and liberation; note discharge pores. D, Single zoospore. E, Formation and liberation of female gametes. F, Formation and liberation of male gametes. G-I, Phases of heterogamous union. J-K, Young plants from zoospores. L,M, Young plants from zygotes. A, J-M, X 315; B-I, X 770.

Ulva reproduces by asexual zoospores (Figs. 3–24C and *D*, 3–25A) and heterogametes (Fig. 3–24E-*I*). If one gathers *Ulva* plants of sufficient maturity, permits them to dry slightly, and then submerges them individually in dishes of sea water under strong unilateral illumination, such dishes soon become green with liberated motile cells. These manifest

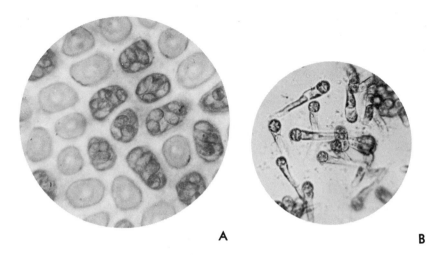

A   B

Fig. 3–25. *Ulva lactuca.* A, Photomicrograph of zoospore formation and empty zoosporangia. B, Young germlings from zoospores. A, X 250; B, X 590.

strong positive **phototaxis.** Careful microscopic examination of the motile cells of the several dishes reveals that three types are produced, each by different plants. Some of them liberate large motile cells (Fig. 3–24C,*D*) which are quadriflagellate; a second group sheds biflagellate gametes of two distinct sizes (Fig. 3–24E-*G*).[4] The small male gametes arise from plants other than those that produce the female ones; *Ulva* is heterothallic. Thus three types of plants, one zoosporogenic and two gametogenic, comprise a population of *Ulva*.

The asexual zoospores grow directly into new plants (Figs. 3–24J-K, 3–25B) which pass through an unbranched filamentous phase. These plants are the male and female gametophytes which liberate the heterogamous gametes at maturity. The zygotes develop into diploid, zoospore-producing plants (Fig. 3–24I,L,M). Meiosis occurs in the first two nuclear divisions in the cells that produce the zoospores, which accordingly

[4] A number of Pacific Coast species of *Ulva* are reported to be heterogamous, but *U. lactuca* on the Atlantic Coast is usually considered to be isogamous. However, the figures of uniting gametes and gametangial cells here reproduced are from camera lucida drawings prepared at Woods Hole, Massachusetts, in 1954.

are haploid. One half of the zoospores of a given zoosporangium develop into male gametophytes and the other half into female; both, of course, are haploid. The life cycle of *Ulva* is entirely similar to that of *Cladophora suhriana*, being diplobiontic and isomorphic; it clearly belongs to Type III (p. 51).

Finally, among the filamentous Chlorophyceae which produce zoospores, *Oedogonium* (Gr. *oedos*, swelling + Gr. *gonos*, seed) remains to be described. It differs from the other genera in that its motile reproductive cells possess a ring of flagella (Figs. 3–26, 3–29). Furthermore,

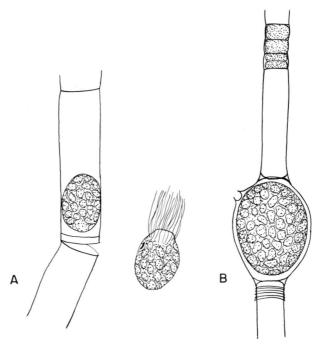

Fig. 3–26.   A, *Oedogonium* sp. Zoospore formation and liberation. B, O. *foveolatum* Wittr. homothallic species with oogonium and antheridium. A, X 315; B, X 500.

growth is intercalary and localized in certain cells on which annular scars indicate the number of cell divisions which have occurred (Fig. 3–27). The cells include segmented, reticulate chloroplasts containing pyrenoids in certain units.

The life cycle of *Oedogonium* is clearly Type I (p. 51) like that of *Ulothrix*. Asexual reproduction is effected by the formation and liberation of single zoospores from vegetative cells (Fig. 3–26A). Sexual reproduction in *Oedogonium* is oogamous. The egg is produced in an enlarged gametangium called the **oogonium** which opens by a pore or fissure just before fertilization (Figs. 3–26, 3–27, 3–29). The sperms arise in pairs in

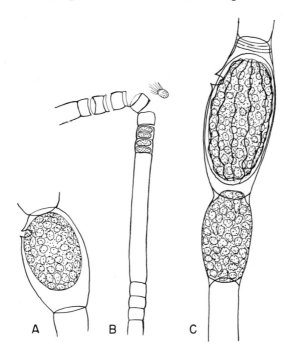

Fig. 3–27. *Oedogonium crenulatacostatum* Wittr. Heterothallic species with both male and female plants well-developed filaments, although male filaments are of smaller diameter. This is the macrandrous condition. A, Oogonium and egg. B, Antheridial filament. C, Immature oogonium and oospore. X 500.

short, often seriate, box-like cells, the **antheridia** (Figs. 3–26 to 3–29). After fertilization, the zygote develops a wall composed of two or more layers, often becomes reddish in color, and enters a period of dormancy (Figs. 3–27C, 3–28). It is liberated by the disintegration of the oogonial wall. The germination of the zygospore into four zoospores is preceded by the meiotic process. The zygospores produced in oogamous sexual reproduction, such as those of *Volvox* and *Oedogonium,* are often called **oospores.** Considerable variation occurs among the numerous species of *Oedogonium* with respect to the distribution of the sexes. These variations are illustrated and explained in the legends of Figs. 3–26 to 3–29.

NONZOOSPORE-PRODUCING TYPES: SPIROGYRA, ZYGNEMA,
COSMARIUM, CLOSTERIUM, AND MICRASTERIAS

Spirogyra (Gr. *speira,* a coil + Gr. *gyros,* curved) and *Zygnema* (Gr.
zygon, yoke + Gr. *nema,* thread), but especially *Spirogyra,* usually are

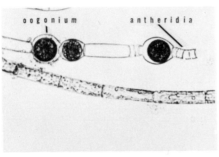

familiar to everyone who has
ever studied biology. These genera often form floating, bright-
green, frothy or slimy masses in
small bodies of water and submerged fields in the spring of the
year and are referred to frequently as "pond scums" by the
laymen. The unbranched filaments, generally unattached,
grow by generalized cell division
and elongation. Masses of the
plants are slimy to the touch, because the filaments are surrounded by watery sheaths, demonstrable by India ink and
methylene blue.

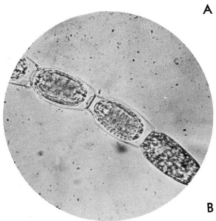

The cell structure of *Spirogyra*
is familiar to many, at least superficially, because of the spiral
arrangement of the ribbon-like
chloroplast or chloroplasts (Figs.
3–30A,B, Fig. 3–31A). However,
this very familiarity and ability
to recognize the plant readily
often result in failure to appreciate the many details of cell

Fig. 3–28. Photomicrographs. A. Homothallic
Oedogonium sp. B, Mature oospores of *O. crenulatacostatum.* X 250.

structure observable by those who will to see them. A careful study of the
cell structure of *Spirogyra* in the living condition, as revealed by an oil
immersion objective, not only is a good test of one's powers of perception,
but also affords an opportunity for observation of detail in three-dimensional relations which can be transferred, with profit to the observer, to
the study of all cells. Species containing one or a few chloroplasts in each
cell are especially favorable for study of the cell structure, which is illustrated in Fig. 3–31A. The living cells of *Spirogyra* are excellent for ob-

servation of protoplasmic streaming or cyclosis, as are those of the desmids. *Zygnema* (Fig. 3–30*E*) differs from *Spirogyra* in having two stellate chloroplastids in each of its cells.

Aside from fragmentation of the filaments, no method of asexual reproduction occurs in *Spirogyra* and *Zygnema*. In *Spirogyra*, after a period of vegetative development, the filaments tend to become apposed. Adjacent cells of contiguous filaments produce papillate protuberances which meet and elongate, thus forcing the filaments apart (Figs. 3–30*B*, 3–31*B*). Ultimately the terminal walls of the contiguous papillae are dissolved, and one of the protoplasts of the pair of connected cells, both of which have lost much of the cell sap from their vacuoles, initiates movement through the tubular connection. Contractile vacuoles, usually present only in flagellate cells, appear in the protoplasts during dehydration and seem to play a role in the process. The two protoplasts and their nuclei unite, and the resultant zygote (Figs. 3–30*C*, 3–31*C*) secretes a thick wall and enters a period of dormancy. There is evidence that the chloroplast of the migrant cell disintegrates subsequently. Sexual reproduction of this type is interpreted

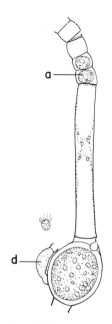

Fig. 3–29. *Oedogonium* sp. Homothallic nannandrous. In this type the dwarf male (*d*) arises from a special "androzoospore" (*a*) which becomes attached to or near the oogonium. X 315.

as **morphological isogamy** with **physiological heterogamy**, the migrant protoplast being considered a male gamete.

At the conclusion of dormancy, the zygospore, which has previously been liberated from the cell wall of the vegetative cell, germinates into a new filament (Figs. 3–30*D*, 3–31*D*). Meiosis precedes germination, but only one filament emerges from each zygospore, because three of the four products of meiosis disintegrate before germination. In some species of *Spirogyra*, papillae from adjacent cells of the same filament establish contact, and the protoplasts of alternate cells function as male gametes with respect to the next cell of the filament, so that zygospores occur in alter-

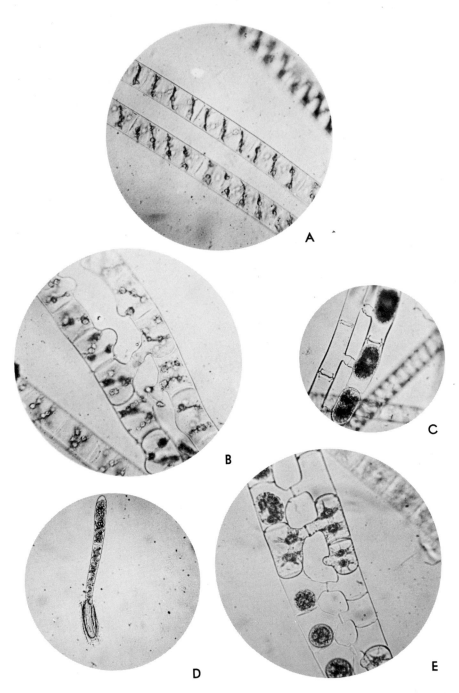

Fig. 3–30. Photomicrographs of *Spirogyra* and *Zygnema*. A, *Spirogyra* sp. Vegetative cells. B and C, Stages in sexual reproduction in different species. D, Zygospore germination. E, *Zygnema* sp. Stages in sexual reproduction. X 250.

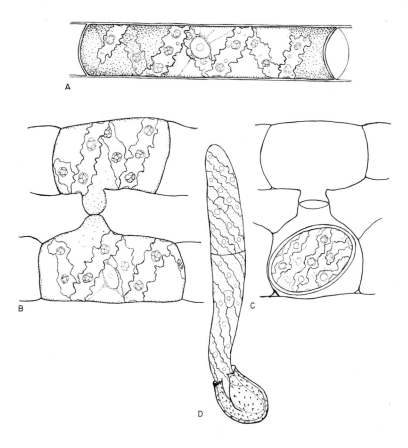

Fig. 3–31.   *Spirogyra sp. A,* Vegetative cell structure (colorless cytoplasm omitted in central portion for greater clarity). *B* and *C,* Stages in sexual reproduction. *D,* Zygospore germination. X 514.

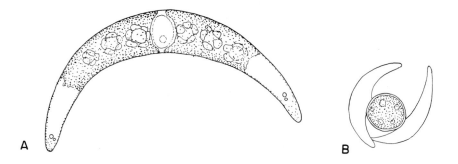

Fig. 3–32.   *A, Closterium parvulum* Wittr. Vegetative cell. *B, C. parvulum.* Sexual reproduction. *A,* X 770; *B,* X 315.

nate cells. This is known as **lateral conjugation,** in contrast with the more usual **scalariform** or ladder-like pattern. As a matter of fact, lateral conjugation might more appropriately be called terminal. The *Spirogyra* life cycle belongs to Type I (p. 51).

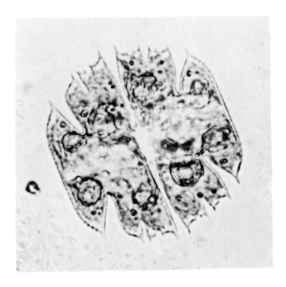

A

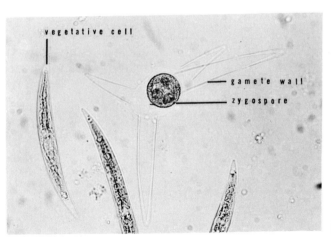

B

Fig. 3–33. *A, Micrasterias semidecandra.* X 540. *B, Closterium littorale Gay.* Vegetative cells and sexual reproduction. X 250.

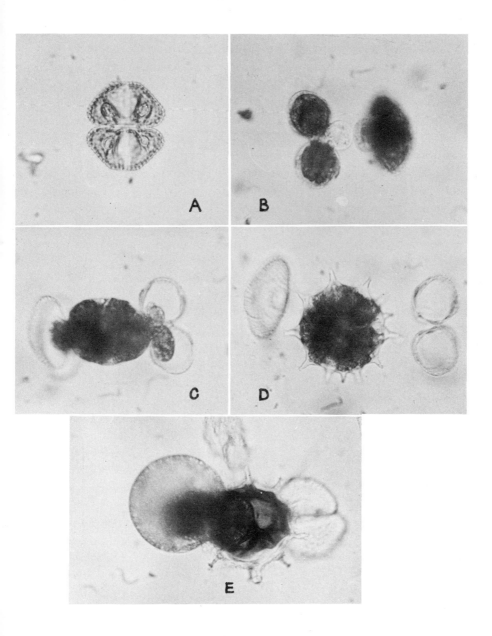

Fig. 3–34. *Cosmarium botrytis* var. *subtumidum* Wittr. A, Vegetative cell. B-D, Sexual reproduction. E, Zygospore germination. X 440. (Photomicrographs by Miss Ann Allen and Dr. R. C. Starr.)

Although they are represented by both unicellular and filamentous genera, the desmids are reminiscent of *Spirogyra* and its relatives because of their cell structure and sexual reproduction. The name "desmid" (Gr. *desmos*, bond) is ascribable to the fact that the cells of a majority of these plants are composed of **semicells** which are mirror images of each other; the connecting region is known as the **isthmus.** As in *Spirogyra*, flagellate motile cells are absent. *Micrasterias* (Gr. *micros*, little + Gr. *asterias*, star) (Fig. 3–33A), *Closterium* (Gr. *kloster*, spindle) (Figs. 3–32, 3–33B), and *Cosmarium* (Gr. *kosmos*, an ornament) (Fig. 3–34), are widely distributed genera representative of the unicellular desmids, although *Micrasterias* cells sometimes are connected in chains. The two semicells of *Micrasterias* (Fig. 3–33A) are separated by a deep incision or **sinus.** The nucleus lies in the isthmus. The cell wall of desmids is composed of several layers, the outermost of which is a rather diffluent pectin. It has been shown in some species that localized secretion of pectin through pores in the wall layers results in movement of the cells.

Asexual reproduction of unicellular genera is by cell division preceded by mitosis. In both *Micrasterias* and *Closterium*, the two products of cytokinesis, each containing a nucleus, regenerate semicells.

Cosmarium is a ubiquitous desmid which has been receiving intensive genetic and cytological analysis. In *Cosmarium botrytis* var. *subtumidum* Wittr. (Fig. 3–34), it has been demonstrated recently that sexuality is heterothallic. When compatible vegetative cells are mixed together in laboratory cultures provided with adequate CO_2, the cells pair within about 48 hours (Fig. 3–34B). This is accomplished through slow movements effected by secretion of pectin at one pole of the cell. The pairs of cells lie together in a mass of common pectin after they have paired. This is followed by opening of the cell walls at the isthmus (Fig. 3–34C) and liberation

Fig. 3–35. *Bryopsis plumosa* (Hudson) C. Agardh. Photomicrograph of vegetative shoot. X 60.

of the protoplasts which unite to form a spiny zygospore (Fig. 3–34D). After a period of dormancy, the zygospore germinates (Fig. 3–34E) to produce two daughter cells. Meiosis occurs during germination, but two of the four products of meiosis disintegrate. *Closterium parvulum* Wittr., unlike *Cosmarium botrytis*, is homothallic (Figs. 3–32B, 3–34).

Tubular (Siphonaceous) Genera: *Bryopsis* and *Codium*

In addition to the unicellular, colonial, filamentous, and membranous types of plant bodies already described among Chlorophyceae, brief mention must be made of one other type, the tubular or **siphonaceous**. Siphonaceous green algae are marine, almost without exception. They may be simple, pinnately branching plants, like *Bryopsis* (Fig. 3–35) or more complex and composed of interwoven tubes as in *Codium* (Figs. 3–36, 3–37). In both these plants the unit of structure is a coenocytic tubular cell whose multinucleate protoplasm is peripherally disposed around a large central vacuole (Figs. 3–35, 3–37). *Bryopsis* (Gr. *bryon*, a moss + Gr. *opsis*, appearance) grows attached to rocks in shallow salt water. *Codium* (Gr. *codion*, a fleece) is a wooly, rope-like plant, the

Fig. 3–36. *Codium tomentosum* (Hudson) Stackh. X ½.

strands of which are composed of interwoven siphons (Fig. 3–37). A majority of the tubular Chlorophyceae exhibit a Type II life cycle (p. 51), as exemplified also by *Cladophora glomerata*. The plants are **diplonts**[5] and meiosis is gametic. The zygotes grow directly into new plants.

Fig. 3–37. *Codium tomentosum*. Portion of branch, surface view of siphons. X 25.

The existence of large and complex plant bodies composed of coenocytic tubes from which transverse septa are lacking, except during reproduction, has led to speculation

---

[5] A diploid organism may be called a diplont.

regarding the relation of such plants to other types of plant body. To some, the extensive growths represent single giant, multinucleate cells. According to others, they are to be interpreted as acellular plant bodies, the individual nuclei and their surrounding cytoplasm being considered to represent cellular units not delimited by cell walls.

SUMMARY AND CLASSIFICATION

One may wonder at the relative length of the discussion of the division Chlorophyta and class Chlorophyceae just concluded, but if he reviews the number and significance of the biological phenomena which they exhibit, no further explanation will seem necessary. They are distinguished from the Cyanophyta (class Myxophyceae) by their possession of highly organized nuclei and chloroplasts, as well as by their pigmentation. In this last respect, among others, they differ from the remaining divisions of algae.

The Chlorophyceae comprise a series of genera with a wide range of body form, including motile unicellular and colonial organisms, nonmotile unicellular and colonial types, branched and unbranched filaments, membranous and tubular organisms. The component cells may be uninucleate or multinucleate (coenocytic) in organization.

The various genera may undergo asexual reproduction by cell division (unicellular forms), by fragmentation (colonial and filamentous types), or by the production of such special reproductive cells as zoospores, aplanospores, autospores, and akinetes. Colonial genera reproduce by autocolony formation.

Many genera of Chlorophyceae exhibit sexual reproduction which involves the union of two cells and their nuclei and the association of their chromosomes and genes. Various grades of sexuality such as isogamy, heterogamy, and oogamy may be observed in the several illustrative genera. In organisms like *Chlamydomonas* and *Chlorococcum*, in which gametes are morphologically indistinguishable from asexual cells, there is evidence that sexuality is primitive and incipient. The gametes of both sexes may occur on one individual (homothallism) or they may be segregated on different individuals (heterothallism). The Chlorophyceae also illustrate a variety of reproductive cycles, herein designated Types I, II, and III (p. 51). These are characterized as follows:

Type I. Organisms which are **haplobiontic** and **haploid**, with **zygotic meiosis.**

Type II. Organisms which are **haplobiontic** and **diploid**, with **gametic meiosis.**

Type III. Organisms which are **diplobiontic**, with **sporic meiosis.**

Alternation in the life cycle in Types I and II is often called **cytological,** in contrast with that of Type III, which is **morphological** (as well as cytological) in the sense that two plants are involved.

The genera of Chlorophyta discussed in the present chapter may be classified as follows:

Division Chlorophyta
  Class 1. Chlorophyceae
    Order 1. Volvocales
      Family 1. Chlamydomonadaceae
        Genus: *Chlamydomonas*
      Family 2. Volvocaceae
        Genera: *Pandorina, Volvox*
    Order 2. Chlorococcales
      Family 1. Chlorococcaceae
        Genus: *Chlorococcum*
      Family 2. Hydrodictyaceae
        Genera: *Pediastrum, Hydrodictyon*
      Family 3. Oocystaceae
        Genus: *Chlorella*
      Family 4. Scenedesmaceae
        Genus: *Scenedesmus*
    Order 3. Ulotrichales
      Family 1. Ulotrichaceae
        Genus: *Ulothrix*
      Family 2. Chaetophoraceae
        Genus: *Stigeoclonium*
    Order 4. Ulvales
      Family 1. Ulvaceae
        Genus: *Ulva*
    Order 5. Cladophorales
      Family 1. Cladophoraceae
        Genus: *Cladophora*
    Order 6. Siphonales
      Family 1. Bryopsidaceae
        Genus: *Bryopsis*
      Family 2. Codiaceae
        Genus: *Codium*
    Order 7. Oedogoniales
      Family 1. Oedogoniaceae
        Genus: *Oedogonium*

Order 8. Zygnematales
  Family 1. Zygnemataceae
    Genera: *Spirogyra, Zygnema*
  Family 2. Desmidiaceae
    Genera: *Micrasterias, Closterium, Cosmarium*

The distinguishing attributes, on the basis of which the orders, families, and their component genera are delimited, are discussed in several of the specialized treatises listed at the conclusion of the preceding chapter. Such characteristics as presence or absence of motility in the vegetative or reproductive phases, structure of the plant body, nature of the chloroplast, and other morphological aspects are involved in the segregation of the various taxa.

In concluding this account of the Chlorophyceae, it should be emphasized that their pigmentation and the storage of the excess photosynthate as starch seem to link them physiologically to the higher land plants more closely than is evident in any other group of algae. For this reason, most speculations regarding the origin of the more complex groups always involve consideration of the morphology and physiology of the division Chlorophyta, class Chlorophyceae.

DISCUSSION QUESTIONS

1. Cite the attributes which distinguish the Chlorophyta from the Cyanophyta.
2. On what basis is motility considered to be a primitive attribute?
3. Explain the meaning and use of the following terms: sexual and asexual reproduction; homothallism and heterothallism; isogamy, heterogamy, and oogamy; zygote, zygospore, and oospore; zoospore and zoosporangium; haplobiontic, diplobiontic, haploid, diploid, haplont, diplont; meiosis, mitosis, and cytokinesis; plasmodesma; stigma; pyrenoid; contractile vacuole; flagellum; protoplast; coenocytic; coenobium; gamete and gametangium; antheridium, oogonium, sperm, and egg.
4. What evidence can you cite which indicates that sexuality in genera like *Chlamydomonas* and *Chlorococcum* may be incipient?
5. Can you make a statement regarding the relative biological advantages of isogamy and oogamy? Explain.
6. Why is the stigma sometimes called the "red eyespot"? Consult your instructor about the experiments of Engelmann, Mast, and Hartshorne.[5]

[5] T. W. Engelmann, Über Licht- und Farbenperception niederster Organismen, *Arch. f.d. ges. Physiol.*, 29:387–400, 1882; J. N. Hartshorne, The Function of the Eyespot in Chlamydomonas, *New Phytol.*, 52:292–297, 1953; S. O. Mast, Structure and Function of the Eye-spot in Unicellular and Colonial Organisms, *Arch. f. Protistenk.*, 60:197–220, 1928.

7. What significance do you attach to the fact that nonmotile organisms produce motile reproductive cells?

8. What result would be realized, in your opinion, if the motile zoospores of *Hydrodictyon* were to be released from the parent cell? Verify by releasing some, if material is available.

9. Give examples of cellular differentiation or division of labor in the Myxophyceae and Chlorophyceae.

10. Describe cell division in *Micrasterias* or *Cosmarium*. Plan an experiment to obtain data on its frequency.

11. In scalariform conjugation in *Spirogyra*, conjugation tubes are often established between more than two filaments. What is the disposition of the zygospores when this occurs?

12. What genetic effect is produced by the disintegration of three of the four nuclei arising by meiosis in *Spirogyra*? Can you cite examples of a similar phenomenon elsewhere in the plant or animal kingdom?

13. Construct a dichotomous key to the genera of Chlorophyceae discussed in Chapter 3.

14. Define the terms unialgal culture, pure culture, clonal culture.

15. Define or explain the terms life cycle, alternation of generations, isomorphic and heteromorphic alternation, cytological and morphological alternation, alternant.

16. Place all the algae with sexual reproduction described in Chapter 3 in Types I, II, or III with respect to life cycle.

CHAPTER 4

Division Phaeophyta

GENERAL FEATURES

The division **Phaeophyta** (Gr. *phaios,* dusky + Gr. *phyton,* plant) includes a single class, the **Phaeophyceae** (Gr. *phaios* + Gr. *phykos,* seaweed). The genera of Phaeophyceae are marine in habitat almost without exception. They occur in the open ocean as well as in quiet estuaries and may be abundant on the muddy bottoms of salt marshes. Approximately 190 genera and 900 species of Phaeophyta have been described. In general, **brown algae** flourish in colder ocean waters and on rocky coasts, where many grow attached in relatively shallow water in the intertidal and sublittoral zones. A number of genera are able to withstand exposure to the atmosphere during low tide, whereas others are sublittoral and continuously submerged. Some of the large genera live in shoal waters, and most thrive in waters with considerable current. Few brown algae occur at great depths. Both annual and perennial genera are known.

The brownish shades of the plant reflect the abundant presence in the plastids of the xanthophyll, **fucoxanthin,** which is dominant over chlorophylls *a* and *c* and the other xanthophylls and beta carotene. The plastids are either single or numerous in each cell and may be elaborate in form (Fig. 4–3B). No starch occurs in Phaeophyceae; instead, the excess photosynthate is stored as a carbohydrate, **laminarin,** as mannitol, or in the form of fat droplets. The nuclei of Phaeophyceae are prominent and highly organized structures. In many genera, centrosomes and astral radiations appear during mitosis as in many animal cells. The protoplast is

70

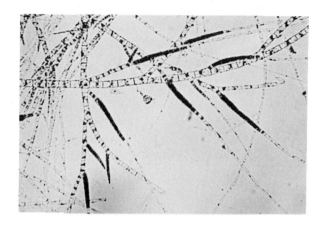

Fig. 4–1. *Ectocarpus siliculosus* (Dillw.) Lyngbye. Photomicrograph of portion of a plant with plurilocular gametangia, X 30.

bounded by a cellulose wall which may be surrounded by a layer composed of a gummy substance, **algin.**

The motile cells of Phaeophyceae are distinctive of the class and differ from those of the Chlorophyta in that they are laterally biflagellate (Figs. 4–3E, 4–9B). Although it has been suggested that the Phaeophyceae originated from unicellular motile organisms with similar lateral flagellation, no such organisms have yet been discovered. In fact, no unicellular Phaeophyceae are known. The simplest type of plant body in the group is the branched filament (Fig. 4–1). Many Phaeophyceae have considerable complexity of structure, as manifested in their leaf-like, stem-like, and root-like organs (Figs. 4–5, 4–6) which exhibit considerable histological differentiation. Certain giant kelps, which attain a length of 50 meters, rival forest trees in stature.

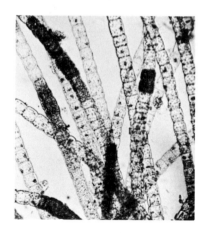

Fig. 4–2. *Pylaiella littoralis* (L.) Kjellm. Photomicrograph of filaments with intercalary gametangia, X 250.

ILLUSTRATIVE TYPES

Filamentous Genera: *Ectocarpus* and *Pylaiella*

Ectocarpus (Gr. *ektos*, outside + Gr. *karpos*, fruit) (Fig. 4–1) and *Pylaiella* (after de la Pylaie, a French phycologist) (Fig. 4–2) are relatively simple types of Phaeophyceae commonly growing epiphytically on larger marine algae. *Ectocarpus* is a branching filamentous plant in which erect filaments arise from an attached prostrate branch system, as in the green alga, *Stigeoclonium*. In *Pylaiella*, occasional cells may divide longitudinally, so that the filaments are multiseriate in part. The apices of the filaments in some species of *Ectocarpus* are almost colorless hairs (Fig. 4–1). A zone of meristematic cells at the base of the hairs increases the length of both the filament and the hairs. This type of in-

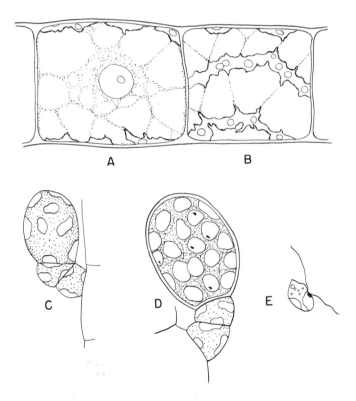

Fig. 4–3. *Ectocarpus siliculosus.* Cell structure, A, median optical section; B, surface view. C,D, Stages in development of unilocular zoosporangium. E, *Ectocarpus mitchellae* Harv. var. *parvus* Taylor. Motile cell from plurilocular organ. X 770.

tercalary growth is said to be **trichothallic.** The mature cells contain band-shaped plastids with pyrenoid-like bodies (Fig. 4–3); the function of the latter is not known.

The life cycle and reproduction of *Ectocarpus* and *Pylaiella* are fundamentally similar to those in *Ulva* and *Cladophora suhriana*—namely,

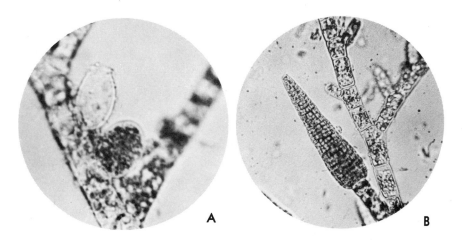

Fig. 4–4. *Ectocarpus* sp. A, Photomicrograph of unilocular zoosporangia, the upper of which has discharged its zoospores. X 590. B, Plurilocular gametangium. X 250.

Type III (p. 51)—in that meiosis is sporic during an isomorphic alternation of generations. Two kinds of reproductive organs may be produced on the diploid sporophytic plants. The terminal cells of lateral branchlets enlarge, and their protoplasts segment endogenously into approximately 32 to 64 portions (Figs. 4–3C,D, 4–4A), each of which becomes pear-shaped and laterally biflagellate (Fig. 4–3E). These are discharged through an apical pore, and after a period of motility they begin to develop into new filaments. The organs producing these zoospores are called **unilocular** (L. *unus*, one + L. *loculus*, small cavity) **zoosporangia**, inasmuch as the zoospores lie within a common cavity. It has been shown that meiosis is accomplished during the first two nuclear divisions in the unilocular zoosporangium, so the zoospores produced from these structures are haploid. By numerous transverse and vertical cell divisions, other lateral branches on the same plants may produce an aggregation of small cubical cells, the protoplasts of each of which also metamorphose into zoospores. Such zoosporangia are said to be **plurilocular** (L. *plus*, more + L. *loculus*), inasmuch as each zoospore is borne

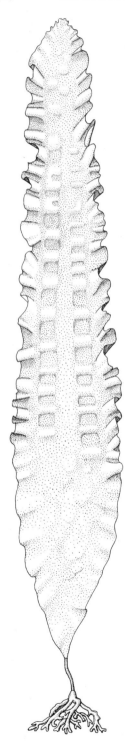

in a separate cell. Zoospores from these plurilocular sporangia are diploid and germinate into filaments like those that produced them. This is a supplementary method which increases the diploid generation. Cultural studies indicate that the haploid zoospores from unilocular sporangia normally develop into haploid gametophytic plants; the latter produce only plurilocular gametangia (Figs. 4–1, 4–4B). Motile cells from these either may unite in pairs to form zygotes, or without union each may produce a new gametophytic plant. Like the diploid, the haploid generation therefore is also increased asexually. Sexuality is isogamous, and the plants are heterothallic. The zygote, without a period of dormancy, develops into a new diploid sporophyte. As in *Chlamydomonas*, sexuality here is not obligate, nor do the gametes differ markedly from the zoospores, for they may develop without sexual fusion into new plants. Both sporophyte and gametophyte may reproduce themselves asexually, so that the alternation of generations is not obligate. Analogous asexual reduplication of sporophyte and gametophyte is rather widespread among the land plants. The life cycles (Type III, p. 51) of *Ectocarpus* and *Pylaiella* are summarized in the diagram p. 75. *Pylaiella* differs from *Ectocarpus* in producing both its unilocular and its plurilocular organs in intercalary positions, not on emergent lateral branches.

The Kelps: *Laminaria* and *Macrocystis*

Laminaria (L. *lamina*, thin plate) (Fig. 4–5) and *Macrocystis* (Gr. *makros*, long + Gr. *kystis*, bladder) (Fig. 4–6), members of the kelp alliance, are of interest not only because of the complexity of their vegetative structure, but also because their

Fig. 4–5. *Laminaria agardhii* Kjellm. Note blade, stipe, and holdfast. X ⅓.

Life Cycle of *Ectocarpus* and *Pylaiella*

Plurilocular
zoosporangium $(2n)$ → Zoospores $(2n)$

Plant $(2n)$ → Unilocular zoosporangium $(2n)$ → Zoospores (n)

Gametes (n)

Zygote $(2n)$ Plurilocular gametangia (n) ← Plants (n)

Gametes (n)

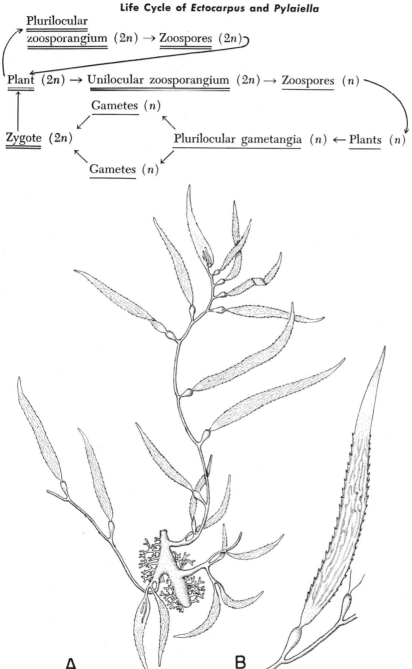

A   B

Fig. 4–6. *Macrocystis integrifolia* Bory. A, Portion of plant, showing holdfasts and branching stipes with blades. X ⅛. B, Single segment enlarged. X ⅜. (Adapted from G. M. Smith.)

life cycle is representative of a type not yet clearly demonstrated in any of the Chlorophyceae, but similar in many respects to that of ferns and

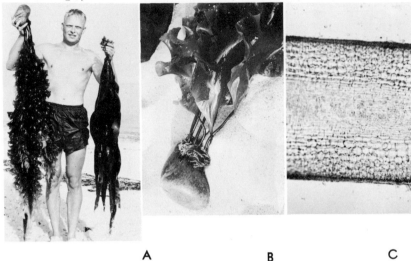

A   B   C

Fig. 4–7. A, *Laminaria agardhii* (left) and *L. digitata* (L.) Edmons. Freshly collected at Sandwich Beach, Mass. X 1/30. B, *L. agardhii.* Detail of holdfasts. X 1/12. C, *L. agardhii.* transverse section of blade (photomicroaraph); note dense photosynthetic cells on both surfaces and central medulla between two cortical layers. X 60.

other vascular plants. *Laminaria* (Figs. 4–5, 4–7) occurs attached to rocks which are submerged even at extreme low tide; it is sometimes known as

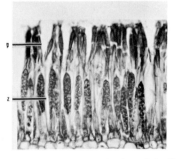

Fig. 4–8. *Laminaria* sp. Section of fertile area consisting of zoosporangia, z., and paraphyses, p. X 215.

the "devil's apron." The plant consists of a branching holdfast, a stipe, and an expanded blade. Growth of the plant occurs at the tip of the stipe and therefore is intercalary. The oldest portion of the blade is the apex. Both blade and stipe are quite complex histologically. Certain cells of the stipe and blade, the "**trumpet hyphae**," have been compared with the sieve tubes of vascular plants. Only the more superficial cells of both stipe and blade are photosynthetic, the central cells having very few plastids (Fig. 4–7C).

Late in the growing season, during the winter and spring on the east

coast, certain superficial cells of the blade elongate and become transformed into unilocular zoosporangia (Fig. 4–8). These occur in sorus-
like patches. Each of these produces 32 to 64 zoospores which are liberated and develop asexually into prostrate, *Ectocarpus*-like branching
filaments that ultimately produce gametangia (Fig. 4–9). Meiosis is
sporic, and occurs in the unilocular zoosporangia, as in *Ectocarpus* and
Pylaiella. The *Laminaria* plant is diploid and sporophytic; the prostrate
branching filaments which develop from the haploid zoospores are

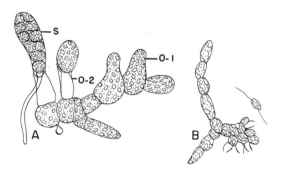

Fig. 4–9. *Laminaria japonica* Aresch. Gametophytes. A, Female gametophyte: 0-1, immature
oogonium; 0-2, oogonium with extruded egg; s, young sporophyte at mouth of oogonium. X 350.
B, Male gametophyte; note cluster of antheridia and sperm. X 450. (Modified from Kanda.)

gametophytic and haploid. The gametophytes are heterothallic and sexuality is oogamous. The antheridia (Fig. 4–9B) are produced as lateral
cells on the male gametophyte; each antheridium produces a minute,
laterally biflagellate sperm. The oogonia (Fig. 4–9A) produce single
eggs which are released but remain attached to the oogonium, so that
fertilization and the development of the embryonic sporophyte occur
in situ (Fig. 4–9A). Without undergoing a dormant period, the zygote
grows into a new sporophyte which ultimately develops the form typical
of the species. The life cycle of *Laminaria* may be summarized as follows:

$$\text{Plant } (2n) \rightarrow \text{Unilocular zoosporangium } (2n) \rightarrow \text{Zoospores } (n)$$
$$\text{Zygote } (2n) \leftarrow \begin{cases} \text{Sperm } (n) \leftarrow \text{Antheridium } (n) \leftarrow \text{Male gametophyte } (n) \\ \text{Egg } (n) \leftarrow \text{Oogonium } (n) \leftarrow \text{Female gametophyte } (n) \end{cases}$$

The life cycle of *Laminaria* and related genera is instructive in a number of respects. It is fundamentally similar to that of *Ulva*, the marine

species of *Cladophora, Ectocarpus,* and *Pylaiella,* all of which have sporic meiosis and alternation of diploid, sporophytic with haploid, gametophytic generations (Type III, p. 51). However, in *Laminaria* the sporophyte and gametophyte differ markedly in size, structure, and longevity; alternation here is **heteromorphic.** The sporophyte is a large, complex, perennial plant, dominant in the life cycle, whereas the gametophytes are microscopic, few-celled, branching filaments and relatively ephemeral. It should be noted that both generations are free-living plants, presumably autotrophic by photosynthesis. In balance of the two generations, the life cycle of *Laminaria* is practically identical with that of ferns and related vascular plants. As a basis for theoretical discussions of the origin and relation of the alternating generations, it must be borne in mind that various genera of algae in the same aquatic environment illustrate alternation of both similar and dissimilar generations. Among the land plants, the alternating generations always are markedly dissimilar morphologically. The partial retention of the egg, and consequently the zygote, within the oogonium, which occurs in *Laminaria,* represents an intermediate condition between their expulsion in many other algae and their permanent retention in the land plants. The significance of these features will be referred to later in our discussion of the land plants.

The Rockweeds: *Fucus* and *Sargassum*

The widely distributed genera *Fucus* (L. *fucus,* rock-lichen) (Fig. 4–10) and *Sargassum* (Sp. *sargazo,* seaweed) (Fig. 4–11) represent still a third type of life cycle which occurs among the Phaeophyceae. *Fucus* grows attached to rocks in the intertidal zone where the plants are exposed at low tide. The plant body, which may attain a length of 2 meters in certain species, is flattened and dichotomously branched. Growth is initiated by the divisions of a clearly differentiated apical cell whose derivatives, by subsequent division, enlargement, and differentiation, build up a rather complex plant body. The plants are attached by multicellular holdfast discs. Prominent **midribs** and **cryptoblasts** (probably sterile conceptacles, described below) and **air bladders** occur in some species (Fig. 4–10).

The production of reproductive cells is localized at the tips of the branches in fertile areas called **receptacles,** which become enlarged and distended because of the internal secretion of large quantities of colloidal compounds (Fig. 4–10). The receptacles bear scattered pustule-like cavities, the **conceptacles,** which communicate with the surrounding

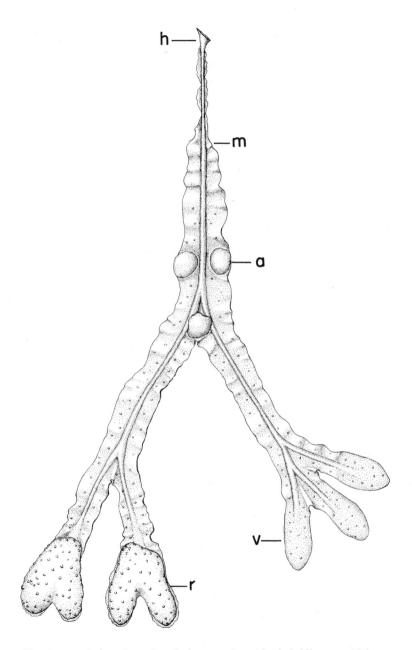

Fig. 4–10. *Fucus vesiculosus* L. portion of plant: *a*, air vesicle; *h*, holdfast; *m*, midrib; *r*, receptacle with conceptacles; *v*, vegetative apex. X 1.

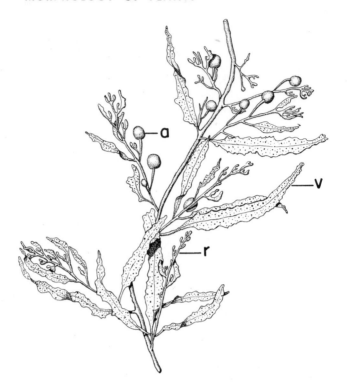

Fig. 4–11. *Sargassum filipendula* C. Ag. Portion of plant: *a,* air vesicle; *r,* young receptacles with conceptacles; *v,* young leaf-like vegetative branch. X 1.

water through narrow **ostioles,** through which filaments protrude (Fig. 4–12). At maturity the conceptacles bear eggs and sperms; these may be either in the same conceptacle, or those which produce the eggs may be on different plants from those producing sperms, depending on the species. Thus *F. vesiculosus* L. is usually heterothallic (Fig. 4–12); *F. spiralis* L., homothallic.

The sperms are laterally biflagellate and produced in groups of 64 from antheridia developed on branching filaments from the wall of the conceptacle (Figs. 4–12A, 4–13A). In *Fucus,* each oogonium, also an outgrowth from the conceptacle wall, produces eight eggs (Figs. 4–12B, 4–13B). The number varies between a maximum of eight and a minimum of one in various genera related to *Fucus.* The conceptacles contain colorless sterile filaments called **paraphyses** (Gr. *paraphysis,* offshoot). Young oogonia and antheridia are uninucleate (Fig. 4–14). The meiotic process

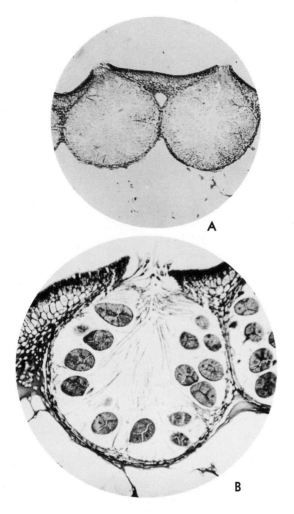

Fig. 4–12. *Fucus vesiculosus.* Median sections of conceptacles through the ostioles. A, Male (antheridial) conceptacles. X 30. B, Female (oogonial) conceptacle. X 45.

is accomplished during the first two nuclear divisions in these structures, the plants themselves being diploid.

Liberation of gametes is closely connected with tidal conditions in some species. At low tide, when the plants are exposed to the drying action of the air, shrinkage of the plant body may result in an extrusion of ripe oogonia and antheridia in gelatinous masses through the ostiole to the surface of the plant. The incoming tide, in submerging these droplets containing the sex organs, effects swelling and dissolution of their walls, so that the individual gametes are set free in the water. However, in other species, extrusion of gametes occurs in continuously submerged

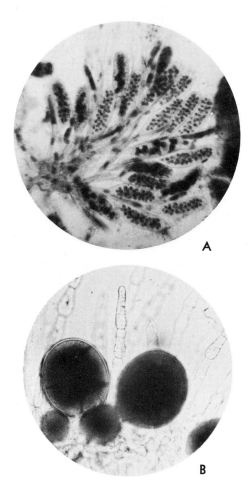

Fig. 4–13. *Fucus vesiculosus.* A, Development of antheridia (from aceto-carmine preparations). X 320. B, Oogonia and paraphyses (living material). X 135.

plants. The eggs are large, spherical, and nonmotile and are penetrated by individual sperms, which swarm about the eggs in great numbers (Fig. 4–15A). Nuclear union follows, and the resulting zygote secretes a thin wall and germinates (Fig. 4–15B), without a period of dormancy,

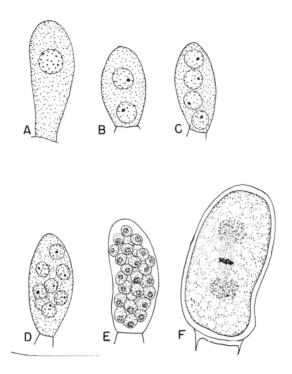

Fig. 4–14. *Fucus vesiculosus.* A-E, Stages in development of an antheridium. F, Young oogonium, meiotic metaphase showing polar radiations. X 770.

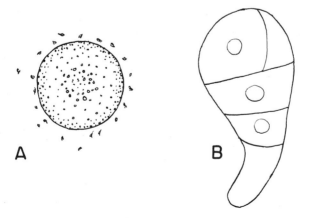

Fig. 4–15. A, *Fucus serratus* L. Egg surrounded by sperms. X 250. (From Thuret and Bonnet). B, *Fucus vesiculosus,* young plant from germinating zygote. (From Nienburg.)

into a new *Fucus* plant. The life cycle of *Fucus* may be summarized as follows:

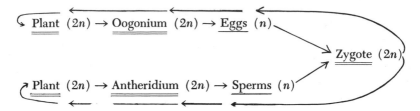

It seems clear from this summary that the life cycle of *Fucus*, like that of *Bryopsis* and freshwater species of *Cladophora*, falls into Type II (p. 51),[1] in which a diploid organism undergoes gametic meiosis and the zygote grows directly into the new plant.

SUMMARY AND CLASSIFICATION

The above account of the genera *Ectocarpus*, *Pylaiella*, *Laminaria*, *Fucus*, and *Sargassum* summarizes the three types of life cycle and reproduction which occur among the Phaeophyceae. Most of the remaining genera of this large alliance correspond in reproduction to one of the types described above; the generic differences are based largely on vegetative morphology. As a group, the Phaeophyceae are sharply characterized and distinct from other algae in their pigmentation and photosynthate, in their almost exclusively marine habitat, their laterally bifiagellate reproductive cells, and the complexity of the plant body in size and internal differentiation achieved in certain genera. Their life cycles have counterparts in certain Chlorophyceae, on the one hand, and in certain vascular plants, on the other. However, no phaeophycean genus with zygotic meiosis has yet been described. The representative

---

[1] The four nuclei present in the so-called oogonia and antheridia at the conclusion of the first two nuclear divisions in these organs have been interpreted by some to be homologous with the nuclei of microspores and megaspores (produced in groups of four from their mother cells) in heterosporous land plants. If this were true, one would have to look upon the "oogonium" and "antheridium," up to the four-nucleate stage, as a "megasporangium" and "microsporangium," respectively. The ensuing nuclear divisions, therefore, would be analogous to those that occur in microspores and megaspores in their production of gametophytes. In the case of *Fucus*, however, the gametophytic phase is markedly abbreviated and approaches a condition most similar to that in certain seed plants whose gametophytes complete development while the spores which produce them are still retained in their sporangia. According to this interpretation, the alternation of generations in *Fucus*, like that in the flowering plants, involves a dominant diploid sporophyte and a much reduced gametophyte, the latter represented by only a few nuclear and cell generations.

genera of Phaeophyta discussed in this chapter may be classified as follows:

Division Phaeophyta
   Class 1. Phaeophyceae
      Subclass 1. Isogeneratae
         Order 1. Ectocarpales
            Family 1. Ectocarpaceae
               Genera: *Ectocarpus, Pylaiella*
      Subclass 2. Heterogeneratae
         Order 1. Laminariales
            Family 1. Laminariaceae
               Genera: *Laminaria, Macrocystis*
      Subclass 3. Cyclosporeae
         Order 1. Fucales
            Family 1. Fucaceae
               Genera: *Fucus, Sargassum*

DISCUSSION QUESTIONS

1. Describe the life cycle and reproduction of *Ectocarpus, Laminaria,* and *Fucus.*

2. Compare these genera with respect to form of plant body and localization of growth.

3. The antithetic theory of alternation of generations postulates that the sporophyte is fundamentally different from the gametophyte, an innovation which appeared in the land plants, and that the primary function of the sporophyte is spore production; vegetative functions of the sporophyte, according to this theory, developed when sporogenous cells became sterile and assumed them. In the light of your knowledge of the Chlorophyceae and Phaeophyceae, evaluate this theory.

4. What possible significance can you attach to the partial retention of the egg, zygote, and young embryo within the oogonium of *Laminaria?*

5. Do you think the Phaeophyceae may have originated from the Chlorophyceae? Give reasons for your answer.

6. If the Chlorophyceae and Phaeophyceae are not closely related in your opinion, how do you interpret the occurrence of the filamentous habit, holdfasts, zoospores, and oogamous reproduction in both groups?

7. Distinguish between cytological, morphological, haplobiontic, diplobiontic, isomorphic and heteromorphic alternation of generations, giving examples of genera of Phaeophyta.

CHAPTER 5

Division Rhodophyta

GENERAL FEATURES

The division **Rhodophyta** (Gr. *rhodon,* rose + Gr. *phyton,* plant) contains a single class, the **Rhodophyceae** (Gr. *rhodon* + Gr. *phykos,* seaweed), commonly called the **red algae.** About 400 genera and 2500 species are known. The Rhodophyceae, like the Phaeophyceae, are predominantly marine organisms; however, several genera like *Lemanea* (Fig. 5–1) and *Batrachospermum* (Fig. 5–2) are widely distributed in streams, lakes, and springs. Marine Rhodophyceae flourish in both littoral and sublittoral zones. Rhodophyceae are very abundant in tropical seas, where they often grow at great depths in clear waters. Many of the marine Rhodophyceae are strikingly beautiful, both in the living condition and when mounted on herbarium sheets.

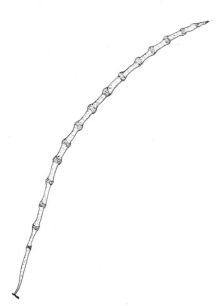

Fig. 5–1. *Lemanea australis* Atk. Single plant. X 2½.

In most genera, chlorophylls *a* and *d* (when present) and the carotenoids are largely concealed by a red pigment, **r-phycoerythrin,**[1] and sometimes by small quantities of the blue pigment **r-phycocyanin.** These pigments absorb light which they transfer

---

[1] "r" to distinguish rhodophycean pigments from those of Cyanophyta.

to the chlorophylls. The numerous genera exhibit a range of color; various shades of red are common, and some plants are almost black. Some species of *Batrachospermum* (Fig. 5–2), on the other hand, are markedly blue-green. The pigments are localized in plastids which may be mas-

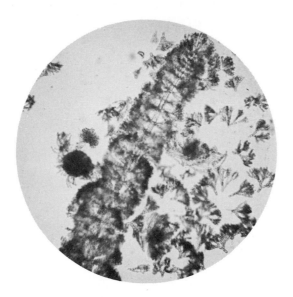

Fig. 5–2. *Batrachospermum* sp. Slightly crushed to show apical growth, single central axis, tufts of photosynthetic filaments, and mass of carpospores at the left. X 60.

sive and single in each cell (Fig. 5–8A), or the plastids may be numerous and disc-like (Fig. 5–13A). The excess photosynthate is stored as a carbohydrate called **Floridean starch**; grains of this substance stain red with iodine-potassium iodide solutions.

The cells of Rhodophyceae may be uninucleate (as in *Nemalion* and *Batrachospermum*) or multinucleate (*Polysiphonia* and *Griffithsia*). The vacuole of large, multinucleate cells is more prominent than in the uninucleate cells of genera like *Nemalion*. The cellulose cell wall is surrounded by a slimy layer. In a number of genera, like *Nemalion*, the filaments are covered, in addition, by copious gelatinous material of rather firm consistency. The walls between two adjoining cells in most of the higher Rhodophyceae are interrupted by structures known as pit connections (Figs. 5–8, 5–10A). The nature and function of these structures remain in doubt. They have been interpreted by some as evidences of protoplasmic continuity between contiguous cells.

Although a few unicellular and colonial rhodophycean genera have been described, a vast majority are filamentous or membranous and foliaceous plants. The basic pattern, however, is filamentous. The development of the plant body is initiated in the activity of one or more apical cells. The membranous Rhodophyceae are less complex internally than similar types of Phaeophyceae.

ILLUSTRATIVE TYPES

Porphyra

The genus *Porphyra* (Gr. *porphyra,* purple) has been chosen here as representative of a group of genera which are considered to be primitive Rhodophyceae. The dark, brown-purple, *Ulva*-like plant bodies of *Porphyra* (Fig. 5–3) grow attached to rocks or larger marine algae in

Fig. 5–3. *Porphyra umbilicalis* (L.) J. Ag. Living plant. X ⅓.

protected bodies of water. They are often inhabitants of the intertidal zone. The fronds may attain dimensions of more than a foot in length. They are composed of one or two layers of cells which are embedded in a rather firm, gelatinous matrix (Fig. 5–4A). The plants are attached to the substratum by rhizoidal holdfasts.

The cells of *Porphyra* contain single, prominent star-like chromatophores which are central in position (Fig. 5–4A). The cells are uninucleate and lack a central vacuole. They also lack the pit connections characteristic of so many of the higher Rhodophyceae. *Porphyra* deviates further from the latter in that its growth is generalized; cell division is not restricted to a certain region of the maturing plant body.

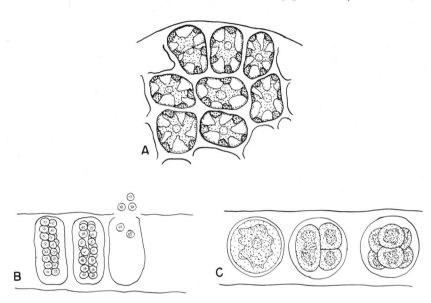

Fig. 5–4. *Porphyra umbilicalis*. A, Surface view of vegetative plant. B, Sectional view, formation and liberation of spermatia. C, Sectional view, stages in carpospore formation. X 315.

Asexual reproduction is accomplished by the formation of nonmotile spores directly from vegetative cells (Fig. 5–5A). In this process the cell undergoes divisions entirely in an anticlinal plane so that the spores lie in approximately a single layer. Upon their liberation, they may undergo slight amoeboid movement before germinating into a filamentous stage. It has recently been demonstrated by laboratory cultures that spores of *Porphyra umbilicalis* (L.) Kütz. var. *laciniata* (Lightf.) sown on sterile shells grow into a branching filamentous phase which had been described as another organism, namely, *Conchocelis rosea* Batters. The life cycle and relationship between these species have not yet been elucidated completely.

Sexual reproduction is of regular occurrence in mature plants of *Porphyra*. The species vary in distribution of the sex organs, some being homothallic and others heterothallic. Sexuality is oogamous in *Porphyra* as it is in all Rhodophyceae. The production of sex organs usually begins near the margins of the plants. Certain cells undergo rapid and repeated transverse and vertical divisions resulting in the formation of from 32

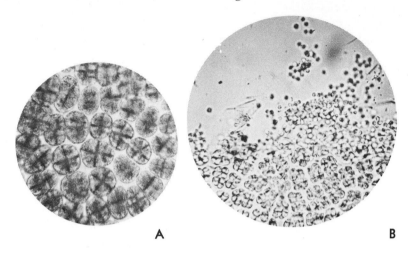

A   **B**

Fig. 5–5. *Porphyra umbilicalis.* A, Surface view of thallus with spores. B, Liberation of spermatia. X 65.

to 128 small cells arranged in tiers (Figs. 5–4B, 5–5B). Each of these small cells functions as a nonmotile male cell, the **spermatium.** In other regions of the same thallus or on other plants (in heterothallic species), certain vegetative cells increase slightly in size and may develop small protuberances which project toward one or both surfaces. These are the female sex organs which are called **carpogonia** (Gr. *karpon,* fruit + Gr. *genes,* generation). The protuberances suggest the **trichogynes** of other Rhodophyceae. The nonmotile male cells, which are passively carried by water currents, become attached to the surface of the carpogonia. The nucleus of one spermatium enters the carpogonium and unites with its nucleus, thus forming a zygote. The latter undergoes nuclear division followed by cytokinesis. Each of the division products divides into four or more cells, so that eight or more protoplasts are developed from each zygote (Fig. 5–4C). There is some evidence that the nuclear divisions of the zygote involve meiosis. The daughter protoplasts, called **carpospores,** which arise from the zygote, are presumably haploid. The carpospores are shed from the plant body by gelatinization of the zygote wall. They lack a firm wall when first liberated and may exhibit amoeboid movements. They ultimately become spherical and walled and undergo cell division to form an unbranched filament; either directly or indirectly (by spore production) this gives rise to the membranous type of plant body. Insofar as it has been investigated, it appears that *Porphyra* is haplobiontic and haplont as to life cycle, but further study is desirable.

Nemalion and Batrachospermum

Nemalion (Gr. *nema,* thread) and *Batrachospermum* (Gr. *batrachos,* frog + Gr. *sperma,* semen) are Rhodophyceae which differ from *Porphyra* in a number of important respects, although both of them are also haplobiontic and haplont. In these genera growth is strictly apical and traceable to one (*Batrachospermum*) or more (*Nemalion*) apical cells. More or less prominent pit connections are present; these give evidence of the pattern of development (Fig. 5–8). *Nemalion multifidum* (Weber and Mohr) J. Ag. is a marine organism which grows attached to rocks that may be exposed at low tide; the living plants have the appearance and texture of gelatinous, worm-like branching cylinders (Fig. 5–6). The plants are an-

Fig. 5–6. *Nemalion multifidum* (Weber and Mohr) J. Ag. Living plants. X ⅓.

chored to the rocks by discoidal bases. In median longitudinal sections or in crushed preparations of apices, it is apparent that the plant body is composed of a number of colorless, central, longitudinal filaments whose tips elongate through the activity of apical cells. From the central filaments, tufts of lateral photosynthetic filaments arise in dense whorls (Fig. 5–7A). The axial and photosynthetic system are both embedded in rather firm slime which they have secreted. The uninucleate photosynthetic cells are somewhat moniliform, and each contains a single massive chromatophore in which a single so-called pyrenoid is embedded (Fig. 5–8A). The function of the latter has not yet been ascertained. The apices of the photosynthetic filaments may be occupied by hair-like cells.

The reproductive organs of *Nemalion* and the higher Rhodophyceae are unlike those of other algae. In some respects, however, they resemble

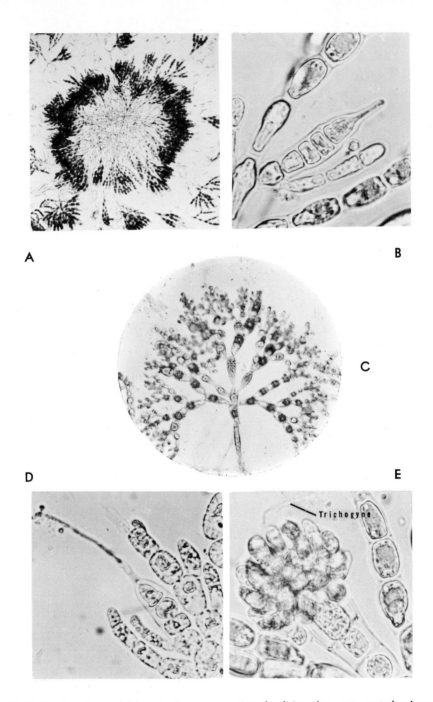

Fig. 5–7. *Nemalion multifidum. A,* Transverse section of a living plant; note central axis and tufts of photosynthetic filaments. X 60. *B,* Young carpogonial branch; note carpogonium and trichogyne. X 500. *C,* Spermatangial tufts. X 250. *D,* Fertilization; note three spermatia on trichogyne, the contents of one having entered (aceto-carmine preparation). X 500. *E,* Cystocarp and immature carpospores. X 250.

those of certain ascomycetous fungi (Chapter 12). The female reproductive organ, the **carpogonium** (Fig. 5–8*B*), is an oogonium with a more or less well-developed protuberance, the **trichogyne** (Gr. *thrix*, hair + Gr. *gyne*, female). The carpogonia are borne on almost colorless lateral branches which arise near the center of a tuft of photosynthetic filaments

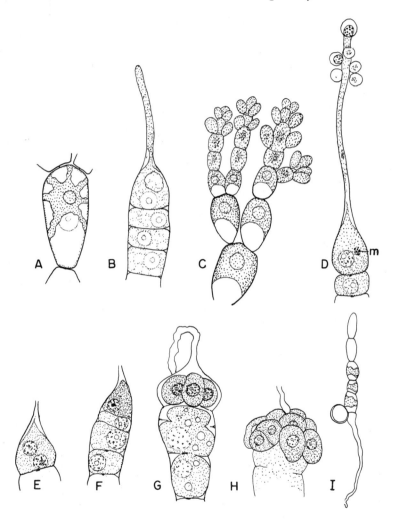

Fig. 5–8. *Nemalion multifidum.* A, Living cell from photosynthetic filament; note asteroidal plastid and axial pyrenoid. B, Four-celled carpogonial branch; note lightly pigmented plastid in carpogonium. C, Spermatangial branch. D, Fertilization: m, spermatial chromatin. E, End of first meiotic division in carpogonium (zygote). F, Completion of first cytokinesis in zygote. G,H, Stages in development of gonimoblasts and carpospores. I, Carpospore germination. A-H, X 770; I, X 315.

(Figs. 5–7B, 5–8B). Other branches on the same plant by successive divisions produce male sex organs, the **spermatangia** (Figs. 5–7C, 5–8C), which are analogous to the unicellular antheridia of other algae. Each spermatangium produces a single **spermatium,** the male gamete, which is discharged at maturity. The spermatia, which are produced and liberated in large numbers, are transported by water currents. When a spermatium makes contact with the trichogyne (Figs. 5–7D, 5–8D), its nucleus divides into two. The wall then dissolves at the point of contact and one of the spermatial nuclei enters the trichogyne. The spermatial nucleus migrates to the base of the carpogonium (Fig. 5–8D), and union of a spermatial with the carpogonial nucleus ensues. Soon after **fertilization,** the zygote nucleus undergoes the meiotic process and the trichogyne withers. A series (Fig. 5–8E,F,G) of mitoses and cell divisions follow, which result in the production of a tuft of short haploid filaments, the **gonimoblasts** (Gr. *gonimos,* productive + Gr. blastos, sprout) (Fig. 5–8H), the apical cells of which become **carposporangia** (Fig. 5–7E), whose protoplasts are liberated as wall-less **carpospores.** The haploid carpospores ultimately germinate (Fig. 5–8I) and develop into gametophytic plants. The life cycle of *Nemalion* may be summarized as follows:

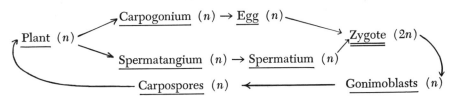

Nemalion, like *Porphyra, Chlamydomonas,* and *Spirogyra,* clearly has a Type I (p. 51) life cycle.

Batrachospermum (Fig. 5–2) is also haplobiontic and haplont, but differs from *Nemalion* in vegetative structure. Instead of the numerous axial filaments and apical cells of the latter, *Batrachospermum* develops from a single apical cell which generates an axial system and tufts of photosynthetic filaments that are loosely verticillate and embedded in slime.

Polysiphonia and Griffithsia

Polysiphonia (Gr. *polys,* many + Gr. *siphon,* tube) and *Griffithsia* (to honor Mrs. Griffiths) illustrate the second of the two types of life cycle which characterize Rhodophyceae. *Polysiphonia* (Fig. 5–9) is a

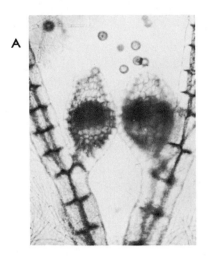

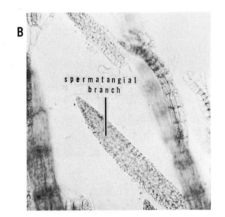

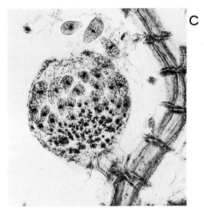

spermatangial branch

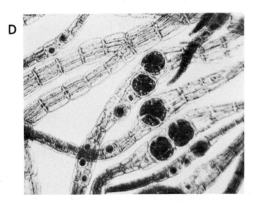

Fig. 5–9. *Polysiphonia* sp. *A,* Living ♀ plants with cystocarps liberating carpospores. X 135. *B,* Living ♂ plant with spermatangial branches. X 30. *C,* Cystocarp, optical section. X 135. *D,* Diploid plants with tetrasporangia (dark bodies). X 60.

branching filamentous plant which frequently grows attached to larger marine algae or rocks. Growth is strictly apical, and the derivatives of the apical cell segment in a regular pattern (Fig. 5–10A) to build up the multiseriate axis, which in some species achieves considerable complexity through superficial cortication. Delicate hair-like branches, the **trichoblasts,** may be present (Fig. 5–9B).

Polysiphonia is diplobiontic in life cycle. The gametophytes are heterothallic, spermatia and carpogonia being produced on different individuals. The sex organs arise from derivatives of the apical cell near the tips of the branches (Fig. 5–10). The curved carpogonial branch of *Polysiphonia* (Fig. 5–10B) at fertilization consists of four almost colorless cells, the distal one of which develops a trichogyne. This branch arises from a pericentral cell which is known as the **supporting cell.** Certain cells at the base and above the carpogonial branch grow up around it forming an urn-shaped envelope, the **pericarp** (Gr. *peri,* around + Gr. *karpon,* fruit) (Fig. 5–9A). The spermatangia and spermatia are borne on lateral branches (Figs. 5–9B, 5–10C) whose pericentral cells produce spermatangial mother cells which give rise to large numbers of colorless spermatangia that are abscised and function directly as spermatia (Fig. 5–10C). As in all Rhodophyceae, the spermatia are borne passively to the trichogyne by water currents. After attachment to the trichogyne, their contents flow into the latter. The spermatial nucleus migrates down through the trichogyne and ultimately unites with the carpogonial nucleus as in *Nemalion.*

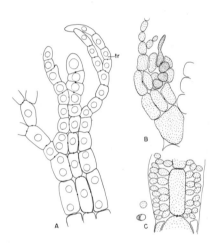

Fig. 5–10. *Polysiphonia harveyi* Bail. A, Apex showing ontogeny; note apical cell, axial cells, pericentral cells, pit connections, and, *tr.,* developing trichoblast. X 388. B, Carpogonial branch (densely stippled). C, Median longitudinal section (m.l.s.) of spermatangial branch. X 770.

Postfertilization development is rather complicated in detail. It involves extensive cell fusions, degeneration of the carpogonial branch, and migration of the zygote nucleus into an **auxiliary cell.** Meiosis does not occur, but mitotic divisions of the zygote nucleus give rise to a number of diploid nuclei which are present in a large fusion cell, the **placental**

cell. Carposporangia, each with a diploid nucleus, are abstricted from this cell and develop seriatim (Fig. 5–11A).

The mature carpospores are liberated through the mouth of the urn-like pericarp (Fig. 5–9A,C) and germinate into diploid plants under suitable conditions. These plants are similar in size and general appear-

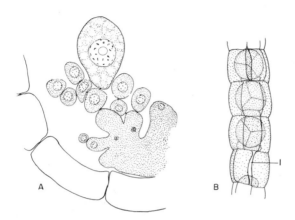

Fig. 5–11. *Polysiphonia harveyi*. A, Placental cell and developing carpospores. X 514. B, Portion of tetrasporic plant; note liberation cleft (*l*). X 126.

ance to the male and female gametophytes, but at maturity they produce **tetrasporangia** which arise on short stalk cells (Figs. 5–9D, 5–11B). Cytological investigation has demonstrated that the two successive nuclear divisions in the tetrasporangium accomplish meiosis, so the four spores produced are haploid. The tetrasporangial wall breaks open and the **tetraspores** are shed through fissures between the pericentral cells (Fig. 5–11B). It has been shown by culture methods that tetraspores develop into gametophytic plants. This rather complicated life cycle of *Polysiphonia* may be summarized as follows:

Male plant (n) → Spermatangium (n) → Spermatium (n)

Zygote $(2n)$

Female plant (n) → Carpogonium (n) → Egg (n)

Tetraspores (n) ← Tetrasporangium $(2n)$ ← Plant $(2n)$ ←

Carpospores $(2n)$ ← Placental cell $(2n)$

Griffithsia is similar in life cycle to *Polysiphonia,* but its vegetative structure is simpler, because the branching filaments are composed of large cells which are not covered by pericentral cells or cortications (Fig. 5–12 A). *Griffithsia globulifera* Harvey, an Atlantic coast species, appears during the summer when the water temperature is relatively high. The bushy growths are attached to stones and pilings in sublittoral habitats and are rosy-pink in color. The multinucleate cells are very large, those

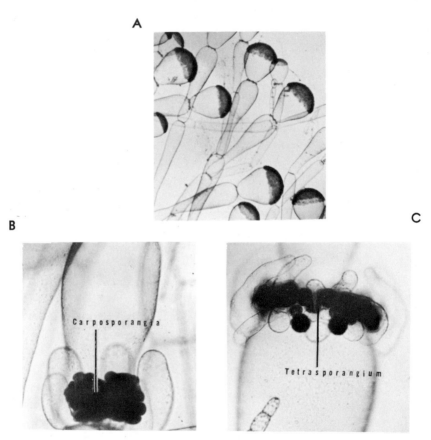

Fig. 5–12. *Griffithsia globulifera* Harvey. Living plants. A, ♂ plant with spermatial caps. X 12½. B, Node of ♀ plant with carposporangia. X 60. C, Node of tetrasporic plant. X 60.

near the base of the branches attaining a length as great as 5 mm. Growth is apical, from a multinucleate cell with dense cytoplasm and without a vacuole. The *apparently* dichotomous branching develops because of the upgrowth of the lateral surface of the cell below an apical cell to form a new growing point. In mature cells the cytoplasm is peripheral; it contains beautiful ribbon-like segmented plastids which are arranged in curved mosaics (Fig. 5–13A). The attaching system of *Griffithsia* is weak and restricted, as evidenced by the frequency with which free-floating plants are encountered. Trichoblasts are present on the axes.

The life history of *Griffithsia* involves three free-living plants, as in *Polysiphonia,* namely, male and female gametophytes, the latter bearing cystocarps at maturity, and **tetrasporophytes.** The male plants are readily recognizable (Fig. 5–12A) because of their cap-like mantles of spermatangial filaments which produce spermatia (Fig. 5–13B) in enormous numbers. The carpogonial branches arise from special three-celled short lateral branches which originate on the free distal surface of vegetative

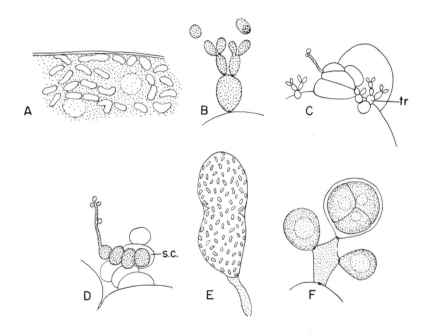

Fig. 5–13. *Griffithsia globulifera. A,* Portion of vegetative cell, surface view; note plastids and nuclei. *B,* Detail of single spermatangial branch. *C,D,* Detail of fertile branches and fertilization: s.c. supporting cell; *tr.,* trichoblast. *E,* Germinating carpospore. *F,* Tetrasporangium mother cell and tetrasporangia. *A,B,* X 770; *C-F,* X 315.

cells (Fig. 5-13C,D). The earliest stages in the development of these branches, and of the carpogonial branches they produce, occur near the growing point of each main axis. The **supporting cell** (*s.c.*) generates a four-celled carpogonial branch which is recurved, as in *Polysiphonia.* After fertilization, the supporting cell gives rise to a special cell, the **auxiliary cell,** with which the fertilized carpogonium becomes united. The zygote nucleus passes from the carpogonium into an auxiliary cell, after which the carpogonial branch withers and is abscised. Further development involves extensive cell fusions to form a placental cell, as well as generation of diploid nuclei within the auxiliary cell and the contiguous regions of the placental cell. Later, gonimoblast initials bud off from the placental cell and initiate the formation of carposporangia which are borne in groups (Fig. 5–12B). Meanwhile, soon after fertilization, the basal cell of the short lateral axis which bears the carpogonial branch gives rise to a number of curved, elongate, involucre-like cells that partially conceal the developing carposporangia and function as a pericarp (Fig. 5–12B).

There is good evidence that the carposporangia germinate (Fig. 5–13E) into plantlets which mature as tetrasporophytes. In these (Fig. 5–12C), the distal portions of vegetative cells bud off a circle of tetrasporangial mother cells which generate three tetrasporangia each (Fig. 5–13F). Meiosis occurs in these while they are small, and each tetrasporangium finally is divided into four tetraspores. When these have been liberated, they develop into male and female gametophytes. A circle of involucral cells surrounds each fertile, tetrasporangium-bearing node (Fig. 5–12C).

The *Polysiphonia* and *Griffithsia* type of life cycle is most similar to that observed among such Chlorophyceae as *Cladophora suhriana* and such Phaeophyceae as *Ectocarpus* (Type III, p. 51). It differs, however, in one important respect. In *Polysiphonia* and *Griffithsia* there is intercalated, between fertilization and the developing tetrasporophyte, a series of cell generations consisting of the diploid placental cell and the carposporangia. This phase has been interpreted by some as still a third alternating phase, the **carposporophyte.** According to this point of view, alternation in *Polysiphonia* and *Griffithsia* involves the haploid gametophytes, the carposporophyte, and finally the tetrasporophyte. There is no phase similar to the carposporophyte in groups of algae other than Rhodophyceae, nor does it occur among the higher plants. The closest approach to it, perhaps, is found in the post-fertilization development in certain ascomycetous fungi, a feature which will be considered in the treatment of that group (Chapter 12).

SUMMARY AND CLASSIFICATION

The genera of Rhodophyceae described in this chapter exhibit two distinct types of life cycle. *Porphyra, Nemalion,* and *Batrachospermum* are haplobiontic with zygotic meiosis (Type I, p. 51), and *Polysiphonia* and *Griffithsia* are diplobiontic with sporic meiosis occurring in the tetrasporophyte. As a group, the Rhodophyceae are sharply segregated from other algae by pigmentation, their storage photosynthate (Floridean starch), and their characteristic reproductive structures which appear elsewhere in the plant kingdom only in the ascomycetous fungi.

The development of a special series of terms for the reproductive organs and cells of the Rhodophyceae is unfortunate in some ways, because it occasions confusion in the minds of those approaching the study of the group for the first time. It seems clear that the carpogonium and spermatangium correspond in function with the oogonium and antheridium, respectively, of other oogamous algae. The permanent retention of the zygote upon the gametophyte, however, marks a deviation rarely seen in other groups of algae, although suggested in the kelps. The continued production of carpospores for considerable periods following fertilization possibly is correlated with this retention, for although the postzygotic filaments may possess pigments, they are nourished largely as a result of their organic connection with the parent gametophyte. Thus, a single act of fertilization, with retention of the zygote, results in the potential production of many more gametophytes than in the plants in which the zygotes are promptly separated from the gametophyte. The genera of Rhodophyta discussed in this chapter may be classified as follows:

Division. Rhodophyta
   Class 1. Rhodophyceae
      Order 1. Bangiales
         Family 1. Bangiaceae
            Genus: *Porphyra*
      Order 2. Nemalionales
         Family 1. Helminthocladiaceae
            Genus: *Nemalion*
         Family 2. Batrachospermaceae
            Genus: *Batrachospermum*
         Family 3. Lemaneaceae
            Genus: *Lemanea*
      Order 3. Ceramiales
         Family 1. Ceramiaceae
            Genus: *Griffithsia*
         Family 2. Rhodomelaceae
            Genus: *Polysiphonia*

DISCUSSION QUESTIONS

1. How does the life cycle of *Polysiphonia* or *Griffithsia* differ from that of diplobiontic Phaeophyceae and Chlorophyceae?
2. Can you see any advantage to the plant in carpospore production?

3. The sex organs of the Rhodophyceae are called spermatangia and carpogonia, although they are similar to the antheridia and oogonia seen in other oogamous algae. Can you suggest a reason for this?

4. If one were to isolate and cultivate separately the four tetraspores from a single tetrasporangium, what result could be expected? Can you cite similar phenomena from other groups of plants or animals?

5. While most Rhodophyceae are marine, a few genera like *Batrachospermum* and *Lemanea* are common in fresh-water streams. What explanation might account for this?

6. Yamanouchi counted 20 chromosomes in nuclear division in the vegetative cells of the female gametophyte of *Polysiphonia violacea*[2] (Roth.) Grev. What would be the chromosome number in the nuclei of the following structures in this plant: spermatium, carpospore, carpogonium, apical cell of the tetrasporophyte, an undivided tetrasporangium, the pericarp, the basal cell of the carpogonial branch?

7. What is the explanation of the words "(Roth.) Grev." after *Polysiphonia violacea* in Question 6 above? Why is Roth. in parentheses? Why is Roth. not so written in "*Batrachospermum moniliforme* Roth."? Search for similar examples in other chapters.

---

[2] Now *P. flexicaulis* (Harv.) Collins.

CHAPTER 6

Divisions Charophyta, Euglenophyta, and Pyrrophyta

INTRODUCTION

The preceding four chapters have presented an account of representatives of the four major groups of algae, namely, the divisions Cyanophyta, Chlorophyta, Phaeophyta, and Rhodophyta. The present chapter includes brief discussions of representative genera of three other alliances of algae which are of widespread occurrence. The groups they represent are treated as coordinate in rank with the four groups already considered, in most current phycological treatises. Numerous genera, in addition to the types here selected, are known in each class, but space does not permit a more extensive treatment of them.

DIVISION CHAROPHYTA

The **stoneworts**, division **Charophyta**, here represented by the genera *Chara* (Latin name) and *Nitella* (L. *nitella*, splendor), are sometimes classified in the division Chlorophyta as a class coordinate with the Chlorophyceae. This reflects the point of view that their morphological deviations from the Chlorophyceae are of insufficient magnitude to warrant their removal to a separate division. In this text, however, for reasons which will be enumerated below, the stoneworts are considered to represent a group of divisional rank coordinate with the Chlorophyta. The division Charophyta contains the single class Charophyceae, order Charales and family Characeae.

Chara (Fig. 6–1) and *Nitella* grow in the muddy or sandy bottoms of

103

clear lakes and ponds or in submerged limestone quarry basins. In such habitats, certain species have the capacity of precipitating calcium carbonate from the water and covering themselves with calcareous surface layers. This last attribute has suggested the names **stoneworts** and **brittleworts.** Calcareous casts of the oogonia of stoneworts have been preserved abundantly as fossils (Fig. 30–3).

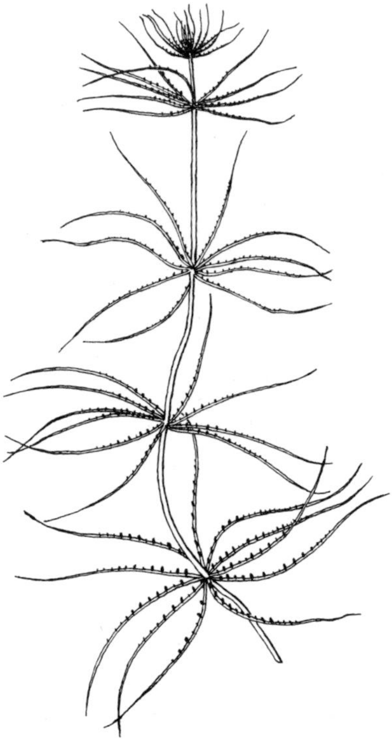

Unlike most fresh-water algae, the Charophyta are plants with macroscopically distinctive features. The markedly whorled and verticillate branching (Fig. 6–1), the organization of the plant body into regular nodes and internodes, and its geometrically regular pattern of ontogeny from a single apical cell (Fig. 6–2) all are features which suggest the Arthrophyta among the vascular plants (Chapter 19). The plant consists of a branching axis on which arise whorls of smaller branches of limited growth, often called "leaves." The lower portions of the axes are anchored to the substratum by branching filaments, the **rhizoids.** Branches arise at the nodes among the leaf bases.

Median longitudinal sections through the apex of the axis (Fig. 6–2) reveal the very regular manner of development which occurs in the stoneworts. All the cells have their origin from the descendants of a prominent, dome-shaped apical cell which cuts off derivatives in a transverse direction, parallel to its basal wall (Fig. 6–2). Each of these segments divides again transversely into a nodal and internodal initial. The internodal cells elongate tremendously and may remain uncovered, as in *Nitella;* or, as in most species of *Chara* (Fig. 6–2), they become clothed with corticating cells which arise from the node above and below a given internode. The protoplasm of the internodal cells streams rapidly in a

Fig. 6–1.   *Chara sejuncta* A. Br. Portion of axis. X 1.

direction parallel to the long axis of the cell; the minute peripheral chloroplasts are embedded in stationary cytoplasm. A prominent vacuole occupies the central portion of the elongate internodal cells which are multinucleate. The nodal initials divide in such fashion as to form two central cells surrounded by one or more rings of cells (Fig. 6–2). The outermost of these are the precursors of the whorled lateral branches or "leaves." The latter develop nodes, internodes, and cortications like those of the main axes in *Chara;* in *Nitella* the leaves are uncorticated.

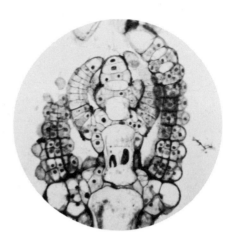

Reproduction in the Charophyta is strictly oogamous and the gametes are produced in specialized complex structures usually called **antheridia** and **oogonia.** Many species are homothallic. The reproductive structures are borne on the leaves (Figs. 6–1, 6–3). A fruiting plant furnishes a

Fig. 6–2. *Chara* sp. Median longitudinal section of apex. X 135.

rather complete series in the ontogeny of the sex organs, if one examines leaves of successively older nodes. The younger sex organs are green; but as development proceeds, the antheridia become orange-red and the oogonia rather blackish-brown (after fertilization) in many species.

The mature male reproductive organ (Figs. 6–3 to 6–6) consists of chains of colorless cells, each of which produces a single sperm, surrounded by several types of sterile accessory cells; the whole structure is stalked. Its surface is composed of eight large, epidermis-like **shield cells** which are orange-red at maturity and contain incomplete, anticlinal septa (Figs. 6–4, 6–5B). To the inner tangential surface of each of these is attached a prismatic cell, the **manubrium** (L. *manus,* hand), which bears one or more isodiametric cells, the **primary capitulum** (L. *caput,* head) (Figs. 6–5B, 6–6A). The primary capitula are all contiguous at the center and give rise to secondary and, in some cases, tertiary capitular cells, which generate the colorless **antheridial filaments** (Figs. 6–5, 6–6A,B). These are composed of chains of box-like cells coiled up within the cavities formed in the male organ by the enlargement of the developing shield

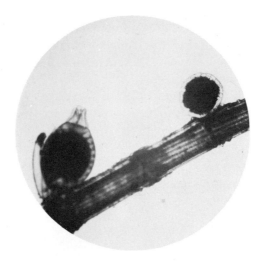

Fig. 6–3.   *Chara sp.* Branch with oogonium (left) and antheridium. X 60.

cells. A single sperm emerges through a pore in the wall of each antheridial cell at maturity. The sperms are liberated by the partial separation of contiguous shield cells.

The female reproductive organ
is less complicated (Figs. 6–5A,
6–6C). It too consists of a fertile
cell, the oogonium proper, surrounded by spirally elongate sterile cells, the **tube cells.** The apices
of these are delimited to form the
five cells (*Chara*) (Fig. 6–3) of
the **corona** or **crown;** there are
two tiers or ten crown cells in *Nitella* (Fig. 6–6C). The female reproductive organ also is pedicellate. At maturity the tube cells
separate from each other immediately under the corona, thus providing pathways for the entrance
of sperms. The single large egg is

Fig. 6–4.   *Nitella* sp. Antheridium showing
shield (surface, wall) cells. X 60.

uninucleate and contains abundant starch grains.

After fertilization the zygote develops a thickened wall, and the

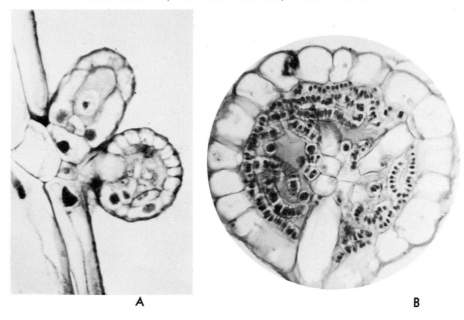

Fig. 6–5. *Chara* sp. A, Median longitudinal section of young oogonium (above) and antheridium. X 135. B, Longitudinal section of older antheridium; note stalk, capitula, one complete manubrium, shield cells, and antheridial filaments. X 250.

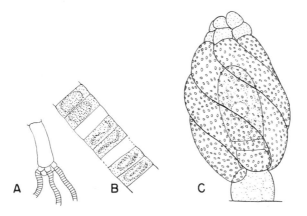

Fig. 6–6. *Nitella* sp. A, Manubrium of antheridium with capitula and antheridial filaments. X 75. B, Segment of antheridial filament. X 770. C, Young oogonium. X 190.

oogonium is abscised from the leaf. The inner walls of the tube cells also thicken and persist as spiral markings on the zygospore (oospore) surface (Fig. 6–7). After a period of dormancy, which is probably followed by meiosis, the oospore germinates (Fig. 6–7) into a juvenile plantlet, all of whose nuclei are the descendants of one of the products of meiosis, as in *Spirogyra*.

Comparison of the morphology of *Chara* and *Nitella*, and other genera of Charophyta, with that of the Chlorophyceae, provides few points of similarity. The complexity of the plant body in the Charophyta is unparalleled among the Chlorophyceae, except, perhaps, in certain marine, siphonalean genera. Furthermore, such features as division into nodes and internodes, cortication of the axes and leaves, and the occurrence of special cellular sheaths around the sexual organs are absent among Chlorophyceae.[1] These reasons, among others, suggest that the stoneworts represent a distinct phyletic line and that, as such, they should be placed in a division separate from the Chlorophyta. It is argued by some that their sex organs suggest affinity with the Hepatophyta or Bryophyta. This claim is denied by others on the ground that the sex organs of the Charophyta are really unicellular, while those of the

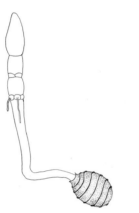

Fig. 6–7. *Nitella* sp. Germination of the oospore. X 10. (Courtesy of Dr. John Dodd.)

Hepatophyta and Bryophyta are multicellular. It is not clear to the writer, however, why the egg protoplast enclosed in a cell wall and surrounded by tube cells in the Charophyta should all together be considered "unicellular," while the egg protoplast of a liverwort or moss, enclosed in its cell wall and surrounded by venter, neck canal, and neck cells, should be considered "multicellular." Even if they are not homologous, both are apparently multicellular organs. If the term antheridium is applied in the Charophyta to one of the colorless cells of the antheridial filament because it produces one sperm, application of similar reasoning would restrict the use of the term antheridium to what is now called a spermatogenous cell or, possibly, an androcyte, in liverworts, mosses, and other plants. Is this not, perhaps, an example of the statement that "Nature mocks at human categories"?

---

[1] Segregation into nodes and internodes may be observed in members of the Chlorophyta, such as *Chaetophora, Draparnaldia* and *Draparnaldiopsis*. Sterile cellular sheaths grow around the oogonia of *Coleochaete* after fertilization.

DIVISION EUGLENOPHYTA

The **Euglenophyta** comprise a small series of organisms, some of which possess both plant- and animal-like attributes. Approximately 25 genera and 335 species arc known. A number of colorless, protozoan-like genera are classified in this alliance, but only the cholorophyllous types are included in the following brief discussion. *Euglena* (Gr. *eu*, good + Gr. *glene*, eye socket), *Phacus* (Gr. *phakos*, lentil), and *Trachelomonas* (Gr. *trachelos*, necks + *monos*, single) are widely distributed in fresh-

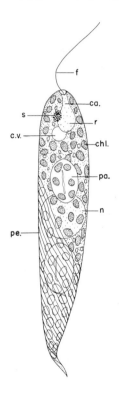

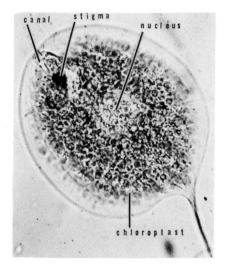

Fig. 6–8. *Euglena* sp. Living individual: *ca*, canal; *chl.*, chloroplast; *c.v.*, contractile vacuole; *f*, flagellum; *n*, nucleus; *pa.*, par- amylum; *pe*, periplast; *r*, reservoir; *s*, stigma. X 250.

Fig. 6–9. *Phacus* sp. Living individual; note stigma, canal, central nucleus, and chloroplasts. X 2400.

water pools, often in such abundance as to form water blooms. At first glance, one would be inclined to classify *Euglena* and *Phacus* (Figs. 6–8, 6–9) as members of the Chlorophyta, but closer study indicates a number of respects in which they differ. In the first place, the protoplast in these genera is unwalled, bounded only by a living, clearly differentiated (punctate, striate, etc.) plasma membrane called the **periplast;** a cellulose wall is absent. Furthermore, the granules of reserve photosynthate, **paramylum,** although similar in appearance to starch grains, fail to give the starch reaction with iodine. Finally, uniflagellate genera are absent among the Chlorophyta. The lack of a cell wall along with the possession of a nonrigid periplast in some species of *Euglena* and *Trachelomonas* permits considerable change in body form, a phenomenon readily observable in the laboratory.

The cell structure of *Euglena* (Fig. 6–8) is typical of the group. In the individual cells a single prominent flagellum is inserted in the anterior portion of the protoplast in an invagination consisting of a tubular **canal** which leads into a broader **reservoir** (Fig. 6–8). A relatively large stigma is adpressed to the canal. The single nucleus is frequently obscured by the chloroplasts, whose shape varies in different species. The chloroplasts may contain pyrenoids with associated grains of paramylum. Large annular grains of paramylum lie free in the colorless cytoplasm of some species of *Englena*. A contractile vacuole empties into the reservoir. Special methods of staining reveal that the flagellum consists of an axial filament surrounded by a sheath; the flagellum is attached to a **basal granule** which lies within the apical canal.

There has been considerable discussion regarding whether these organisms, particularly *Euglena*, are plants or animals. Their chief plantlike attribute is the possession of chlorophyll and with it the capacity for photosynthesis. The occurrence of motility, the presence of a receptor for light stimuli (the stigma), and the anterior invagination (the canal and reservoir) are usually interpreted as animal-like characteristics. Careful study of several species of *Euglena* in bacteria-free cultures indicates that in spite of having chlorophyll, relatively few are completely autotrophic. A greater number require organic supplements such as vitamins. One may regard *Euglena*, therefore, as an organism descended from animal-like ancestors and developing in the direction of the photosynthetic self-sufficiency of plants. According to this view, its animal-like attributes would be considered to be vestigial. However, as seems to be the case in many phylogenetic speculations, there is evidence that the supposed direction of evolution may be quite the reverse.

Multiplication of *Euglena, Phacus,* and *Trachelomonas* is effected by cell division (Fig. 6–10) which follows mitosis. Under certain conditions,

the cells of *Euglena* may withdraw their flagella, secrete a thicker surface layer and copious slime, and remain in a state of nonmotility. Multiplication by cell division may occur in this "Palmella" condition,[2] which
may be of long duration. Conclusive evidence for the occurrence of
sexual reproduction among the Euglenophyta is not available.

Species of *Phacus* (Fig. 6–9) differ from *Euglena* in having rigid
periplasts, so the cell form is fixed and constant. Many species of *Phacus*
are flattened and slightly curved. The protoplasts of *Trachelomonas* (Fig.
6–10) are surrounded by a delicate periplast and a polysaccharide layer,

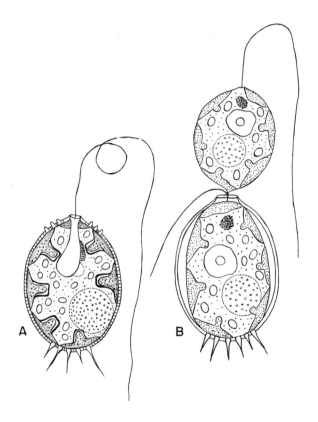

Fig. 6–10. *Trachelomonas armata* (Ehrbg.) Stein. A, Single individual, sectional view. B, Cell
reproduction. X 700. (Courtesy of Dr. K. P. Singh.)

---

[2] Many algae may pass through a "Palmella" stage. This term is derived by analogy from the genus *Palmella* of the Chlorophyceae; here the cells are nonmotile, surrounded by slime which they have secreted, and capable of reverting directly to a
motile condition.

the **lorica.** The latter is variously ornamented and generally impregnated with iron salts.

The division Euglenophyta usually is considered to contain but a single class, the Euglenophyceae, and a single order, the Euglenales, which includes three families. These are delimited on the basis of cytological features such as flagellum structure. The three genera here described are members of the family Euglenaceae, which includes all the chlorophyllous genera.

DIVISION PYRROPHYTA

Like the Euglenophyta, the division **Pyrrophyta** (Gr. *pyrrhos,* reddish + Gr. *phyton,* plant) contains both green and colorless organisms. The Pyrrophyta, represented in this account by the single class Dinophyceae (Gr. *dinos,* whirling + Gr. *phykos,* seaweed, alga), the **dinoflagellates,** formerly were considered to be members of the Protozoa; they are still so classified by many protozoologists. However, nonmotile unicellular and filamentous genera have been discovered that produce motile stages in which the ce'ls are dinoflagellate in character; this indicates an affinity with plant-like organisms.

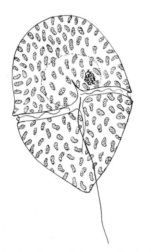

Fig. 6–11. *Gymnodinium* sp. Single individual from fresh-water plankton. X 770.

Dinoflagellates are abundant in both fresh and salt water, where they frequently form an important constituent of the plankton. Marine water blooms of one of these organisms in the Gulf of Mexico have been known to form "red tides" and to result in widespread destruction of fish.

The motile genera as well as the motile cells of nonmotile genera are characterized by the arrangement of their flagella (Fig. 6–11). One of the latter is elongate, usually extending posteriorly with reference to the direction of motion. The second flagellum, which emerges from the same point as the first, lies in a transverse groove in which it undergoes undulating movement. This furrow divides the cell into anterior and posterior portions which may be unequal in size in some genera. A few dinoflagellates, like *Gymnodinium* (Fig. 6–11), lack a cell wall, but in others the wall is prominent (Fig. 6–12) and composed of regularly arranged plate-like segments. Genera with walls of the latter type are often said to be "armored." The walls probably contain cellulose; the empty walls persist for some time after the death of the protoplasts.

Ceratium (Gr. keration, little horn) (Fig. 6–12), Gymnodinium (Gr. gymnos, naked + Gr. dinos), and Peridinium (Gr. peridines, whirled

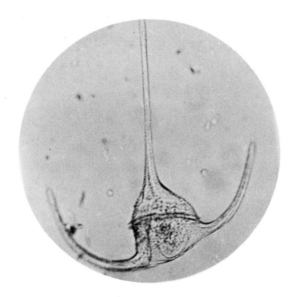

Fig. 6–12.   Ceratium sp. Single individual from marine plankton. X 250.

around) are representatives of the motile type of dinoflagellates of common occurrence in the plankton in bodies of cold water or during the colder seasons of the year. The protoplasts contain discoid plastids which are yellow-brown to dark brown in color. The excess photosynthate is stored as starch or oil. Each cell has a single prominent nucleus and most genera have prominent stigmata as well. Small, noncontractile vacuoles are frequently visible. There is some evidence that certain species of dinoflagellates, although photosynthetic, may undergo holozoic nutrition and ingest solid foods, but the exact mechanism of ingestion is not clearly understood.

Asexual reproduction is by cell division, frequently of cells in a motile condition. In plate-walled genera, each daughter cell receives a portion of the original cell wall. Sexual reproduction has been reported occasionally, but its occurrence should be verified.

DISCUSSION QUESTIONS

1. Summarize the features which distinguish the following groups of algae: Charophyta, Euglenophyta, and Pyrrophyta.
2. Why are the Charophyta known as "stoneworts" and "brittleworts"? To what other algae might this name also be applied for a similar reason?
3. Describe the ontogeny from the apical cell of the plant body of *Chara*.
4. Describe the structure of the male and female reproductive organs of *Chara*. How does the female organ of *Nitella* differ from that of *Chara*?
5. How do the sperms reach the egg of *Chara*? What becomes of the zygospore?
6. Do you consider the Charophyta to be closely related to the Chlorophyceae? Give the reasons for your answer.
7. Why are the Euglenophyta placed in a division other than the Chlorophyta?
8. Summarize the plant-like and animal-like attributes of *Euglena*.
9. How would you prove whether or not a given species of *Euglena* is autotrophic?
10. What facts concerning the occurrence of *Euglena* in nature might lead one to question its capacity for autotrophic nutrition?
11. How do you interpret the presence of a canal and reservoir in *Euglena*?
12. Suggest methods for making the plate-like structure of dinoflagellate cell walls more readily observable.
13. Why are bacteria-free cultures necessary for study of physiological problems in algae?
14. How would you interpret the fact that there are a number of species of colorless dinoflagellates?
15. What significance do you attach to the observation, by a European phycologist, that a brownish, branching, filamentous alga produced zoospores with transverse furrows and one girdling and one trailing flagellum?

CHAPTER 7

Division Chrysophyta

INTRODUCTION

The division **Chrysophyta** includes three classes of algae in whose plastids carotenes and xanthophylls are dominant. Therefore, the cells are varying shades of yellow-green and brown. Their excess photosynthate is never stored as starch but, instead, in the form of another carbohydrate or oil. The distinctive attributes of the division Chrysophyta will be reviewed more fully at the conclusion of this chapter. The Chrysophyta are usually subdivided as follows:

Class I. **Xanthophyceae,** the yellow-green algae
Class II. **Chrysophyceae,** the golden-brown algae
Class III. **Bacillariophyceae,** the diatoms

A brief account of representatives of these three classes is given in the present chapter. More than 300 genera and 5700 species of Chrysophyta have been described.

CLASS XANTHOPHYCEAE

The Xanthophyceae (Gr. *xanthos,* yellow + Gr. *phykos*) are called the "**yellow-green algae**" because their color is distinctly that hue, especially if they are compared directly with members of the Chlorophyta. They were classified formerly among the Chlorophyceae, until it was recognized that several of their attributes differ markedly from those of that group. The yellow-green color results from a combination of pigments, among them chlorophylls *a* and *e,* beta carotene, and a xanthophyll pigment. The pigments are localized in plastids which are usually lens-like or disc-shaped. Droplets of oil and granules of a substance called

115

leucosin are frequently observable in cells of Xanthophyceae. In many genera—*Tribonema* (Fig. 7–2), for example—the cell wall is not homogeneous but is composed of overlapping segments. This attribute is not demonstrable in all Xanthophyceae, however, except by special chemical treatment. The cell wall is silicified in some genera. The flagella of Xanthophyceae are of unequal length (Fig. 7–1*C*).

The Xanthophyceae are predominantly fresh-water organisms, but they may be aerial (moist rocks and other vegetation) or terrestrial in habitat. A few are marine. A number of species have been isolated into culture from subterranean soil samples. The genera of Xanthophyceae, now grouped in a separate class, formerly were distributed among the orders and families of Chlorophyceae whose members they resemble in body structure. Removal of these xanthophycean genera into a separate class revealed that they comprise a series of body types largely parallel to those described in the Chlorophyceae. Space does not permit discussion of a complete array of parallel genera, but four commonly occurring and readily available xanthophycean organisms will be described.

The simplest of these is the unicellular genus *Botrydiopsis* (Gr. *botrydon*, in clusters + Gr. *opsis*, resemblance). *Botrydiopsis* (Fig. 7–1)

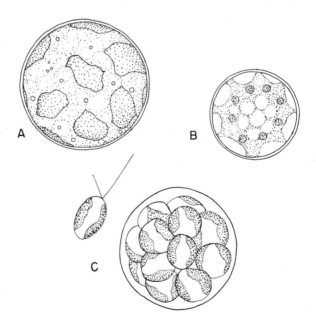

Fig. 7–1. *Botrydiopsis arhiza* Borzi. *A*, Vegetative cell, surface view. *B*, Stained cell with numerous nuclei and plastids. *C*, Zoospore formation and single liberated zoospore. X 1700.

occurs on and in soil, from which it may be isolated readily into unialgal culture. The spherical cells are thin-walled and contain an increasingly large number of lenticular plastids as the cells grow older and larger. The cells are multinucleate (Fig. 7–1B). As in *Chlorococcum*, division of one cell into two does not usually occur in *Botrydiopsis*. Instead, each cell undergoes cleavage to form a number of zoospores (Fig. 7–1C), the number varying with the size of the cell. The zoospores are unwalled and have two flagella of unequal length. After a short period of motility, they round up, secrete walls, and begin their development into vegetative cells. Sexual reproduction has not been observed in *Botrydiopsis*.

The genus *Tribonema* (Gr. *tribo*, rub + Gr. *nema*, thread) is representative of the unbranched, filamentous Xanthophyceae (Fig. 7–2).

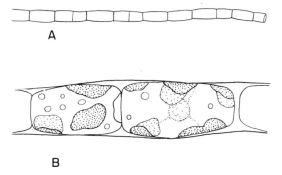

Fig. 7–2. *Tribonema* sp. A, Outline drawing of portion of filament. X 75. B, Two vegetative cells, the one at the left in surface view, the other in optical section. X 500.

Tribonema is cosmopolitan and occurs as floating masses and as overgrowth on submerged sticks and aquatic vegetation during the cooler months of the year. The uniseriate cells are often shaped like somewhat inflated cylinders. Each contains a single nucleus and several discrete, discoidal plastids, decidedly yellow-green in color (Fig. 7-2). *Tribonema* clearly illustrates the fact that certain Xanthophyceae have walls composed of overlapping halves. When the filaments break apart or dissociate, the wall sections may readily be observed to consist of H-shaped segments (Figs. 7–2B, 7–3A), as viewed in optical section. They actually consist of segments of cylinders joined together by a plane, disc-like wall. At the conclusion of cytokinesis in a given vegetative cell, the two daughter protoplasts secrete such a wall segment within the original wall of the parent cell. As in *Ulothrix* among the Chlorophyceae, *Tribonema* reproduces by forming zoospores, but these arise singly within the vegeta-

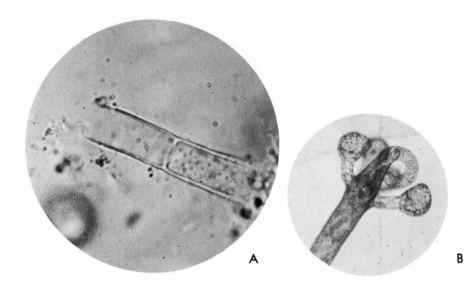

Fig. 7–3. A, *Tribonema* sp. H-shaped wall segment. X 1260. B, *Vaucheria geminata* (Vauch.) DC. Fertile branch with four oogonia and curved antheridium. X 135.

tive cells and have flagella of unequal length. The germling produced by a zoospore has a holdfast, but the mature filaments are rarely encountered in an attached condition. Union of isogamous gametes also has been reported in *Tribonema*.

The terrestrial genus *Botrydium* (Gr. *botrydon*, in clusters) is of widespread occurrence on damp soil, where it may grow in association with

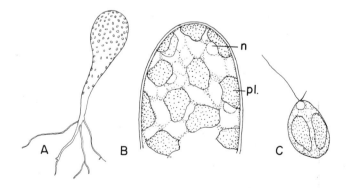

Fig. 7–4. *Botrydium granulatum* (L.) Grev. A, Small vesicle from agar culture. X 75. B, Apex of young plant: *pl.*, plastid; *n*, nucleus. X 700. C, Zoospore. X 1700.

Protosiphon, its chlorophycean counterpart, with which it was long confused. The cells of *Botrydium* (Fig. 7–4) consist of an inflated epiterranean vesicle and a rhizoidal system; the latter is usually richly branched. In many localities the vesicular portion of the plant may attain a size of 2 mm., and it is frequently ornamented with granules of calcium carbonate. Mature plants of *Botrydium* contain a thin peripheral layer of protoplasm surrounding an extensive central vacuole. The protoplasm is composed of a superficial layer of plastids (Fig. 7–4B), and, slightly centripetal to these, there occur numerous minute nuclei embedded in colorless cytoplasm. The rhizoidal portion of the plant contains few if any plastids and is filled with highly vacuolate protoplasm. *Botrydium* reproduces by zoospore and aplanospore formation. The zoospores (Fig. 7–4C) arise by cleavage of the protoplast when the vesicles are submerged in water. The zoospores are facultative isogamous gametes which may unite in pairs to form zygospores. Zoospores may also develop into new plants without union. Meiosis in *Botrydium* is probably zygotic.

No account of the Xanthophyceae, however limited, would be complete without a discussion of the well-known and widespread genus

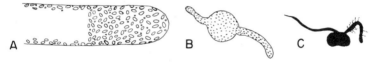

Fig. 7–5. *Vaucheria* sp. A, Apex of vegetative branch, the tip in surface view, the rest in optical section. X 315. B, Germinating zoospore. X 75. C, Stained sperm of *V. pachyderma* Walz. X 1720 (C. from Koch.)

Vaucheria (in honor of Vaucher, a Swiss phycologist), which until recently was included among the Chlorophyceae. Careful examination of its pigments, of its photosynthetic storage products, and of the flagellation of its motile cells (Fig. 7–5C) has demonstrated that the affinities of *Vaucheria* are probably with the Xanthophyceae. Species of *Vaucheria* may be amphibious like certain liverworts. Some flourish in running water or floating or submerged in quiet pools or on moist, undisturbed soil like that in greenhouse flower pots. The plant body consists of an elongate, sparingly branched tube, from which septations are absent except in the reproductive stages or as a response to injury. The central portion of the tube (Fig. 7–5A) is occupied by a large, continuous vacuole, which is separated from the wall by a delicate peripheral layer of protoplasm. Numerous discoidal plastids, which overlie the minute nuclei, occur in this layer. Growth of the siphon-like tubes is apical. Asexual reproduction in the coenocytic *Vaucheria* plant is effected by the formation of large zoospores at the tips of the filaments, which are delimited by septa as zoosporangia (Fig. 7–6A). The protoplast in the sporangium contracts and an interchange of position between nuclei and

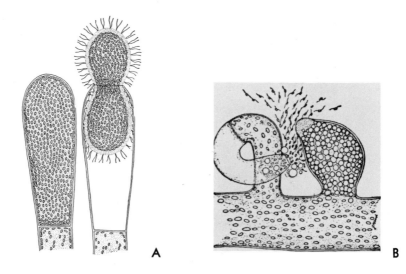

A

B

Fig. 7–6. A, *Vaucheria* sp. Zoospore formation. X 286. B, *V. sessilis* (Vauch.) DC. Mature antheridium and oogonium. X 212. (From G. M. Smith, after Couch.)

plastids occurs, so that the nuclei are now nearer the surface. A pair of equal or slightly unequal flagella is then generated from the surface of the protoplast in the region of each beak-shaped nucleus (Fig. 7–6A). The large compound zoospore is liberated from the terminal zoosporangium and undergoes rather slow, narrowly circumscribed movements. It soon loses its flagella and germinates, frequently from both poles, to form a new *Vaucheria* siphon (Fig. 7–5B).

Sexual reproduction, which is oogamous, is rather striking in *Vaucheria* because of the large size of the sex organs (Figs. 7–3B, 7–6B). These may be sessile on the main siphons or they may occur in groups on special reproductive branches. Both sex organs arise as protuberances into which the streaming protoplasm carries numerous nuclei and plastids. They become segregated from the subtending branch relatively late in their ontogeny. The oogonium is at first multinucleate, but prior to formation of the delimiting septum, all the nuclei except one migrate back into the subtending siphon. At maturity, each oogonium contains a single, uninucleate egg cell. The sperms enter through a pore in the oogonial wall in a special receptive region. The antheridium, which is multinucleate when it is delimited by a septum from its subtending branch, produces a large number of minute, almost colorless, unequally flagellate sperms (Figs. 7–5C, 7–6B). In nature, these are liberated early in the morning. The zygote develops a thick wall soon after fertilization and loses its green pigment. The oogonium containing the zygospore often is abscised from the parent branch. Germination into a new filament, after a period of dormancy, probably involves zygotic meiosis.

This brief account of the genera *Botrydiopsis, Tribonema, Botrydium,* and *Vaucheria* has been presented in order to provide some insight into the attributes of the yellow-green algae, the Xanthophyceae. In spite of the paucity of genera described, it should be apparent that the Xanthophyceae exhibit parallelisms with the Chlorophyceae, insofar as body form is concerned. This parallelism is reflected in the classification of the Xanthophyceae into orders which correspond to those of the Chlorophyceae. The genera described above may be classified as follows:

Division Chrysophyta
    Class 1. Xanthophyceae
        Order 1. Heterococcales
            Family 1. Pleurochloridaceae
                Genus: *Botrydiopsis*
        Order 2. Heterotrichales
            Family 1. Tribonemataceae
                Genus: *Tribonema*
        Order 3. Heterosiphonales
            Family 1. Botrydiaceae
                Genus: *Botrydium*
            Family 2. Vaucheriaceae
                Genus: *Vaucheria*

The Heterococcales correspond to the Chlorococcales of the Chlorophyceae; similar pairs of orders are the Heterotrichales and Ulotrichales and the Heterosiphonales and Siphonales. In spite of the parallelisms, the Xanthophyceae are clearly recognizable by their lack of starch, their pigmentation, their unequal flagellation, and by the overlapping construction of the cell walls in many genera. There is no sound evidence of relationship between the Xanthophyceae and the Chlorophyceae.

CLASS CHRYSOPHYCEAE

The Chrysophyceae (Gr. *chrysos*, gold + Gr. *phykos*), or **golden-brown algae,** are widely distributed in fresh and salt water; but with the exception of a few genera, they are rarely encountered in any great number. Many of the species are planktonic and flourish in bodies of cold water or only in the colder months of the year. The golden-brown color is the result of a combination of pigments including chlorophyll *a*, beta carotene, and two xanthophylls; the abundance of the beta carotene and the xanthophylls masks the chlorophyll in most species. The excess photosynthate is stored in the form of oil droplets or as granules of leucosin, the chemical composition of which is not known with certainty. In a great majority of genera the cells contain one or two parietal plastids and are uninucleate. The surface of the protoplast is often ornamented with small siliceous scales.

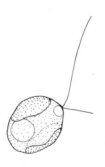

Fig. 7–7. *Ochromonas* sp. Single vegetative cell. X 1700.

The Chrysophyceae, like the Xanthophyceae, represent a series in which types of plant body have developed in a manner parallel to that observed in the Chlorophyceae. In addition, in spite of the fact that the cells possess pigmented plastids, a number of motile genera carry on holozoic nutrition. Many Chrysophyceae are capable of forming siliceous cysts which are often ornamented in various ways. Although a considerable number of genera and species of Chrysophyceae have been found in this country and abroad, with few exceptions they do not seem to be organisms that appear with frequency in collectors' jars. Furthermore, few of them have been grown in culture in the laboratory. For these reasons, only three relatively widely distributed genera—*Ochromonas* (Gr. *ochros*, pale yellow + Gr. *monas*), *Synura* (Gr. *syn*, together + Gr. *oura*, tail), and *Dinobryon* (Gr. *dinos*, whirling + Gr. *bryon*, moss)—will be described.

Ochromonas (Fig. 7–7) is a unicellular motile organism which varies from a spherical to a somewhat irregular shape. The unwalled cells contain one or two pale yellow plastids which are curved and parietal. Two very unequal flagella emerge from the anterior portion of the protoplast. Each cell contains a single nucleus; contractile vacuoles and stigmata are present in the cells of certain species. Actively photosynthetic cells usually contain a single large posterior grain of excess photosynthate, called leucosin. Reproduction is by cell division. The cells may form siliceous cysts with prominent pores.

Synura (Fig. 7–8) is a motile colonial organism in which the individual cells are stipitate and united into spherical clusters. The cells are ovoid and the anterior pole is broader than the stipitate posterior pole. Each is biflagellate and covered with delicate

Fig. 7–8. *Synura uvella* Ehrbg. Single colony. X 700.

siliceous scales. The protoplast contains two parietal concave plastids, a single nucleus, and contractile vacuoles. Cell division augments the number of individuals in a colony. Multiplication is accomplished by fragmentation of the colony and continued growth of the fragments.

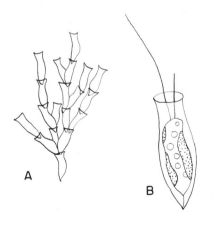

The colonies of *Dinobryon* (Fig. 7–9) are branching and composed of a series of urn- or bell-like loricas, usually widely separated from their contained protoplasts except at the base. Each protoplast has two apical flagella (one of which is markedly longer than the other), usually two plastids, a single nucleus, contractile vacuoles, and a stigma. After longitudinal division, one of the daughter cells moves to the mouth of the lorica, becomes affixed there, and secretes a new lorica. Continuation of this process through a number of divisions results in the formation of dendroid colonies. These

Fig. 7–9. *Dinobryon sertularia* Ehrbg. A, Arborescent colony. X 200. (From G. M. Smith.) B, Single lorica with protoplast enclosed. X 600.

fragment readily and the fragments continue to grow as individual colonies. Isogamous union of two vegetative individuals has recently been reported in *D. Borgei* Lemm.

In addition to the genera described above, nonmotile unicellular colonial and filamentous forms of Chrysophyceae are known. One group of unicellular forms has cells which are amoeboid; the production of pseudopodia effects their movement and is involved in the ingestion of solid foods, an animal-like attribute. The motile Chrysophyceae are most abundant in numbers of genera and species. However, the occurrence of filamentous types indicates that the group contains organisms of algal grade of organization as well as flagellates. The organisms considered in the present account are usually classified as follows:

Division Chrysophyta
   Class 2. Chrysophyceae
      Order 1. Chrysomonadales
         Family 1. Ochromonadaceae
            Genera: *Ochromonas, Dinobryon*
         Family 2. Synuraceae
            Genus: *Synura*

CLASS BACILLARIOPHYCEAE

The **diatoms,** Bacillariophyceae, are at once the best-known, the most numerous (in number of genera, species, and individuals), and economically the most important members of the division Chrysophyta. Diatoms are the despair of the amateur and the joy of the professional microscopist with respect to their structural complexity. Their great beauty and perfection of design rival those of the desmids, but the beauty of diatoms is perhaps more subtle, for it is mostly confined to their cell walls. To appreciate this beauty in full measure, it usually is necessary to dissolve the protoplast with acid and to mount the cells in a highly refractive medium, a process known as "cleaning" the diatoms.

Although some diatoms are bottom dwellers and epiphytes in salt and fresh water, a great number occur in the plankton, where they are of inestimable value in the nutritional cycle of aquatic animals. They are a very ancient group of plants, as indicated by the fossil record. The abundance of diatoms in earlier geological periods is attested by the finding of great deposits of their cell walls—"shells" or frustules, as they are often called. As individual diatoms died in certain bodies of water, they sank to the bottom; here the protoplasts disintegrated, leaving the siliceous cell walls. In this way there were built up great deposits which were exposed in later geological periods and which are now mined as "diatomaceous earth" for use in industrial and technical processes. The economic importance of this substance is tremendous and its uses are many.[1]

At the present time, living diatoms are ubiquitous and important components of algal vegetation. In bodies of fresh water, they seem to be more abundant when the temperature is low. In running water, they often form a brownish coating on submerged rocks and other vegetation.

Diatoms may be strictly unicellular, colonial, or filamentous (Fig. 7–10). They may be divided into two types on the basis of symmetry. In the first, the **pennate** diatoms, exemplified by such genera as *Navicula* (dim. of L. *navis*, boat) and *Pinnularia* (L. *pinna*, feather), the symmetry is bilateral (Fig. 7–10A to F). The second group, the **centric** diatoms, to which many marine genera belong, is characterized by radial symmetry. *Melosira*, a common genus in fresh and salt water, and *Coscinodiscus*, usually marine, illustrate this type (Fig. 7–10G,H).

The taxonomy of diatoms is based almost exclusively on differences in the structure and ornamentation of the cell walls or frustules. The wall is composed of pectic compounds impregnated with silicon dioxide. The diverse types of marking represent thin places or minute pores in the walls; these are rather constant in arrangement and form the basis for species delimitation. The transverse lines seen on the valves of many pennate diatoms represent lines of pores which can be resolved as such with good oil immersion lenses as well as with the electron microscope. The cell wall in all diatoms is composed of two overlapping portions, the **valves;** one is usually slightly larger than the other, much like the bottom and cover of a box (Figs. 7–10D, 7–11C). The larger, cover-like portion is called the **epitheca** (Gr. *epi*, over + Gr. *theke*, case); the smaller is known as the **hypotheca** (Gr. *hypo*, under + Gr. *theke*). The two valves, instead of overlapping each other directly, frequently are attached to a **girdle band** (Fig. 7–11C); this is composed of two overlapping portions. Supernumerary bands may be intercalated between the valves and girdle-band segments; hence the epitheca and hypotheca may be quite widely separated in certain species. The cells are shaped like oblong boxes in *Navicula* (Fig. 7–10A,B) and *Pinnularia* (Fig. 7–10C,D). When viewed from either above or below in valve view, *Pinnularia* cells usually have

---

[1] For a fascinating and informative account of this and other aspects of diatoms, see Paul S. Conger, Significance of Shell Structure in Diatoms, *Smithsonian Report*, 1936, pp. 325–344.

parallel sides and rounded polar portions. A prominent line, the **raphe** (Gr. *raphe*, a seam) traverses each valve (Figs. 7–10A,C,F, 7–11B). When observed in lateral aspect, girdle view, the same cells appear rectangular. Each valve of *Pinnularia* is marked by two series of prominent rib-like lines, the **striae.** In *Navicula*, rows of pores or **punctae** extend from the margin toward the central region of the wall, which, as in *Pinnularia*, is traversed by the raphe. This is interrupted in the center by a clear thickening known as the **central nodule,** and also at each pole by a terminal **polar nodule.** The raphe is wedge-shaped, as viewed in transverse section, and it is believed that streaming cytoplasm on the surfaces of this fissure accounts for the motility observed in the species that have a raphe.

The most conspicuous structures of the diatom protoplasts are the brownish plastids (Figs. 7–10F,H, 7–11A), which are reported to contain, in addition to chlorophylls *a* and *c*, beta carotene and a number of xanthophylls including fucoxanthin, that is present also in Phaeophyta. The plastids may be few in number and massive, as in the pennate diatoms, or numerous and discoidal, as in the centric types. The excess photosynthate is stored in the form of oil or

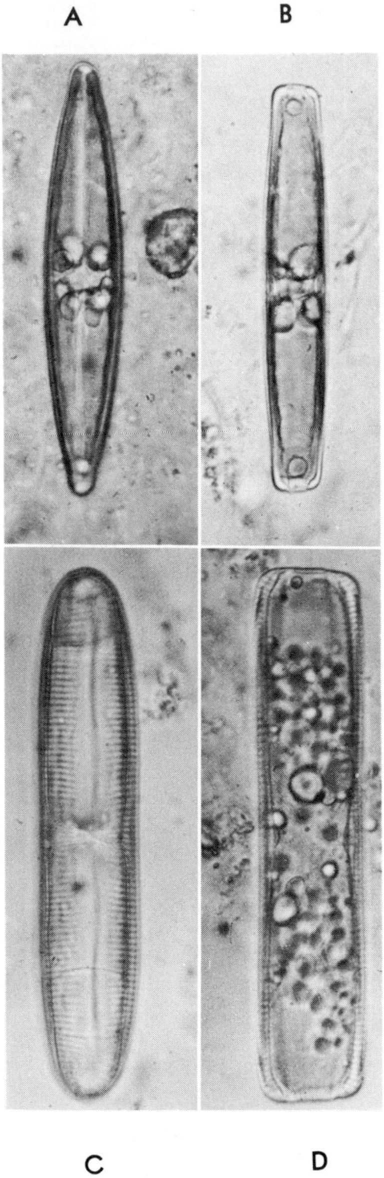

A   B

C   D

Fig. 7–10. Photomicrographs of various Bacillariophyceae. A, Valve, and B, girdle view of a species of *Navicula.* X 540. C, Valve, and D, girdle view of a species of *Pinnularia.* X 540. E, Recently di-

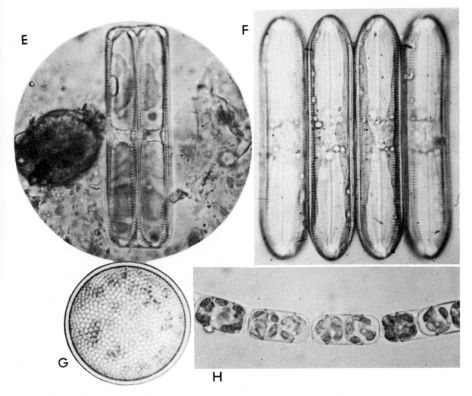

vided cell of *Pinnularia*, girdle view. X 540. F, *Pinnularia sociale.* X 250. G, *Coscinodiscus* sp. Valve view. X 540. H, *Melosira* sp. Girdle view. X 540.

leucosin which is frequently conspicuous in the living cells. The single nucleus usually is readily observable in the center of the cells in pennate genera. In addition to the nucleus, which lies in a bridge of colorless cytoplasm, the central portion of the cell is occupied by a large central vacuole (Fig. 7–11C).

Asexual reproduction in unicellular diatoms is effected by nuclear and cell division (Figs. 7–10E, 7–11D). Immediately after cytokinesis, the original wall contains two protoplasts, each approximately half the volume of the parental one. As the daughter protoplasts enlarge, each secretes a new wall, using the half wall of the parent cell as the epitheca. It is obvious, therefore, that one of the daughter cells thus formed will be slightly smaller than the mother cell, and that if this process were to continue, some of the progeny would become progressively smaller. While there is evidence that this may occur, there is also apparently a compensating ability of the girdle band and valve to increase slightly in size.

Sexual reproduction in pennate diatoms results in the formation of **auxospores** (Gr. *auxo*, increase + Gr. *spora*, spore). These are so called because they are naked protoplasts which increase markedly in size after

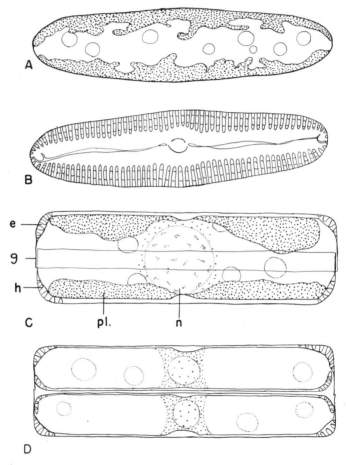

Fig. 7–11. *Pinnularia streptoraphe* Hustd. Living cells. A, Valve view of protoplast. B, Frustule in valve view. C, Cell in girdle view. D, Recently divided individual, optical section, somewhat schematized: e, epitheca; g, girdle band; h, hypotheca; n, nucleus; pl., plastid. X 770.

their formation. Sexuality is superficially similar to that in certain desmids, because the protoplasts of two cells may escape from their walls and unite directly to form a zygote. It differs, however, in that the pennate diatoms are diploid during their vegetative stages, and sexual reproduction is immediately preceded by the meiotic process. In some species—*Navicula halophila* (Grun.) Cl., for example—each member of the pair of vegetative cells forms two gametes, so that two zygotes (auxospores) are formed (Fig. 7–12). The zygotes increase rapidly in size to form auxospores which are larger than the parent cells whose protoplasts functioned as gametes. In this way, when the auxospore has secreted new cell walls it again achieves the maximum size characteristic of the species and functions as a vegetative cell (Fig. 7–12D).

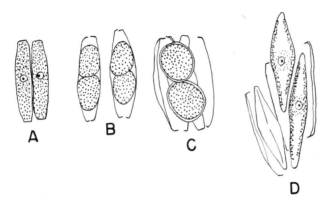

Fig. 7–12. *Navicula halophila* (Grun.) Cl. Stages in sexual reproduction. A, Pairing of cells. B, Formation of two gametes in each cell. C, Two auxospores (zygotes) formed. D, Elongation of auxospores. A-C, X 175; D, X 260. (After R. Subrahmanyan.)

The centric diatoms (Fig. 7–10G,H) are largely marine, but a few also occur in fresh water. Of these, the filamentous genus *Melosira* (Fig. 7–10H) is by far the most widely distributed. It is frequently present in the plankton in sufficient abundance to color the water, but benthic species are also common. The elongate cells, when joined together, are observed in girdle view. The cells contain many small brownish plastids and are uninucleate. The epitheca and hypotheca are joined by connecting bands which seem scarcely to overlap. The valve view of *Melosira* cells, which is circular, becomes apparent when the filaments dissociate into individual cells. *Coscinodiscus* (Gr. *koskinon*, sieve + Gr. *diskos*, disc) is representative of numerous marine species of centric diatoms (Fig. 7–10G). Its cells are markedly flattened in the manner of extremely shallow petri dishes. Sexual reproduction, in one case oogamous, has been reported for a number of centric forms.

The foregoing brief account serves as an introduction to the diatoms.

As a group, they are perhaps the most important of the algae insofar as economic significance is concerned, because of their role in the food cycle of aquatic animals and because of the many uses of diatomaceous earth. While diatoms have received considerable taxonomic study, many other aspects require further investigation. The Bacillariophyceae are clearly delimited from other Chrysophyta by their specialized wall structure, method of wall formation, and sexual reproduction.

The genera of diatoms discussed in the preceding account may be classified as follows:

Division Chrysophyta
    Class 3. Bacillariophyceae
        Order 1. Centrales
            Family 1. Coscinodiscaceae
                Genera: *Melosira, Coscinodiscus*
        Order 2. Pennales
            Family 1. Naviculaceae
                Genera: *Navicula, Pinnularia*

SUMMARY

In concluding this account of the division Chrysophyta, the question remains regarding the propriety of grouping the three classes Xanthophyceae, Chrysophyceae, and Bacillariophyceae into one division, a practice which implies their relationship. Among the attributes which these classes share in common may be listed the brownish color of the plastids that results from the predominance of carotenes and xanthophylls, the frequent deposition of siliceous material in the cell membranes, and the storage of the excess photosynthate as oils. Furthermore, in all genera of one class (Bacillariophyceae) and many of the other two, it has been demonstrated that the cell wall is composed of two overlapping segments. Finally, in some genera of all three classes there has been observed the formation of a unique type of silicified resting cyst, the statospore, which is not found among other algae. In view of these common attributes, the tentative grouping of these classes into one division, Chrysophyta, seems to be justified.

DISCUSSION QUESTIONS

1. What features distinguish the Xanthophyceae from the Chlorophyceae?
2. Cite instances of parallel body structure in these two algal classes.
3. Do you think that Xanthophyceae, like the terrestrial *Botrydium,* may be like the ancestors of the higher land plants? Give the reasons for your answer.

4. What rapid laboratory technique can you suggest for distinguishing Xanthophyceae from Chlorophyceae?

5. In what location and under what conditions would you attempt to collect members of the Chrysophyceae?

6. List the respects in which diatoms are of economic importance.

7. Describe asexual reproduction in unicellular diatoms such as *Pinnularia*.

8. How could you prove that diatom cell walls are impregnated with silica?

9. Speculate on what might happen if you cultivated diatoms in a silicon-free medium.

10. Distinguish between "pennate" and "centric" diatoms.

11. Why is the zygote of pennate diatoms called an auxospore?

12. To what genera of Chlorophyceae are the pennate diatoms similar in respect to type of life cycle?

13. On the basis of supplementary reading, discuss the economic importance of both living and fossil diatoms.

CHAPTER 8

The Algae: Recapitulation

Chapters 2 through 7 have presented a brief account of the several divisions of algae and their component classes, as exemplified by certain illustrative genera. In the discussion of the classification of the plant kingdom in Chapter 1, it was pointed out that the algae, classified in this volume in eight separate divisions, formerly were grouped together in a single class, Algae, in the division Thallophyta. Now that the reader has gained some degree of familiarity with the organisms themselves through mastery of the material in the intervening chapters and especially through laboratory study of the living plants, it may be profitable to reexamine the question of classifying the algae and to present a general comparative summary of their attributes.

A natural classification is one in which the arrangement of the various groups or taxa—namely, the genera, families, orders, classes, and divisions—signifies degree of kinship. To include all the algae in a single class, Algae, implies that they all had a common ancestry, in spite of their present divergences. This would signify, for example, that the blue-green algae, which lack plastids and the type of nuclear organization characteristic of other algae, nevertheless arose from the same stock. Furthermore, it would imply that the range of variations described in the preceding chapters with respect to pigmentation, type of reserve photosynthate, flagella number and insertion, cell wall structure, habitat, body organization, and structure of the sex organs and gametes is of insufficient magnitude to indicate multiplicity of origin. Most modern phycologists are unwilling to accept these implications. The formal class Algae was erected more than seventy years ago, when the diversity of the morphological and physiological attributes of the algae had not been clarified by the studies of many botanists and biochemists. The various types of pigmentation and associated photosynthates are now considered to be characteristics of sufficiently fundamental importance to separate the old class Algae into distinct phyletic lines or divisions. The remaining attributes—namely, flagellation, wall structure, habitat, body organization, and structure of the sex organs—have been used as criteria on the basis of which to delimit taxa lower than the division. For example, the orders Oedogoniales and Ulotrichales among the Chlorophyceae are segregated on such criteria as cell wall structure and flagellation. It must be emphasized once again, and it should be clear from the discussion in earlier chapters, that the classification of plants is subjective. The classification represents a system of presumed relationship carefully elaborated by one or more individuals on the basis of evaluation of the available evidence. The scheme frequently is cemented together by the classifier in a framework of speculation. In a group like the algae, for which the fossil record has not demonstrated the lines of development clearly, the classifier is bound to rely heavily upon the comparative morphology and physiology of the extant genera. It is quite possible, however, that genetic study of physiological attributes of algae may yet furnish evidence that the diversities of pigmentation and photosynthate, currently considered to be of such fundamental importance as to delimit divisions among algae, may represent merely small mutations from an ancestral type. Should this possibility be realized, it might be necessary to replace our currently polyphyletic interpretation of the algae by a monophyletic one.

Review of the type of pigmentation in the several taxa of algae reveals that all contain cholorophyll a, but that only the Chlorophyta and Euglenophyta have chlorophyll b as well. All the algae examined contain beta carotene; the greatest variations occur in the types of xanthophyll pigment present in the cells.

Reserve photosynthates and metabolites may be stored in either soluble or insoluble form. The Chlorophyta and Charophyta are similar to higher green plants in their almost universal storage of the excess photosynthate as starch. Oil is frequently present in addition, in such resting cells as zygospores and cysts. Some of the Dinophyceae also store starch, but a number of genera contain oils. Oil is present as visible droplets in the cells of Chrysophyta. Carbohydrate reserves occur in the cells of Myxophyceae, Phaeophyceae, and Rhodophyceae, but the exact chemical nature of the storage products is not known completely in each case.

Lack of exact knowledge is evidenced by such names as "cyanophycean starch" and "Floridean starch" for the reserve carbohydrates of Myxophyceae and Rhodophyceae, respectively.

Comparison of the several groups of algae with reference to the degree of organization of the plant body is instructive. In every class except the Charophyceae and Phaeophyceae, unicellular genera have been described. Of the classes containing unicellular genera, flagellate motile forms are absent only in the Myxophyceae and Rhodophyceae. Gelatinous and nongelatinous cell aggregates, namely, colonies, occur in several classes of algae. There is evidence that colonial plant bodies represent unicellular types in which the products of cell division have failed to separate. Similarly, the unbranched filament characteristic of a number of genera of Myxophyceae, Chlorophyceae, Bacillariophyceae, and a few Rhodophyceae, may arise in ontogeny from a single cell in which cytokinesis is restricted to one direction. Initiation of cell division in a second direction by certain cells of unbranched filaments results in the branched filamentous type of algal plant body (*Stigeoclonium, Cladophora, Ectocarpus, Griffithsia*). In such genera as *Ulva* and some species of *Porphyra*, continuous cell division in two directions perpendicular to each other and one division in a third direction by each of the cells have resulted in two-layered, sheet-like expanses. Such plant bodies may also arise ontogenetically by continuous branching of primarily filamentous axes in certain Rhodophyceae. Of all the algae, the Phaeophyceae have the largest and most complex plant bodies.

Growth in algae may be generalized (*Merismopedia, Oscillatoria, Spirogyra*) or localized. In the latter case, three types of localization are present in the representative genera which have been described. Apical growth occurs in such plants as *Cladophora, Chara, Nemalion, Batrachospermum, Polysiphonia,* and *Griffithsia.* Intercalary growth is characteristic of *Oedogonium* and filamentous brown algae like some species of *Ectocarpus* and *Pylaiella.* Finally, basal growth is illustrated by *Calothrix, Gloeotrichia,* and *Rivularia* among the Myxophyceae.

The preceding chapters have cited examples of a number of methods of asexual reproduction. Among these may be mentioned cell division, which occurs in a majority of unicellular genera; fragmentation, in colonial and multicellular types; and formation of specialized types of asexual reproductive cells. These may be motile zoospores or nonmotile aplanospores or autospores. All of these possess in common the negative attribute that no union of cells and nuclei is involved in their development into new individuals.

Sexual reproduction—the union of cells and nuclei and the association of chromosomes—is absent only in the Euglenophyta and Cyanophyta of the major groups of algae. In the other taxa, sexuality ranges through isogamous, heterogamous, and oogamous grades. The Charophyta and Rhodophyta are unique in having only oogamous reproduction. The male gamete is actively motile by means of flagella in every group but the Rhodophyta. Both flagellate (*Chlamydomonas*) and nonflagellate (*Spirogyra*) gametes may display evidence of amoeboid activity during union. In algae as in animals, certain secondary characteristics may accompany sexuality. Among the motile unicellular genera, the gametes may be morphologically indistinguishable from vegetative cells. However, in the higher algae, the gametes are markedly differentiated from vegetative cells, and they may be produced frequently in specialized structures, the gametangia. The gametangia in oogamous reproduction are known as antheridia and oogonia. Both sex potentialities may occur on the same individual (homothallism) or each may be present on a separate individual (heterothallism).

The product of sexual union, the zygote, is free-floating in the water in the lower algae (*Chlamydomonas, Ulothrix*, etc.). In others—*Spirogyra* and *Oedogonium*, for example—the zygote is formed within the protective envelope of a parent cell which, however, ultimately disintegrates, thereby freeing the zygote. In *Laminaria* and in all the Rhodophyta, it is retained on the gametophyte after fertilization.

The behavior of the zygote after fertilization varies in different genera of algae, and this is associated with the development of several types of life cycle, shown in the accompanying diagram. In what is regarded as the most primitive and simplest cycle (I), the zygote undergoes meiosis often after a period of dormancy, so the product or products of its germination are haploid (*Chlamydomonas, Spirogyra, Nemalion*, etc.), and the zygote represents the only diploid cell in the life cycle. At the other extreme is the condition (II) in which the zygote, without undergoing dormancy, grows directly into a new individual which is diploid; meiosis occurs in this case when the diploid individual forms gametes (*Cladophora glomerata, Bryopsis*, diatoms). Here the gametes alone, of all the cells involved in the life cycle, are haploid. Both of these types of life cycle may be termed haplobiontic, because only one recognizable plant

Types of Algal Life Cycles

I. Haplobiontic, plant haploid

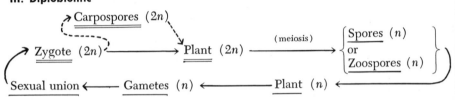

II. Haplobiontic, plant diploid

III. Diplobiontic

body type is present in nature. Haplobiontic organisms undergo alternation only of cytological states, for the diploid or haploid phase, as the case may be, is represented only by a single cell, the zygote or gamete.

Intermediate between these two extremes are the various modifications of diplobiontic life cycles (III). In these, the zygote, without undergoing meiosis, develops into a diploid individual in whose cells meiosis takes place in connection with the formation of asexual reproductive cells which therefore are haploid. These develop into haploid sexual individuals which produce gametes whose union gives rise to zygotes. In this type of life cycle two sets of independent individuals occur in nature. These may be morphologically similar (*Ulva, Cladophora suhriana, Ectocarpus, Griffithsia*) or divergent (*Laminaria*). Hence in morphological alternation the cycle may be isomorphic or heteromorphic. The diplobiontic Rhodophyta have a life cycle like that summarized in Type III, with the interpolation of diploid spores between the zygote and the diploid plant. The origin and relationship of the alternating generations have been alluded to briefly in preceding chapters. This is a question of fundamental importance in any speculation dealing with the development of the higher plants, and it will be referred to repeatedly in the following chapters.

Although this volume is devoted primarily to morphological data, brief mention must be made of the relation of algae to other organisms, and especially of their economic importance. That the algae have a twofold basic biological role becomes clear at once if we speculate regarding the outcome if all aquatic algae were to disappear from the earth. It is clear that all aquatic animal life would also soon be eradicated, for ultimately it is dependent on algal green pastures, not only as a link in the food chain, but because of the role of algae in maintaining an adequate level of oxygen in the animals' environment. The widespread presence of algae in soils suggests that their occurrence there is not fortuitous, and, as a corollary, that they must play some presently undiscovered role in the society of soil organisms.

The value of algae directly as food, indirectly as vegetable manure and for a variety of other purposes, has been appreciated for centuries in oriental countries and to a more limited extent in the western world. Many species of algae are regularly used in the diet of oriental peoples. For example, a species of *Porphyra* known as "laver" has long been culti- vated in Japan by sinking bamboo poles in shallow estuaries; the *Porphyra* spores settle on the poles and develop into the blade-like plants which are subsequently harvested. Various products of algin, derived from the cell walls of coarser Phaeophyceae, are used for several purposes in the textile industry, among them, for waterproofing cloth. Algin has also been used to improve the texture of commercial ice cream. The chemical formula of algin is probably $(C_6H_8O_6)_n$. Colloidal extracts from a num- ber of marine Rhodophyceae, but in this country especially *Gelidium cartilagineum* (L.) Gaillon, are the basis for the purified product known as agar-agar or simply agar. This substance is of paramount importance as the relatively inert agent of solidification of microbiological culture media, but it has a number of additional commercial and medicinal ap- plications. Another red alga, *Chondrus crispus* (L.) Stack, or Irish moss, often called "carragheen," is used in certain coastal localities in this coun- try and abroad as the basis for blanc-mange and other confections. Col- loids extracted from *Chondrus* are widely used in food products such as chocolate milk and ice cream. In addition to the uses of these living algae or products derived from them, algae are important in many other connections. Reference has already been made to the numerous uses of the fossil remains of diatoms known as diatomaceous earth. Finally, unicellular fresh-water algae (*Chlorella*, etc.) are currently the experi- mental organisms in two very important lines of research whose implica- tions for human welfare are obvious. The first concerns the mechanism and energy relations of photosynthesis. The second concerns the large-scale cultivation of the organisms in a controlled environment, for the purpose of obtaining maximum yields to provide possible supplementary sources of food and fuel. More extensive discussions of the topics and organisms alluded to in this chapter and in Chapters 2–7 will be found in the reference works listed at the end of Chapter 2.

DISCUSSION QUESTIONS

1. What plants are usually included in the division Thallophyta? For what reasons? What is the implication of such a practice?

2. Define or explain the terms ontogeny, phylogeny, monophyletic, polyphyletic.

3. What evidence can you cite to indicate that the algae are a polyphyletic group?

4. Discuss pigmentation and reserve photosynthates as they occur in algae. Compare with the land plants in these respects.

5. List the divisions and classes of algae and the attributes which distinguish them.

6. Summarize the types of life cycle that are present in algae and name illustrative genera.

7. Speculate regarding the possible development and relationships of the various types of plant body structure observed in the algae.

8. Discuss sexual reproduction with respect to possible origin, significance, gradation, and distribution of the sexes.

9. a. Where may the algal zygote be located during its formation and at maturity?
   b. What correlations can you make between its location and further development?

10. Distinguish between morphological and cytological alternation of generations, between isomorphic and heteromorphic alternation, between haplobiontic and diplobiontic life cycles, between haplonts and diplonts, between haploid and diploid.

11. Discuss the algae with respect to habitat.

12. How would you go about proving that aquatic animals depend on algae (or other submerged plants) for their existence?

13. State the biological importance of algae.

14. In what respects are algae of economic importance?

15. What is meant by a "culture" of algae? What are pure cultures, unialgal cultures, clonal cultures?

16. In agricultural areas in many parts of the country it has become the practice to excavate for tanks or ponds in which to raise fish for food. Once the water has filled these artificial ponds, commercial fertilizer is added. Exactly how does this affect the fish?

CHAPTER 9

Division Schizomycota

INTRODUCTION TO THE FUNGI (Sensu Lato)

The algae, representatives of which have been described in Chapters 2–8, formerly were grouped as a class, Algae, coordinate with a class, Fungi, in a single division of the plant kingdom, the Thallophyta (Chapter 1). Although this classification has been superseded, the concepts "algae" and "fungi" have persisted, and they serve useful functions. The fungi, in the broadest sense of the term, are sometimes considered to include all the nonphotosynthetic organisms in the plant kingdom below the level of liverworts, mosses, and vascular plants. Although the various organisms thus delimited possess in common the negative attribute of nonphotosynthetic metabolism, they are divergent in so many other important morphological, cytological, and physiological aspects that they no longer are classified in a single group. Instead, they are here treated as five separate phyletic series or divisions, namely, Schizomycota, Myxomycota, Phycomycota, Ascomycota, and Basidiomycota. Discussion of the possible relationships between members of this series is deferred to Chapter 14.

DIVISION SCHIZOMYCOTA

The discussion of the **Schizomycota** (Gr. *schizo*, cleave + Gr. *mykes*, fungus), the **bacteria,** in a volume treating of the morphology of plants, is necessarily brief for several reasons. First, none of the several groups of plants approaches the bacteria in *apparent* simplicity of structure, although there is recent evidence of a higher degree of organization than hitherto had been suspected. Second, the relative simplicity of their

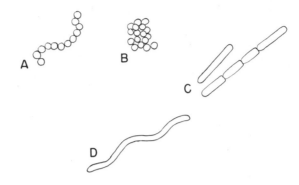

Fig. 9–1.   Some common bacteria. A, *Streptococcus* sp. B, *Staphylococcus* sp. C, *Bacillus* sp. D, *Spirillum* sp. X 3400.

morphology has stimulated and necessitated study of the physiology of bacteria, with the result that their classification is based in large measure on their extremely diverse physiological activities. As a result, the study

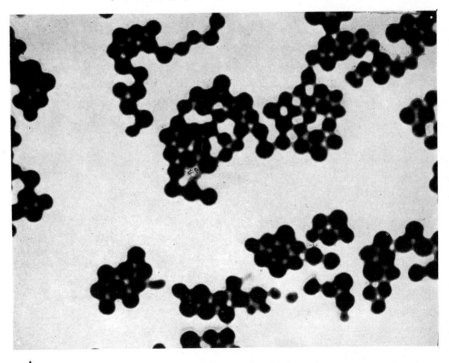

A

Fig. 9–2.   Photomicrographs showing three common shapes of true bacteria (from stained preparations). A, Coccus. B, Bacillus. C, Spirillum. X 2000. (From J. Nowak.)

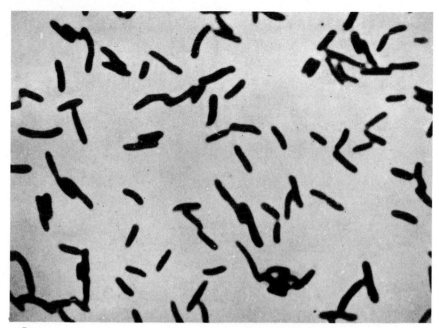

B

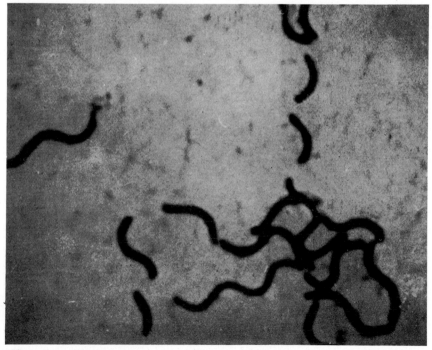

C

of bacteria, originally initiated by botanists, has now come to be recognized as a separate field of biology, namely, bacteriology. Nevertheless, in a treatment of representatives of the plant kingdom and their possible relationships, the bacteria must be reckoned with, particularly in discuss-

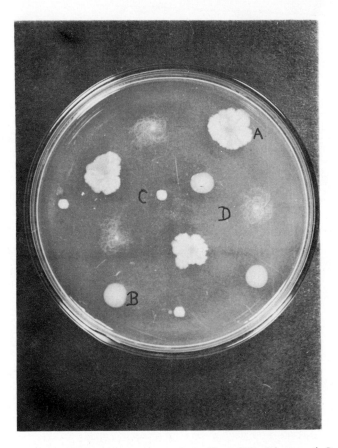

Fig. 9–3. Bacterial colonies on nutrient agar. A, *Bacillus subtilis* Cohn emend. Prazmowski. B, *Escherichia coli* (Migula) Castellani and Chalmers. C, *Streptococcus faecalis* Andrews and Horner. D, *Bacillus cereus* var. *mycoides*, nov. comb. Smith (B. *mycoides* Flügge). X ¾.

ing such fundamental concepts as the nature of primitive life on earth. Furthermore, there are certain cytological aspects of bacteria which seem to parallel those of the Myxophyceae. These are considered by some authorities to be sufficiently significant to warrant classification of the two groups in a single division, the Schizophyta. Approximately 122 genera and more than 1000 species of bacteria have been described. According to the 1948 edition of *Bergey's Manual,* 1630 species of bacteria were known in that year. It is debatable, however, whether bacterial species correspond in scope to those of other plants.

Although bacteria were known to Leeuwenhoek as early as 1683, detailed knowledge of their structure and nutrition goes back only to the last decades of the nineteenth century. Bacteria sometimes are considered to be unicellular fungi which reproduce only by simple fission. A number of genera, however, consist of multicellular chains or filaments, or sporangiate aggregations suggestive of those of certain slime molds to be discussed in the following chapter. In general, bacteria are the smallest living organisms visible with the ordinary light microscope; they frequently have dimensions which range between 0.5 and 2.0 microns in width and 1.0 and 8.0 microns in length. As to cell form, many bacteria fall into three groups (Figs. 9–1, 9–2): those with spherical cells, the **cocci** (Gr. *kokkos,* berry), those whose cells are short rods or cylinders, the **bacilli** (L. *bacillus,* little stick), and those whose cells are curved and twisted, the **spirilla** (Gr. *speira,* coil). Because

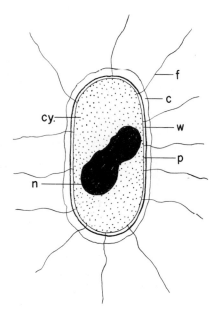

Fig. 9–4. Cell structure in bacteria, schematized: c, capsule; cy., cytoplasm; f, flagellum; n, nuclear material; p, plasma membrane; w, wall. (Modified from Clifton.)

many bacteria are similar in cellular form, it became apparent early that additional criteria must be employed to recognize bacterial genera and their species; these criteria are largely physiological. Many bacteria grow readily on a variety of organic culture media solidified with agar, a colloidal derivative of seaweeds (Fig. 9–3). The growth habit varies considerably among different species.

The individual bacterial cell is delimited from its environment by a cell wall and contains cytoplasmic and nuclear material (Fig. 9–4). The existence of a cell wall has been demonstrated by plasmolysis, by microdissection, and by electron microscopy. The chemical nature of the wall is by no means well known for all bacteria and seems to vary in different species. The wall appears to be composed of a complex carbohydrate of unknown nature and is sometimes referred to as hemicellulose. It is often impregnated with other substances, some of which contain nitrogen. Chitin has been reported in the walls of some bacteria. The cell wall is surrounded, in turn, by a layer of slimy material of variable thickness, which may be present as a recognizable **capsule** (Figs. 9–4, 9–5). The cytoplasm of bacteria devoid of insoluble metabolites appears optically

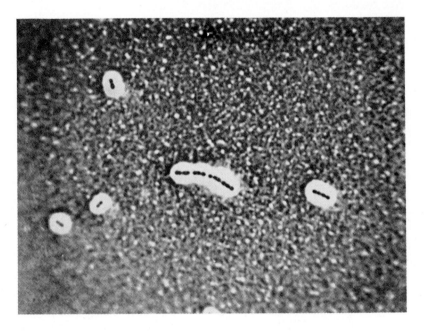

Fig. 9–5.   Photomicrograph of stained streptococci showing capsules. X 1000. (Courtesy of W. D. Frost.)

homogeneous. It is bounded externally by a cytoplasmic membrane. Various granules involved in metabolism frequently are present in the cytoplasm. The question of the organization of the nuclear material is one of the most controversial aspects of the morphology of the bacterial cell. Inasmuch as bacteria maintain certain specific, inheritable attributes through countless series of cell generations, our knowledge of other organisms would indicate that the bacteria possess some physical mechanism of inheritance—in other words, a nuclear mechanism. Recently, as a result of the study of a number of bacteria by special microchemical methods for the detection of desoxyribonucleic acid, which seems to be present universally in the nuclei of higher plants and animals, it was demonstrated that this substance is also present in bacterial cells (Fig. 9–4). Frequently, it takes the form of a somewhat dumbbell-shaped mass which lies parallel to the transverse axis of the cell. This chromosome-like body divides longitudinally prior to cell division; it thus has one of the attributes of chromosomes of higher organisms. It will be recalled that in certain Myxophyceae, similar rod-like bodies have been demonstrated in the central region of the cell. There is apparently a certain precocity in the division of the chromosomal element of some bacteria. In these species, recently divided chromosomes may become separated by partition of the cytoplasm, while actual secretion of the dividing septum may be delayed. Thus a single cell, during active growth, may have its protoplast divided into a number of segments, in some of which the chromosomal element is dividing in preparation for an ensuing cytokinesis, while formation of the transverse walls may lag behind karyokinesis and cytokinesis. Actual separation of daughter protoplasts occurs only after they have secreted these walls.

Some bacteria are nonmotile, but others are actively motile by means of flagella, whose presence can be confirmed only by special illumination or methods of staining. A single flagellum or group of flagella may be present at one pole of the cell or the cells may be covered uniformly with flagella (Fig. 9–4). Various arrangements have been described.

Many of the rod-shaped bacteria have the capacity of forming **endospores** (Fig. 9–6). There is some evidence that these are produced as a result of depletion of the nutrients in the surrounding medium and that they represent condensations of the protoplast within the cell wall. Each spore contains nuclear material and cytoplasm and at maturity is covered by an impermeable wall. Spores are extremely resistant to such unfavorable environmental conditions as high temperatures and desiccation. Upon germination, each spore produces a single vegetative cell. Spore formation in bacteria, therefore, usually is not a means of increasing the number of individuals, but rather a mechanism for survival in adverse environmental conditions.

Until the last decade, it was generally agreed that bacteria lacked sexual reproduction. However, strong genetic evidence of sexuality has been educed recently. The small size of the majority of these organisms no doubt is responsible for failure to obtain convincing cytological evidence of the union of cells and association of their nuclear material. Recent investigations of mutant strains of bacteria have demonstrated that when two mutants, differing in two or more characteristics—in this case biochemical—are cultivated together, certain individuals arise in the mixed culture which combine traits of the original strains. This phenomenon can be explained most satisfactorily by the assumption that cells and nuclei of the two original strains have united and that the fusion

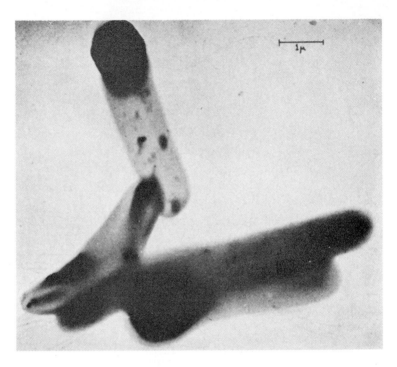

Fig. 9–6. *Clostridium tetani* (Flügge) Holland, with terminal or "drumstick" endospores. X 10,-000. (Electron microscopy.) (Mudd and Anderson, S.A.B. No. 63.)

nucleus has undergone meiosis, with segregation and recombination of the parental attributes in some cases. Convincing cytological proof in support of this hypothesis has not yet been presented. There have been some reports of conjugation of adjacent cells by tubes, but these require confirmation. It is of interest to note, in passing, that the Myxophyceae, which in some respects resemble the Schizomycota, seem to lack sexuality in their life cycles.

The organisms described in the preceding paragraphs are representative of the "true" bacteria, usually classified together in a single order distinct from several orders of "higher" bacteria which are morphologically more complex. One group of the latter, commonly called the **actinomycetes,** is of special interest in several respects. In the first place, the organisms are sometimes classified with the fungi, because their plant bodies are filamentous in organization (Fig. 9–7) like those of many fungi. Furthermore, they produce minute, dust-like spores, conidia (Fig.

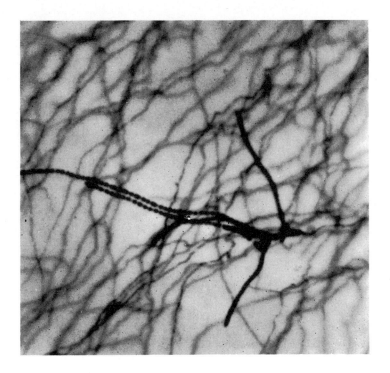

Fig. 9–7. *Streptomyces antibioticus* (Waksman and Woodruff) Waksman and Henrici; hyphae in background, chains of conidia in foreground. X 1500. (Courtesy of Dr. S. A. Waksman.)

9–7), which are similar to those of many fungi. However, the cytological organization of actinomycetes is similar to that of bacteria rather than to that of the fungi. The filaments of actinomycetes, which rarely exceed 1 micron in diameter, form radiating colonies in agar cultures. They are distributed widely in soil from which many strains have been isolated into pure cultures. Three of them, among others—*Streptomyces griseus* (Krainsky) Waksman and Henrici, *S. aureofaciens* Duggar, and *S. rimosus* Routien—yield, respectively, the antibiotics **streptomycin, aureomycin,** and **terramycin.** More than 80 other antibiotic substances have been obtained from species of the genus *Streptomyces*. There is every reason to believe that actinomycetes play an important role in the biology of soil.

A comprehensive account of the nutritional physiology of the bacteria is outside the scope of the present text; it forms a large part of the subject matter of bacteriology. However, several aspects of bacterial nutrition must be considered at this point, not only because of the parallelism with other groups of fungi, but also because of the importance of bacteria in speculations regarding the nature of primitive life.

In respect to nutrition, all plants may be classified as either **autotrophic** (Gr. *autos,* self + Gr. *trophe,* nourishment) or **heterotrophic** (Gr. *heteros,* other + Gr. *trophe*). The chlorophyll-bearing plant is **photoautotrophic,** for it uses energy from the sun in building its food (and its protoplasm) from entirely inorganic substances, in the process known as **photosynthesis.** The presence of chlorophyll, however, is not always an infallible criterion of autotrophism, for, as emphasized in the discussion of the Euglenophyta, certain species of *Euglena* require either organic carbon or nitrogen sources, or both, in their metabolism. On the other hand, the absence of chlorophyll is not a universal manifestation of heterotrophic nutrition, for there are a number of bacteria which utilize the energy released in chemical reactions involving inorganic compounds in synthesizing their food and protoplasm in a **chemoautotrophic** manner. Among these may be mentioned the species of *Nitrosomonas,* which utilize the energy liberated in oxidizing ammonium salts to form nitrites, *Nitrobacter,* which oxidizes nitrites to nitrates, and *Thiobacillus thiooxidans* Beijerinck, which oxidizes sulfur under acid conditions. The energy obtained from these oxidations is utilized in synthesizing protoplasm from inorganic sources. It is clear that autotrophic organisms are entirely independent of other living things, whereas all other living organisms are directly or indirectly dependent upon them and/or each other.

A number of bacteria are photoautotrophic. These organisms are green, brown-red, or purple in color and can be cultivated in an entirely inorganic medium in the absence of oxygen, provided the cultures are illuminated. They contain a magnesium porphyrin compound which is similar to but not identical with chlorophyll. Their photosynthesis differs from that of chlorophyllous organisms in two respects: oxygen is not liberated during the process and the hydrogen donor is not water, but usually a sulfur compound. The photosynthesis of the green and purple bacteria involves a photochemical oxidation of hydrogen sulfide into sulfur or sulfuric acid.

The vast majority of bacteria and fungi are **heterotrophic** (as are animals). The energy they use in building their protoplasm is derived not from the sun or from the oxidation of inorganic compounds but from breaking down complex organic substances produced by other organisms. Heterotrophic species which require living protoplasm of other organisms are known as **parasites** (Gr. *parasitos,* eating at another's table); those that utilize either nonliving organisms or the products of living organisms are known as **saprophytes** (Gr. *sapros,* rotten + Gr. *phyton,* plant). In the account of the fungi (Chapters 11–14), a number of examples of both parasitic and saprophytic organisms will be described. Among the bacteria, some of the species present in human and animal bodies are parasitic; saprophytic species are more widely distributed. Certain fungi other than bacteria which ingest or engulf particles of organic matter are said to have **holozoic** (Gr. *holos,* whole + Gr. *zoion,* animal) nutrition. This, of course, is characteristic of most animals and of certain primitive flagellates.

Microorganisms like bacteria frequently serve as the point of departure for discussions concerning the ultimate origin of life and the nature of primitive life on this earth. In such speculations, knowledge of the types of nutrition is an important prerequisite. Some have postulated that chemoautotrophic organisms represent the most primitive living organisms, inasmuch as they could have existed in darkness and in the purely inorganic environment of the cooling earth crust. According to this view, as the atmosphere cleared sufficiently for the penetration of light rays, photosynthetic organisms, also requiring purely inorganic substances, would have been able to exist. In the final stage, it is postulated that heterotrophic organisms arose as degenerate forms which secondarily lost the ability to chemosynthesize or photosynthesize and grew dependent upon other organisms or their products.

These conjectures have been questioned by those who believe that the evolution of nutritional and energy relations has proceeded in exactly the opposite direction. Their basic assumption is that "organic" substances were present on the earth before the appearance of living organisms. Therefore, they argue, the most primitive organisms would be those which could use organic substances to build their protoplasm, much as certain of our heterotrophic bacteria and fungi do at present. Furthermore, such organisms would require less complex enzyme systems than do chemosynthetic and photosynthetic organisms, which may start their synthetic chain with substances as simple as carbon dioxide. Evolution, beginning with the primitive heterotrophic organisms, proceeded in the direction of increasing capacity for effecting complex biosyntheses from decreasingly complex environmental substances. It culminated in the type of nutrition exhibited by chemosynthetic bacteria, which are able to synthesize their protoplasm and its building units from entirely inorganic substances, utilizing chemical energy. The final step, according to this hypothesis, was the appearance of photosynthetic organisms which developed a capacity for a similar synthesis, using the energy of the sun.

Thus the course of evolution of nutrition and metabolism, like that of many morphological attributes, is interpreted by different scholars as having proceeded in opposite directions. However, the metabolism of microorganisms remains of fundamental importance in all discussions regarding the origin of life.

DISCUSSION QUESTIONS

1. What attributes are possessed in common by bacteria and Myxophyceae? How do they differ?
2. Define or explain the terms autotrophic, heterotrophic, chemoautotrophic, photoautotrophic, chemosynthetic, photosynthetic, parasite, saprophyte.
3. What evidence is there that sexual reproduction occurs in bacteria?
4. Are bacteria the smallest living organisms? Explain.
5. Can most bacteria be identified specifically by microscopic examination alone? Explain.
6. How would you prove that bacterial cells have walls?
7. What types of nutrition occur in bacteria?
8. What type of nutrition do you consider to be the most primitive? Give reasons for your answer.
9. Obligate parasites are those which cannot be cultivated except in a living host. Can you suggest an explanation for this?
10. In what respects are bacterial spores different from those of Myxophyceae?

REFERENCE WORKS ON BACTERIA

Breed, R. S., Murray, E. G. D., and Hitchens, A. P. *Bergey's Manual of Determinative Bacteriology*, The Williams and Wilkins Co., 1948.
De Kruif, P. *Microbe Hunters*, Harcourt, Brace & Company, 1926.
Dubos, R. J. *The Bacterial Cell*, Harvard Univ. Press, 1945.
Frobisher, Martin. *Fundamentals of Bacteriology*, Saunders, 5th ed., 1953.

Grant, Madeline P. *Microbiology and Human Progress,* Rinehart & Co., Inc., 1953.

Henrici, A. T., and Ordal, E. J. *The Biology of Bacteria,* D. C. Heath and Co., 3rd ed., 1948.

Knaysi, G. *Elements of Bacterial Cytology,* Comstock Pub. Co., 1944.

Krueger, Walter. *Principles of Microbiology,* Saunders, 1953.

Oparin, A. I. *The Origin of Life,* The Macmillan Company, 1938.

Salle, A. J. *Fundamental Principles of Bacteriology,* McGraw-Hill Book Co., 3rd ed., 1948.

Sarles, W. B., Frazier, W. C., Wilson, J. B., and Knight, S. G. *Microbiology,* Harper & Brothers, 2nd ed., 1956.

Umbreit, W. W. Problems of Autotrophy, *Bacteriological Reviews 11,* 1947.

Van Niel, C. B. Biochemical Problems of the Chemo-Autotrophic Bacteria, *Physiological Reviews 23,* 1943.

Van Niel, C. B. Comparative Biochemistry of Photosynthesis, *American Scientist, 37,* 1949.

Waksman, S. A., and Lechavalier, H. A. *Actinomycetes and Their Antibiotics,* The Williams and Wilkins Co., 1953.

CHAPTER 10

Division Myxomycota

INTRODUCTION

The **Myxomycota** (Gr. *myxa*, mucus + Gr. *mykes*, fungus) or **slime molds** are characterized especially by their vegetative phase, which is quite unique in respect to nutrition and morphology. Slime molds are relatively inconspicuous elements of the vegetation, but they are objects of great beauty in miniature during the periods when they produce their reproductive structures.[1] The vegetative phase of these organisms is known as the **plasmodium** (Figs. 10–1, 10–2). It occurs on decaying leaves, wood, and soil in moist situations. Inasmuch as most of the vegetative period is spent within or beneath the organic substratum, the plasmodial stage is frequently overlooked. However, if one collects decaying leaves or wood and stores them in moist chambers on damp paper, the plasmodia may often be induced to leave their original substratum and may be maintained for considerable periods in the laboratory.

Fig. 10–1. *Physarum polycephalum* Schw. Plasmodium, X 1.

Illustrative Genera

The following account deals especially with *Physarum polycephalum* Schw. because it is a species readily observable in all stages in the

---

[1] For particularly beautiful illustrations of these plants, see W. Crowder, Marvels of Mycetozoa, *National Geographic Magazine*, 49:421–443, 1926.

laboratory. The plasmodium (Figs. 10–1, 10–2) is a yellow, macroscopically visible mass of multinucleate protoplasm normally in a more or less active state of flowing movement. The protoplasm ingests various organic particles and spores, pollen grains, and microorganisms during its migration; its nutrition is **holozoic** (Gr. *holos*, whole + Gr. *zoion*, animal). The ingested foods lie in vacuoles where they are digested by enzymes secreted by the plasmodial protoplasm. There can be little

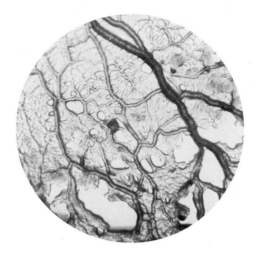

Fig. 10–2. *Physarum polycephalum*. Photomicrograph of portion of plasmodium. X 12½.

doubt that soluble organic matter is also absorbed, so that nutrition is in part saprophytic as well as holozoic. The rate and direction of movement are influenced markedly by external stimuli. Hence plasmodia afford an excellent opportunity for the study of various tactic responses. Motility itself may be observed both macroscopically and microscopically. It consists of a rather regular rhythmic movement in one direction, followed by a short pause and reversal of direction. The prolonged movement, absence of a cellulose cell wall, and capacity for holozoic nutrition have suggested to some biologists that the Myxomycota have affinities with the protozoa; they are sometimes classified with the latter and referred to as Mycetozoa. Their reproductive phases, however, are strikingly plant-like. Movement of the plasmodium may be as rapid as at a rate of 3 cm. per hour in *Physarum*. Plasmodia which have not yet formed reproductive bodies may become concentrated into dormant sclerotia when moisture and/or temperature fall below a certain level. The sclerotia of *Physarum polycephalum* vary from yellow-orange to dark brown in color. They are composed of multinucleate segments called **spherules.** They may give rise to plasmodia again when adequate moisture becomes available.

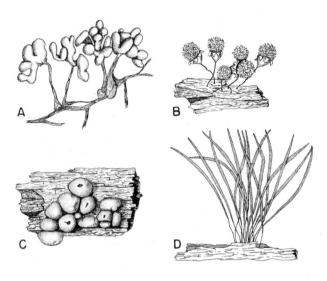

Fig. 10–3. Fruiting bodies—sporangia—of various Myxomycota. A, *Physarum polycephalum.* X 10. B, *Hemitrichia* sp. X 4. C, *Lycogala epidendrum* (L.) Fr. X 1. D, *Stemonitis* sp. X 2.

After a relatively prolonged vegetative phase, which may be lengthened by maintaining high levels of moisture and nutriment, the plasmodium enters the reproductive phase and produces **sporangia** (Fig. 10–3A). This may be hastened by withholding food. Yellow plasmodia, among various species of slime molds, require light to form sporangia. Blue light, 4360A, is especially efficacious in inducing sporangium production in *P. polycephalum.* The plasmodium begins to undergo concentration at one or more localized points, usually those more highly illuminated and drier. As the process continues, the fruiting body characteristic of the genus is produced (Figs. 10–3, 10–4). This may be irregular in form, not markedly different from that of the plasmodium, or it may consist of several or many individual sessile or stalked sporangia. In *Physarum polycephalum* the sporangia are dichotomously lobed, blackish at maturity, and supported on stalks (Fig. 10-3A). During sporangial development, the plasmodium usually discards much detritus at the base of the sporangia, forming a **hypothallus** (Gr. *hypo,* under + Gr. *thallos,* bloom or branch); the remainder is used to produce a rather firm outer stratum, the **peridium** (Gr. *peridion,* small wallet or case), over the sporogenous region.

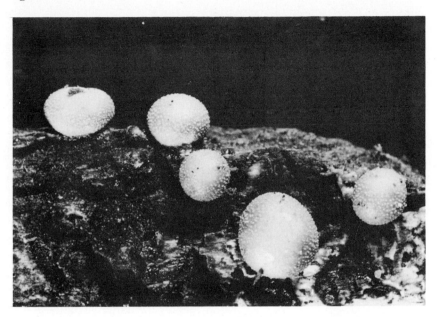

Fig. 10–4. *Lycogala epidendrum.* Sporangia. X 5.

When the protoplasm aggregates, the young fruiting bodies consist of somewhat vacuolate masses of protoplasm with numerous minute nuclei. As development proceeds, the nuclei increase in number by mitosis, and progressive cleavage is initiated both from the plasma membrane ad-

jacent to the peridium and from the surface membranes of numerous vacuoles; hence a large number of spores is ultimately produced. In the meantime, depending on the species, nonliving material may be deposited in and on the surfaces of canal-like vacuoles. When the spo-rangium is thoroughly mature and dry, the former vacuoles persist as a system of threads (Fig. 10–5), the **capillitium** (L. *capillitium,* hair).

The sporangial peridium is rup-

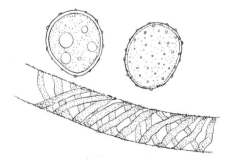

Fig. 10–5. *Hemitrichia vesparium* (Batch.) Macbr. Spores and portion of capillitium; spore at left in optical section, at right in surface view. X 1700.

tured at maturity and the liberated spores are carried away by air currents. Those which settle on favorable substrata soon undergo germination, although they may retain their viability for a number of years. The spores of *P. polycephalum* have punctate walls and are uninucleate (Fig. 10–6A). The germinating spores usually give rise to but one or two motile cells. These are irregular in shape, and somewhat amoeboid; they develop two unequal flagella. Spore germination in *Fuligo*, another genus, is illustrated in Fig. 10–6B. These motile products of spore germination have been observed to ingest bacteria and other minute fragments of nutriment. It has been demonstrated in some genera of slime molds that these amoeboid or flagellate motile cells are potentially gametes which may unite in pairs to form amoeboid zygotes. This occurs in *P. polycephalum*. In each zygote, repeated mitotic nuclear division occurs without cytokinesis, so that a multinucleate plasmodium is ultimately produced. The latter grows very rapidly; for example, a 1 cm.-square piece of plasmodium of *P. polycephalum* increased to 25 sq. cm. in area within seven days when supplied with fungus mycelium for food.

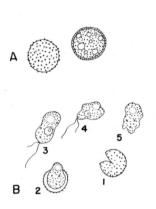

Fig. 10–6. A, Physarum polycephalum. Spores. X 770. B, Fuligo sp. Spore germination: 1, empty spore case; 2, emergent protoplast; 3,4, flagellated spores; 5, amoeboid stage. X 770.

Conclusive evidence as to the exact time and place of meiosis is lacking at present.[1] It is clear, however, that it must occur sometime between the initiation of the plasmodium and the germination of the spores to form the potential gametes. Furthermore, there is good evidence that sexuality is unnecessary for the completion of the life cycle in certain species. For example, it has been demonstrated in cultures that the progeny (swarm cells and amoebae) of a single spore of one species of *Physarella* can form a plasmodium and sporangia without undergoing sexual fusion. In the light of the available evidence, it is probable that

---

[1] In a personal communication, Ian K. Ross, Department of Botany, McGill University, reports that meiosis occurs just after the formation of the capillitium and just prior to spore formation.

the various genera and species of Myxomycota differ in respect to type of life cycle.

A number of genera and species of slime molds other than *Physarum* are of common occurrence on substrata that are subject to prolonged periods of moisture. These include decaying wood and leaves, moist soil, and grass. *Stemonitis, Lycogala,* and *Hemitrichia* (Figs. 10–3, 10–4) are genera which are widely distributed in such habitats.

Brief mention must be made also of two other organisms, namely, *Dictyostelium* and *Plasmodiophora,* usually classified as Myxomycota, which differ in important respects from the organisms described above. *Dictyostelium* (Fig. 10–7), an inhabitant of soil, differs from *Physarum* and similar slime molds in that its plasmodial stage is an aggregate of amoeboid cells, called **myxamoebae,** which retain their individuality instead of uniting to form a multinucleate mass of protoplasm. These myxamoebae remain associated during their holozoic phases, engulfing and digesting bacteria and other nutriment. They ultimately gather at one point on the substratum to form a stalked sporangium called a **sorocarp.** The fertile, globular apex liberates walled cells which function as spores and germinate, forming other amoebae. It has recently been reported that during the early stages of aggregation to form the sorocarp, numbers of amoebae unite in pairs and form zygotes. These soon undergo zygotic meiosis in which the chromosome number $n = 7$ has been observed clearly.

In addition to holozoic organisms like *Physarum* and *Dictyostelium,*

Fig. 10–7. *Dictyostelium mucoroides* Brefeld. Single fruiting body. X 14. (From Harper.)

several parasitic genera are often classified with the Myxomycota. One of these, *Plasmodiophora brassicae* Wor., parasitizes the roots of plants in the mustard family, especially those of cabbage, causing a deformation of the roots and a condition known as "club root."

SUMMARY AND CLASSIFICATION

In conclusion, it may be noted that the Myxomycota are of interest to the biologist because of the combination of plant and animal attributes they display. Their naked, plasmodial stages afford an excellent opportunity for the study of protoplasm, while the delicate beauty and design of the minute sporangia have attracted the attention of many students. As noted above, the slime molds are often classified by zoologists as members of the phylum Protozoa. When treated by botanists, they are generally considered to include at least three series which are accorded varying rank by different authors. The organisms discussed in this chapter may be classified as follows:

Division Myxomycota
    Class 1. Myxomycetes
        Order 1. Physarales
            Family 1. Physaraceae
                Genus: *Physarum*
        Order 2. Stemonitales
            Family 1. Stemonitaceae
                Genus: *Stemonitis*
        Order 3. Liceales
            Family 1. Lycogalaceae
                Genus: *Lycogala*
        Order 4. Trichiales
            Family 1. Trichiaceae
                Genus: *Trichia*
    Class 2. Acrasiomycetes
        Order 1. Acrasiales
            Family 1. Acrasiaceae
                Genus: *Dictyostelium*
    Class 3. Plasmodiophoramycetes
        Order 1. Plasmodiophorales
            Family 1. Plasmodiophoraceae
                Genus: *Plasmodiophora*

DISCUSSION QUESTIONS

1. What characteristics distinguish the Myxomycota from other fungi?
2. In what habitats would you look for slime molds?
3. How do the plasmodium and sporangiate stages of Myxomycota differ in their tactic responses? Describe possible experiments to demonstrate such responses.
4. In what respect is the nutrition of Myxomycota unlike that of other fungi?
5. Is the capillitium cellular? Explain, describing its origin.
6. Summarize the life cycle and reproduction of *Physarum polycephalum*.
7. List the animal- and plant-like attributes of slime molds.
8. If you were cultivating Myxomycota in the laboratory, in what form could you supply the essential elements?

9. How does *Dictyostelium* differ from other slime molds like *Physarum?*

REFERENCE WORKS ON FUNGI[2]

Alexopoulos, C. J. *Introductory Mycology,* John Wiley and Sons, Inc., 1952.

Bessey, E. A. *Morphology and Taxonomy of Fungi,* The Blakiston Co., 1950.

Buller, A. H. *Researches on the Fungi,* Vols. 1–6, Longmans, Green and Co., Vol. 7, University Press, Toronto, 1909–1950.

Christensen, C. M. *The Molds and Man,* Univ. of Minnesota Press, 1951.

Crowder, W. Marvels of Mycetozoa, *National Geographic Magazine,* 49:421–443, 1926.

Fitzpatrick, H. M. *The Lower Fungi. Phycomycetes,* McGraw-Hill Book Co., Inc., 1930.

Foster, J. W. *Chemical Activities of Fungi,* Academic Press, 1949.

Gauman, E. A., and Wynd, F. L. *The Fungi,* Hafner and Co., 1952.

Gwynne-Vaughan, H. C. I., and Barnes, B. *The Structure and Development of the Fungi,* Cambridge Univ. Press, 1937.

Krieger, L. C. C. Common Mushrooms of the United States, *National Geographic Magazine,* 37:387–439, 1920.

Lindegren, C. C. *The Yeast Cell, Its Genetics and Cytology,* Educational Publishers, Inc., 1949.

Lister, A. *A Monograph of the Mycetozoa,* British Museum, 1925.

MacBride, T. H., and Martin, G. W. *The Myxomycetes,* The Macmillan Company, 1934.

Ramsbottom, J. *Mushrooms and Toadstools,* Collins, 1953.

Smith, G. M. *Cryptogamic Botany,* McGraw-Hill Book Co., Inc., Vol. 1, 1955.

Sparrow, F. K. *Aquatic Phycomycetes,* Univ. of Michigan Press, 1943.

Wolf, F. A., and Wolf, F. T. *The Fungi,* John Wiley and Sons, Inc., 2 vols., 1947.

---

[2] For use with Chapters 10–14.

CHAPTER 11

Division Phycomycota

INTRODUCTION

The division **Phycomycota** (Gr. *phykos*, alga + Gr. *mykes*, fungus) contains a rather heterogeneous group of fungi, which may be distinguished from the Myxomycota by the absence of a plasmodial stage and from the Schizomycota by differences in cell organization. The Phycomycota are readily distinguishable from the Ascomycota and Basidiomycota by the lack of spores characteristic of those divisions. The **mycelium,** the vegetative filamentous stage, also is distinctive in the Phycomycota, being either nonseptate[1] or incompletely septate and coenocytic. An individual branch of the mycelium is called a **hypha.** Both parasites and saprophytes occur among the Phycomycota. The name of the division reflects the opinion of those who see in its members evidences of relationship to the algae. The Phycomycota considered in this chapter represent five different groups of organisms. These are the chytrids, *Allomyces*, the water molds, *Albugo*, and bread mold.

ILLUSTRATIVE TYPES

Chytrids

The chytrids are the simplest of the Phycomycota. They are often microscopic and may be unicellular. However, vegetative and reproductive portions may be separated by partitions as in siphonalean algae like *Bryopsis*, and as in *Vaucheria*. A division of labor is apparent in the vegetative phases of some genera, as indicated by the development of

---

[1] A. H. Buller (*Researches on Fungi,* vol. V, pp. 86–134) has shown that the septa in many Ascomycota and Basidiomycota are incomplete and traversed by streaming protoplasm.

rhizoidal processes with tapering extremities (Fig. 11–1), somewhat like those of the alga *Botrydium*. In other genera, rhizoidal branches are absent.

Many parasitic species inhabit such hosts as algae, aquatic fungi, and the submerged portions of higher plants. Others, like *Synchytrium*, occur on terrestrial plants such as the hog-peanut, *Amphicarpa bracteata* (L.) Fern. Dormant reproductive bodies of chytrids are abundant in the soil and in submerged decaying vegetation. Accordingly, a number of species may be obtained readily for study by immersing various types of "bait,"

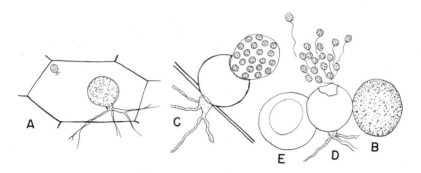

Fig. 11–1. *Rhizophydium globosum* (Braun) Rabenhorst, on leaf cells of *Elodea. A,* Young and almost mature thalli on leaf cell. *B,* Vegetative thallus. *C-E,* Formation and liberation of zoospores. X 410.

such as onion scale epidermis, untreated cellophane, pollen grains, chitinous substances, bleached leaves, etc., in pond water and suspensions of soil and water.

Rhizophydium globosum (Braun) Rabenhorst represents one of the simpler chytrids (Fig. 11–1). It occurs on dead or moribund aquatic fresh-water vegetation. Infection is effected by a posteriorly uniflagellate zoospore, which settles on the surface of the host, withdraws its flagellum, and secretes absorptive branches into a host cell (Fig. 11–1A). The fungus protoplast increases in size by absorbing nutriment from the host protoplasm (Fig. 11–1B) or its remains. After a period of vegetative development, during which increase in nuclear number occurs, the protoplast of the parasite undergoes cleavage to form a number of uniflagellate zoospores. These are liberated at maturity (Fig. 11–1C,D) through an apical orifice (Fig. 11–1E). The zoospores produce new infections.

Polychytrium aggregatum Ajello is representative of the chytrids in which a branching system, the **rhizomycelium,** often is developed by the vegetative individual (Fig. 11–2), which is saprophytic and present in decaying vegetation. Reproduction is accomplished by posteriorly uniflagellate spherical zoospores (Fig. 11–2B), which settle on the substratum and produce a branching penetration tube. The latter grows in length and diameter, producing a continuous branch system, the rhizomycelium, within and upon the surface of the substratum. At different loci on the rhizomycelium, terminal and intercalary swellings become delimited by septa and develop into zoosporangia (Fig. 11–2A). These are

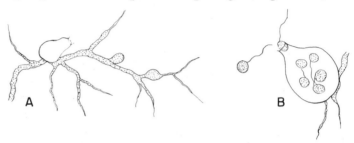

Fig. 11–2. *Polychytrium aggregatum* Ajello. A, Portion of plant body with developing zoosporangia. X 315. B, Liberation of zoospores. X 770.

variously shaped, spherical to pyriform, and are either smooth or tuberculate. Both types of sporangia are uninucleate when first formed, but a period of mitotic nuclear division increases the nuclear number. Progressive cleavage of the zoosporangium protoplast into uninucleate zoospores follows. These are discharged from a short beak at the tip of the sporangium (Fig. 11–2B). The individual zoospores gradually become motile and swim away from the mass. Sporangial **proliferation,** in which a new sporangium is regenerated within the empty wall of a former one, is of common occurrence. In addition to *Polychytrium* and *Rhizophydium,* many other genera and species of chytrids have been described.

Allomyces

Unlike the chytrids, which are either strictly unicellular or possess only rhizoidal processes, the plant body of *Allomyces* (Gr. *allo,* other + Gr. *mykes*) consists of a well-developed branching mycelium (Figs. 11–3A, 11–4A) anchored by rhizoidal absorptive branches which penetrate the substratum. The organism, which occurs in moist soil and aquatic habitats in nature, grows readily in laboratory cultures on split hemp seeds or other organic substrata. Branching in *Allomyces* is typically dichotomous, and growth is apical. Superficially the mycelium appears to be septate, but careful scrutiny of the septations indicates that they are incomplete and that the protoplasm is continuous throughout the plant (Fig. 11–3B). The plant body with its many nuclei is coenocytic.

After a period of vegetative growth, the mycelium enters the reproduc-

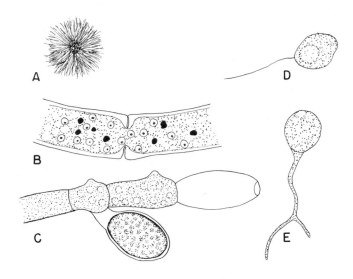

Fig. 11–3. *A, Allomyces* sp. Habit of growth on hemp seed in water culture. X 1. *B-E, Allomyces macrogynus* Emerson. *B,* Median longitudinal section of hypha; note multinucleate condition and false septum. *C,* Three seriate thin-walled zoosporangia, the apical one empty, and a thick-walled (meiosporangium) on lateral branch. *D,* Zoospore. *E,* Zoospore germination. B,D,E, X 770; C, X 315.

tive phase. In *A. macrogynus* Emerson, the terminal portions of the mycelium become delimited as zoosporangia (Fig. 11–3C). The portion of the hypha just below the sporangial septum may form a new branch; hence the originally terminal sporangial initial becomes secondarily lateral in position. As development proceeds, it becomes apparent that two types of sporangia may be produced. The first of these are thin-walled, ephemeral, and colorless and are produced early in development. The second type is thick-walled, persistent, and brown and occurs later (Figs. 11–3C, 11–4B). Both types of sporangia contain a number of nuclei at the time of their formation; this number is increased by division as the sporangia mature. During development, the thin-walled sporangia undergo progressive cleavage to form a number of posteriorly uniflagellate zoospores (Fig. 11–3D). These are liberated at maturity through a pore in the sporangial wall (Fig. 11–3C). The zoospores serve as agents for increasing the number of thalli, and under suitable conditions a large number of asexual generations is produced in this manner. Only 36 to 48 hours is required for a mature thallus to develop from a zoospore.

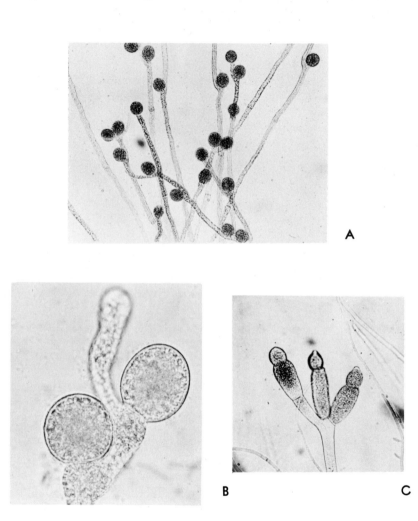

Fig. 11–4. *Allomyces* sp. A, Mycelium with thick-walled zoosporangia. B, Thick-walled, meiosporangia. C, *A. macrogynus*. Male (terminal) and female gametangia. A, X 70; B, x 250; C, x 125.

The thick-walled, resistant zoosporangia (Fig. 11–5A) called **mei-osporangia** can withstand long periods of desiccation and temperatures up to 100° C. for short periods and still retain their viability. These sporangia also are multinucleate. It has recently been demonstrated that their nuclei persist for long periods in the prophase stages of meiosis, even when the sporangia have been dried. Transfer to water breaks their dormancy and stimulates further development. This consists in the completion of the nuclear divisions, which are meiotic, and the formation of approximately 48 uniflagellate zoospores. The haploid chromosome number in A. *macrogynus* Emerson is 14 or 28 (depending on the race); the

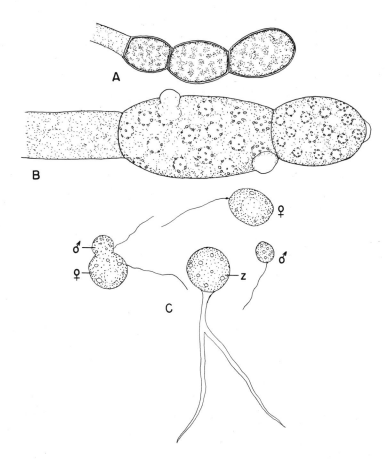

Fig. 11–5. *Allomyces macrogynus.* A, Chain of meiosporangia. X 315. B, Male (terminal) and female gametangia; note exit papillae and clusters of granules which mark nuclear position. X 770. C, Gamete union and zygote germination: z, zygote. X 1700.

haploid number in A. *arbuscula* Butler is 8 or 16. The zoospores from resistant sporangia settle on available substrata and develop into plants which form only gametangia, not zoosporangia.

The gametangia, as they first appear on the vegetative branches, occur in pairs (Figs. 11–4C, 11–5B), but those produced subsequently may be borne in chain-like series. In their development the male gametangia produce an orange-red carotenoid pigment which is dissolved in droplets of oil in the gametes. The female gametangia remain colorless throughout their development. Both types of gametangia undergo progressive cleavage to form uninucleate gametes. The male gametangia contain more nuclei than the female, and as a result the male gametes are considerably smaller than the female (Fig. 11–5C). Both are liberated through pores and unite in pairs under suitable environmental conditions (Fig. 11–5C). *Allomyces macrogynus,* therefore, is heterogamous and homothallic.

The zygote settles on an available substratum and develops (Fig. 11–5C) into a mycelium which develops only zoosporangia, not gametangia. Cultural and cytological studies have demonstrated the occurrence of isomorphic alternation of a diploid, asexual, zoospore-producing sporophyte with a haploid, sexual, gamete-producing gametophyte in *Allomyces macrogynus.* The life cycle of *Allomyces macrogynus* may be summarized as follows:

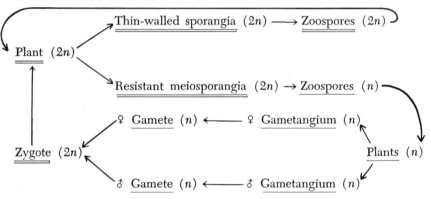

The life cycle here is similar to that of *Cladophora suhriana* and *Ectocarpus siliculosus* (Type III, pp. 51, 136). Deviations from this life cycle may occur in certain strains. In *Allomyces cystogenus* Emerson, the gametophyte is represented only by cysts which arise from the haploid zoospores of resistant sporangia. These cysts form isogametes, and the products of their union grow into diploid, zoosporangium-bearing plants.

The Water Molds

The widespread genera *Saprolegnia* (Gr. *sapros,* rotten + Gr. *legnon,* border) and *Achlya* (Gr. *achlys,* mist) are representative of a considerable number of Phycomycota known as **water molds.** The great majority of the species is saprophytic, but a few parasitize fish and other aquatic animals. They are commonly observable as a cottony halo on the bodies of dead insects which have fallen into the water. These fungi can be readily obtained for laboratory study by using small pieces of coagulated egg albumen or boiled hemp seeds as bait in pond water and aqueous soil suspensions.

The plant body of the water molds differs from that of *Allomyces* in the absence of partial septa and in the lesser regularity of branching. Septa are formed at the bases of the reproductive organs (Figs. 11–6, 11–8) or in response to injury. As in *Vaucheria,* the tubular plant body is multinucleate, the minute nuclei lying in the thin peripheral cytoplasm which surrounds the central

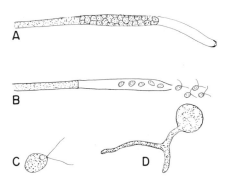

Fig. 11–6.   *Saprolegnia* sp. A, Proliferative zoosporangium. B, Liberation of primary zoospores. C, Single zoospore. D, Zoospore germination. A,B, X 75; C,D, X 770.

vacuole. Absorptive rhizoidal branches penetrate the substratum and serve the function of anchorage (Fig. 11–6D).

After a period of vegetative development, the reproductive phases, asexual at first, are initiated by the development of cylindrical zoosporangia (Figs. 11–6, 11–7). These are elongate and terminal and undergo cleavage, forming a considerable number of biflagellate zoospores (Fig. 11–6) which are liberated (Figs. 11–6, 11–7) through a terminal pore. The apex of the hypha just posterior to the zoosporangium may then protrude as a lateral branch or it may project up through the empty zoosporangium to form a second crop of zoospores; this is an example of **proliferation** (Fig. 11–6A). After a period of motility, the liberated pyriform zoospores (Fig. 11–6C) withdraw their flagella, become spherical, and secrete walls, thus forming aplanospores. The latter germinate later to form reniform zoospores, one from each aplanospore; these also encyst after a period of motility. In germination to form a new plant, the cysts produce delicate hyphae known as germ tubes (Fig. 11–6D). The occurrence of two motile periods is termed **diplanetism.** *Achlya* may be distinguished from *Saprolegnia* in that its primary zoospores remain clustered and become aplanospores at the mouth of the zoosporangium. In *Saprolegnia,* in contrast, the primary zoospores are dispersed. Under some environmental conditions, probably mainly nutritional, segments of the coarse mycelium may become irregularly swollen and densely granular. These **gemmae** (L. *gemma,* bud) may germinate into new mycelia under favorable conditions.

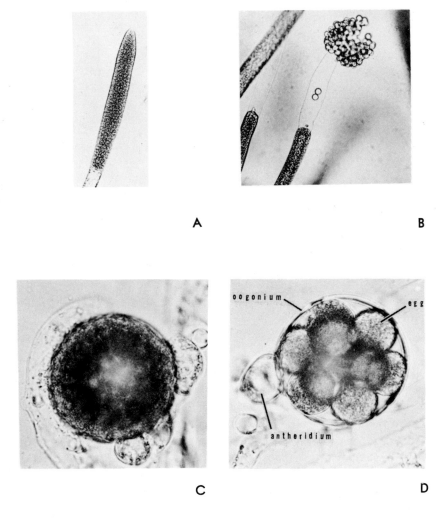

Fig. 11–7. *Achlya* sp. A, Zoosporangium containing zoospores. X 135. B, Liberation of zoospores. X 175. C, Young oogonium with male branch applied to its surface. X 540. D, Older oogonium with eggs and antheridium at the surface. X 540.

Following a series of asexual generations, the mycelium initiates sexual reproduction. *Saprolegnia* and *Achlya* differ from *Allomyces* in that both male and female gametes are nonmotile. The male and female gametangia develop as lateral branches on the mycelium. Some species are homothallic and others heterothallic. Careful study of the development of the sex organs in *Achlya* has revealed a process of unsuspected complexity, involving the secretion of a number of complex chemicals which

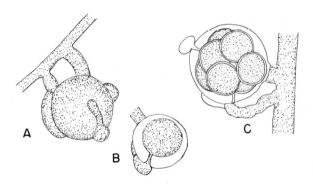

Fig. 11–8. *Saprolegnia* sp. A, Young oogonium with male branch attached. B, Oogonium with single egg at fertilization. C, Oogonium with oospores (zygospores) and empty antheridia. X 315.

influence the course of development. The female gametangia, here known as **oogonia,** arise from lateral hyphae whose swollen apex is delimited by a septum (Figs. 11–7C, 11–8). The multinucleate protoplast of the oogonium undergoes cleavage into a number of multinucleate portions, each of which becomes spherical and ultimately uninucleate through the degeneration of all but one of the nuclei in each segment. The male gametangium, the **antheridium** (Figs. 11–7, 11–8B,C), consists of the delimited portion of a slender, branching hypha which envelops the oogonium. It penetrates the oogonium and eggs by means of tubular protuberances called **fertilization tubes** (Fig. 11–8B,C). The antheridia are multinucleate, and contact and penetration of each egg by a fertilization tube make possible the union of male and female nuclei which follows. After fertilization, the zygotes rapidly develop thick walls which obscure their contents. The dormant zygote is known as the **oospore;** details of its germination are not well known, nor are the cytological features of the life cycle. There is some evidence, however, that meiosis is zygotic.

Albugo

The genera of Phycomycota so far described are all similar in that they are saprophytic in nutrition and aquatic in habitat. *Albugo* (L. *albus*, white), on the contrary, is a parasitic genus which occurs on a number of hosts. *A. candida* (Pers.) Kuntze occurs on certain genera of

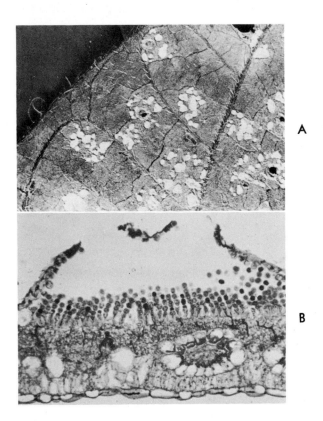

Fig. 11–9. *Albugo bliti* (Bis.-Bern.) Kunze. A, Portion of infected leaf of a species of *Amaranthus*. B, Section of infected leaf showing ruptured epidermis, conidiophores, and conidia. X 125.

mustards (Cruciferae). *A. ipomeae-panduranae* (Schwein.) Swing. is widespread on sweet potatoes and certain morning-glories, and *A. bliti* (Bis.-Bern.) Kunze occurs on species of *Amaranthus*. Leaves of infected plants become covered with conspicuous mealy white spots or patches (Fig. 11–9A) which are caused by eruptions of large numbers of spores below the epidermis (Fig. 11–9B). Because of their lesions, infected plants are said to have **white rust.** The formation of the spores is preceded by the development of a vegetative mycelium which spreads through the host tissues from the site of the primary infection; the mycelium is entirely intercellular. The fungus obtains its metabolites by forming small, protuberant, papillate branches, **haustoria** (L. *haustor*, one who·draws), which penetrate some of the host cells.

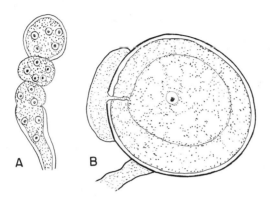

Fig. 11–10. *Albugo bliti.* A, Conidiophore and conidia. B, Oogonium, egg, and antheridium; note residual cytoplasm around egg. X 770.

In spore formation, a number of multinucleate hyphal tips push out between the mesophyll cells and enlarge terminally (Figs. 11–9B, 11–10A). After several nuclei have migrated into the enlarged tip, the latter is delimited by an annular centripetal ingrowth of the wall. The tip of the hypha below the delimited spore now enlarges and is ultimately cut off like the first. The spores thus are produced in chains in basipetal succession, the oldest spore being farthest from the spore-producing hypha. Continued spore production brings about a localized uplifting of the epidermis (Fig. 11–9B), which is finally ruptured, and the mature spores escape freely. They are often called **conidia** or **conidiospores** (Gr. *konis,* dust). However, in view of their subsequent development, in which each "conidium" may function as a zoosporangium, undergoing cleavage to form as many zoospores as there are nuclei present, these spores are sometimes interpreted as sporangia. Each may therefore be called a **conidiosporangium.**

The mealy, dust-like spores are readily disseminated by air currents; and if they settle on moist surfaces of leaves of the host species, they germinate either by germ tubes or by producing zoospores. The biflagellate zoospores become spherical after a period of motility, encyst, and then develop delicate hyphal tubes which usually enter the host through a stoma. The infection is spread in this way.

Sexual reproduction may follow asexual later in the growing season. The sex organs are produced from the tips of hyphae among the mesophyll cells of the leaf (Fig. 11–10B) and are suggestive of those of the water molds. After the hyphal tips have enlarged considerably, they are segregated from the remainder of the hyphae by cell walls. The antheridia are smaller than the oogonia, but both are multinucleate. As the oogonium matures, the protoplasm becomes rather densely aggregated in the center, leaving a more watery, vacuolate periplasm at the periphery. By the time of fertilization, all but one of the nuclei of the oogonium disintegrate; the remaining nucleus functions as the egg nucleus. The antheridium, which is appressed to the oogonium, now produces a small hyphal protuberance that penetrates the oogonial wall and grows through the periplasm, into the central dense cytoplasm containing the egg nucleus (Fig. 11–10B). After nuclear union, a multilayered wall is secreted by the zygote, whose nucleus divides soon after fertilization, until about 32 nuclei are formed. In the spring, further nuclear division and, finally, cleavage occur. In this manner, the zygote gives rise to a large number of biflagellate zoospores which reinfect the leaves of the next season's plants. No convincing evidence of the time and site of occurrence of meiosis is available.

The sexual organs of *Albugo candida* are superficially similar to those of *Saprolegnia* and *Achlya*. The oogonia differ, however, in the production of a single egg which is delimited from the remaining cytoplasm (periplasm) by free cell formation. In *Saprolegnia* and *Achlya*, on the other hand, even in those cases when only one egg is developed, there is no residual cytoplasm.

Rhizopus nigricans and Related Molds

Perhaps the most familiar of all Phycomycota is *Rhizopus* (Gr. *rhiza*, root + Gr. *pous*, foot), one of a large group of phycomycetous molds. *R. nigricans* Ehr., commonly known as **black bread mold** because of its occurrence on that substratum, frequently appears in damp, warm weather. *Rhizopus* and related genera may be present on all sorts of organic matter including dung, fruit, and fleshy fungi, when there is sufficient moisture to support growth. Its spores are almost always present in the atmosphere, as evidenced by the frequency with which it can be obtained when moistened bread and other organic substances are exposed to air currents and then maintained in a humid atmosphere. *Rhizopus oryzae* has been isolated from human beings with fatal cerebral disorders.

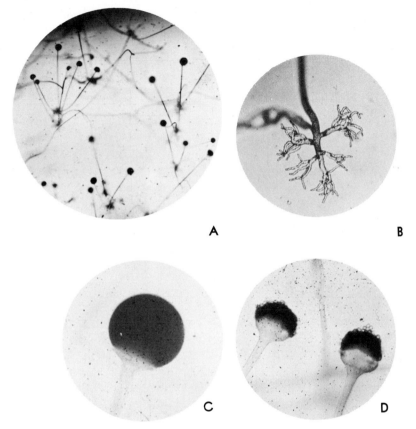

Fig. 11–11. *Rhizopus nigricans* Ehr. A, Habit of growth; note sporangiophores, sporangia, stolon-like hyphae, and absorptive bases. X 12½. B, Enlarged view of absorptive hyphae. X 125. C, Mature sporangium. X 135. D, Dehiscent sporangia; note columella and spores. X 135.

The mycelium is a cottony white mass during the vegetative phase but presents a sooty appearance at the time of sporulation. This is caused by the presence of large numbers of black-walled spores. Although the mycelium, as in most Phycomycota, is nonseptate and coenocytic, it exhibits considerable differentiation. Certain branches creep over the substratum much like stolons in higher plants (Fig. 11–11A). Also like stolons, the portions of the horizontal hyphae that make contact with the substratum produce rhizoidal branches (Fig. 11–11B), which serve as absorptive organs and secrete digestive enzymes. After a short period of vegetative development, groups of unbranched, elongate hyphae arise from the absorptive branches, forming erect hyphae whose tips become enlarged with nuclei and cytoplasm as increase in length ceases. These are known as **sporangiophores,** because their apices develop into sporangia (Fig. 11–11A,C,D).

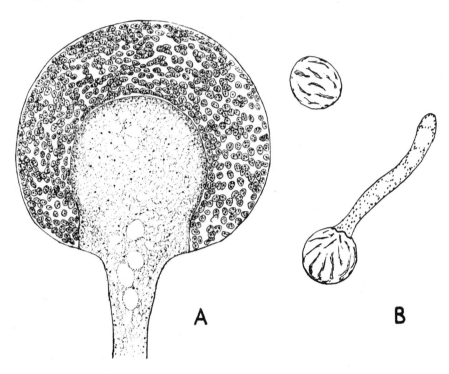

Fig. 11–12. *Rhizopus nigricans.* A, Median longitudinal section of sporangium; note wall, columella, and spores. X 520. (From Swingle.) B, Spore and germinating spore, the latter after 6 hours on potato-dextrose agar. X 770.

The sporangia are formed in the following manner. As the enlarging tips of sporangiophores attain their characteristic size (Fig. 11–11C), the peripheral cytoplasm becomes dense and the central portion remains vacuolate. The two regions are segregated from each other by the coalescence of a series of vacuoles which are present in a dome-like arrangement. A wall finally is secreted between the two portions of the protoplasm (Fig. 11–12A). The central sterile portion is called the

columella (L. *columella,* dim. of column); the peripheral portion is fertile and sporogenous. As the sporangium matures, the sporogenous protoplasm undergoes progressive cleavage, with the ultimate production of large numbers of minute spores (Fig. 11–12A), each of which contains several nuclei and develops a black wall (Fig. 11–12B). The outer sporangial wall is extremely delicate and readily torn. When this occurs, the exposed spores are quickly carried away by air currents; the naked columella remains (Fig. 11–11D). The spores germinate readily on moist substrata (Fig. 11–12B).

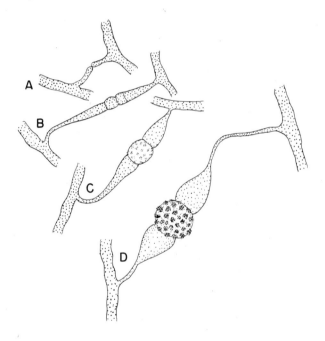

Fig. 11–13. *Rhizopus nigricans.* Sexual reproduction. A, Meeting of compatible hyphae. B, Delimitation of coenogametes. C, Young zygote and suspensors. D, Mature zygospore, enlarged suspensors. X 75.

Rhizopus nigricans is heterothallic and considered to be isogamous in sexual reproduction. When spores of two sexually compatible strains are planted in reasonably close proximity in agar cultures, sexuality soon becomes manifest. Hyphae of the two strains which come in contact increase in size at their tips. Transverse septa are soon laid down, so that the multinucleate tip of each branch is delimited from the remainder of the hypha. The delimited portions are called gametangia or considered to be multinucleate gametes, and the subtending hyphae are known as **suspensors.** The walls between the tips of contiguous gametangia dissolve, with the result that the cytoplasm and nuclei then lie free within a single lumen (Fig. 11–13). During this period, the nuclei in the uniting gametangia increase in number; subsequently, many nuclei unite in pairs, but some supernumerary nuclei remain. A thick wall is secreted by the zygote (Fig. 11–13*D*). The supernumerary nuclei disintegrate so that the mature zygospore contains only diploid nuclei.

Germination of the zygospore has been observed infrequently, but there is some cytological evidence that the nuclear divisions which occur during germination are meiotic. This evidence is also supported by genetic studies of genera related to *Rhizopus*. It is probable that the germinating zygospore gives rise to a sporangiophore and sporangium.

A number of genera similar to *Rhizopus* are widespread on organic substrata. *Mucor* (L. *muceo,* be moldy) is similar to *Rhizopus* except that its sporangiophores arise from the main hyphal branches, rhizoids being absent at their bases. *Phycomyces,* also heterothallic, produces sporangiophores which may attain a length of four inches. Its zygospores are made conspicuous by the development of dark, branching projections on the arched suspensors. The genus *Pilobolus* (Gr. *pilos* ball + Gr. *bolos,* a throwing) is an interesting dung-inhabiting mold. Its resistant spores pass unharmed through the digestive tract of animals. Horse dung, if stored in a moist chamber, soon becomes covered with the positively phototropic sporangiophores of this organism (Figs. 11–14, 11–15). Each of them bears a terminal black sporangium (Fig. 11–14*B*). Unlike that of *Rhizopus,* the sporangial wall of *Pilobolus* is firm and the sporangium is abscised as a unit. The sporangiophores originate in the afternoon from the mycelium just below the surface of the substratum. In early evening their tips enlarge to form sporangia. Shortly after midnight a subsporangial swelling appears (Fig. 11–14*A*) which explodes late the following morning because of excess turgor pressure. The sporangia and their spores (Fig. 11–14*C*) thus are forcibly ejected for distances as great as six feet.[2]

SUMMARY AND CLASSIFICATION

The name Phycomycota reflects the views of those who speculate that these fungi have been derived from algal progenitors which have

---

[2] For more detailed discussion of this and spore dispersal mechanisms in plants see: T. C. Ingold, *Spore Discharge in Land Plants.* Clarendon Press, 1939.

lost their chlorophyll and have entered upon either a saprophytic or a parasitic mode of life. This concept is based largely upon the similarity of the nonseptate mycelium of the Phycomycota to the tubular, nonseptate filaments of siphonalean Chlorophyceae and such Xanthophyceae as *Vaucheria* and *Botrydium*. The superficial similarity of the oogamous reproduction of such genera as *Saprolgenia* and *Albugo* to that of oogamous algae like *Vaucheria*, and of the isogamous conjugation of *Rhizopus* to that of *Spirogyra* and the desmids, no doubt has served to make the hypothesis of algal origin an attractive one to some mycologists. Others look upon these supposed similarities as examples of parallel and independent evolution, pointing out that although colorless genera of algae are well known, they continue to store starch, a storage product which is absent in most fungi. Furthermore, because so many Phycomycota possess zoospores with one flagellum, a condition rarely encountered among algae, these same students are inclined to look upon the Phycomycota as a group with protozoan affinities.

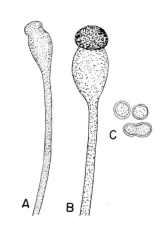

Fig. 11–14.   *Pilobolus* sp. A,B, Stages in sporangium development. X 15. C, Spores. X 315.

As far as is known, all Phycomycota, with the exception of some species of *Allomyces,* are haplobiontic in their life cycle, with zygotic meiosis. All grades of sexuality occur, from the union of motile isogamous gametes in certain chytrids and the nonmotile isogametes of *Rhizopus,* through the heterogamous sexuality of *Allomyces,* to the advanced oogamy described above in *Saprolegnia, Achlya,* and *Albugo*. The last-named genus is of interest in that it offers a clue, in its alternate methods of conidial germination, to the origin of the change in method of sporulation effected by the assumption of a terrestrial habitat by originally aquatic fungi.

The organisms representative of the Phycomycota which have been discussed in this chapter may be classified as follows:

Division Phycomycota
    Class 1. Phycomycetes
        Order 1. Chytridiales
            Family 1. Synchytriaceae

Genus: *Synchytrium*
Family 2. Phlyctidiaceae
Genus: *Rhizophydium*
Family 3. Cladochytriaceae
Genus: *Polychytrium*

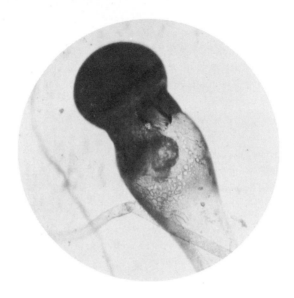

Fig. 11–15. *Pilobolus* sp. Enlarged view of sporangium. X 315.

Order 2. Blastocladiales
Family 1. Blastocladiaceae
Genus: *Allomyces*
Order 3. Saprolegniales
Family 1. Saprolegniaceae
Genera: *Saprolegnia, Achlya*
Order 4. Peronosporales
Family 1. Albuginaceae
Genus: *Albugo*
Order 5. Mucorales
Family 1. Mucoraceae
Genera: *Mucor, Rhizopus, Phycomyces, Pilobolus*

DISCUSSION QUESTIONS

1. Which of the genera of Phycomycota discussed in this chapter do you consider to be the most primitive? Give the reasons for your answer.
2. Give a summary of the morphology and life cycle of each of the genera described in this chapter; include reference to nuclear condition.

3. What similarities can you see in comparing sexual reproduction in *Rhizopus* and *Spirogyra?* How does their reproduction differ?

4. In what respects is sexual reproduction in *Saprolegnia* and *Albugo* similar to that in *Vaucheria?* How does it differ?

5. Define the terms hypha, mycelium, haustorium, intercellular, host, conidium, suspensor, sporangial proliferation, rhizomycelium, obligate parasite, saprophyte.

6. If the Phycomycota are algal in origin, to what alga might *Rhizophydium* be related?

7. To the life cycle of what algae does that of *Allomyces macrogynus* correspond?

8. How would you ascertain the nutritional requirements of a saprophytic fungus?

9. What attributes distinguish the Phycomycota from the Schizomycota and Myxomycota?

CHAPTER 12

Division Ascomycota

INTRODUCTION

The Ascomycota (Gr. *askos*, bladder + Gr. *mykes*, fungus) differ from the Phycomycota in that their mycelium is usually septate, even if incompletely so, the cells thus delimited being either uninucleate or multinucleate. Furthermore, as a result of sexual reproduction, a sac-like hypha, the **ascus,** is developed in which typically eight (Fig. 12–14*H*), but sometimes more or fewer, **ascospores** are produced. The asci may be single and scattered or they may be aggregated into a specially differentiated fruiting body, the **ascocarp** (Gr. *askos* + Gr. *karpos*, fruit). The structure of the sex organs themselves varies considerably among the many genera of Ascomycota; therefore it will be described separately in connection with each of the type genera selected. Finally, motile cells are absent in the Ascomycota. Four types of Ascomycota will be considered in the present chapter. These include the yeasts; the brown, green, and pink molds; the powdery mildews, and fleshy forms.

ILLUSTRATIVE TYPES

The Yeasts

The yeasts are ascomycetous fungi in which an extensive mycelium is not produced; hence the plant body is unicellular. In some genera, however, rudimentary mycelium development may take place under certain conditions. Furthermore, the asci usually are produced singly and are free-floating in the medium, not protected by special sterile outgrowths.

Schizosaccharomyces (Gr. *schizo*, cleave + Gr. *saccharon*, sugar + Gr. *mykes*) is a unicellular organism which occurs in nature on such fruits as grapes and figs. Certain species of *Schizosaccharomyces* are the agents of fermentation in tropical beers. The cells of *S. octosporus* Beijer. are spherical to ellipsoidal in shape, vacuolate and uninucleate (Fig. 12–1). Multiplication is effected by cell division which follows nuclear

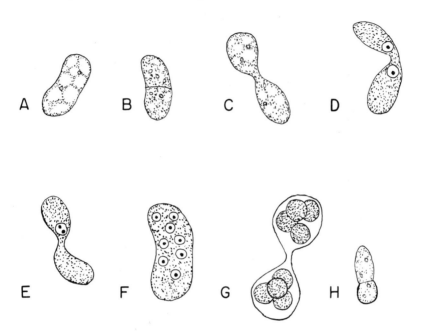

Fig. 12–1. *Schizosaccharomyces octosporus* Beijer. A, Vegetative cell. B, Cell division. C, Cell union (isogamy). D, Same as C, stained. E, Zygote with fusion nucleus. F, Free nuclei of ascus about which ascospores will be delimited. G, Ascus with ascospores. H, Ascospore germinating. X 1700.

division (Fig. 12–1B). Recently divided cells may remain adherent or they may separate promptly. After several days' growth in laboratory cultures, sexuality occurs. In this process (Fig. 12–1C to G), two adjacent cells produce short protuberances which meet; the tips of the protuberances dissolve, and plasmogamy and karyogamy follow. The zygote nucleus soon undergoes three successive nuclear divisions resulting in the formation of eight nuclei (Fig. 12–1F). Each of these is the center around which an ascospore is delimited (Fig. 12–1G), leaving residual cytoplasm called **epiplasm**. This method of cytokinesis is known as **free-cell formation**. The zygote is transformed directly into a single ascus which liberates the ascospores ultimately; the latter contain abundant starch. They produce new generations of plants asexually by nuclear and cell division (Fig. 12–1H). It has been demonstrated recently that meiosis occurs in the ascus during the nuclear divisions which follow karyogamy.

Saccharomyces cerevisiae Hansen, a **brewers' yeast** (Fig. 12–2), is representative of the budding yeasts which occur in nature on various fruits. The ovoidal cells of *Saccharomyces* (Gr. *saccharon,* sugar + Gr. *mykes*) contain a rather large nucleus and are rather complex cytologically. Multiplication occurs by **budding** (Fig. 12–2A to C), during which nuclear division takes place. One of the daughter nuclei migrates into the bud, which subsequently enlarges and becomes segregated from the parent cell. Rapid budding may result in the formation of short chains of cells. Under certain environmental conditions, ordinary vegetative cells may become transformed into asci, each of which usually produces four ascospores (Fig. 12–2D). It has been demonstrated that the ascospores from a single ascus, if isolated into individual culture vessels, will germinate to form spherical vegetative cells which will continue to reproduce by budding as long as the four cultures remain separated. However, when the cells of the four strains are brought together into one culture, union of the haploid cells in pairs establishes a diploid population. Furthermore, two of the ascospores of a given ascus are of one mating type and two are of another. The diploid vegetative cells of S. *cerevisiae* function as asci under certain conditions. Therefore, there occurs an alternation between two distinct phases in the life cycle of S. *cerevisiae,* namely, between diploid cells (potential asci), which reproduce asexually by budding, and haploid cells, which also reproduce by budding. The latter are derived from the germinating ascospores.

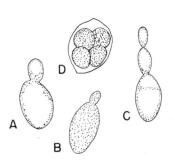

Fig. 12–2. *Saccharomyces cerevisiae* Hansen. A-C, Budding vegetative cells. D, Ascus with ascospores. (A and C, optical section.) X 1700.

The importance of various types of yeast to man, because of their biochemical activities, can scarcely be described adequately. They are used as agents of alcoholic fermentation, especially in the brewing and baking industries, and for this reason they have been the subject of intensive cytological, genetic, and physiological investigations.

Brown, Green, and Pink Molds

The brown, green, and pink molds are here represented, respectively, by the genera *Aspergillus* (L. *aspergo*, sprinkle), *Penicillium* (L. *penicillus*, pencil), and *Neurospora* (Gr. *neuron*, nerve + Gr. *spora*). These three genera contain mostly saprophytic species that occur commonly on a wide variety of organic substrata such as foods and fruits on which they produce the phenomenon of moldiness. *Penicillium* and *Aspergillus* are frequent contaminants of laboratory cultures. The former is often the agent of the mildewing of leather and clothing. Many species of *Penicillium* are greenish in color when fruiting; those of *Aspergillus* are frequently yellowish or dark brown. The spores of these genera are ubiquitous in air and soil. *Neurospora*, on the other hand, is pink and is known as pink bakers' mold.

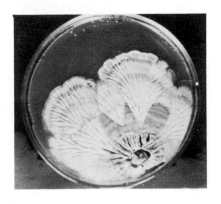

Fig. 12–3. *Penicillium notatum* Westling. Week-old culture on potato-dextrose agar. X ½.

All have a well-developed mycelium (Fig. 12–3) which is extensive and septate (Fig. 12–4). It absorbs food from the substratum by haustorial branches. The nuclear condition in the mycelium is variable; further cytological study is needed. In *Penicillium notatum* Westling, the

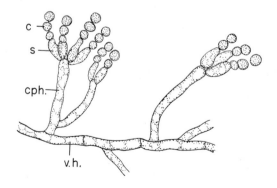

Fig. 12–4. *Penicillium notatum. v.h.*, vegetative hypha; *cph.*, conidiophore; *s*, sterigma; *c*, conidia. X 770.

apical hyphae are usually uninucleate, but older hyphae become multi-nucleate because of the absence of cytokinesis following mitosis. After some vegetative growth has occurred, the older portions of the mycelium

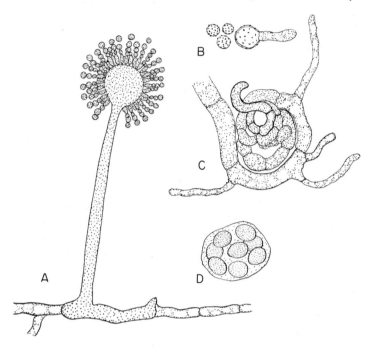

Fig. 12–5. A, *Aspergillus niger* van Tiegh. Vegetative hyphae, conidiophore, sterigmata and conidia. X 315. B, Spores and spore germination, the latter after 20 hours on potato-dextrose agar. X 770. C, *Aspergillus chevalieri* Mangin. Ascogonial coil. X 770. D, Ascus and ascospores. X 1700.

produce asexual spores, **conidia.** In both *Penicillium* and *Aspergillus*, these are produced in specially differentiated fruiting heads (Figs. 12–4, 12–5) called **conidiophores** (Gr. *konis*, dust + Gr. *phoros*, bearer). The conidiophores of *Penicillium* are short-celled hyphae which are terminated by somewhat bottle-shaped cells (Fig. 12–4) called **sterigmata** (Gr. *sterigma*, support). Each of these produces a chain of conidia, the oldest conidium being farthest from the tip of the sterigma. The older spores are readily dislodged from the chains by air currents or other slight disturbances; hence it is sometimes difficult to obtain satisfactory microscopic preparations unless one uses relatively young fruiting branches. The color of the fungi during spore production is the result of the maturation of large numbers of conidia whose walls are pigmented. Conidia germinate readily into new mycelia (Fig. 12–5B).

In *Aspergillus*, the fruiting head arises from a **foot cell** (Fig. 12–5A). The apex ultimately becomes spherical as growth in length ceases, and is covered with densely ranked sterigmata, sometimes in two series. The tip of the sterigma is a spore-producing tube whose nuclei divide. One of each pair of division products migrates into the tube, the tip of which is delimited by cytoplasmic division. This tip enlarges to become a conidium (Fig. 12–5A). Repetition of this process results in the seriate arrangement of conidia on each sterigma, the oldest being farthest from the sterigma.

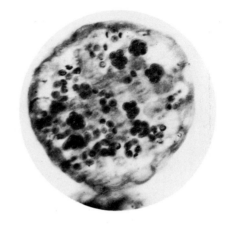

Fig. 12–6. *Penicillium* sp. Section of cleistothecium, asci, and ascospores. X 590.

Our knowledge of the details of sexuality in *Aspergillus* and *Penicillium* is incomplete, but in some species special female hyphae, the **ascogonia**, have been described (Fig. 12–5C). The cytological aspects of sexuality in these molds have not been satisfactorily elucidated. Differentiated antheridia are absent in many species, but nuclear pairing has been found to take place in the ascogonium, from which branching **ascogenous hyphae** then arise. These give rise to sac-like cells, the asci (Fig. 12–5D). It has been demonstrated that in *Aspergillus Fischeri* Westling the ascogonial cells are binucleate when they generate ascogenous hyphae. Each ascus typically produces eight ascospores by free-cell formation; the spores are liberated by the breakdown of the ascus wall. While the ascogenous hyphae and asci are maturing, sterile interwoven hyphae form a loose protective layer about them. The whole structure is frequently globose, and inasmuch as it lacks an opening it is called a **cleistothecium** (Gr. *kleistos*, closed + Gr. *theke*, case). The cleistothecium (Fig. 12–6) is one of several types of **ascocarp**, the general term for ascomycetous fruiting bodies. The asci of *Penicillium*, like those of *Aspergillus*, are borne in cleistothecia. The ascospores, which are liberated by decay of the cleistothecial wall, germinate into conidia-forming mycelia.

A number of species of *Aspergillus* and *Penicillium* are notable for both harmful and beneficial activities. Among the former may be listed the propensity for spoilage and decay of foods, especially bread, fruits, and fruit products, and the destruction of leather and textiles in damp climates. Several species of *Aspergillus* and *Penicillium* are pathogenic in animals and man. Other species, however, are of great benefit to mankind in several connections. Certainly the most noteworthy of these is the antibiotic substance **penicillin**, secreted by *Penicillium chrysogenum* Thom and *P. notatum* Westling. *Penicillium roqueforti* Thom and *P. camemberti* Thom should be more widely appreciated than they seem to be for their role in imparting distinctive flavors to Roquefort and Camembert cheeses, respectively, during ripening.

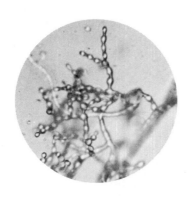

Fig. 12–7. *Neurospora sitophila* Shear and Dodge. Conidia. X 250.

In *Neurospora,* the conidiophores are not markedly differentiated from the vegetative hyphae (Fig. 12–7). Some races of this genus produce minute microconidia in addition to those of ordinary size; the latter are called macroconidia in such organisms. The conidial walls are responsible for the pink color of the fungus. Our knowledge of the details of sexuality in *Neurospora* is still incomplete, a surprising fact in view of the intensive genetic studies of this fungus. In *N. sitophila* Shear and Dodge, the young ascogonium, a curved septate hypha with several nuclei in each cell, becomes covered with several layers of interwoven sterile hyphae. Certain cells of the ascogonium produce long, tenuous, trichogyne-like branches which penetrate the sterile hyphal layers surrounding the ascogonium. It has been demonstrated that not only the large conidia but also the microconidia and even vegetative hyphae and trichogynes of one strain may unite with the trichogynes and vegetative hyphae of another compatible strain. In this way presumably, nuclei of the two strains are brought together into the same mycelium, and ultimately into the ascogonial coil. The latter now gives rise to ascogenous hyphae whose tips enlarge to form elongate asci. Meanwhile, the sterile layer surrounding these has increased in extent and organized itself into a flask-shaped structure (Fig. 12–8A,B), at the apex of which a small aperture, the **ostiole,** develops. This type of ascocarp is known as a **perithecium** (Gr. *peri,* around + Gr. *theke*).

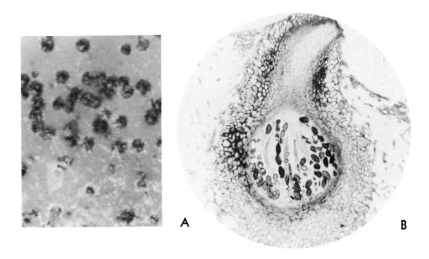

Fig. 12–8. *Neurospora sitophila.* A, Perithecia on agar. X 6. B, Perithecium, median longitudinal section. X 135.

The young asci of *Neurospora* are binucleate. It is generally agreed that the two nuclei of each ascus represent descendants of nuclei of the two compatible strains originally brought together in trichogynal or other types of plasmogamy. In further development, nuclear fusion takes place in each ascus. This is soon followed by three successive nuclear divisions during which meiosis is accomplished. The asci at this stage contain eight linearly arranged nuclei. These, with a portion of their surrounding cytoplasm, are finally segregated from the residual cytoplasm of the ascus by free-cell formation (Fig. 12–9). The mature ascospores become binucleate as a result of mitosis within each spore. At maturity they are discharged from the perithecium through its ostiole. The mature spore walls are ribbed, an attribute which suggested the generic name.

The ascospores germinate readily in laboratory cultures, giving rise to a mycelium which produces only perithecial rudiments and conidia, unless contact is made with a mycelium or conidia of a compatible strain. It has been shown experimentally that four of the eight ascospores of each ascus of *N. sitophila* give rise to one compatible strain, and that the other four are of the opposite type. Various species and races of *Neurospora* have provided the basis for important genetic and biochemical studies. It should be noted that the necessity for fusion between two strains of *N. sitophila* for maturation of the perithecia is analogous to the **self-incompatibility** found in certain types of flowers rather than to the

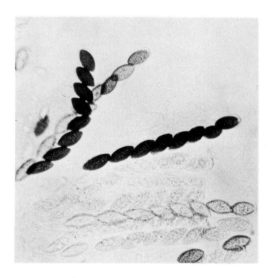

Fig. 12–9. *Neurospora* sp. Asci with ascospores. X 900. (Courtesy of Dr. Jay C. Murray.)

heterothallism present in many algae and fungi. As in certain flowers, both types of reproductive organs are present but fail to function; the controlling factor here apparently is physiological.

Powdery Mildews

The powdery mildews are so called because they form a mealy, powdery white stratum on the surfaces of leaves in a number of plants. Their mycelium is obligately parasitic on a specific host. All attempts to grow them for prolonged periods in artificial culture have thus far failed. Examples of powdery mildews which infect well-known plants are the following: *Microsphaera alni* (DC.) Wint. on lilacs, *Erysiphe cichoracearum* DC. on garden plantain, *Sphaerotheca pannosa* (Wallr.) Lev. on roses, and *Erysiphe graminis* DC. on cereal grains. The mycelium spreads over the leaf from the original point of infection (Fig. 12–10A) and obtains nourishment by means of haustoria which penetrate into the epidermal cells (Fig. 12–10C). The hyphal cells of most species are uninucleate. After a period of vegetative growth, certain hyphae produce erect branches which form conidia in chains (Fig. 12–10B). These are blown about by air currents and germinate, initiating new infections,

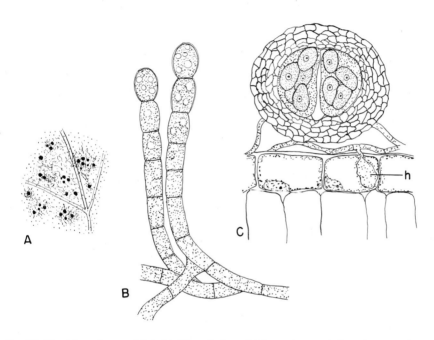

Fig. 12–10. *Microsphaera alni* (DC.) Wint. **A,** Superficial mycelium and cleistothecia on lower surface of lilac leaf. X 5. **B,** Conidiophore and seriate conidia. X 315. **C,** Section of stained cleistothecium on upper surface of lilac leaf: h, haustorium. X 440.

especially under humid conditions. This cycle, frequently repeated, rapidly spreads the fungus.

Sexual reproduction and ascocarp formation occur later in the growing season. The sex organs, which precede the cleistothecium, are not highly differentiated but consist of short hyphae that curve around each other. One has been identified as an antheridium and the other as the ascogonium. The walls between these dissolve at one point of contact, and the antheridial nucleus is reported to migrate into the ascogonium. Nuclear union is probably delayed, as in other Ascomycota. Descendants of the sexual nuclei are distributed among the cells of the ascogenous hyphae. The latter, depending on the genus, give rise to one or more asci (Fig. 12–10C). Soon after the sex organs have developed, vegetative hyphae at their base form a sterile protective layer which becomes the wall of the cleistothecium. Three successive nuclear divisions occur in each ascus, so eight potential ascospore nuclei are developed. In some species each of these is delimited to form an ascospore by free-cell formation. In others, fewer ascospores are produced, and the supernumerary

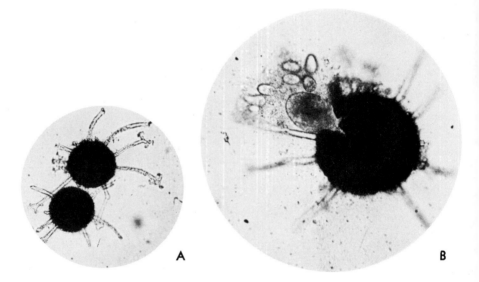

A   **B**

Fig. 12–11. *Microsphaera alni. A,* Cleistothecia with appendages. X 135. *B,* Enlarged view of crushed cleistothecium showing unsegmented ascus and free ascospores. X 250.

nuclei disintegrate in the epiplasm. The cleistothecia (Figs. 12–10C, 12–11) usually remain on the leaves when the latter are shed, and dissemination of the ascospores does not occur until the following growing season. Ascospores which come to rest on the leaves of the proper host plant are capable of initiating a new conidial cycle.

Cup Fungi

The final group of Ascomycota to be considered in this chapter is known as the **cup fungi,** because their fleshy, often brightly colored, conspicuous ascocarps are usually cup-, urn-, or saucer-shaped (Fig. 12–12). Such an ascocarp is called an **apothecium.** The cup fungi are for the most part saprophytes that occur on a wide variety of organic substrata

Fig. 12–12.   *Pyronema confluens* Tul. (among *Funaria* plants). X 6.

such as rich soil, decaying wood, dung, burlap, and fallen fruit. Several genera are inhabitants of burned-over or sterilized soil. The apothecia vary from a millimeter in diameter up to the size of small tea cups. In some genera the apothecia are stalked.

Although the fruiting body is somewhat ephemeral, its formation is in all cases preceded by an extended period of vegetative activity on the part of the mycelium, which ramifies in the substratum, absorbing nutriment. In a few genera the vegetative mycelium reproduces itself asexually by conidia, but these are entirely absent in others. There is good reason to believe that the apothecium arises as a result of sexuality; but the latter has been clearly demonstrated only in a few species, and even in these there is a difference of opinion regarding the cytological details of the process. *Pyronema* (Gr. *pyr,* fire + Gr. *nema,* thread) (Fig. 12–12) has been investigated frequently regarding its cytological and sexual features. In this genus well-differentiated antheridia and ascogonia are developed (Fig. 12–13).

In *Pyronema confluens* Tul., an inhabitant of burned-over ground, where it is frequently associated with the moss, *Funaria* (Fig. 12–12), the multinucleate antheridia and ascogonia arise in clusters from the tips of lateral hyphae (Fig. 12–13). Each sex organ contains between 100 and 200 nuclei. The apex of the ascogonium is prolonged into a trichogyne-like tube at maturity. The trichogyne at first is separated from the ascogonium by a septation. As development proceeds, the tip of the trichogyne establishes contact with an antheridium, and dissolution of the walls takes place at the point of contact (Fig. 12–13A). Trichogynes of several ascogonia may establish contact with the same antheridium, and several antheridia and ascogonia may be involved in the formation of a single apothecium. Antheridial nuclei migrate into the multinucleate

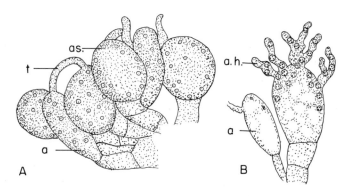

Fig. 12–13. *Pyronema confluens.* A, sex organs: *a*, antheridium; *as.*, ascogonium; *t*, trichogyne. X 420. B, Postfertilization ascogonium with ascogenous hyphae, *a.h.* X 500. (From Gwynne-Vaughan and Williamson.)

ascogonium through the trichogyne, whose basal septum is dissolved at this stage but develops again after the nuclear migration. The male and female nuclei become associated in pairs. During the earliest stages of this process, sterile hyphae grow around and envelop the functioning sex organs, ultimately forming the apothecial wall.

Following nuclear association, slender **ascogenous hyphae** protrude from the surface of the ascogonium (Fig. 12–13B). A number of nuclei migrate into these and multiply there by mitosis. Ultimately the ascogenous hyphae are divided into binucleate cells which give rise to the asci by a process known as **crozier formation** (Fig. 12–14). Although this process is probably involved in the formation of the asci of a majority of Ascomycota, the cup fungi are especially favorable for demonstrating it. The tip cell of a branch of an ascogenous hypha becomes recurved (Fig. 12–14A), like a crozier, and its two nuclei undergo mitosis, with their spindles oriented in such a manner that at the completion of nuclear division two nuclei (one descendant of each of the original sexual nuclei, presumably) lie in the apical bend of the crozier; one nucleus lies at the apex of the recurved hypha, and one at the proximal portion of the ascogenous hypha. Cytokinesis follows, producing a uninucleate terminal ("ultimate") cell, a binucleate intermediate ("penultimate") cell, and a uninucleate basal ("antepenultimate") cell (Fig. 12–14A). The binucleate penultimate cell enlarges to form the ascus (Fig. 12–14B,C). In certain species, the ultimate cell may reunite with the antepenultimate cell and again undergo crozier formation. The yellow-orange pigment of the

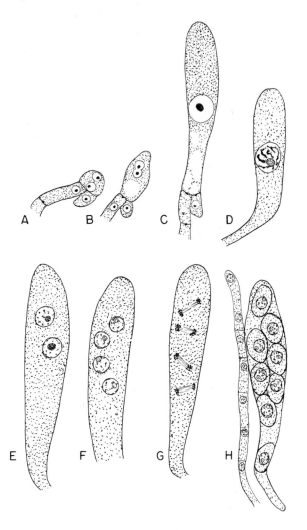

Fig. 12–14. *Pyronema confluens.* Ascus and ascospore development. A-C, Crozier formation and origin of the ascus. D-G, Successive nuclear divisions in the ascus. H, Paraphysis and ascus with delimited ascospores and residual cytoplasm. X 770.

paraphyses and other sterile hyphae of the *Pyronema* apothecium is responsible for its color.

Nuclear union follows in each ascus (Fig. 12–14*B*). Three successive nuclear divisions (Fig. 12–14*D* to *G*) occur, resulting in the formation of eight haploid nuclei. These are incorporated into ascospores by free-cell

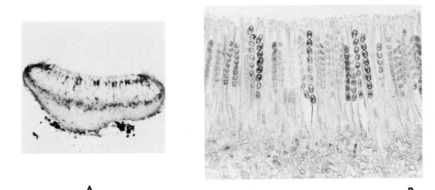

A   B

Fig. 12–15. *Pyronema confluens.* A, Median section of apothecium; note hymenial layer. X 30. B, *Peziza* sp. Enlarged view of portion of hymenium, showing asci and ascospores. X 320.

formation (Fig. 12–14*H*). The ascospores germinate, producing a multinucleate mycelium in which the sexual cycle is repeated; *Pyronema confluens* is homothallic.

The inner surface of the apothecium in cup fungi, the **hymenium,** is composed of intermingled columnar asci and sterile paraphyses (Fig. 12–15). The remainder of the apothecium is made up of sterile interwoven hyphae which form **pseudoparenchyma,** as viewed in section. Spore discharge is explosive in many species, and large numbers of spores may be disseminated simultaneously in visible puffs.

Although *Pyronema* has been chosen here as the type genus to illustrate reproduction in the cup fungi, its apothecia are relatively small and inconspicuous, and plane or almost convex. The apothecia of *Peziza, Patella, Urnula,* and *Bulgaria* are widely distributed, larger, and more conspicuous than those of *Pyronema;* they are flat or concave. Unfortunately, however, their life cycles have not been worked out as completely as that of *Pyronema.*

SUMMARY AND CLASSIFICATION

Of the representative genera of Ascomycota described above, all are saprophytic with the exception of the powdery mildews, which are obligate parasites. Except for the unicellular yeasts, the vegetative phase regularly consists of a branching, septate mycelium, which may be composed of uninucleate (powdery mildews) or multinucleate hyphae. Some yeasts may develop short, mycelium-like stages under certain conditions. For this reason, they often have been interpreted as organisms reduced from higher, strictly mycelial genera.

The life cycle of most Ascomycota consists of an asexual phase in which conidia are produced, and a sexual phase whose zygote, either directly as in the yeasts, or indirectly as in other genera, produces asci. Indirect ascus formation involves the production of ascogenous hyphae. The vegetative cells of *Saccharomyces* are diploid; they become transformed directly into single asci. In the higher Ascomycota, there is an interval between plasmogamy and karyogamy; the fusion cell produces ascogenous hyphae which give rise to asci in which karyogamy occurs. In *Saccharomyces*, as a result of one fertilization, many agents of propagation (in this case, ascospores) are produced. Further examples of the same phenomenon among the algae and other groups of plants will occur to the reader.

Both the conidial and the ascogenous (ascus-forming) stages may be well developed, as in the powdery mildews, *Neurospora*, and certain species of *Aspergillus* and *Penicillium*, or one or the other phase may be absent from the life cycle. Thus, for many species of *Aspergillus* and *Penicillium*, no ascogenous stages have been discovered. In many cup fungi, on the other hand, no conidial stages have been observed.

The Ascomycota exhibit considerable range of variation with reference to the production of differentiated sex organs. Among the yeasts, the haploid vegetative cells function directly as gametes, as in the alga *Chlamydomonas*. In the higher forms, markedly differentiated sex organs may be present, as in *Pyronema*. Among the powdery mildews, the so-called antheridia and ascogonia are scarcely distinguishable. Ascogonia have been observed in a number of ascogenous forms of *Aspergillus* and *Penicillium*, but differentiated male organs are rarely present. In *Neurospora*, the number of alternate mechanisms by which approximation of sexually compatible nuclei can be effected suggests that the true male sex organs may have been lost.

As to the origin of the Ascomycota, several hypotheses have been presented. According to one, they have been derived from the Rhodophyta. Evidence listed in support of this view is the absence of motile cells in both groups, the similarities between the ascocarp (especially cleistothecia and perithecia) and the cystocarp of Rhodophyceae, the occurrence in some Ascomycota of nonmotile spermatia and trichogynes, and the resemblance between diploid gonimoblasts of certain Rhodophyceae and the ascogenous hyphae of the Ascomycota. At first glance, the marked physiological differences between the Rhodophyceae and Ascomycetes would seem to present an insurmountable barrier to relationship. It has been pointed out, however, that several species of extant Rhodophyceae have lost their pigments and are parasitic on other Rhodophyceae. In opposition to the theory of rhodophycean origin of the Ascomycota, there has developed a theory of origin from the Phycomycota. According to this view, the Ascomycota in which the zygote directly forms ascospores (as in certain yeasts) are considered primitive and derived from Phycomycota. Genera with highly differentiated sex organs and ascogenous hyphae are considered to have evolved from yeast-like ancestors. Supposed homologies between sex organs, gonimoblasts, and ascogenous hyphae and cystocarps and ascocarps of Ascomycetes and Rhodophyceae are interpreted by proponents of the theory of phycomycetean origin of the Ascomycota as examples of parallel development. A satisfactory solution to these questions is not available in the present state of our knowledge.

The genera of Ascomycota discussed in this chapter may be classified as follows:

Division Ascomycota
  Class 1. Ascomycetes
    Order 1. Endomycetales
      Family 1. Endomycetaceae
        Genera: *Schizosaccharomyces, Saccharomyces*
    Order 2. Aspergillales
      Family 1. Aspergillaceae
        Genera: *Aspergillus, Penicillium*
    Order 3. Sphaeriales
      Family 1. Fimetariaceae
        Genus: *Neurospora*
    Order 4. Erysiphales
      Family 1. Erysiphaceae
        Genera: *Erysiphe, Microsphaera, Sphaerotheca*

Order 5. Pezizales
Family 1. Pezizaceae
Genera: *Pyronema, Peziza, Ascobolus, Patella, Urnula, Bulgaria*

DISCUSSION QUESTIONS

1. What characteristics distinguish the Ascomycota, as a group, from the Phycomycota?

2. Of what economic importance are such Ascomycota as *Aspergillus, Penicillium, Neurospora, Saccharomyces,* and the powdery mildews?

3. What aspects of the life cycle of Ascomycota require further investigation, in your opinion?

4. If a given race of *Neurospora sitophila* produces ascogonia, trichogynes, macroconidia, and microconidia but still requires "mating" with another race to produce mature ascospores, is this not heterothallism? Explain, giving the reasons for your answer.

5. How does the production of ascospores from the zygote of *Schizosaccharomyces* differ from the production of zoospores from the zygote of *Chlamydomonas?*

6. Define or explain the following terms in comparative fashion: ascocarp, apothecium, perithecium, cleistothecium.

7. How would you determine whether or not a certain ascomycetous fungus is homothallic or heterothallic?

8. Where does segregation of genes take place in Ascomycota?

9. What genus of Ascomycota has been most extensively employed in genetic investigations?

10. Why are such organisms especially favorable for correlating genetic and cytological data?

11. Define free-cell formation. How does it differ from progressive cleavage and repeated bipartition?

12. Where would you search for cup fungi in nature?

13. Where and when would you attempt to collect powdery mildews in the perithecial stage?

14. Describe a possible procedure to determine whether or not the powdery mildews are heterothallic.

15. Outline the methods and procedures you would use to investigate the life cycle and reproduction of an unknown cup fungus.

CHAPTER 13

Division Basidiomycota

INTRODUCTION

The **basidium** (Gr. *basis*, di.-pedestal) is as characteristic of Basidiomycota (Gr. *basis* + Gr. *mykes*) as the ascus is of Ascomycota. Like the ascus, the young basidium or its immediate precursor (either a hypha or a spore) contains two nuclei which unite to form a fusion nucleus, which in two ensuing divisions undergoes the meiotic process. The mycelium of the Basidiomycota is always septate; its cells may be either uninucleate or binucleate. The basidia, each of which typically produces **basidiospores,** either are borne directly at the tips of vegetative hyphae or may arise as outgrowths of germinating spores. The basidia may or may not be aggregated in fruiting bodies called **basidiocarps.** The Basidiomycota include two groups. To the first belong organisms, like the rusts and smuts, whose basidia are produced as a result of the germination of a thick-walled spore (Fig. 13–5). The second group includes the mushrooms, puffballs, and jelly fungi, in which the basidia are specialized hyphal tips (Fig. 13–16) that do not arise from spores. In this volume, four series representative of these two groups will be considered—the rusts, the smuts, the mushrooms, and a group of miscellaneous organisms.

ILLUSTRATIVE TYPES

Rusts

The rusts are a very large assemblage of fungi (perhaps 7000 species) which are obligate parasites on vascular plants. Recently, however, the mycelium of one species has been maintained in artificial culture. Their common name was suggested by the rust-colored, streaked, or linear lesions that infections produce on various parts of host plants. The genera and species of rusts exhibit considerable complexity in their life cycles, in the types of spores they produce, and in their physiological relationships to one or more hosts. They are of tremendous economic importance because their presence markedly reduces the yield in infected plants, particularly of fruits and cereal grains.

Fig. 13–1. *Puccinia graminis* Pers. Uredinial lesions on wheat stem. X 2.

One of the most widely distributed and best-known rust species is *Puccinia graminis* Pers. (after T. Puccini, Italian anatomist), the numerous races of which parasitize various cereal grains, among them corn,

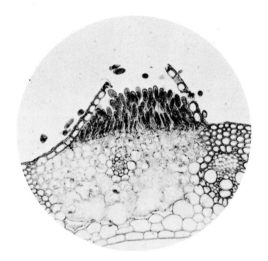

Fig. 13–2. *Puccinia graminis.* Transverse section of uredinium on wheat leaf. X 135.

wheat, oats, barley, and rye. Distinct strains or races infect each of these hosts. The leaves and stems of infected plants bear small, rust-colored, usually linear streaks or lesions which are manifestations of the presence of the fungus (Fig. 13–1). A magnified view of one of these (Fig. 13–2) reveals that the epidermis of the infected organ has been lifted up by the formation of a **uredinium** (L. *uredo*, blight), a group of rust-colored spores, each of which is stalked. During the growing season of the host plant the infection spreads through the agency of these spores, the **urediniospores**[1] (Figs. 13–2, 13–3A). These are blown about by air currents after they have been liberated from the uredinium; and if they chance to reach other leaves or stems of the host species, they can germinate under suitable conditions. A delicate hyphal tube emerges from one of several pores in the urediniospore wall, grows over the sur-

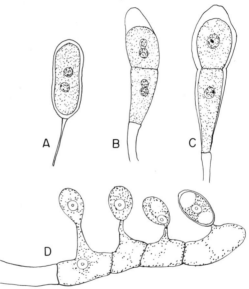

Fig. 13–3. *Puccinia graminis.* A, Single urediniospore. B, Immature teliospore before nuclear fusion. C, Mature teliospore, each cell with a diploid nucleus. D, *Gymnosporangium* sp. Tip of basidium with four basidiospores. X 770.

face of the leaf, and enters it through a stoma. Once inside the leaf, the primary hypha branches and spreads through the intercellular spaces. The mycelium thus formed grows at the expense of the host protoplasm, from which it obtains nutriment by means of intracellular haustorial

---

[1] The terminology used follows that of J. C. Arthur, *The Plant Rusts (Uredinales)*, John Wiley and Sons, 1929. There are a number of synonyms for the terms used to describe reproductive structures in the rusts. These may be summarized as follows:

uredinium: uredosorus	**basidium:** promycelium
urediniospore: urediospore,	**basidiospore:** sporidium
uredospore	**spermagonium:** pycnium
telium: teleutosorus	**spermatium:** sperm cell, pycniospore
teliospore: teleutospore	**aeciospore:** aecidiospore

branches. After seven or eight days, certain branches of the mycelium aggregate at localized points between the mesophyll and epidermal cells
of the leaves and just below the epidermis of the stems, where they produce a new generation of urediniospores (Fig. 13–2). It has been estimated that the mycelium arising from the germination of a single
urediniospore may produce several thousand urediniospores; hence the
spread of the fungus through a field of grain is very rapid, especially
when the relative humidity is high. The urediniospore cycle may be repeated many times during the growing season of the host.

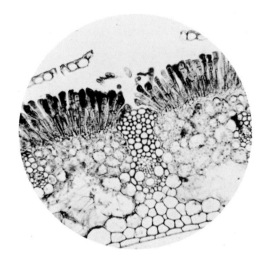

Fig. 13–4. *Puccinia graminis.* Transverse section of wheat leaf with telial lesion. X 135.

As the latter approaches maturity, the rust-colored lesions are gradually replaced by some of darker color, the **telia** (Gr. *telos,* end). Microscopic study reveals that these darker sori contain another type of spore,
a two-celled one, whose walls are deeply pigmented at maturity. These
teliospores (Figs. 13–3B,C, 13–4), so called because they are produced
at the end of the season, are borne on a mycelium that arises from a
germinating urediniospore; they may occur either in separate sori or
mixed with urediniospores. The thick wall of each of the teliospore cells
is homogeneous except for a single germination pore.

The teliospores of *Puccinia graminis* apparently require a period of
dormancy and low temperature before they develop further. Some are
shed from the telia on the host plants before or during harvesting and

fall to the ground; others remain in the telia on the stubble. The germination of the teliospores of another rust, *Gymnosporangium*, is illustrated in Figs. 13–3D and 13–5. After a suitable period of dormancy, each cell of the teliospore germinates by producing a slender colorless hypha, whose apical portion soon divides into four cells. Each of these develops a minute sterigma on which a single, thin-walled **basidiospore** is produced.

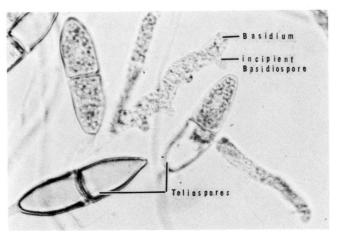

Fig. 13–5. *Gymnosporangium* sp. Germinating teliospores. X 540.

The slender septate hypha which produces the basidiospores is called the **basidium.** Germination of the teliospores, formation of the basidium and basidiospores, and discharge of the latter are very rapid processes which may take only a few hours. The basidiospores are violently discharged from their sterigmata and caught up by air currents; they may be carried great distances.

The thin-walled basidiospores of *Puccinia graminis* are capable of germinating to form a mycelium only if they chance to fall upon the leaves or young stems of several species of barberry, among them *Berberis vulgaris* L. The germination hypha from the basidiospore penetrates the cuticle of the leaf and enters an epidermal cell, where it absorbs metabolites, begins to branch, and forms a mycelium which is mostly intercellular, nutriment being obtained by haustoria.

Certain mycelial branches aggregate at localized spots between the upper mesophyll cells and epidermis; within six days after the original infection by the basidiospore, they form somewhat flask-shaped organs, the **spermagonia** (Fig. 13–6). Spermagonia may also be produced on the

lower surface of the leaf. The apex of the spermagonium ruptures the
leaf epidermis at maturity; through its ostiole there project slender,
curved hyphae, the **periphyses.** The central portion of the spermagonium
is composed of columnar hyphae which form chains of minute, conidia-
like cells, the **spermatia** (Fig. 13–7B). The latter are discharged through
the ostiole in a syrupy liquid and spread over the leaf surface near the
orifice of the spermagonium. Meanwhile, other branches of the mycelium

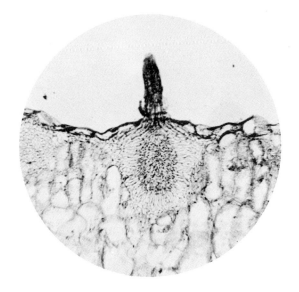

Fig. 13–6. *Puccinia graminis.* Median longitudinal section of spermagonium in upper surface of
barberry leaf; note projected periphyses and central mass of spermatia. X 250.

from the original basidiospore infection have grown through the leaf in
all directions. Usually there are produced near the lower surface of the
leaf a number of densely interwoven masses of hyphae which appear
yellow-orange to the naked eye. As development continues, each of these
hyphal snarls grows into a somewhat bell-shaped cup whose outer surface .projects through the ruptured lower epidermis of the leaf (Figs.
13–7A, 13–8). A few of these structures may also be borne on the upper
epidermis. The basal cells within each of these cup-shaped **aecia** (Gr.
aikia, injury) give rise to chains of orange-colored spores, the **aeciospores**,
which are usually separated by compressed intercalary cells (Fig. 13–7C).
As the latter disintegrate, the mature aeciospores are violently discharged
from their cups, often to a distance as great as 8 mm. It is thought that

the intercalary cells play a role in this violent dissemination of the spores. The latter, which may number as many as 11,000 in a single cup, are caught up by air currents. If they chance to fall upon young stems or leaves of grain plants, they germinate and produce an intercellular mycelium by which the urediniospore cycle is again initiated. The aecial cups occur in groups (Fig. 13–7A), each of which may include between

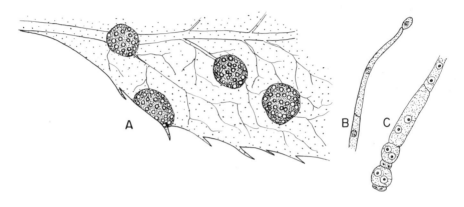

Fig. 13–7. *Puccinia graminis.* A, Aecia on lower surface of barberry leaf. X 2½. B, Hypha bearing spermatium. X 770. C, Hypha bearing aeciospores. X 770.

four and thirty-five cups. By calculating the number of spores in a cup, the number of cups in a group, the number of groups on a leaf, and the total number of leaves, it has been estimated that a single barberry bush might produce 64,512,000,000 aeciospores!

From this account of the life cycle of *Puccinia graminis,* two facts, among others, are especially noteworthy. In the first place, the fungus produces five distinct types of reproductive cells, namely, urediniospores, teliospores, basidiospores, spermatia, and aeciospores. Second, two hosts, a cereal grain and barberry, are usually required for the completion of its cycle. The latter attribute is characteristic of **heteroecious** (Gr. *heteros,* other + Gr. *oikos,* house) rusts.

Special attention must now be given the question of nuclear condition in *Puccinia graminis,* as it is correlated with the life cycle and successive appearance of the various spore types. Stained preparations of urediniospores and the mycelium which produces them reveal that both are binucleate, as is also the mycelium which gives rise to teliospores. Each cell of the teliospore likewise is binucleate at the time of its formation.

The two nuclei in each cell unite during the maturation of the teliospore, so that each now contains a diploid nucleus. Cytological evidence in another species of *Puccinia*, *P. malvacearum* Bert., and in *Gymnosporangium* indicates that the two diploid nuclei of the teliospore undergo meiosis during germination, the four nuclei of the septate basidium resulting from this process. Genetic evidence proves that meiosis occurs at the same point in the life cycle of *P. graminis*. In the latter, the chromosome number is approximately $n = 5$. The basidiospores therefore contain haploid nuclei, as does the primary mycelium which they produce within

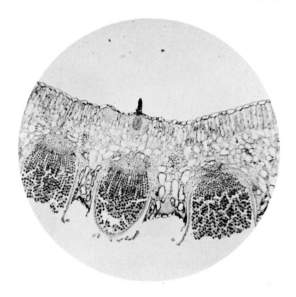

Fig. 13–8. *Puccinia graminis*. Transverse section of barberry leaf, spermagonium above and aecia below. X 60.

the barberry plant. The spermagonia and spermatia also apparently contain haploid nuclei, as well as the hyphae which aggregate to form the rudimentary aecium. The aeciospores themselves, however, are regularly binucleate; the origin of this condition has been under investigation for many years. There is now considerable evidence that the binucleate hyphae in the aecial stages of *P. graminis* and other rusts may arise in a variety of ways. Soon after infection of the leaf by the basidiospore and during the production and exudation of spermatia, haploid receptive hyphae may protrude through the stomata and between the epidermal cells of the leaf much like trichogynes among the Ascomycota and

Rhodophyta. These may unite with spermatia, whose nuclei migrate into the trichogyne-like hyphae, multiply, and migrate further, thus "diploidizing" the originally haploid mycelium. It has also been reported that spermatia may unite with receptive hyphae of the spermagonia themselves, that certain cells of the young aecium may send to the leaf surface trichogynous branches which receive spermatial nuclei, and finally, that hyphal fusions between different haploid basidiosporal infections may take place within the tissues of the leaf. The conjugate $n + n$ nuclear condition apparently can be initiated by several mechanisms; but unless it is initiated, the aecia usually remain sterile and fail to mature their aeciospores.

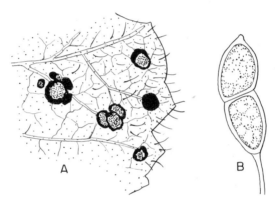

Fig. 13–9. *Puccinia malvacearum* Bert. A, Lesions on lower surface of hollyhock leaf. X 4. B, Teliospore. X 770.

It has been demonstrated experimentally that some rusts—*P. graminis*, for example—are heterothallic. Infections of the barberry leaf arising from the germination of a single basidiospore may produce spermagonia and rudimentary aecia; but fertile, spore-producing aecia do not develop as a result of such infections. Furthermore, in heterothallic rusts, two of the four basidiospores produced by a basidium are "plus" and two are "minus" as to compatibility, as a result of segregation during meiosis. Unless compatible nuclei are brought together into the aecial rudiment by one of the several methods listed above, the aecium fails to mature. In other rusts, infection by a single basidiospore is sufficient to produce fertile aecia; such species are regarded as homothallic. There is good evidence that insects play an important role in carrying plus and/or minus spermatia to compatible receptive hyphae. The life cycle of *Puccinia graminis* may be summarized as follows:

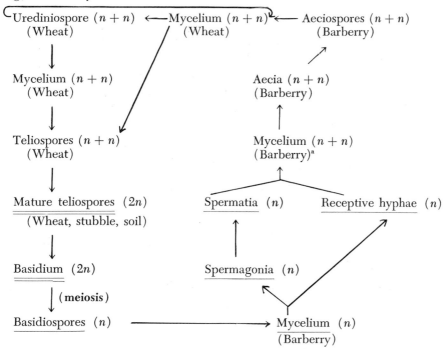

Rusts like *Puccinia graminis* which produce binucleate spores—in this case aeciospores and urediniospores—in addition to teliospores, are said to be **macrocyclic.** Those in which the teliospore is the only binucleate spore are said to be **microcyclic.** *Puccinia malvacearum* Bert., the widespread rust of hollyhocks and related plants, is here chosen to represent the life cycle of a microcyclic rust (Fig. 13–9). There is some evidence that this species is homothallic. In the life cycle of *P. malvacearum,* only two types of spores, teliospores and basidiospores, are produced. Reinfection is accomplished by thin-walled basidiospores which are binucleate as a result of a mitosis that takes place shortly after their formation. The basidiosporal germ tube enters the hollyhock epidermal cell and forms a short primary mycelium of uninucleate hyphae. These give rise to a more permanent mycelium which spreads through the leaf in both intercellular and intracellular fashion. Where hyphae from two different basidiosporal infections meet in the leaf, abundant anastomoses occur which involve

[a] Diploidization may be accomplished by alternate methods (see text).

nuclear migrations as well. This is sometimes interpreted as evidence that *P. malvacearum* is heterothallic. It is thought that this process initiates the binucleate mycelium which becomes aggregated at certain loci near both leaf surfaces. A new generation of teliospores is produced on these hyphae which soon rupture the leaf epidermis. The two nuclei in each teliospore cell unite during maturation of the spore. Meiosis and formation of a basidium and basidiospores occur during teliospore germination. The teliospores of *P. malvacearum* do not require a period of dormancy before germination.

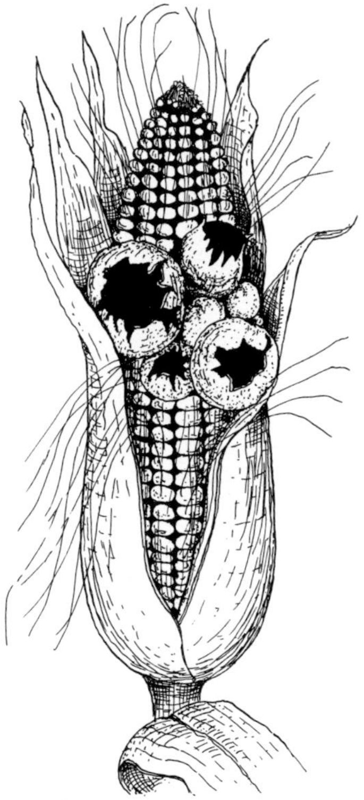

Puccinia graminis and *P. malvacearum* represent two extremes in type of life cycle among rusts. The former is heteroecious, requiring two hosts, and macrocyclic. It produces five types of reproductive cells. *P. malvacearum* is autoecious, confined to one host, and produces only teliospores and basidiospores. A number of other rust species fall between these two extremes with respect to degree of complexity of life cycle.

Smut Fungi

Although the smut fungi are parasitic Basidiomycota, some of them have been induced to complete their life cycles in laboratory cultures. The smuts which parasitize cereal grains are of tremendous economic importance. In epidemic years they have caused the loss of millions of bushels of grain. Their presence on the host is usually strikingly manifest by the sooty-black malformations on the fruiting spikes and vegetative portions of the plant.

Ustilago zeae (Beckm.) Unger, the **corn smut,** occurs in most spectacular fashion in the ears and tassels of the plant, where it causes immense, enlarged growths (Fig. 13–10). These tumor-like galls of *Ustilago* (L.

Fig. 13–10. *Ustilago zeae* (Beckm.) Unger. Corn smut on ear of bantam corn. X ½.

ustus, burned) are black at maturity. The color results from the transformation of the mycelium in the swollen host tissue into a mass of countless dark-walled spores (Fig. 13–11) which are binucleate. The spores
are called **chlamydospores** (Gr. *chlamys*, cloaked + Gr. *spora*) or, some-

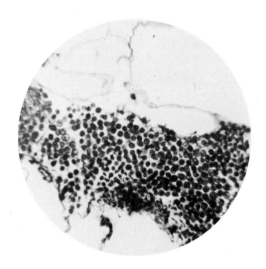

Fig. 13–11.   *Ustilago zeae.* Infected host cells filled with chlamydospores. X 250.

times, teliospores. The two nuclei in the young spore undergo union as
the spore wall thickens.

The epidermis of the host, which at first covers the growing gall-like
enlargement, is finally ruptured. The interior of the mass is composed of
large numbers of chlamydospores, in-
termingled with the remains of sterile
hyphae and host cells. The chlamydospores are readily disseminated by air
currents and can germinate immediately, or they may undergo dormancy
until the next growing season of the
host. Upon germination, the thick
spore wall is ruptured by the protrusion of a delicate basidial hypha which
becomes divided into four linearly arranged cells (Fig. 13–12), each containing a single haploid nucleus. The

Fig. 13–12.   *Ustilago zeae.* Germinating
chlamydospore with basidium and basidiospores. X 770.

nucleus in each cell of the basidium divides mitotically to form two nuclei, one of which migrates into a thin-walled basidiospore that is budded off each basidial segment. Each of the latter may continue to produce additional basidiospores. It has been demonstrated, by the technique of single spore isolation and culture, that meiosis occurs during the division of the primary basidial nucleus, i.e., the fusion nucleus of the chlamydospore. Therefore, the basidiospores are usually of two kinds in their sexual potentialities. Host plants inoculated with a single basidiospore fail to develop typical smut galls.

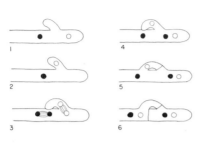

Fig. 13–13. Stages in cell division and clamp connection formation in the mycelium of Basidiomycota, schematized; black nuclei represent one type and white nuclei another type of compatible nuclei. By comparing 1 and 6 and intervening figures, note maintenance of original nuclear complement. (Modified from Alexopoulos.)

The basidiospores which chance to fall on the meristematic epidermis of young host tissues form delicate germination tubes which penetrate it and develop an intercellular mycelium, nourished by intracellular haustorial branches. The cells of this mycelium are uninucleate. The binucleate mycelium which produces the gall-like growth is initiated by fusions of hyphae, **somatogamy**, from different basidiosporal infections that chance to be in close proximity within the host. The infected region of the plant undergoes cell enlargement as a result of the presence of the fungus, and a new gall is ultimately produced. Other species of *Ustilago* cause smut diseases in different cereal grains. *U. tritici* Körn causes "loose smut" of wheat, and *U. avenae* (Pers.) Jens. causes a similar disease of oats. In addition to the origin of the binucleate (dikaryotic) mycelium by somatogamy described above, other mechanisms occur among smuts to effect the same result. For example, the dikaryotic mycelium is initiated in some smuts by conjugation of compatible basidiospores, often called **sporidia.** Once initiated, the binucleate condition of the mycelium of many smuts and other Basidiomycota is maintained by the formation of **clamp connections,** a phenomenon illustrated in Fig. 13–13 and described in its legend.

Mushrooms

The mushroom or toadstool (Fig. 13–14) represents the fruiting body or **basidiocarp** of the fungus. Aggregation of the basidia into basidiocarps does not occur among the rusts and smuts. In the mushrooms, countless basidia and basidiospores are produced on the surface of the **gills.** The mushroom itself appears after a long period of vegetative development by a saprophytic mycelium which permeates the substratum, usually rich soil, decaying leaves or wood, or other organic debris. The mycelial branches are often twisted together in rope-like strands called **rhizomorphs.** By the time the mycelium has matured sufficiently to produce basidiocarps, its cells are binucleate.

Among laymen, the term "mushroom" usually is employed to designate edible basidiocarps, whereas "toadstool," used as the antonym, signifies inedible or deleterious species. Morphologically, both mushrooms and

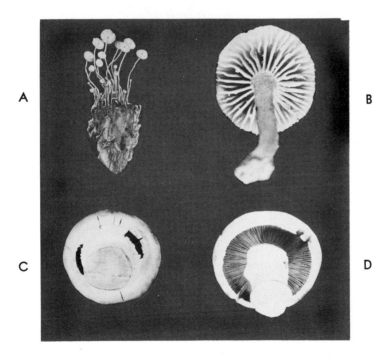

Fig. 13–14. *A,* Wood-inhabiting mushroom, *Marasmius rotula* (Scop.) Fr. X ⅔. *B,* Single basidiocarp of *Marasmius,* ventral view of pileus and gills. X 2½. *C,D, Agaricus campestris* L. ex Fr. Stages in development of the basidiocarp; note partially ruptured velum in C. X ⅜.

toadstools are basidiocarps. As a matter of fact, very few forms are poisonous, although a number are unpalatable or otherwise unpleasant. In spite of many popular "rules" for distinguishing edible and poisonous mushrooms, "the only certain test is eating. . . . To know whether a fungus is safe to eat, we must be able to recognize it and know its proved reputation."[2] The most poisonous species are members of the genus *Amanita,* the toxicity of which varies with the species.

The mushroom originates as a minute ball of interwoven hyphae which increases in size and soon develops the familiar "button" stage. In sectional views, the closely interwoven cells give the appearance of paren-

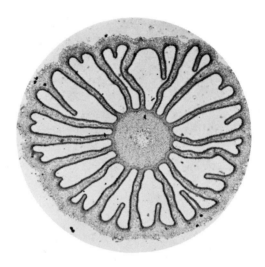

Fig. 13–15. *Coprinus* sp. Transverse section of pileus and gills, the latter covered with the fertile hymenium. X 30.

chyma tissue, but their origin, from interweaving hyphae, indicates that they are merely **pseudoparenchymatous.** The immature, button stages may be produced in large numbers within the substratum, from which they emerge very rapidly following a rainfall. The word "mushroom" is commonly used metaphorically to exemplify the epitome of rapid growth. The latter is effected by the absorption of large quantities of water by the hyphae, which become extremely turgid and enormously stretched. In some genera, like *Coprinus* (Gr. *kopros,* dung), the basidiocarp is raised by elongation of the stipe early in the morning; all its spores are shed by afternoon, after which it deliquesces.

The basidiocarp of the mushroom (Fig. 13–14), as it appears above the substratum, consists of an expanded, frequently disc-like portion, the **pileus** (L. *pileum,* cap), which is subtended by the stalk or **stipe** (L.

[2] Ramsbottom, *Mushrooms and Toadstools,* Collins, 1953, p. 35.

stipes, branch). The entire basidiocarp may be covered during early development by a membranous tissue which ruptures as the mushroom enlarges. Its remnants are visible in some genera as scales on the upper surface of the pileus and as a cup, the **volva,** at the base of the stipe. The ventral surface of the pileus consists of radiating plates of hyphae, the **gills** (Fig. 13–14), whose arrangement, color, and structure are of taxonomic value in distinguishing various genera. The ventral surface of the pileus is often covered during its development by a membrane, the **velum** (Fig. 13–14*C*); its remnants may persist as an **annulus** on the stipe.

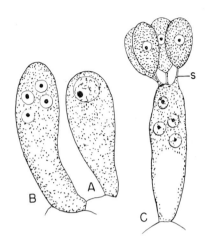

Fig. 13–16. *Coprinus* sp. Stages in basidiospore formation. A, Young basidium with single diploid nucleus. B, Nuclear products of meiosis. C, Basidiospores, sterigmata, and supernumerary nuclei in basidium: s, sterigma. X 1700.

The gills (Fig. 13–14) comprise the fertile region of the basidiocarp. They are composed of a series of interwoven hyphae (Fig. 13–15) whose enlarged terminal cells protrude from the gill surface and function as basidia. Unlike the rusts and smuts, the basidia here arise from vegetative hyphae, not from teliospores or chlamydospores. A section of a mushroom gill, prepared at the proper point in development, shows a series of stages in the production of basidia and basidiospores. The surfaces of the gills are covered by a fertile layer of basidia in various phases of development, and of **paraphyses** or sterile cells. Specialized cells, the **cystidia,** whose function is not entirely clear, are intermingled with the basidia of certain species. The surface layer of the gill is called the **hymenium.** The basidia and paraphyses are borne on hyphae which form a subhymenial layer, and the central portion of the gill is composed of elongate hyphae which form a **trama.** The young basidia, as well as the sterile hyphae of the basidiocarp, are binucleate, but the two nuclei of the former unite early in development (Fig. 13–16*A*). The enlarged diploid nucleus then undergoes two nuclear divisions (Fig. 13–16*B*), during which meiosis occurs. It has been reported that the chromosome number in *Agaricus campestris* L. ex Fr. (Gr. *agarikon,* mushroom), the commercially cultivated mushroom of the United States, is $n = 9$. Following meiosis, each of the four haploid nuclei migrates into a sterigma, which enlarges at the tip to form a basidiospore (Fig. 13–16C). These are produced gradually by all the basidia, so that tremendous numbers of spores are shed from each pileus. One may gain some idea of their enormous numbers by placing a pileus, ventral surface down, on a suitable piece of paper, covering it with a bell jar, and examining the spore print which appears. It has been estimated that a single basidiocarp of *Agaricus campestris,* four inches in diameter, produces about sixteen billion spores during the five to six days of spore discharge. Two-spored races occur in a number of mushrooms. In these, each basidiospore receives two of the four haploid basidial nuclei. Cultivated races of *Agaricus* are usually two-spored.

The liberated basidiospores germinate promptly, if they chance to fall upon a suitable substratum. Each produces a primary mycelium with uninucleate cells. Many species have been grown in artificial culture. It has been demonstrated that some genera of mushrooms are homothallic and others are heterothallic. In homothallic species, mycelium from a single basidiospore will ultimately produce a basidiocarp. In heterothallic species, on the other hand, the haploid mycelium remains sterile unless it is diploidized by a suitable compatible strain. Diploidization gives rise to a mycelium with binucleate cells, a **dikaryotic** condition. Diploidization may be accomplished by somatogamy or by union of hyphal segments, **oidia.** In heterothallic species, the nuclei which unite in the young basidia are the descendants of the original pair or pairs of compatible nuclei brought together at the time of diploidization. It has been shown experimentally that two of the four spores contain nuclei of one sexual type and that two have nuclei of the other. Spores of homothallic species apparently contain both sexual potentialities in their nuclei.

Cultivation of the field mushroom, *Agaricus campestris,* has become an important commercial enterprise. Mushroom cultivation was practiced in France early in the seventeenth century. Mushroom mycelia are inoculated into specially prepared beds, containing a mixture of soil, leaves, and manure called compost; these beds are kept moist and at a suitable temperature. Blocks of such compressed soil mixture containing the mycelium are often spoken of as mushroom "seed" or "spawn."

Other Basidiomycota

In addition to the rusts, smuts, and mushrooms, several other representatives of the Basidiomycota are of widespread occurrence. These will be treated briefly in the following account.

JELLY FUNGI

Fruits of *Tremella* (L. *tremo*, tremble) and *Auricularia auricularis* (S. F. Gray) Martin are saprophytes on decaying logs in damp situations. They are most conspicuous after periods of prolonged rainfall. The basidiocarp

Fig. 13–17.   *Tremella lutescens* (Pers.) Fr. Basidiocarps on decaying wood. X ¾.

of *Tremella* (Fig. 13–17) is usually yellow, markedly convoluted, and of gelatinous consistency. *Auricularia* (Fig. 13–18), the "ear fungus," is brown in color and, although gelatinous, is somewhat firmer. The saprophytic vegetative mycelium ramifies through the substratum, producing

Fig. 13–18.   *Auricularia auricularis* (S. F. Gray) Martin. Basidiocarp. X ¾.

basidiocarps after a period of vegetative development. The mycelial cells are binucleate at the time the fruiting bodies are developed, but the exact origin of this condition is not known with certainty. It presumably results from somatogamy of uninucleate primary mycelia.

The basidia and basidiospores of these genera are of interest to students of the phylogeny of fungi, because they exhibit similarities both to the basidia of mushrooms and to those of rusts. In *Tremella,* the basidia occur all over the surface of the basidiocarp and are bathed in a gelatinous exudate secreted by the mycelium. This arrangement recalls the vegetative structure of such Rhodophyceae as *Nemalion* and *Batrachospermum.* It has been demonstrated that nuclear union, followed by meiosis, takes place in each basidium as it develops. Cytokinesis follows the formation of four nuclei in such a manner that the basidium is divided into four cruciately arranged cells. Each of these produces an elongated sterigma-like protuberance which gives rise to a basidiospore on the surface of the gelatinous basidiocarp.

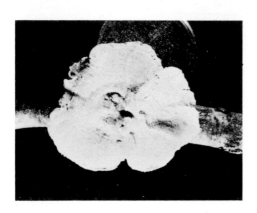

Fig. 13–19. *Polyporus* sp. Basidiocarp on twig. X 3/7.

In *Auricularia,* the entire under surface of the basidiocarp also is fertile. Nuclear union is followed by meiosis and production of four nuclei in the developing basidium. Here, however, cytokinesis divides the basidium into a chain of four cells very similar to the arrangement in the rusts. Each cell of the four-celled basidium now develops an elongate, sterigma-like hypha which grows to the surface of the basidiocarp and produces a basidiospore. The latter are violently discharged from the sterigmata.

PORE FUNGI

The pore fungi comprise the Basidiomycota in which the hymenial layer is developed as a layer over the surface of pores or tubes in the basidiocarp (Fig. 13–20). The pores are often visible to the unaided eye. The basidiocarp may be superficially similar in form to that of the mushroom, as in the genus *Boletus* (Gr. *bolites,* mushroom), or it may occur as a shelf-like or bracket-like outgrowth on living trees and timber, as in the genus *Polyporus* (Gr. *polys,* many + Gr. *poros,* pore) (Fig. 13–19). The basidiocarp of bracket fungi may be soft in texture or woody or leathery; it may be annual or perennial. The appearance of the basidiocarp is preceded by an extensive development of vegetative mycelium within the substratum. The vegetative mycelium is dikaryotic at the time the fruiting body makes its appearance. There is evidence that somatogamy occurs in several species. In perennial types, countless basidiospores are shed from the basidiocarp during its existence. Fig. 13–20 shows a portion of a section through the fruiting body of *Boletus*. The wall of each pore is covered with a layer of hymenium, much like that in mushrooms. Each basidium forms four basidiospores which are explo-

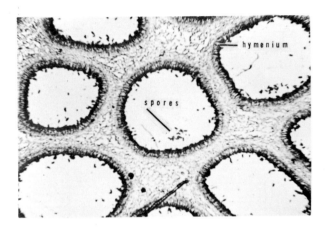

Fig. 13–20. *Boletus* sp. Transverse section of segment of basidiocarp; note spores, and pores lined with hymenium. X 60.

sively discharged from their sterigmata. Little information is available as to the details of the life cycle in these pore fungi; the nuclear condition and reproductive phases are unknown for a majority of genera. The pore fungi are of great economic importance as the cause of the rotting of standing and stored timber; they are probably largely saprophytic, although some attack sapwood which contains living cells.

PUFFBALLS

In concluding this short treatment of the Basidiomycota, brief mention must be made of the puffball type (Fig. 13–21). The basidiocarp in these organisms always remains closed until after the basidia have matured their basidiospores. Indeed, in some genera, the basidiocarp never opens, the spores being disseminated only after the decay of the wall. In others, like *Lycoperdon* (Gr. *lykos*, wolf + Gr. *perdomai*, break wind), *Calvatia* (L. *calvus*, bald), and *Geastrum* (Gr. *ge*, earth + Gr. *aster*, star) (Fig.

3–21), one or more small ostioles develop on the surface of the basidiocarp; the basidiospores are emitted in puffs through these, when the basidiocarps are subjected to pressure. Our knowledge of cytological and reproductive features of the puffballs is scanty.

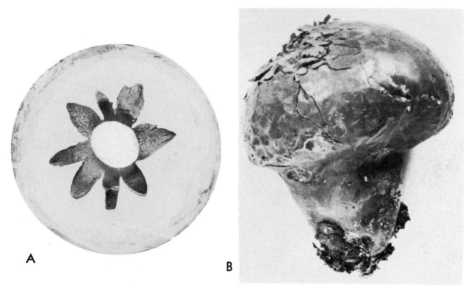

A
B

Fig. 13–21.   A, *Geastrum* sp. Basidiocarp of an "earth star." X 1½; B, *Calvatia* sp. X ½.

SUMMARY AND CLASSIFICATION

The representative genera of Basidiomycota described in the preceding sections of this chapter comprise a rather heterogeneous assemblage of fungi which, however, possess in common the attribute of producing a structure called the basidium. The basidium itself is not uniform in structure or time of occurrence in the life cycle. In the mushrooms, jelly fungi, pore fungi, and puffballs, the basidia appear directly on the mycelium as enlarged terminal hyphal tips (Fig. 13–16). In the rusts and smuts, on the other hand, the basidium always develops as the result of the germination of a thick-walled spore, the teliospore or chlamydospore (Figs. 13–5, 13–12). As to the structure of the basidium itself, the genera described exhibit variation. In the mushrooms and pore fungi, the basidium is nonseptate, and the postmeiotic nuclei migrate directly into the basidiospores as they are formed. In the rusts, certain jelly fungi, and *Ustilago zeae*, the postmeiotic nuclei are segregated as the basidium becomes septate, each ultimately occupying a separate cell of the basidium.

Obvious manifestations of sexuality, such as specially differentiated gametes and gametangia, are usually absent in the Basidiomycota, and somatogamy prevails. For these reasons, sexuality is often said to be reduced in this assemblage of fungi. On the other hand, in many other organisms in which sexuality is considered to be highly developed—as in isogamous species of *Chlamydomonas, Spirogyra,* and *Rhizopus,* for example—highly differentiated gametangia and gametes are also lacking. The primary manifestations of sexuality, the union of cells and nuclei and the association of chromosomal and gene complements, are obviously present in the Basidiomycota, in spite of the absence of such secondary criteria as specialized gametes and gametangia. It is quite true that plasmogamy and karyogamy may be separated in time for an exceptionally long interval (*Puccinia graminis*), but descendants of the original pairs of nuclei of opposite sex potentiality, brought together at plasmogamy, are maintained by conjugate nuclear division, and one or more pairs of these descendant nuclei ultimately unite in the teliospore, chlamydospore, or basidium. Clamp connections are associated with the maintenance of the dikaryotic condition in many Basidiomycota.

The Basidiomycota are frequently divided into two groups on the basis of basidium structure. The illustrative genera discussed in this chapter may be classified as follows:

Division Basidiomycota
 Class 1. Hemibasidiomycetes (basidium septate or consisting of a thick-walled teliospore or chlamydosopore and its germ tube)
  Order 1. Uredinales (Rusts)
   Family 1. Pucciniaceae
    Genera: *Puccinia, Gymnosporangium*
  Order 2. Ustilaginales (Smuts)
   Family 1. Ustilaginaceae
    Genus: *Ustilago*
  Order 3. Tremellales (Jelly fungi)
   Family 1. Tremellaceae
    Genus: *Tremella*
  Order 4. Auriculariales (Jelly fungi)
   Family 1. Auriculariaceae
    Genus: *Auricularia*
 Class 2. Holobasidiomycetes (basidium nonseptate, one-celled, a hyphal tip)

Subclass 1. Hymenomycetes (basidia exposed to air, discharging their basidiospores freely at maturity)

Order 1. Agaricales (Gilled fungi)

Family 1. Agaricaceae

Genera: *Agaricus, Coprinus*

Order 2. Polyporales (Pore fungi)

Family 1. Polyporaceae

Genus: *Polyporus*

Family 2. Boletaceae

Genus: *Boletus*

Subclass 2. Gasteromycetes (basidia and basidiospores permanently enclosed in basidiocarp, or enclosed until basidiospores have matured)

Order 1. Lycoperdales (Puffballs)

Family 1. Lycoperdaceae

Genera: *Lycoperdon, Geastrum, Calvatia*

DISCUSSION QUESTIONS

1. In outline form, summarize the life cycle of *Puccinia graminis*. How does it differ from that of *P. malvacearum?* Distinguish between macrocyclic and microcyclic rusts. Give an account of the nuclear cycle in *P. graminis.*

2. Can you suggest any *a priori* reasons why mycologists have failed, with few exceptions, to cultivate rusts independently of their specifically required host plant? How would you proceed in attempting to do so?

3. Why has the eradication of barberry bushes not caused the disappearance of the wheat rust?

4. Sexual reproduction in rusts has been compared with that in the Rhodophyceae. What evidences of parallelism can you cite?

5. How do you account for the frequent occurrence of mushrooms in circles or "fairy rings"?

6. How do you explain the rapid appearance of mushrooms after a rain?

7. Define the terms basidium, basidiocarp, basidiospore, conjugate nuclear division, hymenium, diploidize, somatogamy, dikaryotic.

8. How would you determine whether or not a given rust fungus is homothallic or heterothallic? A mushroom? A smut?

9. Is it always necessary to count the chromosome number to establish the occurrence of meiosis?

10. How do rusts and smuts reduce the yield of cereal grains?

11. The introduction of nuclei of one strain into the mycelium of another, in Ascomycota and Basidiomycota, has been called "diploidization." Does this involve the production of diploid nuclei? Explain.

12. In view of the tremendous number of spores produced by such organs as the mushroom basidiocarp and the aecium of the rusts, why is the world not overrun with mushrooms and rusts?

13. Male and female sex organs are absent in most Basidiomycota. Is sexual reproduction present in your opinion? Give the reasons for your answer.

14. Consult one or more of the references listed at the end of Chapter 10 for an account of the life cycle of rusts other than *Puccinia*. On the basis of your reading, cite variations from the *Puccinia* type.

CHAPTER 14

Fungi Imperfecti; Lichens; Recapitulation of the Fungi

FUNGI IMPERFECTI

In concluding the several chapters dealing with fungi, brief mention must be made of a great group of organisms known as **Fungi Imperfecti** or **Deuteromycetes** (Gr. *deuteros,* second + Gr. *mykes*). These organisms, which include both parasitic and saprophytic species, produce only asexual reproductive cells, namely, **conidia** or **chlamydospores,** at maturity. The spores may be borne directly on the mycelium (Fig. 14–1), or on conidiophores which develop within or upon special fruiting structures, such as **pycnidia** (Gr. *pyknos,* dense) (Fig. 14–2), composed of densely interwoven hyphae. When cultivated under controlled environmental conditions properly manipulated, a number of fungi once included in this alliance have been induced to undergo sexual reproduction and thus complete their life cycles. The spores produced as a result of sexual reproduction have been ascospores in a majority of species, but basidia and basidiospores have developed in a few. It seems evident that the species of Fungi Imperfecti represent alternate stages of Ascomycota and Basidiomycota in which the characteristic asci and ascospores or basidia and basidiospores are produced rarely, if ever. The Fungi Imperfecti are classified in an artificial system which emphasizes the location of the conidiophores and the color and structure of the conidia. Further consideration of this group is beyond the scope of the present volume.

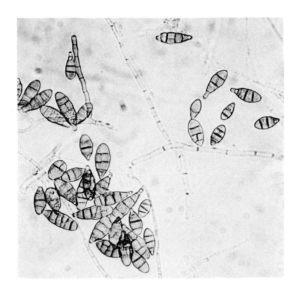

Fig. 14–1. *Alternaria* sp. An imperfect fungus with septate chlamydospores. X 540.

LICHENS

The organisms known as lichens might be classified as a separate division of the plant kingdom, were it not for the marked artificiality of such a grouping. Such a hypothetical division might be named the *Mycophycophyta* (Gr. *mykes,* fungus + Gr. *phykos,* alga + Gr. *phyton,* plant), a name which emphasizes that these organisms are dual in nature, consisting of an algal and a fungal component that grow together to form a plant body of consistently recognizable structure and appearance. Because the component organisms are members of other divisions—the Cyanophyta, Chlorophyta, Ascomycota, and Basidiomycota—the lichens usually are not classified as a separate division but in-

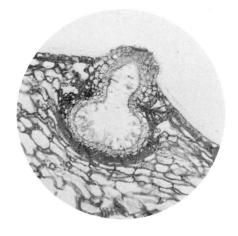

Fig. 14–2. *Sphaeropsis malorum* Pk. An imperfect fungus parasitic on apples. Median longitudinal section of a pycnidium on the surface of an apple. X 135.

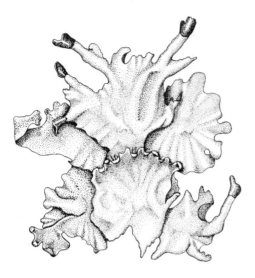

Fig. 14–3. *Peltigera rufescens* (Neck.) Hoffm. Portion of thallus with fertile lobes. X ⅔.

stead are often grouped with the fungi. This probably stems from the circumstance that in a majority of lichens the fungus grows more rapidly than the alga, its mycelium forming a sort of framework within which the algal cells develop.

Lichens are ubiquitous plants. They occur in a great variety of habitats, ranging from the bare surfaces of exposed rocks to the frozen substrata of arctic regions. Many of them flourish on decaying wood and undisturbed soil rich in organic debris. Tree bark supports an extensive flora of lichens (Fig. 14–4B). Some species are able to survive long periods of desiccation, and others thrive in extremely moist habitats. A number grow as epiphytes on the bark and branches of trees. Rock-inhabiting lichens are important agents in initi-

| A | B |

Fig. 14–4. A, Granite rock with *Parmelia caperata* Ach., *p*, and *Umbilicaria papulosa* (Ach.) Tuck., *u*, X ⅓. B, Portion of tree trunk with lichens. X 1/30.

ating soil formation. Their secretions etch the rock which is then readily broken down by ice and other physical agents to form a primitive type of soil. As organic remains from lichen vegetation become incorporated among the rock particles, higher forms of vegetation are established. A few marine lichens are known.

The exact relationship between the organisms comprising a lichen thallus are by no means completely understood. Some look upon a lichen as a fungus parasitizing an alga, while, at the same time, the former is connected with the substratum. Support for this view is afforded by the lichens in which the fungus hyphae are connected to the algal cells by means of **appressoria** or haustoria (Fig. 14–9). On the other hand, the fungus component of a number of lichens has been grown successfully in artificial culture media, so the supposed parasitism is not obligate or highly specialized. Furthermore, in spite of the inferred parasitism, the algal cells grow and multiply for long periods

Fig. 14–5. *Cladonia chlorophaea* (Flk.) Spreng., with cups, and *C. cristatella* Tuck., X ½.

within the lichen thallus without apparent injurious effects from the fungus. Other investigators interpret lichens as manifestations of a type of **symbiosis** (Gr. *syn*, together + Gr. *bios*, life), with benefit accruing to each partner. The alga is surrounded and mechanically protected by the meshwork of fungus hyphae which absorb and adsorb water, mineral salts, and organic materials from the substratum. The fungus, presumably by means of appressoria or haustoria, diffusion from the algal cells, or autolysis of the latter, is supplied with a source of carbohydrate and organic nitrogen compounds. Our knowledge of the physiological relations between fungi and algae in lichens is colored to some extent by teleological

Fig. 14–6. *Cladonia sylvatica* (L.) Hoffm. X ½.

considerations and speculation. While it is obvious that the algal component of lichens occupying xeric habitats like bare rocks could not and does not exist alone in the same environment, it is more difficult to be

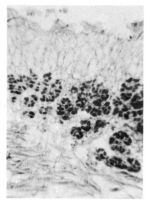

convinced that the algal component of lichens growing in moist habitats is benefited by association with a fungus. In fact, it seems probable that the fungus hyphae surrounding the algae may reduce their rate of photosynthesis by shading. However, again considering the case of the xerophytic lichen on a bare rock surface, it is reasonable to suppose that the fungus

Fig. 14–7.   *Peltigera rufescens.* Transverse section of thallus; note algal (dark cells) and fungal components. X 250.

component could not exist in such a habitat, devoid of organic

metabolites, unless it were supplied by the alga. Again, in the case of lichens of moist soil and bark habitats, it seems probable that the substratum itself can supply a great part of the organic materials re-

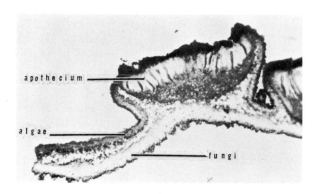

Fig. 14–8.   *Umbilicaria papulosa.* Transverse section of thallus and apothecium. X 60.

quired by the fungus, so that association with an alga would seem to be superfluous. Furthermore, it is well known that algae can utilize available organic matter to supplement their nutritional requirements. In summary, it is difficult to generalize with assurance concerning the physiological relations between the component organisms of lichens.

Further investigation of this question, based on pure culture studies of the organisms grown separately and together, would undoubtedly clear up some of our current uncertainties.

In the great majority of lichens, the fungus component is ascomycetous, probably related to the cup fungi or to perithecium-forming genera. In a few lichens, the fungus is one of the Basidiomycota, often one of the mushrooms. The algal components are usually myxophycean genera like *Gloeocapsa, Nostoc,* and *Stigonema,* or chlorophycean genera like *Trebouxia* (a *Chlorococcum*-like genus) (Fig. 14–9).

The plant body of the lichen may be leaf-like or **foliose** (*Peltigera, Parmelia, Umbilicaria*) (Figs. 14–3, 14–4), crust-like or **crustose,** or branching and cylindrical or **fruticose** (*Cladonia, Usnea*) (Figs. 14–5, 14–6). In most lichens, the fungus forms a general network around the algal cells. It often looks pseudoparenchymatous because of the dense interweaving of its hyphae. As a result, considerable internal differentiation of the thallus may be present (Figs. 14–7, 14–8). The surface hyphae may assume a somewhat epidermis-like configuration, which in genera like *Peltigera* (L. *pelta,* shield)

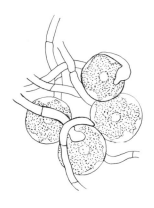

Fig. 14–9. *Parmelia caperata.* Soredium. X 315.

absorbs water slowly, if at all. The hyphae below the epidermal layer form the upper cortex. The algal cells lie immediately beneath this (Fig. 14–7), among loosely woven fungus hyphae. The central portion of the thallus, the medulla, is also composed of a loose network of hyphae below which a dense lower cortex may be present. The medullary hyphae are longitudinal in orientation in *Peltigera* and function in conduction. Special absorbing hyphae, the **rhizines,** enter the substratum from the lower surface of the thallus. The rhizines of *Peltigera* are complex bundles of hyphae which have anastomosed by fusion of young hyphal tips. They conduct water rapidly in the capillary spaces among the component hyphae and also in their lumina, as demonstrated by experiments with water-soluble dyes.

Multiplication of the lichen thallus is effected by fragmentation, as the older portions of the plant body die and leave the growing regions isolated. A number of lichens produce special bodies, the **soredia** (Gr. *soros,* heap), for propagation (Fig. 14–9). These are small fragments of the thallus consisting of one or more algal cells surrounded by fungus hyphae. The soredia are readily detached from the thallus and, when borne to suitable environments by air currents, may develop into new plants. In *Cladonia chlorophaea* (Flk.) Spreng. the soredia are borne in goblet-like structures (Fig. 14–5).

In addition to multiplication of the lichen as a unit, the component organisms also reproduce independently. Under conditions of abundant moisture, the algal member may undergo rapid growth and cell division, thus outstripping the enveloping fungus; groups of algal cells are thus set free into the substratum. In many lichens, the fungus regularly produces ascocarps and asci (Figs. 14–3, 14–4, 14–8, 14–10); the ascocarp may be a perithecium or an apothecium (Figs. 14–3, 14–8, 14–10), or have some other form. The picturesque red tips of certain ascending branches of *Cladonia cristatella* Tuck. (Fig. 14–10), for example, are aggregations of asci. It has been demonstrated in a number of genera that the formation of the ascocarp is preceded by the development of a coiled ascogonium, often with a trichogyne, which is probably fertilized by a spermatium. Cytological details are unknown in most cases.

Fig. 14–10.   *Cladonia cristatella.* Ascus-bearing branches. X ⅔.

The mature ascocarp may be elevated on a stipe above the thallus or it may be sessile or even sunken. The hymenial layer of the apothecium is composed of densely intermingled asci and paraphyses (Fig. 14–11A,B); the wall of the ascocarp may be composed only of fungus hyphae, or it may be overgrown by an alga-containing layer of the thallus. The ascospores vary among the various genera in form and number of component cells. They are discharged explosively from the apothecia and usually germinate readily if they fall upon a favorable substratum.

It is clear that both the algal component and the spores of the fungus, once separated from the parent thallus, initiate an independent existence. The synthesis of a new lichen thallus depends upon the fortuitous proximity of a germinating fungus spore and algal cells of the species with which the fungus has been associated in the parent lichen thallus. For this reason it is questionable whether ascospores play an important role in the multiplication of lichens, as such. It is probable that fragmentation and soredium production are more efficacious in this connection.

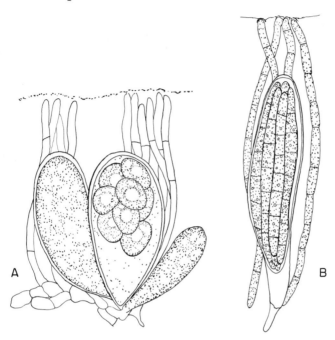

Fig. 14–11.   A, *Parmelia caperata*. Asci and paraphyses. B, *Peltigera rufescens*. Ascus with septate ascospores and paraphyses. X 770.

Lichens have been neglected by most botanists, except for a few who have occupied themselves almost exclusively with the taxonomy of these interesting plants. Careful physiological studies of the components, grown separately and together in laboratory culture under controlled conditions, would probably augment our understanding of these organisms.

It is difficult to assign lichens a natural position in any plan of classification of the plant kingdom. If they were classified with the group of ascomycetous or basidiomycetous fungi to which their fungus component is related, as some have suggested, the importance of the algal component would be minimized. The opposite objection might be raised, were they to be classified on the basis of their algal components. In the present volume, therefore, they have been assigned no formal position in the classification of the plant kingdom but are treated in the chapter that concludes the discussion of the algae and fungi.

RECAPITULATION OF THE FUNGI

Chapters 9 through 13 contain a brief survey of organisms known as fungi in the broad sense of the term, as exemplified by descriptions of the structure and reproduction of certain selected genera and species. It was stated in Chapter 1 that in older systems of classification the algae and fungi were grouped together in a single division, Thallophyta, within which the fungi comprised a class coordinate with the algae. It became clear long ago that the bacteria and slime molds represent series fundamentally distinct from the remainder of the fungi. The characteristic cell structure of the bacteria, with respect to wall structure, nuclear organization, flagellation, and their endospore formation, mark them as a group apart. It seems quite logical, therefore, to consider them as a phyletic unit or division, although future investigation may reveal that the assemblage is a heterogeneous one. The slime molds differ from the bacteria in their nuclear organization, and from the bacteria and other fungi in their possession of naked amoeboid stages (the plasmodium and pseudoplasmodium), as well as in their holozoic manner of nutrition. In spite of the stationary sporangial stages of slime molds, a number of distinguished mycologists are of the opinion that they are more closely related to protozoa than to fungi. For these reasons, the slime molds, like the bacteria, are usually considered to represent a distinct phyletic group and are accorded divisional rank.

The three remaining groups of fungi, treated in this volume as separate divisions—namely, the Phycomycota, Ascomycota, and Basidiomycota—are assigned class rank and combined into a single division, Eumycophyta, by a number of mycologists. Approximately 3585 genera and 40,-000 species are included in this alliance. If the division is indeed the expression of phyletic unity, such a grouping would indicate close kinship among phycomycetous, ascomycetous, and basidiomycetous fungi. When one reviews the attributes which these several classes of fungi have in common, attributes which might serve as evidences of kinship, the results are not convincing, if speculation is distinguished from knowledge. These organisms do possess the negative attribute of nonphotosynthetic nutrition, but they share this with the great majority of Schizomycota and Myxomycota. Their most striking common characteristic, perhaps, is the structure of their plant bodies, which, for the most part, are composed of branching filaments, the mycelium. It should be noted, however, that the occurrence of branching filamentous plant bodies in the Chorophyta, Phaeophyta, Rhodophyta, and Cyanophyta is considered evidence of parallel development rather than of relationship among these algae. It should be interpreted in similar fashion in the fungi. The Phycomycota, Ascomycota, and Basidiomycota certainly are distinct enough from each other, with respect to their reproduction, to warrant our considering them as separate phyletic groups of divisional rank.

There are two important divergent points of view, among others, regarding the relationship of these three groups of fungi. According to one hypothesis, the fungi are probably derivatives of algae which have lost their photosynthetic capacity. This view is based upon similarities between the structure of the siphonalean Chlorophyceae and the mycelium of the Phycomycota, on the occurrence of flagellate motile cells in the lower Phycomycota and Chlorophyta, and on the similarity between the reproductive phases of the Ascomycota and the Rhodophyta. On the other hand, the flagellate motile cells of the lower Phycomycota and the absence of chlorophyll have suggested a protozoan origin to other mycologists.

There is no unanimity of opinion regarding the relation of the Phycomycota to the other two groups of fungi. According to some mycologists, the ascus is the homologue of the zygote of the Phycomycota, and the formation of ascospores by free-cell formation is interpreted by them as a derived condition. If this is granted, the unicellular yeasts, in some of which the zygotes produce ascospores directly, are probably the simplest Ascomycota. The genera with indirect ascus formation from ascogenous hyphae are considered to be derived types in this hypothesis. On the basis of similarities in reproduction reviewed in Chapter 12, other mycologists have suggested that the Ascomycota have been derived from a rhodophycean ancestry. To them, the yeasts are secondarily simplified or **reduced** organisms which originated from more complex mycelial ancestors. Most students of the fungi are of the opinion that the Basidiomycota have originated from an ascomycetous ancestry, and they interpret the basidium as the homologue of the ascus. They support this theory by emphasizing that nuclear union and meiosis occur in both basidium and ascus, that the special mechanisms involved in maintaining the dikaryotic condition which precedes the ascus and basidium (crozier formation and clamp connections, respectively) are similar, and that both organs form spores, albeit those of the ascus are endogenous and those of the basidium exogenous. On the basis of these considerations, it should be clear to the reader that so-called evidence of relationship among the several groups of fungi is largely founded on speculation and hypothesis. As such, it should not be accepted as final. In the writer's opinion, the available evidence is inadequate to indicate common origin for the Phycomycota, Ascomycota, and Basidiomycota, and accordingly they have been classified as separate divisions in this book.

As compared with the range of complexity of types of plant body in the algae, the fungi are more homogeneous, for the vegetative phases are either unicellular or composed of amorphous masses of mycelia. In complexity, however, the spore-bearing bodies of the Ascomycota and Basidiomycota surpass the fertile tracts of algae.

Both asexual and sexual reproduction are involved in the life cycles of a majority of the fungi. Zoospores and gemmae of the aquatic genera and air-borne spores of the higher genera of Phycomycota, the conidia of the Ascomycota, and the urediniospores and aeciospores of the Basidiomycota are all clearly asexual reproductive bodies. Such spore types as ascospores and basidiospores, while asexual in the sense that they can continue development into a mycelium without sexual union, nevertheless are closely associated with sexual phenomena which precede their formation. The absence of differentiated sex organs in many Ascomycota and Basidiomycota, together with alternate paths of effecting association and ultimate union of compatible nuclei, suggest that asexual and sexual phenomena in the higher fungi are not mutually exclusive.

When one attempts to interpret life cycles among the fungi in the light of their range in the algae, difficulties soon arise. It is quite clear that in respect to life cycle, such genera as *Saprolegnia, Achlya,* and *Rhizopus* are similar to *Chlamydomonas, Spirogyra,* and *Nemalion,* that is, haplobiontic with haploid plant bodies. The life cycles of *Allomyces macrogynus* and *Saccharomyces cerevisiae,* with their isomorphic alternation of generations, are similar in all fundamental respects to those of *Cladophora suhriana, Ulva,* and *Enteromorpha.* Difficulties present themselves, however, in comparing life cycles of the higher Ascomycota and Basidiomycota with those of algae. While it is tempting to homologize ascogenous hyphae, basidioferous hyphae, and diploid rhodophycean gonimoblasts, it must be remembered that the latter are diploid, not dikaryotic, and that normally dikaryotic cells are unknown among algae.

In conclusion, brief mention must be made of the relation and importance of fungi to mankind. Although most people are painfully aware of their harmful or inconvenient and unpleasant activities—among them production of a number of diseases of plants, animals, and human beings; decay of foods, textiles, and building materials; and such aesthetic offenses as mildews—the countless useful activities of these organisms are usually not appreciated sufficiently. One has but to mention such processes as acetic and lactic acid fermentations by bacteria and the role of the latter in the nitrogen cycle; the relation of the yeasts to the alcohol, baking, and brewing industries; the important antibiotics, which, like penicillin and streptomycin, are of fungus origin; and finally the relation of molds to the ripening of highly prized cheeses, to be reminded of some of the beneficial activities in which fungi have a stellar role.

DISCUSSION QUESTIONS

1. Discuss the nutritive relations between the algal and fungus components in lichens.
2. What types of algae occur in lichens?
3. What types of fungi are present in lichens?
4. How do lichens reproduce?
5. How would you go about isolating and growing the components of a given lichen?
6. How would you go about resynthesizing the lichen?
7. Why are lichens sometimes called "soil builders"?
8. List the distinctive attributes of the divisions of fungi.
9. What evidence is usually cited in support of the practice of grouping the Phycomycota, Ascomycota, and Basidiomycota in a single division?
10. Do nonphotosynthetic organisms occur only in the animal kingdom and among the fungi? Explain.
11. Assume that all fungi (including bacteria and slime molds) were to disappear from the earth tomorrow. What immediate and what ultimate results would you predict, if this occurred?

REFERENCE WORKS ON LICHENS

Fink, B., *The Lichen Flora of the United States,* Univ. of Michigan Press, 1949.
Nearing, G. G., *The Lichen Book,* published by author, Ridgewood, N.J., 1947.
Schneider, A., *A Textbook of General Lichenology,* Clute and Co., 1897.
Smith, A. L., *Lichens,* University Press, Cambridge, 1921.

CHAPTER 15

Division Hepatophyta

INTRODUCTION TO THE LAND PLANTS

Chapters 2 through 14 included a discussion of the algae and fungi, both of which were formerly classified together in the single division, Thallophyta. It will be recalled that the algae differ from the fungi in their autotrophism by photosynthesis, whereas the fungi, with the exception of a few types of bacteria, are heterotrophic organisms. With the rarest exceptions, the plants to be described in the present and succeeding chapters are, like the algae, also photoautotrophic. Although the algae are mostly aquatic organisms, with terrestrial representatives in a minority, the remaining groups of photosynthetic plants are primarily land dwellers. However, almost every division provides examples of genera which probably have taken to the water from an originally terrestrial habitat.

When one compares the bodies of the aquatic algae with those of terrestrial plants, it becomes evident that most of the complexities of the latter are manifestations of adaptation to existence in a drying atmosphere. As compared with postulated aquatic ancestors, the land plant is a pioneer in a harsh and unfavorable environment. Aquatic plants are bathed continuously in a solution containing the inorganic materials which are used in the synthesis of their protoplasm. On the contrary, large portions of the bodies of terrestrial plants are not in direct contact with water and dissolved nutrients, and, furthermore, are subject to the evaporation of a large percentage of the water that has been absorbed. Study of the structure of land plants reveals a variety of both morphological and physiological adaptations to terrestrial life. The degree and efficiency of these modifications are undoubtedly correlated with the habitats of land plants in relation to moisture and with the very survival of the plants themselves.

The **Hepatophyta** (Gr. *hepar*, liver), commonly called liverworts,[1] are certainly among the most primitive extant land plants. Several of the genera included in this group are aquatic organisms; the remainder, with few exceptions, are restricted to moist habitats. In some of them the plant body is scarcely more complex, internally and externally, than that of such algae as *Ulva*. The liverworts are considered by many botanists to be "allies" of the mosses with which they are usually grouped in a single division, Bryophyta, by those who hold this view. In this text, for reasons that will be cited after the student has become familiar with both groups, the liverworts and mosses are classified in separate divisions. The division Hepatophyta here is considered to include two distinct classes, the **Hepatopsida** (Gr. *hepar*, liver + Gr. *opsis*, appearance of) or liverworts, and the **Anthoceropsida** (Gr. *anthos*, flower + Gr. *keras*, a horn + Gr. *opsis*) or horned liverworts.

CLASS 1. HEPATOPSIDA

Introduction

The gametophyte is the dominant phase in the heteromorphic alternation of the liverworts. This class contains approximately 175 genera and 8500 species, which are grouped into orders and families on the basis of differences in the structure of their gametophytic and sporophytic phases. If one attempts to list first in the class the organisms which exhibit the greatest simplicity, he is at a loss to make a decision, for a low or high degree of complexity in both sporophyte and gametophyte does not coincide in the same organism. Furthermore, attributes which morphologists agree are simple may be divergently interpreted as either primitive or reduced. Thus, for example, on the basis of structure of the sporophyte alone, *Ricciocarpus* and *Riccia* deserve first place if simplicity is 'the criterion; but their gametophytes, which are internally differentiated, are more complex than those of genera like *Pellia*, *Pallavicinia*, and *Sphaerocarpos*. Three types of gametophytic plant body may be distinguished among the Hepatopsida to be discussed in this text: 1. the ***Riccia-Ricciocarpus-Marchantia*** type: thallose or blade-like organ-

---

[1] The name "liverwort" was first applied to the genus *Conacephalum* because of an imagined resemblance of its lobes to the lobes of the liver.

isms, with some degree of internal differentiation of tissues; 2. the *Pellia-Pallavicinia-Sphaerocarpos* type: thallose genera in which simplicity of external form is associated with a minimum of internal differentiation; 3. the *Porella* type: lobed and leafy organisms in which the external form is complex, but which are almost chlorophycean in their internal simplicity. Genera exemplifying these types of organization will be described in the following paragraphs.

Illustrative Genera

RICCIA AND RICCIOCARPUS

Vegetative Morphology. Most species of *Riccia* (after P. F. Ricci, an Italian botanist) lead an entirely terrestrial existence, frequently

Fig. 15–1.   *Riccia fluitans* L. On soil. X 1⅓.

occurring as rosettes on the surface of undisturbed soil when sufficient moisture is available. *Riccia fluitans* L. (Fig. 15–1) and *Ricciocarpus natans* (L.) Corda (from *Riccia* + Gr. *karpon*, fruit) (Fig. 15–2), however, lead an amphibious existence. Both have the capacity to develop vegetatively when stranded on moist soil as well as when submerged (*R. fluitans*) or floating (*R. natans*) on quiet waters. The individual plants of *Ricciocarpus* taper posteriorly from a broad, dichotomously lobed anterior growing region. The posterior portion of the plant is continually sloughing off as growth occurs at the tip. Increase in number of individuals occurs when branches become separated or when death and decay extend to the region of a dichotomy. Plants which contain mature sporophytes may attain a length of 2.5 cm. Four or more rows of **ventral scales** are present on the lower surface of each plant. The scales, which are a single cell layer thick, are often purple in color because of the presence of a pigment dissolved in the cell sap. Unicellular protuberances, or **rhizoids,** emerge from the cells of the lower surface of terrestrial plants and penetrate the substratum.

The apparent midrib in *Ricciocarpus* is in reality a bifurcating fissure that extends deeply into the plant body from the dorsal surface. Observed in transverse section (Fig. 15–3), this furrow is approximately in the form of an inverted Y. The lower portion of the plant is composed of rather

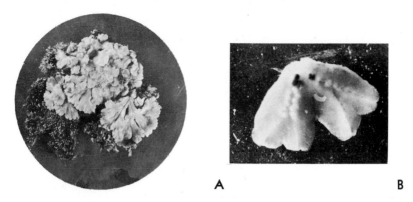

Fig. 15–2. *Ricciocarpus natans* (L.) Corda. *A,* Plants on soil. X 1. *B,* Aquatic plant with developing sporophytes in dorsal furrow. X 2.

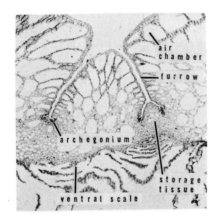

Fig. 15–3. *Ricciocarpus natans.* Transverse section of thallus just posterior to a dichotomy; note two Y-shaped dorsal furrows with archegonia, air chambers, ventral storage tissue, and scales. X 30.

Fig. 15–4. *Ricciocarpus natans.* Dorsal surface of thallus. X 60.

compact parenchyma cells which contain few chloroplasts and function as storage cells; these are covered above by several tiers of air chambers. The latter are responsible for the spongy appearance of the plants when they are viewed in dorsal aspect under low magnifications (Fig. 15–4). The walls of the air chambers are built up of photosynthetic parenchyma (chlorenchyma) cells rich in chloroplasts. The cells of the upper surface

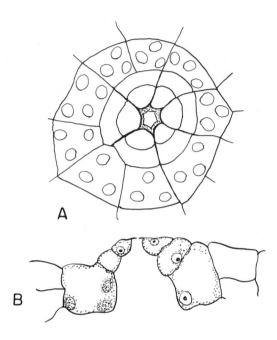

Fig. 15–5.   *Ricciocarpus natans.* A, Surface, and B, sectional views of an air pore and surrounding epidermal cells. X 410.

contain only a few poorly developed plastids and function as an epidermis. That their outer walls are cutinized at least delicately is suggested by the occurrence of apertures, one corresponding to each air chamber, on the upper surface of the plant body (Figs. 15–4, 15–5). The epidermal cells surrounding the aperture are modified in structure (Fig. 15–5). In *Riccia,* the air chambers are usually merely narrow fissures between the sheets of photosynthetic cells.

Growth of the plant body of *Ricciocarpus,* and of almost all land plants, is localized at the apex, where one or more prominent meristematic cells, the **apical cells,** and the cells derived from them undergo orderly divisions which augment the tissues of the plant. A median sagittal section through the plant body demonstrates its ontogeny (Fig. 15–6).

Reproduction.   Other than vegetative reproduction by fragmentation noted above, increase in number of individuals in *Ricciocarpus* is the ultimate result of sexuality. The reproductive organs are sunken in chambers in the floor and walls of the dorsal furrow when they are mature

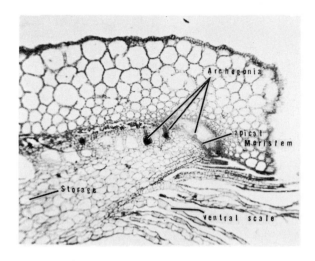

Fig. 15–6. *Ricciocarpus natans.* Median longitudinal section of apex, perpendicular to upper surface of thallus; note apical meristematic region, developing ventral scales, ventral storage tissue, dorsal air chambers, and developing archegonia. X 30.

(Figs. 15–3, 15–6, 15–7). However, a study of their development demonstrates that they arise from single cells, that they first protrude from the surface of the furrow, and that they become secondarily sunken in chambers because of the upgrowth of the surrounding cells (Figs. 15–6 to 15–8). The liverwort plant body is gametophytic. *Ricciocarpus* is homothallic, for the male and female sex organs arise on one and the same plant. The **antheridia** appear first in young plants and are followed by the **archegonia,** the term applied to the female reproductive organs in the land plants. Inasmuch as both types of sex organs come from derivatives of the apical cells (Fig. 15–6), the

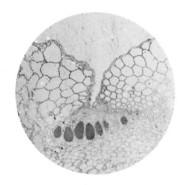

Fig. 15–7. *Ricciocarpus natans.* Transverse section of thallus with antheridia in furrow. X 30.

earlier-formed antheridia are posterior in the furrow to the later-formed archegonia. Plants like *Ricciocarpus,* in which the male sex organs develop before the female, are said to be **protandrous** (Gr. *proteros,* prior +

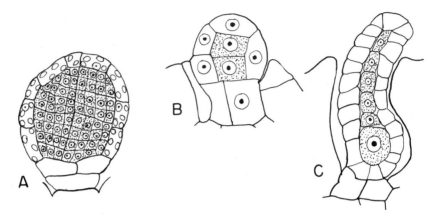

Fig. 15–8. *Ricciocarpus natans.* Sex organs. A, Median longitudinal section of young antheridium with stalk, sterile jacket, and spermatogenous cells. X 546. B,C, Development of the archegonium. In C, note neck, venter, egg, ventral canal cell, and neck canal cells. B, X 1028; C, X 546.

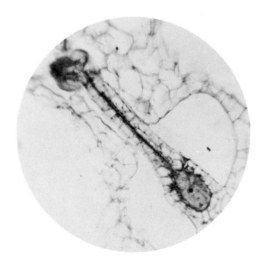

Fig. 15–9. *Ricciocarpus natans.* Median longitudinal section of archegonium with zygote; note opened neck of archegonium. X 250.

Gr. *ander,* male), while those in which archegonia are produced first are said to be **protogynous** (Gr. *proteros* + Gr. *gyne,* female). Sex organs usually appear only in floating plants of *Ricciocarpus,* but they may develop in occasional terrestrial individuals. Floating plants which bear only antheridia are young individuals in which archegonia have not yet developed. Plants bearing archegonia are older ones in which the antheridia have been lost through decay of the posterior portion of the individual.

The antheridia and archegonia are arranged in three or more rows in the dorsal furrow (Fig. 15–7). They differ from gametangia of the algae, with the exception of the plurilocular gametangia of the Phaeophyta, the antheridia and oogonia of the Charophyta, and those of certain fungi, in their multicellular construction. Unlike the plurilocular gametangia of the Phaeophyta, however, the sex organs of the land plants are always composed, in part, of sterile cells.[2] The antheridium (Fig. 15–8A) consists of a short **stalk** and a single layer of surface cells, the **sterile jacket,** which encases the small, cubical **spermatogenous cells** in which the sperms are organized. The archegonium (Figs. 15–6, 15–8B,C) is flask-like, consisting of an axial row of cells, the **egg, ventral canal cell,** and **neck canal cells,** surrounded by a jacket of sterile cells that form the slender **neck** and **venter.**[3]

Because of the marked protandry, it is probable that sperms from other plants often fertilize the later-maturing archegonia, a process of **cross-fertilization.** The neck canal cells and ventral canal cell disintegrate as the archegonium matures, providing the motile sperms with a passageway to the egg (Fig. 15–9). Sexual reproduction in *Ricciocarpus* and all land plants is oogamous.

Shortly after its formation, the zygote of *Ricciocarpus* begins to undergo a series of nuclear and cell divisions which produce a spherical mass of tissue within the venter of the archegonium (Fig. 15–10). As in such algae as *Cladophora, Ulva, Ectocarpus, Laminaria, Griffithsia,* and *Polysiphonia,* the divisions of the zygote nucleus are mitotic, so diploid tissue is formed. The venter of the archegonium becomes two-layered by **periclinal** (Gr. *peri,* around + Gr. *klino,* bend) divisions which occur immediately after fertilization (Fig. 15–10B); and by continuous **anticlinal**

---

[2] Some students of phylogeny, who postulate an algal ancestry for the land plants, have been impressed by an apparent similarity between the sex organs of the latter and the plurilocular gametangia of Phaeophyta. The current view, that the Phaeophyta and Chlorophyta are parallel rather than closely related groups, offers scant encouragement to such speculations.

[3] The ventral canal cell and neck canal cells often are considered to represent vestigial female gametes which have become functionless, a view which is fraught with mechanical difficulties, unless one postulates that at the time they were still functional all the female gametes were shed into the water; otherwise, only the most distal (represented by the first neck canal cell near the neck orifice) could have been reached by a sperm.

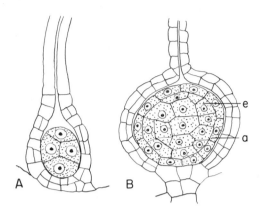

Fig. 15–10. *Ricciocarpus natans.* A, Median longitudinal section of archegonium with four-celled sporophyte. X 125. B, Same, older sporophyte differentiated into *a*, amphithecium, and *e*, endothecium. X 125.

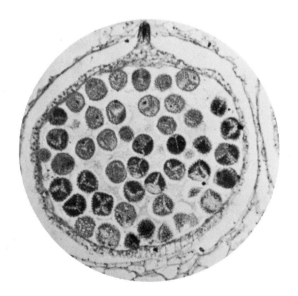

Fig. 15–11. *Ricciocarpus natans.* Median longitudinal section of archegonium (calyptra) containing sporophyte with tetrads of spores. X 125.

(Gr. *anti,* against + Gr. *klino*) divisions, the archegonial venter keeps pace with the growth of the diploid tissues within it (Figs. 15–10, 15–11).

A differentiation of the latter occurs during development as a result of periclinal divisions in the outermost layer of cells, which segregate a peripheral layer, the **amphithecium** (Gr. *amphi*, around + Gr. *theke*, case), from the central mass of tissue, the **endothecium** (Gr. *endon*, within + Gr. *theke*) (Fig. 15–10B). When the endothecium has increased to about 400 cells, enlargement of the diploid tissue occurs, and the endothecial cells separate and become free-floating in the liquid in the amphithecial wall. Traces of a green pigment, presumably chlorophyll, in the form of dispersed or aggregated droplets appear in both the amphithecial and endothecial cells during their development.

The endothecial cells now undergo two successive divisions during which the chromosome number of the diploid tissue ($2n = 8$) is reduced

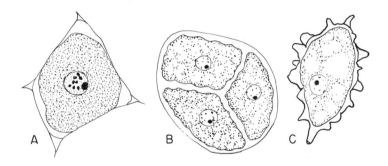

Fig. 15–12. *Ricciocarpus natans*. Sporogenesis. A, Spore mother cell in prophase of meiosis. B, Tetrad of spores. C, Sectional view of mature spore. X 770.

($n = 4$) (Fig. 15–12). Each of the cells now contains four haploid nuclei, tetrahedrally arranged. Cytokinesis follows, and the original floating cells are transformed into groups of four coherent haploid cells, each a **spore tetrad** (Figs. 15–11, 15–12B).

The inner layer of the archegonial venter disintegrates at about this stage, with the result that the spore tetrads are surrounded by the diploid amphithecium and the outermost layer of the archegonial venter. The latter, which covers the developing diploid tissue in many land plants, is known as the **calyptra** (Gr. *kalyptra*, veil). The members of the spore tetrad now thicken their walls by secreting a somewhat corrugated, blackish surface layer (Fig. 15–12C) and separate from each other.

Meiosis in *Ricciocarpus* and in all land plants is sporic and intermediate in the life cycle, rather than zygotic or gametic. The cells which undergo meiotic divisions and form spore tetrads are usually called **spore mother cells** or primary sporocytes in the land plants. The four products of nuclear and cell division of each spore mother cell become the spores.

The spherical mass of diploid tissue within the enlarged archegonial

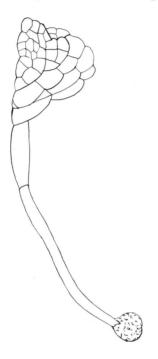

venter is called the **sporophyte.** One unfamiliar with life cycles in the algae, on the one hand, and with those in the higher plants, on the other, would be at a loss to understand this designation, literally "spore plant," because the slightly chlorophyllous, spherical mass of tissue scarcely would pass muster as a "plant." However, comparison of its attributes with those of the free-living sporophytes of certain algae and of higher plants provides evidence that it possesses the characteristics of diploidy, asexuality, and spore production generally associated with free-living sporophytes. Furthermore, it is similar in origin and in ultimate function, so that on grounds of **homology** (Gr. *homo*, same + Gr. *lego*, speak), application of the designation "sporophyte" seems to be justified.

Fig. 15–13. *Ricciocarpus natans.* Spore germination. X 62.

No special mechanism for dissemination of the spores is present in *Ricciocarpus.* The older, posterior sporophytes mature first (Fig. 15–2*B*), as evidenced by their blacker color, which results from the thickening deposited on the spore walls. As the thallus grows apically and decays in the older portions, the spores are liberated into the water. The germination of the spores (Fig. 15–13) occurs in the southern United States late in the summer or in early autumn on damp mud on the margins of ponds as the water level recedes. The plants remain terrestrial until they become submerged by the rise in the water level which accompanies autumn and winter rains and spring thaws. The germinating spores give rise to plants like the original gametophytes. When submerged by the rising water level, the apices, which are not anchored by rhizoids, are detached and float to the surface where

Fig. 15–14. *Marchantia polymorpha* L. Vegetative plants with gemma cups. X ½.

they initiate large colonies of floating plants which multiply early in the spring by fragmentation. A typical hepatophytan life circle may be summarized as follows:

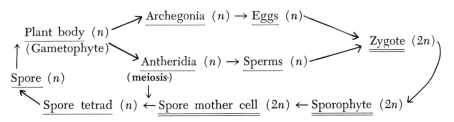

MARCHANTIA

Vegetative Morphology. The manifestations of internal differentiation and specialization already noted in *Riccia* and *Ricciocarpus* are still more pronounced in *Marchantia* (after N. Marchant, a French botanist), a genus (Fig. 15–14) entirely terrestrial in habitat. *M. polymorpha* L., perhaps the most widespread species, often grows on moist soil on which the vegetation has been burned. *M. paleacea* Bertol. grows on moist limestone rocks, and *M. domingensis* Lehm. and Lindenb. lives on moist clay banks. The plant body of *Marchantia polymorpha* is larger

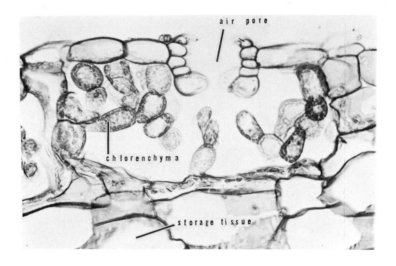

Fig. 15–15. *Marchantia polymorpha.* Transverse section of upper surface of thallus; note air pore, photosynthetic cells above, storage tissue below. X 1100.

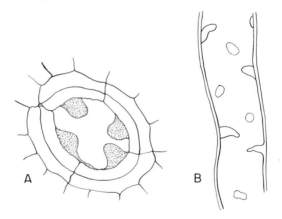

Fig. 15–16. *Marchantia polymorpha.* A, Surface view of air pore. X 410. B, Portion of tuberculate rhizoid bisected longitudinally. X 770.

than that of *Ricciocarpus* and *Riccia;* under favorable conditions of moisture and nutrition, it may exceed four inches in length. It also is dichotomously lobed and branched (Fig. 15–14), exhibiting the apical growth (Fig. 15–17) and posterior decay common to most Hepatophyta.

The upper surface of the plant is conspicuously divided into polygonal air chambers, each with a central pore (Figs. 15–15, 15–16A). Numerous rhizoids emerge from the ventral surface of the thallus; both smooth-walled and tuberculate-walled rhizoids are produced (Fig. 15–16B). The ventral scales of *M. polymorpha* are arranged in six or eight rows. The tuberculate rhizoids originate from the portions of the ventral surface under the scales or near them. The smooth-walled rhizoid develop near the mid-portion of the ventral surface. Bundles of tuberculate rhizoids from below the scales converge toward the mid-

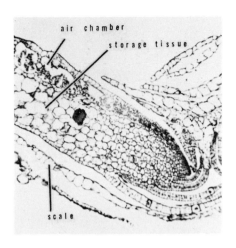

Fig. 15–17. *Marchantia paleacea* Bertol. Median longitudinal (sagittal) section of apex; note apical meristem, developing scales, air chambers above, and storage tissue below. X 135.

rib. It has been shown that the scales and bundles of rhizoids are involved in the rapid conduction of water by capillarity over the ventral surface.

It is apparent from sections (Figs. 15–15, 15–17) that the upper portion of the plant is composed of a single layer of air chambers, and that the remainder is made up of densely arranged parenchymatous cells which contain few chloroplasts and probably serve as storage cells. The cells forming the walls and floor of the air chamber, on the other hand, are filled with plastids. Although the photosynthetic portion of *Marchantia* is more restricted in proportion to total thickness than that in *Ricciocarpus* and *Riccia,* the richly branched, cactus-like, dwarf chlorenchyma filaments of *Marchantia* comprise a photosynthetic region of considerable extent. The specialized cells surrounding the pore of each air chamber are typically arranged in four ringed tiers of four in *Marchantia polymorpha* (Figs. 15–15, 15–16A). The uppermost and lowest tiers are arranged in circles of smaller diameter; hence the whole structure is somewhat barrel-shaped. The tiered cells contain only a few chloroplasts, probably nonfunctional, when they have matured. Members of the lowermost tier may protrude into the central cavity (Fig. 15–16A). Median longitudinal sections cut perpendicular to the surface of the plant body demonstrate the method of development of the various tissues and the origin of the scales (Fig. 15–17).

Fig. 15–18. *Marchantia domingensis* Lehm. and Lindenb. Plants showing air pores and gemma cups. X 2.

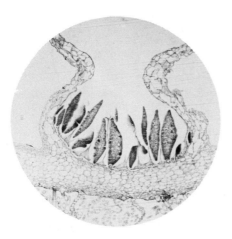

Fig. 15–19. *Marchantia polymorpha.* Transverse section of plant and longitudinal section of gemma cup; note ventral scales, rhizoids, and mucilaginous material in gemma cup. X 30.

Fig. 15–20. *Marchantia polymorpha.* Antheridiophores (left) and archegoniophore. X 1⅓.

Reproduction. In their development, the young plants of *Marchantia* are at first entirely vegetative. Later on, vegetative plants produce special propagative bodies, the **gemma cups** (Figs. 15–14, 15–18), on their dorsal surfaces. Each gemma cup gives rise to a continuously developing series of minute, doubly notched, somewhat lens-shaped bodies, the **gemmae** (L. *gemma*, a bud), which are attached to the bottom of the cup by small stalks (Fig. 15–19). When the cups have been flooded with water, the gemmae are rapidly released by the swelling of gelatinous substances secreted by cells that line the base of the cup. They float away from the parent plants, and those that are carried to favorable substrata undergo bipolar growth from the two apical notches, ultimately forming pairs of young plants. It has been observed that splashing raindrops cause the ejection of gemmae for distances as great as two feet. Gemmae are special fragments of the parent plant which can regenerate new plants, a phenomenon widespread in the Hepatophyta and Bryophyta, and similar in principle to the fragmentation of certain algae, on the one hand, and to vegetative propagation of vascular plants, on the other.

Sexual reproduction in *Marchantia* is manifested only under proper environmental conditions. Such factors as length of daily period of illumination and paucity of nitrogen, among others, play important roles in evoking it. The rather generalized distribution of sex organs along the dorsal surface of the plant body observed in *Riccia* and *Ricciocarpus* is absent in *Marchantia*. In it, the fertile regions of the plant body are restricted and they are raised on specialized negatively geotropic branches, often called **gametophores** (Fig. 15–20). The plants are strictly heterothallic, the antheridia arising on stalked, disc-headed branches, the **antheridiophores,** and the archegonia on **archegoniophores,** whose spoke-like processes are usually nine in number. That these rather bizarre structures are to be interpreted as modified branches of the plant body is indicated by

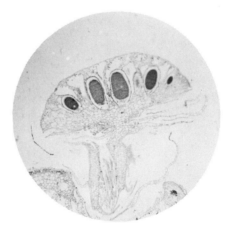

Fig. 15–21. *Marchantia polymorpha.* Median longitudinal section of young antheridiophore; note antheridia, dorsal air chambers and ventral storage region of disc, ventral scales of disc at right, rhizoids at left. X 30.

the presence of rhizoids and scales on the lower surfaces and of air chambers and pores on the upper ones. The stalks of these sexual branches, with their dorsiventrality as observed in transverse section, and scales and rhizoids also give evidence of branch-like structure (Figs. 15–21, 15–22).

Both the archegoniophores and antheridiophores originate as minute button-like excrescences at the apices of certain branches whose further elongation in a horizontal plane is thus terminated. Careful study of the ontogeny of archegoniophores and antheridiophores has revealed that their lobing is an expression of dichotomy repeated in rapid succession.

The antheridia occur in radiating rows just below the surface of the disc of the antheridiophore, the youngest and last-formed near the margins (Fig. 15–21). At maturity, each antheridium is sunken in a chamber which is connected by a narrow canal to a surface pore. Discharge of the biflagellate sperms takes place through these canals and pores. In at least one species of *Marchantia*, there is evidence that the discharge of sperms in the presence of water involves a centripetal distention of the wall cells of the antheridium and of the air chamber, as well as a swelling of the walls of the spermatogenous cells. The pressure generated in this manner ruptures the upper cells of the antheridial wall and the sperms ooze out in smoke-like columns. In the columns they may be observed actively rotating in their mother cells from which they ultimately are liberated.

The archegonia also occur seriately but are located on the *apparent* ventral surface of the archegoniophores between the proximal portions of the radiating spoke-like rays (Fig. 15–22). The words "apparent ventral surface" are used, because in reality the archegonia arise from dorsal derivatives of apical cells, but excessive growth of the dorsal surface

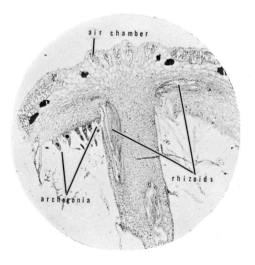

Fig. 15–22. *Marchantia polymorpha*. Median longitudinal section of archegoniophore; note dorsal air chambers, scales and rhizoids, and archegonia to the left. X 30.

results in an inversion of the portion that bears archegonia. The latter thus become suspended, neck downward, in radiating rows from the under surface of the archegoniophore (Fig. 15–22). The rows of archegonia, with the last-formed in each group nearest the stalk of the archegoniophore, are separated by fringed involucral membranes. The antheridia and archegonia of *Marchantia* are quite similar to those of *Riccia* and *Ricciocarpus*, although somewhat more massive in structure.

Fertilization of the first-formed archegonia occurs before the elongation of the archegoniophore stalk, and because of the differing degrees of maturity of the antheridia in a single antheridiophore, discharge of the sperms, effected by flooding, probably continues over a considerable period. Fertilization of the later-formed archegonia probably takes place after their elevation above the plant body. This indicates either that the sperms remain viable for long periods or that they reach the archegonia through splashing or by swimming through the surface films of water on the archegoniophores. Raindrops falling on antheridiophores have been observed to splash the sperms for distances up to two feet. That the elongation of the archegoniophore stalk is not dependent upon fertilization is evidenced by its occurrence even in segregated female plants in which fertilization has not taken place.

Although the eggs of many archegonia on an archegoniophore may be fertilized, not all of the zygotes develop into mature sporophytes, possibly because of crowding and insufficient nutrients. The more mature

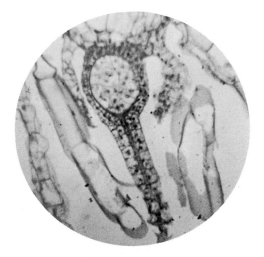

Fig. 15–23. *Marchantia polymorpha.* Median longitudinal section of archegonium with young sporophyte; note developing pseudoperianth. X 250.

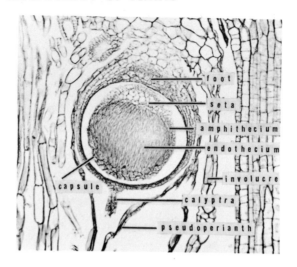

Fig. 15–24. *Marchantia polymorpha*. Median longitudinal section of immature sporophyte within calyptra; note foot, seta, capsule, endothecium, and ampithecium. X 135.

sporophytes usually occur near the periphery of each radiating group, corresponding in position to that of the first mature archegonia. Successive transverse and longitudinal divisions of the zygote result in the formation of a spherical mass of diploid tissue enclosed in the venter (Fig. 15–23). The latter undergoes cell divisions, increases in size, and remains as a covering layer, the calyptra (Gr. *kalyptra*, veil) as in *Ricciocarpus*. During these stages, a collar-like layer, the **pseudoperianth**, grows down over each archegonium (Fig. 15–23).

Further development of the sporophyte results in differentiation and specialization not present in the sporophyte of *Ricciocarpus*. Certain cells of the young sporophyte enlarge and grow through the base of the venter into the compact storage tissue of the archegoniophore, forming an anchoring and absorptive organ, the

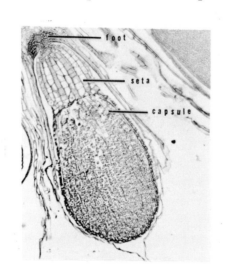

Fig. 15–25. *Marchantia polymorpha*. Median longitudinal section of older sporophyte. X 40.

foot. Enlargement of the opposite pole also occurs, so the sporophyte is differentiated ultimately into three regions (Figs. 15–24, 15–25): an enlarged **foot**; an intermediate short cylindrical region, the **seta**; and a fertile region, the **capsule** or sporangium. In the capsule the differentiation of the tissues into amphithecium and endothecium, observed in *Ricciocarpus*, also takes place (Figs. 15–24, 15–25). At first, all the cells in the endothecial portion of the capsule are similar, but differentiation into

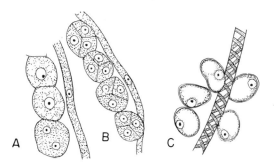

Fig. 15–26. *Marchantia polymorpha.* Sporogenesis. A, Spore mother cells and precursor of elaters. B, Elater precursor and tetrads. C, Mature spores and elater. X 770.

rows of spherical cells and elongate cells follows (Fig. 15–26). The rows of spherical cells function as spore mother cells (Fig. 15–26A) and, as in *Ricciocarpus*, undergo two successive nuclear and cell divisions during which meiosis is accomplished. The members of the spore tetrads (Fig. 15–26B) finally separate, and the individual spores thicken their walls (Fig. 15–26C). The remaining cells of the endothecium, which have elongated, secrete spirally arranged thickenings on the inner surfaces of their cell walls, after which their protoplasts disintegrate (Fig. 15–26C). These pointed elongated cells are called **elaters** (Gr. *elater*, driver) and are sensitive at maturity to slight changes in atmospheric moisture. They seem to have a role in effecting gradual rather than simultaneous spore dispersal.

Examination of sections of living sporophytes during their development reveals that they contain abundant chloroplasts, often with enclosed starch grains, an indication that photosynthesis occurs actively. While there is little doubt that organic substances as well as water and dissolved salts are absorbed from the parent gametophyte through the foot and transported through the seta into the capsule, it is also quite evident that the sporophyte of *Marchantia* (and all Hepatophyta) are photoautotrophic to some degree. When one compares the independent autotrophic sporophytes of such Chlorophyta as *Cladophora suhriana,* which have no physical connection with the gametophyte, with those of *Ricciocarpus* and *Marchantia,* he may interpret the paucity of chlorophyll and photosynthetic activity in *Ricciocarpus* and their abundance in *Marchantia* in one of two ways: either the paucity is primitive and the presence of the chlorophyll incipient, or these are manifestations of reduction in *Ricciocarpus.* It seems to the writer that in the light of comparison with the sporophytes of the algae, especially those of the Rhodophyceae, it is probable that permanent retention of the sporophyte of the Hepatophyta (and Bryophyta) upon the gametophyte has been accompanied by a loss of primary photosynthetic ability and, secondarily, the adoption of a facultative heterotrophic form of nutrition by the sporophyte.

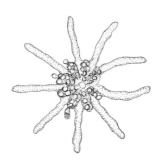

Fig. 15–27. *Marchantia polymorpha.* Ventral surface of archegoniophore with maturing sporophytes. X 3.

Up to the time sporogenesis is complete, the sporophytes are surrounded by several protective layers which seem to function in preventing premature drying, namely, the calyptra, the pseudoperianth, and, in addition, the two involucral membranes (Fig. 15–25). When the spores have matured, elongation of the seta pushes the capsule of the sporophyte out through calyptra, pseudoperianth, and the involucres (Fig. 15–27). As elongation ceases, the capsule dehisces into a number of petal-like segments from within which the elaters and spores form a protuberant mass. The spores are carried away by air currents; those that fall on favorable substrata germinate and ultimately form new gametophytes. Two of the spores of each tetrad grow into male and two into female gametophytes. Similarly, the gemmae from potentially male plants and those from potentially female plants always grow into male and female plants, respectively.

A number of genera related to *Marchantia* occur commonly in moist habitats. Among them may be mentioned *Reboulia, Mannia, Lunularia,* and *Conacephalum,* the last-named of special interest because endosporic divisions take place within the capsule before its dehiscence, as in certain vascular plants.

PELLIA

Vegetative Morphology.   In marked contrast with the progressively more elaborate internal differentiation observable in the plant bodies of *Riccia, Ricciocarpus,* and *Marchantia,* the thallose genera *Sphaerocarpos* (Gr. *sphaira,* sphere + Gr. *karpon,* a fruit), *Pellia* (after Leopoldi Pelli-Fabroni a Florentine lawyer), *Pallavicinia* (after L. Pallavicini, Archbishop of Genoa), and *Metzgeria* (after Johannes Metzger of Staufen, Germany) exhibit marked internal simplicity. In *Sphaerocarpos, Pallavicinia,* and *Metzgeria,* for example, the greater portion of the plant body consists of a single layer of uniform chlorenchymatous cells, quite similar to those of such membranous algae as *Ulva,* the sea lettuce, of the Chlorophyta. Because of their wider distribution, availability, and larger size, *Pellia* and *Pallavicinia* will be emphasized in the following account.

Pellia (Fig. 15–28) is encountered frequently on moist stream banks in

Fig. 15–28. *Pellia epiphylla* (L.) Corda. Clump of plants from a bog. X 2/5.

shady woods where the soil is neutral or acid in reaction. It may be submerged during high water. The irregularly dichotomously branching plant bodies (Figs. 15–28, 15–29) are smaller, smoother in appearance, and usually a brighter green in color than those of *Marchantia polymorpha.* The smooth appearance of the plants is due to the absence of pores and air chambers on their upper surface. Numerous rhizoids arise from the ventral surface of each branch along the thickened central portion. Ventral scales are absent, but mucilage-secreting glandular hairs occur in the region of the growing points (Fig. 15–30). The margins of the plants may be slightly lobed and ruffled. As in many other Hepatophyta, anterior growth and branching and posterior decay of the plant body result in vegetative multiplication by fragmentation; gemmae are absent in *Pellia.*

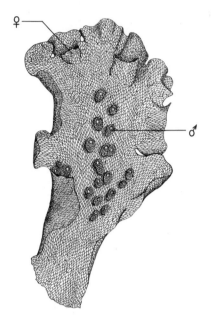

Growth is strictly apical and may be traced to the division of a single dome-shaped apical cell with a curved base (Fig. 15–30). This cell undergoes mitoses and cytokineses; and the derived cells, cut off in a direction parallel to the curved basal wall, add to the tissues of the plant body by subsequent divisions. Transverse sections of a branch reveal the absence of internal differentiation, as compared with *Marchantia.* There is a gradual diminution in thickness of the branches from the center toward each margin so that the latter are monostromatic. All the cells of the plant body contain chloroplasts. The superficial layers are not noticeably differentiated as epidermal cells.

Fig. 15–29.   *Pellia epiphylla.* One lobe of thallus with antheridial and archegonial involucres. X 7.

Reproduction.   *Pellia epiphylla* (L.) Corda, a species widely distributed in the United States, is homothallic and strongly protandrous. However, the antheridia are slow in maturing and still contain viable sperms when the archegonia have matured. In habitats where the plants have overwintered, the old dark thalli produce light-green branches early in the spring. After a period of vegetative development, these attain sexual maturity, some of the dorsal derivatives of the apical cell differentiating as antheridia (Fig. 15–29, 15–31). These occur scattered on the dorsal surface of the plant in the central portion of each branch. Each antheridium is protected by an involucre-like layer of cells. Somewhat later in the season the same plants produce archegonia at their apices (Figs. 15–29, 15–32). The archegonia arise on a mound of tissue formed from derivatives of the apical cell. The latter ultimately gives rise to an archegonium, so that further elongation of the branch apex is terminated.

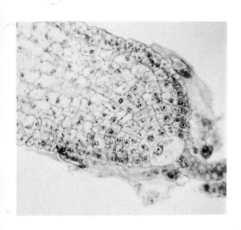

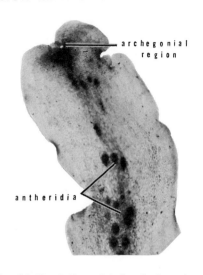

Fig. 15–30. *Pellia epiphylla*. Median longitudinal section of thallus apex perpendicular to upper surface; note homogeneous tissue, apical cells, and mucilaginous glands near latter. X 175.

Fig. 15–31. *Pellia epiphylla*. Surface view of thallus with ♂ and ♀ (apical) reproductive organs. X 12½.

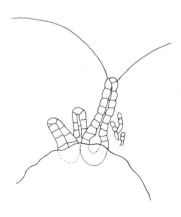

Fig. 15–32. *Pellia epiphylla*. Apex of thallus with archegonia, schematized. X 125.

Fig. 15–33. *Pellia epiphylla*. Archegonial complex; two enlarged archegonia containing sporophytes. X 16.

This condition is said to be **acrogynous** (Gr. *akros*, topmost + Gr. *gyne*, female). The entire archegonial group, composed of fifteen or more archegonia, is covered by an involucral layer. The archegonia of *Pellia* differ from those of *Marchantia* in that they are slightly stipitate and the necks are composed of only five vertical rows of neck cells, in contrast to the six in *Marchantia*.

It has been demonstrated that rapid movement of films of capillary water takes place on both surfaces of the *Pellia* plant. There is little doubt that such films of water, as well as heavy rains and dews, accumulate in the space between the antheridial wall and the antheridial chamber and aid in the dehiscence of the antheridia and liberation of the sperms. The latter are among the largest in the Hepatophyta and Bryophyta, attaining a length of 70 microns. They are released by rupture of the antheridial wall and emerge in gelatinous discs from which their movements ultimately liberate them. The close proximity of the thallus branches and of the antheridia and archegonia on a single branch insures abundant fertilizations. Although the eggs of several of the archegonia on one receptacle may be fertilized, normally only one develops into a mature sporophyte (Fig. 15–33). The others abort but remain recognizable during the early stages of development of the functional sporophytes.

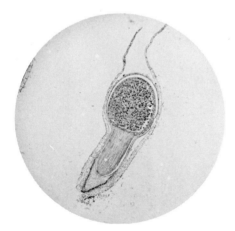

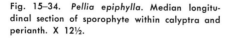

Fig. 15–34. *Pellia epiphylla.* Median longitudinal section of sporophyte within calyptra and perianth. X 12½.

Fig. 15–35. *Pellia epiphylla.* A, Distal portion of seta and capsule of mature sporophyte. B, The capsule of A at dehiscence. X 12½.

A transverse division of the zygote initiates the formation of the sporophyte which is later differentiated into foot, seta, and capsule regions. Growth of the sporophyte of *P. epiphylla* in the eastern United States progresses as far as the spore mother cell stage before midwinter;

development is then arrested until the following spring. The dormant sporophytes are protected by the basal portion of the receptacles, by their calyptras, and also by the involucral outgrowth (Fig. 15–34). As in *Marchantia,* the cells of all the regions of the sporophyte contain abundant starch-filled chloroplasts, which indicates active occurrence of photosynthesis during ontogeny. The capsule wall in the immature sporophyte consists of several layers of cells. The interior of the capsule becomes differentiated into lobed spore mother cells and elongate cells, the precursors of the elaters. Some of the latter cells are oriented with one end, in each case, at the base of the capsule, thus forming what is called an **elaterophore.** Following meiosis in the four-lobed spore mother cells, the members of the spore tetrads separate, and each undergoes a limited number of nuclear and cell divisions within the spore wall so that by the time of their dissemination the spores have already begun development. As maturity approaches, the outermost layer of cells becomes thickened and brown in color, except for four vertical rows of cells which remain thin-walled. When the spores are multicellular, the seta lengthens and raises the capsule above the gametophyte (Fig. 15–35). Elongation of the seta is very rapid; it may increase in length within three or four days from 1 mm. to 80 mm. Setae 110 mm. long are common in shady ravines. The spherical capsule dries when elongation has been completed; it dehisces violently (Fig. 15–35) when contraction ruptures the four rows of thin-walled cells, and many of the spores are simultaneously disseminated. Others remain in the meshes of the twisted elaters which are attached at the base of the opened capsule (Fig. 15–35). Spores that are carried by air currents to proper habitats continue their development into *Pellia* thalli (Fig. 15–36).

PALLAVICINIA

Vegetative Morphology. *Pallavicinia* (Fig. 15–37) is similar to *Pellia* in a great many respects. Its elongate, rather sparingly branched, ribbon-like thalli, approximately 4 mm. wide, occur on moist, humus-rich soil. The plants can withstand periodic submersion. Branching is largely monopodial in *P. lyellii* (Hook.) S. F. Gray. The branches originate from the ventral side of the thallus near the prominent midrib. Numerous smooth-walled rhizoids emerge from the midrib region and penetrate the substratum. The plant body is clearly differentiated into midrib and lateral wings; the latter are one cell layer thick and somewhat undulating. Growth of each branch is localized in the region of a prominent apical cell which is slightly sunken in the thallus apex because of the more rapid growth of the wings at that point. The central portion of the midrib (Fig. 15–38) is occupied by a group of elongate, pitted-walled

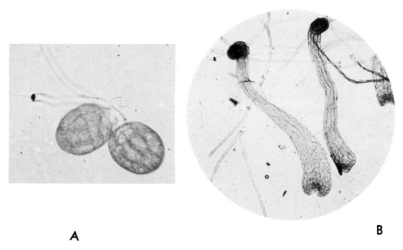

A   B

Fig. 15–36. *Pellia epiphylla.* Spore germination. A, 48 hours after spores were shed. X 125; B, 45 days later. X 30.

cells which have been shown experimentally to function in the conduction of water. The wings of the thallus are composed of photosynthetic parenchyma cells rich in chloroplasts.

Reproduction. *Pallavicinia lyellii* is heterothallic. The male plants are slightly smaller than the female with which they are usually intermingled in dense colonies (Fig. 15–37A). The antheridia are produced on the dorsal surface of the thallus in linear order on both sides of the midrib (Fig. 15–37B). Each antheridium is short-stalked and is covered during development by a scale-like involucre (Fig. 15–38). The fringed involucres of several antheridia may become more or less confluent (Fig. 15–37B). The archegonia, which are also produced above the midrib, are borne in groups on receptacles (Fig. 15–37C). As is obvious from the figure, formation of archegonia does not inhibit elongation of the branch as it does in *Pellia. Pallavicinia,* therefore is **anacrogynous.** The archegonia of a given group, between eighteen and thirty in number, mature at different rates. As in *Pellia,* the archegonia are stipitate, with elongate necks composed of five vertical rows of neck cells (Fig. 15–38B). Each archego-

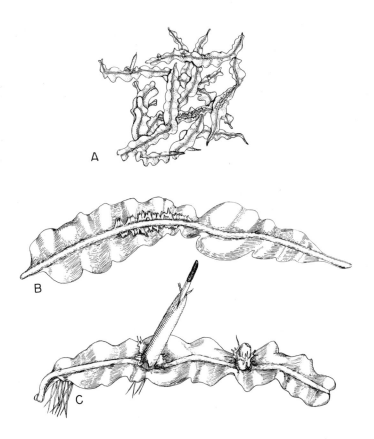

Fig. 15–37. *Pallavicinia lyelli* (Hook.) S. F. Gray. A, ♂ and ♀ plants. X 1. B, Enlarged view of ♂ branch. X 3. C, Enlarged view of ♀ plant with emergent sporophyte. X 3.

nial group is surrounded by an involucre which becomes fringed (Fig 15–37C). As the first archegonia mature, a ring-like layer, the **perianth**, appears at their base. Immediately after fertilization, the perianth grows rapidly, forming a prominent cylindrical protuberance from within the involucre (Fig. 15–37C).

Development of the sporophyte follows much the same pattern as that described for *Pellia*, the first division of the zygote being transverse. Here too, only one sporophyte usually matures on one receptacle (Fig. 15–37C). The calyptra attains a thickness of four or five cells and keeps pace with the developing sporophyte, which is surrounded by three pro-

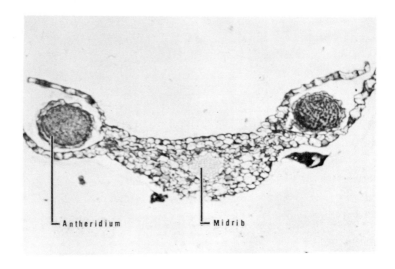

A

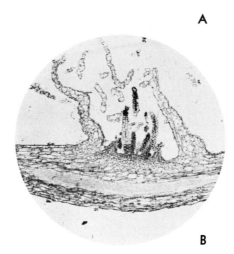

B

Fig. 15–38. *Pallavicinia lyelli.* A, Transverse section of thallus; note midrib and antheridia. X 30. B, Transverse section of thallus through archegonial receptacle; note midrib, archegonia, and involucre. X 30.

tective sheaths of gametophytic origin (Fig. 15–39). Meiosis of the lobed spore mother cells (Fig. 15–40) reduces the chromosome number from $2n = 16$ to $n = 8$. Following elongation of the seta, the spores (Fig. 15–41) are shed by the longitudinal division of the capsule wall into four portions (Fig. 15–41B). In most individuals these remain united at the

Fig. 15–39. *Pallavicinia lyelli.* Dissection of living sporophyte within calyptra; note aborted archegonia at base. X 12½.

Fig. 15–40. *Pallavicinia lyelli.* Lobed spore mother cell in prophase of meiosis, and immature elater. X 770.

apex so that the capsule opens by four longitudinal slits. The germinating spores (Fig. 15–42) grow into a new generation of ribbon-like *Pallavicinia* plants.

SPHAEROCARPOS

In concluding the account of these genera of Hepatopsida whose plant bodies are both externally and internally simple, brief mention should be made of *Sphaerocarpos* (Fig. 15–43). *Sphaerocarpos* is widespread, especially in the southern and western parts of the United States, during the late winter and spring. It is encountered frequently on the

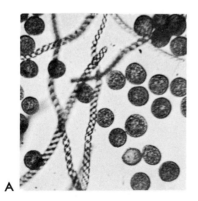

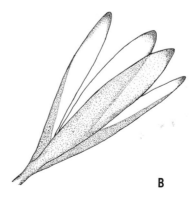

Fig. 15–41. *Pallavicinia lyelli.* A, Spores and elaters. X 250. B. Dehiscent capsule. X 25. (B, courtesy of Professor H. W. Bischoff.)

moist soil of unplowed fields. At first glance the dense colonies give the appearance of mounds of large *Botrydium* plants because of the conspicuous urn-like involucres of the female plants (Fig. 15–43B). The male plants are more minute and readily recognizable macroscopically by their purple color (Fig. 15–43A).

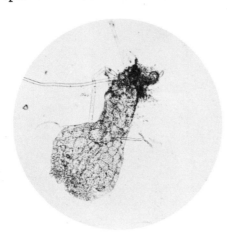

The sex organs are borne on the dorsal surface of the strictly heterothallic plants. Each antheridium and archegonium becomes surrounded by a hollow outgrowth of the thallus, the involucre, during its development. The archegonial involucres grow rapidly after fertilization and stand above the thalli in dense columnar fashion (Fig. 15–43B). The zygote develops into a sporophyte which is differentiated into foot, seta, and

Fig. 15–42. *Pallavicinia lyelli.* Germling plant from spore 31 days after germination. X 60.

capsule; but the entire structure is smaller than that in other genera described above, and the seta does not elongate. Some of the spore mother

A   B

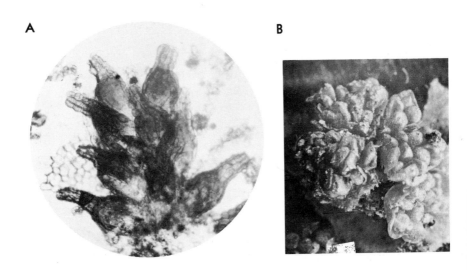

Fig. 15–43. *Sphaerocarpos texanus* Aust. A, ♂ thallus with antheridia. X 60. B, ♀ thalli with involucres. X 3½.

cells become starch-filled and fail to divide. These are often interpreted as rudimentary elaters. In some species (like *S. texanus* Aust.) the spores remain permanently united in tetrads, even after they have been shed by the decay of older portions of the gametophyte.

Sphaerocarpos has been the object of numerous genetic and cytological studies which have revealed that the heterothallic gametophytes differ in their chromosome constitution. The nuclei of the female plants contain a special **X** or a female-determining chromosome, and those of the male plants contain a **Y** or male-determining chromosome. *Sphaerocarpos* was the first plant in which sex chromosomes were discovered. Thus, in meiotic divisions during sporogenesis, the descendants of the parental sex chromosomes, brought together at fertilization, are segregated so that two of the spores of the tetrad are male-producing and two are female-producing. While this type of chromosome mechanism in relation to sex suggests that present in such insects as *Drosophila*, the fruit fly, it should be noted that sex in the gametophyte of *Sphaerocarpos* is manifested only after the sex chromosomes have been segregated, whereas in the diploid insect body it is expressed only when they become associated in the same nuclei.

PORELLA AND OTHER LEAFY TYPES

Vegetative Morphology. In a third group of Hepatopsida, exemplified by *Porella* (origin of name unknown), *Frullania* (in honor of Leonardo Frullani, a Florentine statesman), and *Scapania* (Gr. *skapanion*, spade, a reference to the flattened perianth), histological simplicity is combined with more complex external form. These genera are representative of the most abundant series of Hepatopsida, the leafy liverworts, and are colonists of moist soil, moist stones, and moist tree bark. A few, like certain species of *Porella* and *Frullania*, can survive in habitats that are xeric for long intervals. Others grow as periodically submerged aquatics.

Porella (Fig. 15–44) and other leafy liverworts superficially resemble prostrate mosses, from which they can usually be distinguished by their leaves, which lack midribs. Furthermore, their leaves are almost universally only one cell layer thick, whereas those of many mosses are often more complex. The plant body is composed of rather flattened, branching leafy axes from whose under surfaces emerge scattered rhizoids that penetrate the substratum. The paucity of rhizoids in many genera indicates that they play a minor role in water absorption. In many cases their major role seems to be anchorage. Inasmuch as the leaves and stems lack a cuticle, absorption occurs directly through the leaf and stem cells which are closely appressed to the moist substratum except at their growing tips. Moreover, the dense colonial habit of most genera, coupled with the partial overlapping of their leaves as well as the folded lobing of the leaves in some genera, provides extensive appressed surfaces between which water may be held by capillarity.

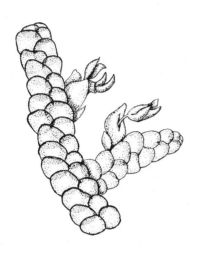

Fig. 15–44. *Porella platyphylloidea* (L.) Lindb. Branch of ♀ plant with dehiscent sporophytes. X 5.

The morphology of *Porella* will be described in some detail in illustrating the attributes of leafy liverworts; special features of other genera will be cited in comparison. *Porella pinnata* L. and *P. platyphylloidea* (L.) Lindb. are of widespread occurrence. They grow on moist rocks, tree bark, and occasionally on soil. The plants form densely interwoven mats, closely applied to the substratum, but the youngest portions of the branches are ascendant. The plants are approximately 3 mm. in width and rather abundantly branched in monopodial fashion. The branches originate from the ventral portion of the axes and correspond in origin to ventral leaf lobes.

The plant body develops from an apical cell, from which derivatives are successively delimited in three directions (Fig. 15–45). These derivatives, by further orderly cell divisions, contribute to the stem and to the formation of new leaves. The latter are arranged in three regular rows along the axes, but only two rows are visible in dorsal aspect (Fig. 15–44). The plants are strongly dorsiventral, and the third row of leaves, called **amphigastria**, is visible only ventrally (Fig. 15–46). When rhizoids are present, they arise from the basal portions of the amphigastria. In ventral aspect, plants of *Porella* seem to possess five rows of leaves, but in reality only three are present. The impression that there are five rows is due to the occurrence of ventral lobes on each of the dorsal leaves (Fig. 15–46); the former are more or less closely pressed against the dorsal portions of the leaves. The leaves themselves consist of a single layer of rather uniform chlorenchymatous cells. The stems show little internal differentiation. *Porella* and many other leafy Hepatopsida are remarkable

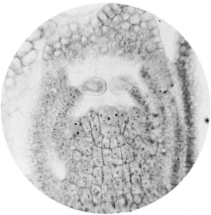

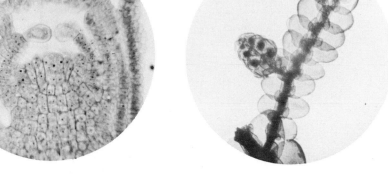

Fig. 15–45. *Porella platyphylloidea.* Median longitudinal section of apex. X 250.

Fig. 15–46. *Porella platyphylloidea.* Ventral view of shoot with antheridial branch (left). X 32.

in their tolerance of prolonged and periodic drying. The osmotic properties and water relations of the component cells have not been fully investigated, but there is every indication that they must differ from those of other plants which also lack cuticles but which are unable to withstand desiccation.

Reproduction. The common *Porella platyphylloidea* is strictly heterothallic, the male plants being slightly narrower than the female, a condition suggestive of *Pallavicinia* and certain macrandrous species of *Oedogonium.* The antheridia are borne singly in the axils of densely overlapping leaves on projecting cone-like lateral branches (Fig. 15–46). Each globose antheridium, which is attached to the leaf axil by a rather long stalk two cells in width, bears numerous sperms (Fig. 15–47). At maturity, if sufficiently moist conditions prevail, the upper jacket

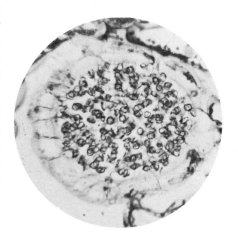

Fig. 15–47. *Porella platyphylloidea.* Section of antheridium containing mature sperms. X 250.

cells of the antheridium separate from each other at its apex, curve back, and liberate the sperms.

The archegonia are produced on short lateral branches of other plants. The archegonial branches are scarcely different from young vegetative

branches until later in their development and therefore are difficult to recognize. After fertilization, the development of a somewhat inflated perianth surrounding the group of archegonia adds to the prominence of the archegonial branch (Fig. 15–48). Eight to ten archegonia occur in each group, one of them derived from the apical cell itself. *Porella* therefore is acrogynous. The archegonia are stipitate, with scarcely swollen venters and five rows

Fig. 15–48. *Porella platyphylloidea.* Portion of shoot with archegonial branch. X 25.

of neck cells (Fig. 15–49).

The abundance of maturing sporophytes, which may be observed in

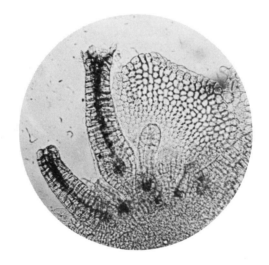

Fig. 15–49. *Porella platyphylloidea.* Living archegonia. X 125.

female plants of *Porella* collected early in the spring, indicates that numerous fertilizations have occurred the preceding autumn. Little information is available regarding the mechanism by which the sperms reach maturing archegonia; but the fact that male and female plants grow intermingled in dense mats, along with the extensive, continuous capillary

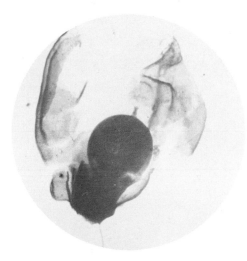

Fig. 15–50. *Porella platyphylloidea.* Living sporophyte in calyptra. X 30.

spaces that exist between the plants, the substratum, and the overlapping leaf surfaces, suggests that a convenient avenue is available for the dissemination of sperms.

Although the eggs of several archegonia in each branch may be fertilized, only one of the zygotes usually develops into a sporophyte. The others abort but often persist at the base of the calyptra of the fertile archegonium (Fig. 15–50). The cells of the sporophyte contain abundant chlorophyll during the later stages of their development and are undoubtedly photoautotrophic to some degree. The sporophyte is surrounded by the enlarging calyptra, by the common archegonial envelope, the perianth, which is somewhat trihedral in form, and by the basal involucral leaves of the archegonial branch. The sporophyte is differentiated ultimately into a capsule, a seta, and a rather poorly developed foot (Fig. 15–51). The spore mother

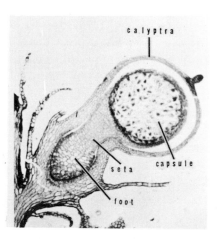

Fig. 15–51. *Porella sp.* Median longitudinal section of sporophyte in calyptra. X 30.

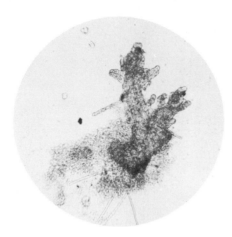

Fig. 15–52. *Porella platyphylloidea.* Leafy shoot arising from protonema, 96 days after spore germination. X 60.

cells are lobed like those of *Palla-vicinia,* and the capsule wall is two to four layers in thickness. After sporogenesis and matura-tion of the spores and elaters, the seta elongates, thrusting the cap-sule out from its protective en-velopes, and dehiscence of the lat-ter then takes place along four vertical rows of thin-walled cells (Fig. 15-44).

The rather large spores of *Por-ella* may undergo precocious and endogenous divisions before they are shed from the capsule, as in *Pellia* and *Conacephalum.* They develop into an amorphous struc-ture which gives rise to one or more leafy axes (Fig. 15–52).

In leafy liverworts other than *Porella,* certain deviations are note-worthy. In *Scapania,* the complicate-bilobed leaves are constructed with the dorsal lobe smaller than the ventral, so that the plants give the illu-sion of growing upside down. Unlike *Porella,* up to six antheridia are subtended by each leaf of the male branch in *Scapania.* In many species of *Frullania,* the complicate-bi-lobed leaves have ventral lobes that are sac-like (Fig. 15–53). These have been shown to serve as water reservoirs, but their effi-ciency in storing water is not markedly greater than that of other portions of the plant body. In this genus, tufts of elaters re-main attached to each of the four valves of the dehiscent capsule (Fig. 15–54).

In concluding this brief account of representative genera of the leafy liverworts it should be em-phasized again that this is the largest and most successful group

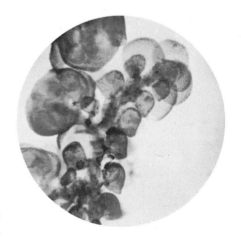

Fig. 15–53. *Frullania* sp. Ventral view of shoot; note antheridial branches at the left and sac-like ventral lobes of leaves. X 60.

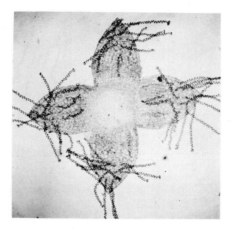

Fig. 15–54. *Frullania* sp. Frontal view of dehiscent capsule with elaters attached to valve apices.
X 60.

of Hepatopsida, if success be judged by such criteria as number of individuals and species, and range of habitat. The group is of great interest taxonomically and morphologically in its exemplification of infinite variation in morphological details connected with the relation of the plants to water.

CLASS 2. ANTHOCEROPSIDA

Introduction

The Anthoceropsida, or **horned liverworts,** are given ordinal rank and included in the Hepatopsida by some authorities. However, while superficially suggestive of certain thallose Hepatopsida, the members of the Anthoceropsida differ in a number of important attributes, and their segregation into a separate class appears to be warranted. The features in which they differ from members of the Hepatopsida are both gametophytic and sporophytic. The Anthoceropsida include five genera and approximately 320 species.

Anthoceros

VEGETATIVE MORPHOLOGY

Anthoceros (Gr. *anthos,* flower + Gr. *keras,* horn) (Figs. 15–55, 15–56) and *Notothylas* (Gr. *noton,* the back + Gr. *thylas,* a bag—from

Fig. 15–55. *Anthoceros carolinianus* Michx. Colony on moist soil. X ⅔.

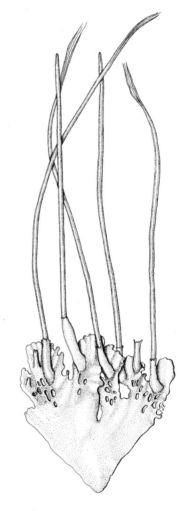

Fig. 15–56. *Anthoceros carolinianus.* Marginal lobes of thallus; note antheridial craters and developing sporophytes. X 1 7/10.

the bag-like involucre on the dorsal surface) are widely distributed in the temperate zone as well as in other parts of the world. Both are inhabitants of moist soil, although *Anthoceros* sometimes lives on moist rocks. In both habitats they are frequently overshadowed by other vegetation. Some species of *Anthoceros—A. laevis* L., for example—are perennial whereas others, like *A. carolinianus* Michx., are annual in habit. In the southeastern United States *A. carolinianus* is a winter-spring annual. The gametophytes appear on the soil in the late autumn, produce sex organs during the winter, and mature their sporophytes during April and May, after which the plants disappear.

In uncrowded conditions in the field, the thallus of *A. carolinianus* develops an orbicular form. The dark-green plant bodies have a rather dull, greasy appearance and are somewhat fleshy and brittle in texture. In the vegetative condition they suggest such thallose genera as *Pellia* and related forms; however, they can be distinguished readily by features to be described below.

The orbicular shape of the thallus reflects frequently repeated dichotomies during the early phases of growth; somewhat laciniate lobes may
project from the margins of the
plants (Figs. 15–55, 15–56). The gametophytes are anchored to the soil
by smooth-walled rhizoids which
arise from the ventral surface. The
lower surfaces of the plants of *A. carolinianus* are interrupted by minute
fissures which communicate with
mucilage chambers. The latter frequently contain colonies of the myxophycean alga *Nostoc* which has
been reported to fix free nitrogen.

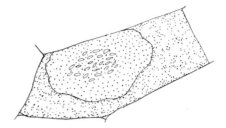

Fig. 15–57. *Anthoceros carolinianus.* Thallus cell; note massive chloroplast with "pyrenoid" segments. X 770.

Were this to be substantiated, it would be indicative of a relationship
similar to that between bacteria and legumes. With the exception of the
ventral mucilage chambers, the plants lack internal differentiation (Fig.
15–58*B*). The component cells are chlorenchymatous and differ from
those of the Hepatopsida in containing single massive chloroplasts in
which are embedded a number of proteinaceous segments that have been
designated **pyrenoid bodies** because of their reported change into starch
grains (Fig. 15–57). Vegetative reproduction occurs by the separation
of marginal lobes from the parent thallus and, in some species of *Anthoceros,* by the formation of tuber-like bodies capable of regenerating into
new gametophytes.

REPRODUCTION

Careful studies of laboratory cultures of a number of species of
Anthoceros have revealed that some (*A. laevis,* for example) are heterothallic, whereas others (*A. carolinianus*) bear antheridia and archegonia on the same gametophyte. The sex organs arise in rows from dorsal
derivatives of the marginal apical cells. *A. carolinianus* is markedly
protandrous, so that its antheridia lie back from the apices in each rosette
(Fig. 15–58*A*); however, antheridia and archegonia may be borne in alternating zones. Although the sex organs are derived from superficial
dorsal cells, they are sunken within the gametophyte at maturity because
of their method of development, in which the antheridial initial undergoes periclinal division. The antheridia arise from the innermost cell

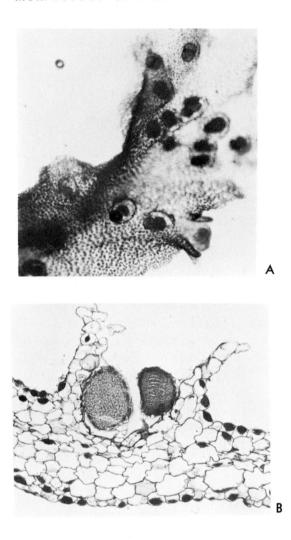

Fig. 15–58.   *Anthoceros carolinianus.* A, Surface view of lobe with antheridia. X 30. B, Transverse section of thallus with antheridia. X 125.

resulting from this division and therefore are endogenous (Fig. 15–58*B*). As many as four antheridia may arise in a single group and proliferation may increase the number. They occur in small chambers in the dorsal surface of the gametophytes (Figs. 15–56, 15–58). Cavities containing mature antheridia are recognizable to the unaided eye as small, orange-

yellow pustules. The color results from the transformation of
the chloroplasts in the antheridial jacket cells into chromoplasts.
When the antheridia are mature,
the superficial cells of the antheridial cavity break down, per-
mitting water to come in contact
with the antheridia. These dehisce at their apices and liberate
large numbers of extremely minute biflagellate sperms.

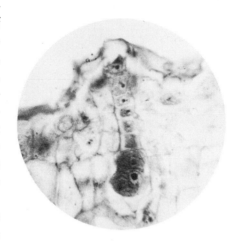

Fig. 15–59. *Anthoceros carolinianus.* Median longitudinal section of archegonium. X 600.

The archegonia, which lie
nearer the margins of the thallus
in homothallic species of *Anthoceros,* are also completely sunken
within the dorsal surface (Fig.
15–59). The position of the young archegonia is indicated clearly by
mounds of a mucilaginous substance (Fig. 15–60). The apex of the archegonial neck is surmounted by four or five cover cells, and the neck itself
is composed of six vertical rows of neck cells. The latter are difficult
to recognize, because they are so
closely associated with the surrounding cells of the gametophyte, but they are evident in a
surface view of the thallus, after
the cover cells have disintegrated.
The axial row of cells of the archegonium is composed of the
egg, ventral canal cell, and four
or five neck canal cells. As the
archegonium matures, the tip of
its neck becomes covered with
a mound of mucilage into which
the disintegrating ventral canal
and neck canal cells are extruded,
after the cover cells have separated.

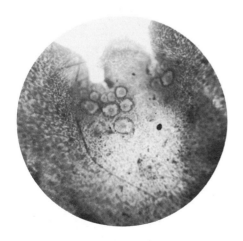

Fig. 15–60. *Anthoceros carolinianus.* Surface
view of thallus lobe with archegonia; note
transparent globule over each neck. X 30.

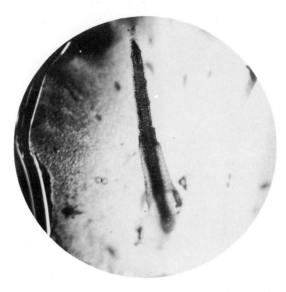

Fig. 15–61.   *Anthoceros carolinianus.* Young sporophyte emerging from involucre; note embedded foot. X 12½.

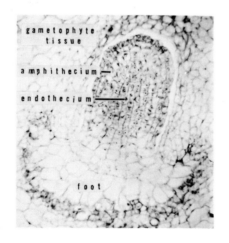

Fig. 15–62.   *Anthoceros carolinianus.* Median longitudinal section of young sporophyte before emergence from thallus; note foot, amphithecium, and endothecium. X 125.

After fertilization in *Anthoceros,* numerous zygotes regularly complete their development into sporophytes. The latter are elongate, cylindrical, needle-like structures which project from the upper surface of the thallus (Figs, 15–55, 15–56, 15–61). In their ontogeny, the zygote undergoes a longitudinal division followed by two additional divisions which form eight cells, in two tiers, within the archegonial venter. The lowermost tier of the octant, by further multiplication, gives rise to the sterile foot of the sporophyte (Fig. 15–62). The upper tier undergoes a series of transverse divisions that form a columnar structure which becomes differentiated into an outer, amphithecial layer and an inner, endothecial zone, by periclinal divisions. The amphithecial layer, by further periclinal divisions, ultimately becomes about six cell layers deep, and the endothecium becomes four cells deep by further divisions (Fig. 15–64). Early in the development

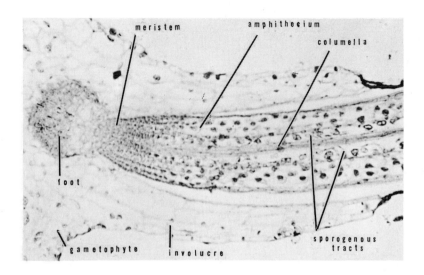

Fig. 15–63. *Anthoceros* sp. Median longitudinal section of base of sporophyte; note foot, meristematic zone, columella, sporogenous tracts, sterile photosynthetic ampithecium, gametophyte, and involucre. X 95.

of the sporophyte, the region that corresponds to the seta of the liverwort sporophyte becomes actively meristematic and functions as an intercalary meristem much like that in *Laminaria*, so that the sporophyte increases in length by growth near its base. As a result, the cylindrical sporophyte emerges from the gametophyte, lifting up or pushing aside a portion of the gametophyte (Figs. 15–61, 15–63). The elongation of the sporophyte by intercalary growth may continue for several months. Sporogenesis and spore dissemination are continuous and progressive in *Anthoceros*, not simultaneous as they are in the sporophytes of the Hepatopsida.

Considerable histological differentiation is present in the more mature regions of the sporophyte (Figs. 15–63, 15–64). The entire endothecium remains sterile and is called the **columella.** It is composed of elongate thin-walled cells which probably function in conduction (Fig. 15–65).

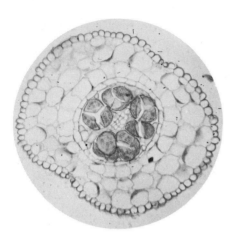

Fig. 15–64. *Anthoceros* sp. Transverse section of sporophyte in region of spore tetrads; note central columella, spore tetrads, photosynthetic portion of the amphithecium, epidermis, and stomata. X 250.

The surface layer of the amphithecium is cutinized; it serves as an epidermis and develops stomata whose guard cells are thickened along the stomatal aperture (Fig. 15–66). The wall layers are also photosynthetic and play an important role in the nutrition of the sporophyte. The innermost layers of the amphithecium develop into sporogenous tissue the cells of which, in older regions of the developing sporophyte, separate, become spherical, and function as spore mother cells (Fig. 15–67), each giving rise to a tetrad of spores as a result of the meiotic process. It is worthy of note that one of the earliest accounts of the origin of cells by division, published about 120 years ago, was based on a study of living spore mother cells of *Anthoceros*. Certain groups of potentially sporogenous cells remain sterile, elongate, and function as elaters (Fig. 15–65). Because of their multicellular condition and

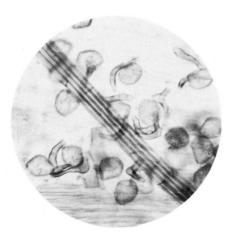

Fig. 15–65. *Anthoceros carolinianus.* Columella, mature spores, and elaters. X 250.

Fig. 15–66. *Anthoceros carolinianus.* Epidermis of sporophyte with stoma and guard cells. X 250.

lack of spiral thickening, they are sometimes referred to as "pseudo-elaters." As the spores near the apical portion of the sporophyte mature, the surrounding tissues lose their chlorophyll and become dry and brown.

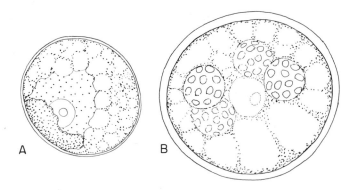

Fig. 15–67. *Anthoceros carolinianus.* Spore mother cells. A, Young, with single chloroplast. B, Older, with four chloroplasts. X 770.

During ontogeny, while the walls of the epidermal cells of the more mature portions of the sporophyte thicken, the common walls between the vertical rows of cells in the shallow grooves on the surface of the sporo-

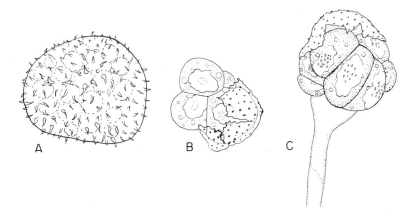

Fig. 15–68. *Anthoceros carolinianus.* A, Mature spore, surface view. X 770. B,C, Stages in spore germination. X 315.

phyte remain thin-walled. Thus dehiscence of the sporophyte into two valves begins near the apex of the sporophyte and extends toward the base as development proceeds. The two valves and the elaters exhibit twisting hygroscopic movements which have a role in the dissemination of the spores. The valve apices may remain adherent or they may separate (Figs. 15–55, 15–56).

Stages in spore germination and the development of young gametophytes are illustrated in Fig. 15–68. It has been reported that sex chromosomes are present in heterothallic species such as *A. laevis;* in this species two spores of a tetrad develop into male and two into female gametophytes.

SUMMARY AND CLASSIFICATION

In summarizing this account of the representatives of the Hepatophyta discussed in this chapter, attention will be devoted first to the question of their classification, now that the basic facts of their morphology have been presented. As noted in the introductory section, the liverworts and mosses are classified together in a single division, Bryophyta, almost universally. The reasons for placing these groups in separate divisions, Hepatophyta and Bryophyta, as is done in this text, will be enumerated at the conclusion of the following chapter. It still remains to arrange the representative genera of Hepatophyta in the higher categories or taxa such as families, orders, and classes. A comprehensive survey of the complete classification of these organisms presupposes familiarity with a wider range of genera than has been described. However, the criteria which are used to delimit the higher categories in the liverworts and horned liverworts should be sufficiently familiar at this stage to permit of some discussion.

No single scheme of classification of these plants has met with universal approval. Some authorities consider the liverworts and horned liverworts sufficiently different morphologically to warrant their separation into separate classes (Hepatopsida and Anthoceropsida) of coordinate rank, as has been done in this text. Others reduce the Anthoceropsida to ordinal rank and include them in the liverwort class. The following classification includes the representative genera discussed in this chapter:

Division Hepatophyta
  Class 1. Hepatopsida (Liverworts)
    Order 1. Marchantiales
      Family 1. Ricciaceae
        Genera: *Riccia, Ricciocarpus*

Family 2. Marchantiaceae
   Genera: *Marchantia, Conacephalum, Lunularia*
Order 2. Jungermanniales
   Family 1. Sphaerocarpaceae
      Genus: *Sphaerocarpos*
   Family 2. Metzgeriaceae
      Genera: *Pellia, Pallavicinia, Metzgeria*
   Family 3. Jungermanniaceae
      Genera: *Porella, Frullania, Scapania*
Class 2. Anthoceropsida (Horned liverworts)
   Order 1. Anthocerotales
      Family 1. Anthocerotaceae
         Genera: *Anthoceros, Notothylas*

In discussing a classification such as this, a question at once arises regarding the criteria that were considered in grouping or segregating the several categories. Whether they be considered in relation to a class or an ordinal rank, the attributes which distinguish the liverworts and horned liverworts are fairly striking and numerous. Among them may be cited such features of the gametophytic phase of *Anthoceros* as possession of single massive chloroplasts containing pyrenoid bodies in each cell, and the endogenous development of antheridia and archegonia. As contrasted with those of Hepatopsida, the sporophytes of the Anthoceropsida, as exemplified by *Anthoceros*, are elongate cylindrical structures with marked internal complexity and long-continued development. The latter is effected by an intercalary meristematic zone which adds continuously to the sporophytic tissues. These include a cutinized epidermis with functional stomata, a zone of photosynthetic parenchyma cells, a fertile sporogenous layer, and a central sterile columella composed of elongate cells which function in conduction. Furthermore, unlike those of the Hepatopsida, the sporophytes of *Anthoceros* are dehiscent into two valves. These characters, among others, are interpreted as manifestations of fundamental dissimilarity from the members of the Hepatopsida.

Within the class Hepatopsida, the characteristics which distinguish the Marchantiales from the Jungermanniales are also both gametophytic and sporophytic. The gametophytes of the Marchantiales, unlike those of the Jungermanniales, always have some degree of internal differentiation into photosynthetic and storage regions. A specially differentiated epidermis with air pores may be present (*Marchantia*), as well as ventral scales. Rhizoids, two types of which may occur (*Marchantia*), are of primary importance in absorption for terrestrial members of the Marchantiales. The sporophytes in this order are either undifferentiated spheres or, if differentiated into foot, seta, and capsule regions, they are irregularly dehiscent. The gametophytes of Jungermanniales, on the other hand, show little internal differentiation, their tissues being largely chlorenchymatous. In the families Sphaerocarpaceae and Metzgeriaceae, the plant bodies are thallose or ribbon-like, with smooth or undulate margins. In the Jungermanniaceae, the plants are leafy, with the leaves in two lateral rows and frequently in a third ventral row. With the exception of *Sphaerocarpos,* in which the spores are liberated by disintegration of the gametophyte and capsule wall, dehiscence of the capsule in the Jungermanniales usually occurs by splitting into four valves.

The arrangment of classes and orders presented above is based on the view that evolution in the Hepatophyta has been in the direction of increasing complexity in both sporophyte and gametophyte. That such an arrangement is not always feasible is apparent in the circumstance that the Ricciaceae, whose sporophytes are the simplest among those in the land plants, are listed before the Metzgeriaceae, whose gametophytes are simpler than those of the Ricciaceae. According to some authorities, the history of the sporophyte generation in the Hepatophyta has been one of increasing complexity through sterilization of potentially sporogenous tissue. Thus, according to this view, the foot, seta capsule, and elaters are interpreted as manifestations of progressive sterilization. This tendency is said to culminate in the sporophyte of *Anthoceros,* which is perhaps the most complex in this division. Other students of the liverworts read the series in quite the opposite direction. According to them, the leafy Jungermanniales represent the primitive stock, from which both the Marchantiales and the Anthoceropsida have been derived by secondary simplifications known as **reductions.** As evidence of leafy ancestry, the ventral scales of the Marchantiales and the involucres of the Metzgeriaceae are often cited.

In discussing the phylogeny of a group, the most important evidence is frequently found in the fossil record. However, the few fossil representatives of the Hepatophyta which have been discovered do not differ from living genera and they shed no light on the origin or relationship of the extant types. Furthermore, the origin of the liverworts from algal stock, from which they are universally considered to have arisen, is likewise unsupported by evidence other than speculative, although the fossil record undoubtedly is incomplete.

Finally, discussion of the Hepatophyta, which are usually conceded to represent the most primitive land plants, affords an excellent opportunity to examine the relationship between the gametophytic and sporophytic phases of the life cycle. If the ancestors of the Hepatophyta are to be sought among the algae, the relationship of the sporophyte and gametophyte in the latter is relevant to the discussion of the same phenomenon in the liverworts. It will be recalled that in all the Chlorophyceae discussed in an earlier chapter, the zygote is free or is set free from the parent plant after its formation, so that further development is independent of the gametophyte. In the Rhodophyceae and fungi whose zygotes are retained on the parent plant, the subsequent development of the zygote seems to have been modified as a result, especially in regard to nutrition. In the land plants, the retention of the zygote within the archegonium and parent gametophyte is permanent. Although retention and intimate association with the parent gametophyte may have resulted in marked morphological variations in the structure developed from the zygote, its capacity for autotrophic nutrition by photosynthesis seems to have been deeply rooted, for evidence of its persistence is available in the widespread occurrence of photosynthetic tissues in the sporophyte generation of Hepatophyta and Bryophyta. It is doubtful, however, whether in any member of these divisions the sporophyte leads an entirely autotrophic existence while enclosed in gametophytic tissues, inasmuch as the foods elaborated by the gametophyte are available to the developing sporophyte through diffusion. But this should appear no more remarkable than the repeatedly demonstrated fact that in all groups of photoautotrophic green plants, individuals can lead a facultatively heterotrophic existence when suitable organic compounds are supplied.

That photosynthesis and other vegetative functions were attributes of the sporophyte generation, as it is observed among the algae, seems also to be true of the sporophytic phase of the Hepatophyta, for only in *Ricciocarpus* (and probably also in *Riccia*) are organized chloroplasts absent from the sporophytic tissues. Instead of interpreting the presence of chlorophyll in the liverwort sporophyte as evidence of its secondary assumption of vegetative functions by sterilization of originally sporogenous tissues, one is equally justified in citing the same phenomenon as a vestigial attribute of free-living algal ancestors. This second interpretation supports the homologous theory of the origin and nature of the alternating generations, according to which sporophytes are considered to be modified gametophytes and not fundamentally different from them in organization. The alternate hypothesis, that spore production is the primary function of the sporophyte and that vegetative functions were assumed secondarily as a result of the sterilization of potentially sporogenous tissue, is corollary to the antithetic theory. This interprets the two alternating generations as fundamentally different and looks upon the sporophyte as an entirely new phase secondarily interpolated into the life cycle. The bearing of evidence from other groups of plants on these theoretical aspects of the life cycle will be presented again where relevant in later chapters.

DISCUSSION QUESTIONS

1. With reference to the structure of the gametophytic phase, which genera of the Hepatophyta do you consider most simple? Which most complex? Give the reasons for your answers.

2. With reference to the sporophytic phase, which of the Hepatophyta do you consider most simple? Which most complex? Give the reasons for your answers.

3. What phenomenon among Chlorophyceae can you cite as similar to gemma formation?

4. To what type of algal life cycle is that of the Hepatophyta most similar? How does it differ?

5. What attributes distinguish sporophytes and gametophytes? Do they occur among algae? Explain.

6. Can the terms "haplobiontic" and "diplobiontic" be applied appropriately to the Hepatophyta? Explain.

7. What factors seem to be involved in effecting the distribution of liverworts?

8. Can you suggest a mechanism, and explain its operation, for the occurrence of heterothallism in *Sphaerocarpos?* In *Marchantia?* How, then, can you explain homothallism in genera like *Ricciocarpus?*

9. Can you suggest any biological advantages which may accrue from the fact that in Hepatophyta meiosis is delayed until sporogenesis?

10. What significance do you attach to the occurrence of chlorophyll in the sporophytes of the Hepatophyta? What is the source of the inorganic salts, carbon dioxide, and oxygen used by the sporophyte?

11. In what respects do rhizoids differ from roots and rhizomes?

12. How do the sex organs of Hepatophyta differ from those of algae? Are there exceptions?

13. According to some morphologists, the sporophytes of Hepatopsida afford evidence that there has occurred a progressive sterilization of potentially sporogenous tissue to form vegetative or somatic tissues. Cite evidence in support of this statement.

14. In the same connection, it has been postulated that *all* vegetative tissue of the sporophyte has arisen by sterilization of sporogenous tissue. What evidence do the algae provide in this connection?

15. Define or explain sporophyte, gametophyte, homology, apical growth, complicate-bilobed, amphigastrium, foot, elater, spore mother cell, tetrad, calyptra, protandrous, periclinal, anticlinal.

16. In your opinion, to the gametophytes of which of the Hepatopsida is that of *Anthoceros* most similar? How does it differ?

17. On what grounds is one justified in segregating *Anthoceros* from liverworts?

18. What innovations are present in the sporophyte of *Anthoceros* as compared with those of the Hepatopsida?

19. How could one distinguish a vegetative gametophyte of *Anthoceros* from that of *Pellia?*

20. What is the origin of the elaters of *Anthoceros?*

21. How would you plan an experiment to clarify the role of the endophytic *Nostoc* which occurs in *Anthoceros?*

22. Each young spore mother cell of *Anthoceros* contains one chloroplast. Each young spore also contains one. Explain. Why do the cells of the sporophyte not contain two chloroplasts since they are diploid?

23. What significance do you attribute to the occurrence of stomata on the *Anthoceros* sporophyte?

24. Describe an experiment to ascertain the degree of autotrophism of the *Anthoceros* sporophyte.

25. Describe an experiment which might prove whether or not the columella functions in conduction.

26. How could you prove whether or not the gametophyte of *Anthoceros* is autotrophic?

REFERENCE WORKS ON HEPATOPHYTA AND BRYOPHYTA[4]

Bower, F. O. *Primitive Land Plants,* Macmillan & Company, Ltd., 1935.

Campbell, D. H. *The Structure and Development of Mosses and Ferns,* The Macmillan Company, 1928.

Campbell, D. H. *The Evolution of the Land Plants (Embryophyta),* Stanford Univ. Press, 1940.

Conard, H. S. *How to Know the Mosses,* H. E. Jaques, 1944.

Frye, T. C., and Clark, L. *Hepaticae of North America,* Univ. of Washington Press, Parts I–V, 1937–1947.

Goebel, K. *Organography of Plants, Especially of the Archegoniatae and Spermatophyta* (English ed., transl. I. B. Balfour), Clarendon Press, Part 2, 1905.

---

[4] For use with Chapters 15 and 16.

Grout, A. J. *Mosses with a Hand-Lens and Microscope,* published by the author, 1903.

Grout, A. J. *Mosses with a Hand-Lens,* published by the author, 1924.

Grout, A. J. *Moss Flora of North American North of Mexico,* published by the author, 1928–1940.

Haupt, A. W. *Plant Morphology,* McGraw-Hill Book Co., Inc., 1953.

Smith, G. M. *Cryptogamic Botany, Vol. II, Bryophytes and Pteridophytes,* McGraw-Hill Book Co. Inc., 1955.

Verdoorn, F. *Manual of Bryology,* Martinus Nijhoff, 1932.

Wardlaw, C. W. *Embryogenesis in Plants,* John Wiley and Sons, Inc., 1955.

CHAPTER 16

Division Bryophyta

INTRODUCTION

As noted at the beginning of the preceding chapter, the division **Bryophyta,** as conceived by most taxonomists, includes the liverworts, horned liverworts, and the mosses. In the present text, however, the liverworts and horned liverworts are classified together in a separate division, the Hepatophyta; hence the division Bryophyta, as here constituted, has narrower limits, since it includes only the mosses. Some 600 genera and 14,000 species are included in the Bryophyta. It generally is agreed that there are three basically different morphological types among mosses. This occasions the division of the group into three classes as follows: Class 1. **Sphagnopsida,** the peat mosses; Class 2. **Mnionopsida,** the "true" mosses; and Class 3. **Andreaeopsida.** Because of their rather restricted occurrence and few members, the Andreaeopsida will be treated only briefly in the concluding section of this chapter.

CLASS 1. SPHAGNOPSIDA: *SPHAGNUM*

Habitat and Vegetative Morphology

The class **Sphagnopsida** includes only a single genus, *Sphagnum* (Gr. *sphagnos,* kind of moss), which is represented by many species. The spongy, pale-green mats and mounds of *Sphagnum* (Fig. 16–1) are familiar to all who have frequented the out-of-doors, especially in those regions where the soil is not markedly alkaline. *Sphagnum* typically is an inhabitant of wet pools, bogs, and swamps and often occurs abundantly around the shores of ponds and lakes. Its rapid growth under such conditions, and its voracious water-holding capacity, frequently combine to completely "fill in" fairly large bodies of water. At one stage in this process, that in which the plants form a dense surface mat over the water below, so-called **quaking bogs** are formed. In certain parts of the world—Ireland, for example—the plant is gathered, dried, compressed, and used as fuel. Its antiseptic and highly absorptive qualities have been responsible for its use in a number of circumstances. Among these may be cited its use as dressings for wounds, especially during wars, as packing material about the roots of living plants in transit, and as colloidal material for increasing the water-holding capacity of soils.

Fig. 16–1. *Sphagnum* sp. Several axes; note excurrent and decurrent branches. X ½.

The individual plants are closely matted together, but careful study reveals that each terminates in a dense series of apical branches. In addition, the stem bears other branches of two kinds. The **excurrent branches** are more or less horizontal in position and project outward from the main axes; the other branches are **decurrent**, pendulous and usually twisted about the axes (Fig. 16–1). The densely intertwined condition of the individual plants, the wick-like action of their decurrent branches, the overlapping leaves, and finally the special cellular modifications of the latter all increase the water-holding capacity of the *Sphagnum* plant. Mature plants lack rhizoids and all absorption takes place through the leaf and stem surfaces.

The development of the individual plant may be traced to a single apical cell at the tip of the stem (Fig. 16–2). This cell is triangular in transverse section, and three rows of derivative cells are regularly produced. By further cell divisions these give rise to the young leaves and tissues of the stem. The three-ranked origin of the leaves becomes ob-

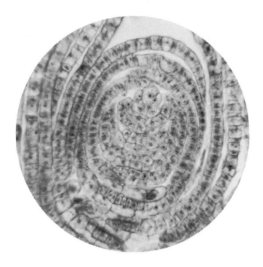

Fig. 16–2. *Sphagnum* sp. Median longitudinal section of stem apex; note apical cell and developing leaves. X 250.

scured in older parts of the branches.

The stem of the main branches is composed of a central region surrounded by a cortex (Fig. 16–3) of hyaline cells; the cortex of the branches is composed of larger hyaline cells. The cortical cells are primarily water storage cells. It is doubtful that the cells of the central strand function efficiently in conduction. Instead, fluids are conducted by the wick-like branches and the numerous capillary surfaces in the densely interwoven plants.

The **leaf primordium** (L. *primordium,* beginning or origin) develops into a mature leaf through the activity of an apical cell whose derivatives arise as a result of cell division in two directions (Fig. 16–2). The cells of young leaves are at first uniform in size

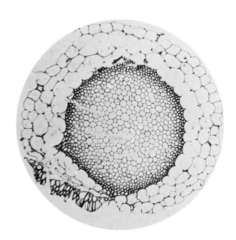

Fig. 16–3. *Sphagnum* sp. Transverse section of branch; note central cells surrounded by water storage cells of cortex (preparation slightly torn). X 60.

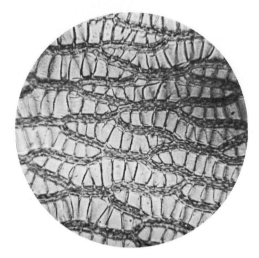

Fig. 16–4. *Sphagnum* sp. Portion of leaf showing alternate large water storage cells and small photosynthetic cells. X 250.

Fig. 16–5. *Sphagnum* sp. Antheridial branch. X 7.

and shape; but as development proceeds, cell divisions occur in such a pattern that the mature leaf is composed of large colorless cells between which there are smaller photosynthetic cells (Fig. 16–4). The colorless cells are nonliving at maturity, are often thickened with annular-spiral markings, and frequently are perforated by circular pores. They store large quantities of water. The reduced number and smaller size of the photosynthetic cells and the abundance of the colorless water storage cells account for the pale-green color of the mature plants.

Reproduction

The leafy *Sphagnum* plant sometimes is called the **leafy gametophore** (Gr. *gamos*, marriage + Gr. *phora*, bearer), inasmuch as it bears the sex organs when mature. Some species are homothallic and others heterothallic. The antheridia occur in short lateral branches (Fig. 16–5) near the apex of a main axis and are reddish or light purple in color. The leaves of the branch are closely overlapping and suggest the antheridial branches of the leafy liverworts. Each leaf bears a single antheridium in its axil (Fig. 16–6). The antheridium is rather long-stalked, as in *Scapania* and *Porella,* but differs from the antheridium of the Hepatopsida in that its development involves the activities of an apical cell. The sperms of *Sphagnum* are biflagellate.

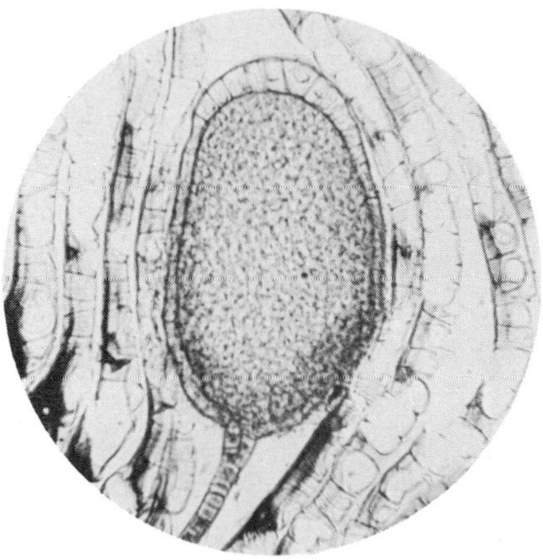

Archegonia are also borne on short lateral branches. The apical cells of these branches, as in acrogynous liverworts, ultimately give rise to an archegonium so

Fig. 16–6. *Sphagnum* sp. Median longitudinal section of antheridium containing mature sperm. X 125.

that increase in length of the branch ceases. In *Sphagnum palustre* L., three archegonia are usually formed on a single archegonial branch (Fig. 16–7). Mature archegonia are massive and pedicellate. Their necks are elongate and curved and are composed of five or six rows of neck cells. The eight or nine neck canal cells become disorganized as the archegonium matures.

Fertilization has been infrequently observed in *Sphagnum* but seems to occur in the late autumn and winter in the eastern portion of the United States. At Highlands, N.C., for example, at an altitude of 4000 feet, the young sporophytes of *S. palustre* are already in the spore mother cell stage early in May, but dehiscence of the capsule and dissemination of the spores does not

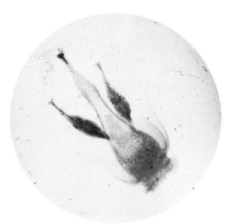

Fig. 16–7. *Sphagnum* sp. Enlarging archegonium containing sporophyte; and two sterile archegonia. X 30.

occur until late June or early July. *S. squarrosum* Perc. and other species have mature sporophytes in July in northern Michigan. The zygote of only one of the archegonia usually develops into a sporophyte (Fig. 16–7); the other two archegonia may persist for some time at the base of the fertile one. The first division of the zygote is transverse, and further division in the same direction results in the formation of a short chain of diploid cells. Approximately the upper half of this chain continues nuclear and cell division to form the capsule region of the sporophyte; an extremely short seta and haustorial foot develop from the lower cells. Early in development, the foot and seta regions of the sporophyte exceed the fertile portion in size. The cells of the sporophyte contain actively photosynthetic chloroplasts throughout their development. The sporophyte remains covered by the calyptra and leaves of the gametophore until just before spore dissemination. An endothecium and amphithecium are differentiated early in the development of the sporophyte, in its upper portion. The sporogenous tissue arises from the innermost layer of the amphithecium and becomes four layers deep; it occupies a dome-like position within the capsule (Fig. 16–8). The central sterile tissue, which arises from the endothecium, is called the columella, as in *Anthoceros*. The sterile cells of the amphithecium are covered by an epidermis in which pairs of apparently nonfunctional guard cells develop. The basal portion of the sporophyte consists of a short nonfunctional seta region and an enlarged foot (Fig. 16–8).

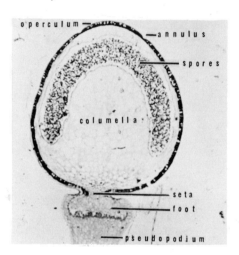

Fig. 16–8. *Sphagnum* sp. Median longitudinal section of sporophyte; note pseudopodium, foot, seta region, columella, spores, annulus, and operculum. X 25.

All the potentially sporogenous cells undergo sporogenesis and form tetrads of spores. Meiosis is accomplished during these divisions, so the spores are haploid. No elaters or other sterile cells, such as those observed in many Hepatophyta, occur in the Bryophyta.

As the spores mature, they secrete a brown sculptured wall, and the sterile tissues within the capsule become dehydrated. Meanwhile, the walls of the cells composing the outer part of the capsule thicken and also become brown. A circular layer of cells, the **annulus** (Figs. 16–8,

Fig. 16–9.   *Sphagnum squarrosum* Pers. Branch with mature sporophytes. X 3.

16–9), near the apex of the capsule remains thin-walled and is
torn when the upper portion of
the capsule, the **operculum,** and
spores are explosively shed. Just
before this, the stem of the gametophore which bears the sporophyte elongates rapidly (Figs.
16–1, 16–9), thus raising the entire sporophyte above the gametophore. This elongated stem is
called the **pseudopodium.** Its
function is similar to that of the
seta of the Hepatophyta and
Bryophyta other than *Sphagnum.*
The explosive discharge of the
spores is audible and the spores
may be ejected for distances as great as 10 cm.

Fig. 16–10.   *Sphagnum* sp. Protonema with
young leafy plant. X 12½.

The spores of *Sphagnum* can germinate immediately after being shed
from the capsule. If they do so in crowded cultures, they form alga-like
filaments which ultimately develop flattened, spatulate apices. A spore

that is well separated from others forms a minute thallose structure, the **protonema**, very early in its development. The posterior marginal cells of this structure produce multicellular rhizoids which anchor it to the substratum. Each protonema ultimately gives rise to a single leafy shoot or **gametophore** (Fig. 16–10) which develops from one protonematal cell. The first few leaves of the young gametophore lack the cellular dimorphism characteristic of *Sphagnum* leaves; this character appears gradually, beginning with the fourth or fifth leaf. The rhizoidal branches of the protonema frequently give rise to secondary protonemata from their apical cells.

Summary

In summarizing the morphology and life cycle of the peat moss, *Sphagnum*, a number of noteworthy features may be emphasized. Although the mature plants lack rhizoids and specialized conducting tissue, they attain a stature which exceeds that of any of the Hepatophyta and rivals that of the largest mosses which have well-developed rhizoids and supporting and conducting tissues. This probably is effected by their growth in dense mats in marshy soil or water, where the individual plants are able to furnish each other with mutual mechanical support. The numerous adaptations for storage and conduction of water are significant. Among them may be cited the matted growth of the leafy gametophores, the overlapping of the leaves and branches, the presence and wick-like action of the decurrent branches, and the occurrence of special water storage cells in the leaves and cortex of the stems.

The pedicellate antheridia suggest those of leafy liverworts; the long-necked stalked archegonia are more massive than those of other Bryophyta. The activity of an apical cell in the formation of the sex organs is characteristic of the Bryophyta and absent in the Hepatophyta, except in such acrogynous forms as *Pellia* and *Porella*.

The structure and dehiscence of the sporophyte capsule are strikingly different from those of the Hepatophyta. It should be noted that relatively less sporogenous tissue develops in the capsule of *Sphagnum* as compared with that of Hepatophyta, and that sporogenesis is simultaneous, unlike that of *Anthoceros*. As in the latter, however, the central region of the capsule is occupied by a sterile columella which involves the entire endothecium, the sporogenous tissue of *Sphagnum* also arising from the innermost layer of the amphithecium. Perhaps the most important departure in the life cycle of *Sphagnum*, as compared with that of Hepatophyta other than *Porella,* is the occurrence of a precursor, the protonema, which arises from the germinating spore.

CLASS 2. MNIONOPSIDA

Habitat and Vegetative Morphology

The **Mnionopsida,** the so-called "true mosses," include approximately 600 genera, the largest number among the Bryophyta. In spite of their abundance, they display a remarkable uniformity in structure and life cycle. A number of representative genera, listed herewith, have been selected to illustrate the attributes of the class:

Atrichum (Gr. *atrichos,* hairless)
Aulocomnium (Gr. *aulos,* tube + Gr. *mnion,* moss)
Bryum (Gr. *bryon,* moss)
Buxbaumia (after J. C. Buxbaum, a German botanist)
Ceratodon (Gr. *keras,* horn + Gr. *odon,* tooth)
Dicranum (Gr. *dikranos,* two-headed)
Fissidens (L. *fissus,* cleft + L. *dens,* tooth)
Fontinalis (L. *fontinalis,* fountain)
Forrstroemia (after the Rev. Forsström, a West Indian collector of
  the 18th century)
Funaria (L. *funarius,* pertaining to a rope)
Grimmia (after Dr. J. F. K. Grimms, a physician and botanist of
  Gotha)
Leucodon (Gr. *leukos,* white + Gr. *odon,* tooth)
Mnium (Gr. *mnion,* moss)
Neckera (after de Necker, an 18th-century French botanist)
Orthotrichum (Gr. *orthos,* straight + Gr. *trichos*)
Pogonatum (Gr. *pogon,* beard)
Polytrichum (Gr. *polytrichos,* very hairy)

While *Sphagnum* is relatively limited in distribution, occurring only in boggy or aquatic habitats, representatives of the Mnionopsida may be collected from xeric, mesic, and hydric environments. The great majority, however, live under moderately moist conditions rather than in extremely wet habitats. *Fissidens* and *Fontinalis* are often submerged in small streams. *Mnium* and certain species of *Bryum* are mosses of very moist substrata but are not submerged. *Orthotrichum* and *Grimmia,* on the other hand, are examples of numerous xerophytic mosses. Terrestrial species grow on various substrata such as rock, tree bark, and wood, and on moist soil. Members of the group are often pioneers on freshly exposed, bare soil surfaces, where they rapidly carpet the substratum with their filamentous, branching protonematal phases. In this connection they are no doubt of considerable importance in preventing incipient erosion. Some mosses are perennial, forming increasingly dense mats each year on a given substratum. Others are annuals which frequently develop in the fall or winter in temperate climates.

As in the genus *Sphagnum*, the gametophyte generation of the Mnionopsida is represented in the life cycle by two phases, the **protonema** (Gr. *protos*, first + Gr. *neme*, thread) and the **leafy gametophore.** In most genera the protonema is a branching filament, in contrast to the spatulate protonema of *Sphagnum*. This protonema ultimately produces a number of leafy shoots which often are known as leafy gametophores because they produce sex organs at maturity. In a few mosses, like *Buxbaumia* and one species of *Pogonatum*, the protonematal stage is long-lived and persistent, the leafy gametophore phase in such genera being correspondingly reduced. The zygote develops into a sporophyte borne on the female gametophore. The complexity of the sporophyte in the Mnionopsida is unparalleled among Hepatophyta and other Bryophyta.

Because of the large number of genera available which furnish suitable material for the study of the moss life cycle, a number of them will be referred to in the following account. Moss spores shed from the capsule of a mature sporophyte germinate promptly if they are carried to a suitable environment. Their germination and subsequent development may be followed readily in laboratory cultures in which the spores have been sown on the surface of agar that contains inorganic salts. In *Funaria hygrometrica* (L.) Schreb., the cord moss, each spore is covered with a brown outer wall which ruptures on the swelling of the spore protoplast (Fig. 16–11). The spores of *Funaria* will not germinate unless they are illuminated. At germination, the spore protoplast may protrude at both poles of the spore. The germ tube enlarges rapidly and soon gives rise to a branching filamentous system as a result of repeated nuclear and cell division. Growth of the protonema is apical. Its cells are rich in lens-shaped chloroplasts. The protonema may be readily distinguished from terrestrial green algae by the discrete, lens-like plastids, together with the oblique position of the end wall of its component cells (Fig. 16–12). The protonema from a single spore of *Funaria hygrometrica* may cover an area 16 inches in diameter within several months. Some branches of the protonema are superficial, whereas others penetrate the substratum, often developing brown walls. Transitional types are common. After a period of growth and vegetative activity, certain cells of the *Funaria* protonema undergo nuclear and cell divisions in which an apical cell is differentiated which gives rise to three series of derivative cells. These apical cells and their derivatives, which may occur on both surface and subterranean branches of the protonema, soon look like minute buds (Fig. 16–13). With the continued activity of the apical cell, each gives rise to a young leafy gametophore (Fig. 16–14). In laboratory cultures at 22° C., on inorganic salt-

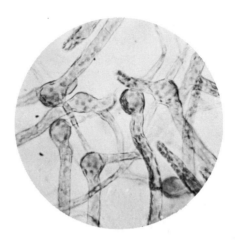

Fig. 16–11. *Funaria hygrometrica* (L.) Schreb. Bipolar spore germination; note slender rhizoid and photosynthetic filament. X 60.

agar media illuminated at 150 foot-candles intensity, gametophore formation is usually initiated within sixty days after spore germination. A protonema arising from a single spore can produce a large number of leafy

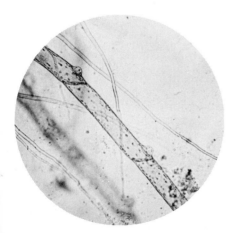

Fig. 16–12. *Funaria hygrometrica*. Protonematal branches with oblique septa. X 250.

Fig. 16–13. *Funaria hygrometrica*. Initiation of leafy plants on gametophores. X 60.

gametophores rather than one as in *Sphagnum;* this accounts for the densely colonial growth of young moss plants. The protonematal branches function as absorbing organs for young gametophores. As the latter increase in age and stature, rhizoids, which are much like subterranean protonematal branches, arise from the bases of the stems.

Fig. 16–14. *Funaria hygrometrica.* Leafy plant attached to protonema and rhizoids. X 12½.

Continued development of the gametophore is effected by the activity of the apical cell and its derivatives. In a majority of mosses, the leaves in young plants are arranged in three rows, the result of the order in which the derivatives are cut off from the apical cell of the stem. In older plants, the three-ranked leaf arrangement is often disturbed. In a few mosses—*Fissidens,* for example—the occurrence of leaves in two ranks is correlated with the presence of an apical cell from which only two rows of derivatives are produced.

Stems of many mosses are differentiated into three regions: a superficial epidermal layer, a thick cortex, and a central strand. The latter may be composed of both thick-walled and thin-walled cells, as in *Polytrichum* (Fig. 16–15). Living cells of many moss stems are actively photosynthetic. In genera like *Pogonatum,* increase in stem length may be very limited, whereas in others, like *Polytrichum,* the stem may attain a length of six or more inches.

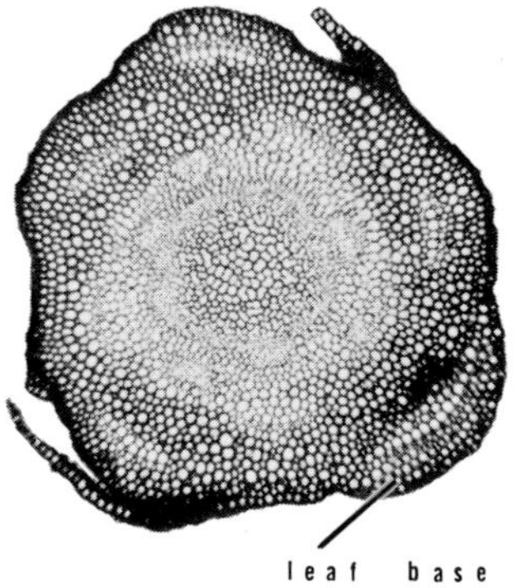

Development of the leaves in the Mnionopsida may be traced to the

Fig. 16–15. *Polytrichum* sp. Transverse section of stem of leafy plant. X 60.

activity of an apical cell which gives rise to cells from two of its surfaces. The young leaf is composed of only a single layer of cells, but in some genera the central region becomes thicker, forming a midrib. This is composed of elongate cells some of which are thickened and function in support. *Funaria* is typical of the mosses whose leaf structure is relatively simple (Fig. 16–14), but *Polytrichum* and *Atrichum* leaves exhibit considerable complexity (Fig. 16–16). In these, the many-layered blade is considerably expanded and sclerotic. From its upper surface arise a number of parallel lamellae of thin-walled photosynthetic cells which are separated from each other by narrow fissures. These are protected from desiccation by inrolling of the sclerotic leaf surface.

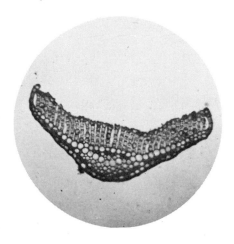

Fig. 16–16. *Polytrichum* sp. Transverse section of leaf; note photosynthetic lamellae on upper surface of leaf. X 125.

The mature leafy plants of most Mnionopsida are anchored to the substratum by systems of multicellular rhizoids with oblique terminal walls (Fig. 16–17). As noted above, the rhizoidal system of the young plant is composed largely of protonematal branches. Secondary rhizoids may arise from the superficial cells of the stems and leaf bases. In some genera (*Polytrichum*) they become twisted into rope-like masses. Older rhizoids are usually brown-walled and contain few chloroplasts. It has been demonstrated in many mosses that such environmental stimuli as wounding may effect the production of protonematal branches from almost any portion of the plant body, including the stem, leaves, and even parts of the sporophyte. The rhizoids may give rise to secondary protonemata and ultimately to young gametophores.

Reproduction

The leafy plants of most mosses have been observed to produce sex organs at maturity. For this reason they are often called gametophores. These organs may be borne either at the apex of the main axis,

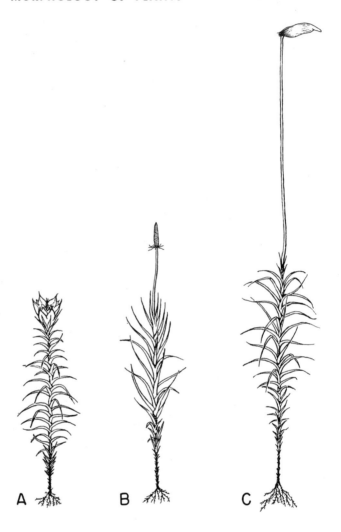

Fig. 16–17.   *Polytrichum* sp. A, ♂ plant. B, ♀ plant with young sporophyte covered by calyptra. C, ♀ plant with almost mature sporophyte. X 1½.

as in *Polytrichum* and *Atrichum,* or in special lateral branches in other genera (species of *Mnium,* for example). The distribution of sex organs varies among the several genera. In *Polytrichum* and *Atrichum* the gametophores are clearly heterothallic, as manifested by the dimorphism of the male and female plants (Figs. 16–17, 16–18). *Funaria,* although homothallic, produces antheridia and archegonia in separate branches of the same plant (Fig. 16–19). *Funaria* is protandrous and the male branch first overshadows the female, which is a lateral branch of it. In certain species of *Mnium,* on the other hand, antheridia and archegonia occur in the same group at the stem apex. Sexual as distinct from vegetative apices in mosses may often be recognized by the occurrence of somewhat

A

B

Fig. 16–18.   *Polytrichum* sp. A, Clump of ♀ plants with sporophytes. X ⅔. B, Apices of ♂ plants with antheridial cups. X ½.

modified leaves about the sex organs. The apices of male individuals of heterothallic species (Figs. 16–17, 16–18B) are cup-like. Certain identification of branches bearing archegonia is more difficult; it is best made by periodic study of *apparently* vegetative apices of a given species at a time when some individuals of the same species bear antheridia. Periods when sex organs are present differ in various moss species, in different seasons, and in different latitudes. After they have produced sex organs and sporophytes, new vegetative shoots may proliferate through the old sexual apices (Fig. 16–18B), or new branches may arise below the apices that have borne sporophytes.

Development of both the antheridia and archegonia in the Mnionop-

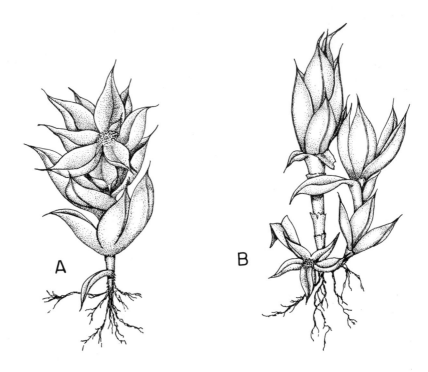

Fig. 16–19. *Funaria hygrometrica.* A, ♂ shoot at fertilization. B, ♀ branches after fertilization with withered ♂ branch. X 4. (♂ and ♀ branches are attached when immature.)

sida involves the activity of apical cells. Sterile hair-like or bulbous fila-ments and modified leaves, all called **paraphyses,** occur among the sex organs of the Mnionopsida (Fig. 16–20). It has been suggested that the paraphyses function in preventing drying of the sex organs by increasing the surface on which capillary water may be held. The antheridia (Fig. 16–20) and archegonia (Fig. 16–21) are massive, readily visible to the naked eye in many cases, and always considerably larger than those of the Hepatophyta. Both types of sex organs are pedicellate. The arche-gonia (Fig. 16–21) have extremely long, often twisted necks composed of six vertical rows of neck cells which enclose a correspondingly long series of neck canal cells. These and the ventral canal cell disintegrate when the archegonium is mature, thus providing an unobstructed pas-sageway to the egg.

In many mosses the chloroplasts of the antheridial jacket cells are

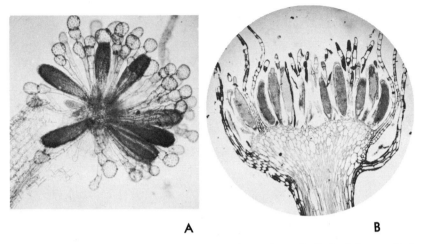

A   B

Fig. 16–20.   A, *Funaria hygrometrica*. Antheridia and paraphyses. X 60. B, *Mnium* sp. Median longitudinal section of antheridial head; note antheridia and paraphyses. X 30.

transformed into chromoplasts when the antheridia are mature; hence ripe antheridia may be recognized by their red color. The spermatogenous cells within the jacket layer divide repeatedly, forming a columnar mass of rather minute cubical cells. At the conclusion of these divisions, the protoplast of each minute cell becomes organized as a biflagellate sperm (Fig. 16–23). Mature antheridia undergo dehiscence if they are submerged in water. This is ac-complished by the absorption of water by the jacket cells; their increased turgidity causes expan-sion of the spermatogenous cells in a vertical direction, with the result that one or more specially modified apical cells of the an-theridium are ruptured. The sperms ooze out slowly from the opened antheridium (Fig. 16–22) and at first are surrounded by the walls of the spermatogenous cells (Fig. 16–23). The sperms at the surface of the mass become motile within these cells and are shed

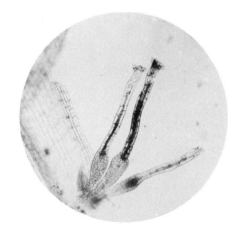

Fig. 16–21.   *Funaria hygrometrica*. Archegonial complex just after fertilization. X 60.

from the cells which produced them, in a hyaline, vacuolate vesicle of cytoplasm bounded by the plasma membrane (Fig. 16–23). The flagella, which are attached to the spirally coiled nucleus, project through and are attached partially to the surface of the plasma membrane on which they undergo undulating movements which causes the vesicle to turn in the water. Ultimately, the vesicle disappears and the sperm swims rapidly and freely in the water (Fig. 16–23C).

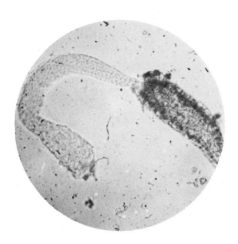

Fig. 16–22. *Funaria hygrometrica.* Antheridium shedding sperm. X 125.

The way in which sperms reach the archegonial necks of homothallic mosses can be readily understood. Probably the moisture of a heavy dew is sufficient to stimulate antheridial dehiscence and suffices for the sperms to swim to the necks of the proximate archegonia. In the case of heterothallic species, where the colonies of male and female gametophores frequently are separated by considerable

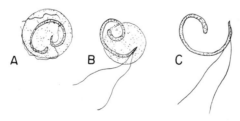

Fig. 16–23.   *Funaria hygrometrica.* Stages in development of functional sperm. A, Sperm with protoplast; note partially free flagella. B, Flagella entirely free. C, Free-swimming sperm; protoplast has been sloughed. X 770.

Fig. 16–24. *Funaria hygrometrica.* Early embryonic sporophyte. X 600. (From Campbell.)

distances, it is more difficult to explain the *apparent* frequency of fertilization as evidenced by the production of abundant sporophytes on the female plants. It has been suggested that the splashing raindrops in a heavy rain probably account for the distribution of the sperms. In view of the paucity of cytological investigations of mosses, the possibility of **parthenogenetic** (Gr. *parthenos,* virgin + Gr. *genesis,* origin) develop-ment of the egg in some cases cannot yet be excluded.

The ontogeny of the sporophyte from the zygote has been investi-gated more thoroughly in *Funaria* than in any other moss, and the fol-

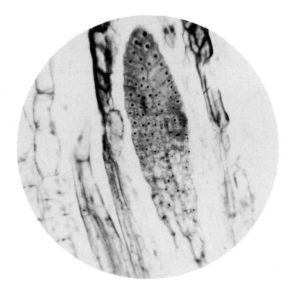

Fig. 16–25. *Funaria hygrometrica.* Late embryonic sporophyte within venter; note apical cell above. X 250.

lowing account emphasizes development in that genus. The first division of the zygote is transverse. An apical cell is differentiated early by divi-sions in both hemispheres (Fig. 16–24). Subsequent development of the sporophyte is traceable to the activity of these two apical cells and their derivatives. The apical growth of the sporophyte (Fig. 16–25) of the Mnionopsida is a deviation from that in the Hepatophyta and from the transient activity of the apical cell in the young sporophyte of *Sphagnum.*

The bi-apical development of the sporophyte of *Funaria* is prolonged and results in the formation of a spindle-like structure within the arche-gonium (Fig. 16–26). The lower apical cell and its derivatives form the lower portion of the sporophyte, the base of which digests its way through the archegonial pedicel into the stem tissue of the gametophore, functioning as a **foot.** The upper apical cell and its derivatives are even more active and develop the major portion of the sporophyte.

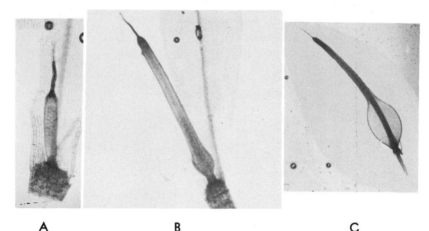

A   B   C

Fig. 16–26. *Funaria hygrometrica.* Further development of sporophyte. A, Sporophyte within calyptra, stage corresponding to that in Fig. 16–25. X 30. B, Elongation of sporophyte, inflation of calyptra. X 30. C, Further inflation of calyptra; foot region of sporophyte dissected from gametophore. X 12½.

Serial transverse sections, beginning at the apex of the cylindrical sporophyte, reveal that the derivatives of the apical cell divide so as to form an endothecium which is at first composed of four quadrately ar-

Fig. 16–27. *Polytrichum* sp. Capsule at extreme right covered by hairy appendages of calyptra, the latter removed from the other specimen to show the capsule. X 2.

ranged cells surrounded by eight primary amphithecial cells. By continued periclinal and anticlinal divisions the amphithecium and endothecium increase in thickness and circumference.

The cells of the archegonial venter at first undergo divisions, and the venter becomes distended (Figs. 16–25, 16–26), so that the young sporophyte is enclosed within the archegonium for a time; but the rapid and inexorable enlargement of the sporophyte soon ruptures the venter. In this manner, the archegonial neck and upper portion of the venter are raised above the leaves of the gametophore. The distal portion of the archegonium, which surmounts the apex of the sporophyte, now is called the **calyptra** (Figs. 16–17*B,C*, 16–27, 16–28). In *Polytrichum* (Fig. 16–27), the major portion of the calyptra is composed of thick-walled protonema-like branches which arise from the venter soon after fertilization and expand during development of the sporophyte.

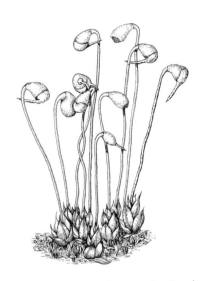

Fig. 16–28. *Funaria hygrometrica.* Female branches with maturing sporophytes; note setae and capsules, one of the latter having shed its peaked calyptra and operculum. X ¾.

Although the moss sporophyte is chlorophyllous throughout development, there can be little question that elaborated foods as well as water and inorganic salts from the gametophore are transferred to the young sporophyte through the foot. The sporophyte of most true mosses exceeds in stature and complexity that of any Hepatophyta and other Bryophyta. In duration of development, it is surpassed only by the sporophyte of *Anthoceros*. The sporophytes of *Funaria* (Fig. 16–28) may exceed two inches in length, and those of species of *Polytrichum* (Figs. 16–17, 16–18) may attain a length of six inches.

The sporophyte remains a needle-like, cylindrical structure until apical elongation has ceased. At that time the distal portion of the sporophyte becomes much enlarged and differentiated into the **capsule** (Fig. 16–28). The major portion of the sporophyte below the capsule functions as a **seta;** the short **foot** is embedded in the gametophore. The central cells of

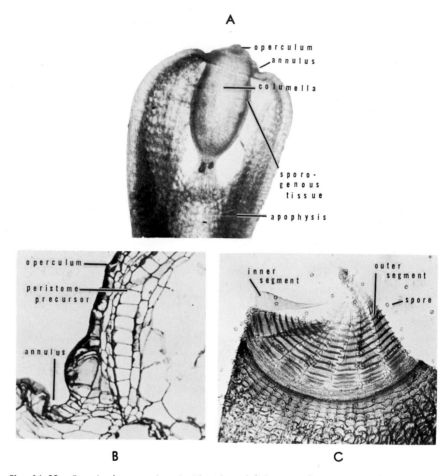

Fig. 16–29. *Funaria hygrometrica.* A, Dissection of living capsule; note operculum, annulus, columella, sporogenous tissue, and photosynthetic tissue within capsule wall. X 30. B, Median longitudinal section of developing peristome segment and adjacent regions; note annulus and thickening of outer and inner tangential walls of cell layer 5. X 125. C, Portion of peristome of mature *Funaria* capsule, showing outer and inner portions. X 125.

the seta are thin-walled and probably function in conduction. As the sporophyte matures, profound changes occur in the capsule region; it becomes a rather complicated, highly differentiated structure, whose organization is illustrated in Fig. 16–29. In *Funaria* and certain other mosses, the basal portion of the capsule remains sterile, enlarges somewhat, and is actively photosynthetic; this region is known as the **apophysis.** Its epidermis bears guard cells and stomata. The upper portion of the capsule contains both sterile and fertile cells. The latter (Fig. 16–29A), ultimately two layers in extent, arise from the outermost layers of the endothecium and are arranged in the form of a barrel or urn, with the distal portion wider than the proximal. The cells within the region of sporogenous tissue in the central portion of the capsule form a **columella** which represents the entire endothecium, except the sporogenous tissue. The cells external to the sporogenous tissue remain sterile and form photosynthetic tissue and the capsule wall (Fig. 16–29A). Relatively late in development, the

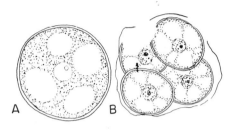

Fig. 16–30. *Funaria hygrometrica.* A, Spore mother cell. B, Spore tetrad. X 770.

sporogenous cells function as spore mother cells, each undergoing meiosis to form a tetrad of spores (Fig. 16–30). As in *Sphagnum,* elaters are absent in the Mnionopsida. The apical portion of the capsule is entirely sterile and undergoes considerable differentiation. The outer layers thicken and are shed ultimately as a cap-like **operculum** which is loosened as the thin-walled cells below the rim-like **annulus** at its base dry out (Fig. 16–29).

In *Funaria* (Fig. 16–29B), the fifth layer of cells from the surface layer of the operculum becomes differentially thickened and at maturity dries out, forming a ring of tooth-like segments, the **peristome** (Gr. peri, around

Fig. 16–31. *Atrichum* sp. Bisected capsule showing peristome with cellular teeth attached to epiphragm. X 30.

+ Gr. *stoma,* mouth) (Fig. 16–29C.) This thickening also extends for a short distance centripetally from the tangential walls along the horizontal walls. As a matter of fact, inasmuch as the thickening of the tangential walls involves the cell layers adjacent to the fifth (the fourth and sixth), three cell layers are actually involved in peristome formation in *Funaria*. The vertical, radial walls of the fifth layer remain unthickened. As these cells dry, they split along the thin radial walls, thus freeing the outer tangential walls and the inner tangential walls. In *Funaria*, the peristome consists of two layers of sixteen segments each. These are attached to a ring of thick-walled cells which form the rim of the capsule.

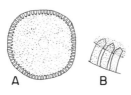

Fig. 16–32. *Polytrichum* sp. A, Frontal view of capsule showing cellular teeth attached to epiphragm. X 8. B, Detail of peristome. X 35.

Meanwhile, the thin-walled cells within the capsule dry, and it contains a powdery mass of cellular debris intermingled with spores. The persistome teeth are hygroscopic, responding to slight changes in humidity by expansion and resultant curving. As they dry, they become somewhat arched and lift the operculum from the capsule apex. They remain arched and separated from each other during periods of low humidity, but in dampness or rain they expand longitudinally and laterally and thus cover the mouth of the capsule. Because of such mechanisms, spore dissemination in the Mnionopsida is almost always a gradual process.

Fig. 16–33. *Fissidens* sp. Portion of peristome showing bifid teeth. X 60.

The variation in structure and mechanism of the peristomes of mosses is a fascinating subject which can be pursued readily at low magnification, with the aid of only a hand lens. In some genera, like *Atrichum* (Fig. 16–31) and *Polytrichum* (Fig. 16–32) and their relatives, the short peristome teeth of the angular capsule are cellular instead of being composed only of cell walls, as in *Funaria*. Furthermore, in these plants, the teeth are short and are attached to a membranous layer, the **epiphragm**, which covers the mouth of the capsule. A number of other widely distributed mosses have double, acellular peristomes like those of *Funaria*. Among these may be cited *Aulocomnium, Mnium,* and *Bryum*. In other genera with acellular peristomes, a single ring of teeth is formed because only the inner tangential walls of the peristome-forming cells become thickened. *Fissidens* (Fig. 16–33),

Dicranum, and *Ceratodon* are mosses with single peristomes. Among commonly encountered genera, *Physcomitrium* is an example of a moss in which a peristome is altogether lacking. Finally, there is evidence that dryness does not always effect the opening of the capsule mouth and spore dissemination. In species of *Leucodon, Neckera,* and *Forsstroemia,* for example, the wet peristome opens the mouth of the capsule and thus enhances egress of the spores.

Summary

In summary, a number of features in the morphology and reproduction of the Mnionopsida are worthy of note. The gametophyte includes two separate phases, the preliminary protonema, with few exceptions a branching filament (in contrast to the spatulate protonema of *Sphagnum*), and leafy gametophores which are produced from buds on the protonema. At maturity the gametophores develop sex organs in either homothallic or heterothallic fashion, depending on the species. The sex organs are large and pedicellate and develop through the activity of apical cells. The zygote gives rise to the sporophyte, whose development is bi-apical. The mature sporophyte is composed of foot, seta, and capsule, the last more complex than that of the Sphagnopsida and Hepatophyta. The sporophyte is actively photosynthetic from the earliest stages of development, and particularly so in the apophysis of the capsule, where stomata and guard cells are present in many genera. The sporogenous tissue is restricted in amount and arises as a double layer from the outermost cells of the endothecium; unlike that of the Sphagnopsida, it does not overarch the columella. A complicated mechanism, the peristome, related to spore dissemination, is organized at the mouth of the capsules in the Mnionopsida. The sporophyte in this class exceeds that of other Bryophyta in stature and complexity.

CLASS 3. ANDREAEOPSIDA

As noted at the beginning of this chapter, the third class of Bryophyta, the Andreaeopsida, are represented by only two genera, both of them rather restricted in distribution. *Andreaea* (Fig. 16–34), the granite moss, is an inhabitant of rocks. The minute mosses are blackish and occur in dense clumps. *Andreaea* possesses attributes of both the Sphagnopsida and the Mnionopsida. Among these may be cited the early stages of germination within the spore wall, the strap-like protonema, suggestive of the protonema of *Sphagnum,* the dehiscence of the capsule by four vertical slits, and its elevation by a pseudopodium. The general habit of the plant, however, is more like that of the Mnionopsida.

SUMMARY AND CLASSIFICATION

The division Bryophyta is often considered to include mosses and their "allies," namely, the liverworts and horned liverworts. This concept of the scope of the division dates back to the late eighteenth century. Now that representatives of these groups have been described, it may be profitable to review the morphological attributes they possess in common and those in which they differ, with the purpose of reaching some conclusion regarding their origin and relationship, if any. It will be recalled that in the division Hepatophyta, the Hepatopsida were considered to include three series, as follows: (1) the *Riccia-Ricciocarpus-Marchantia* group, in which external simplicity of body form is combined with internal differentiation; (2) the *Pellia-Pallavicinia-Metzgeria-Sphaerocarpos* group, in which both external and internal simplicity are combined; and (3) the *Porella* group, in which lack of internal differentiation is associated with external complexity. The Anthoceropsida are here represented only by *Anthoceros*, the horned liverwort, whose morphological attributes were summarized in the preceding chapter. Representatives of two groups of Bryophyta—*Sphagnum* of the Sphagnopsida and *Funaria* and *Polytrichum* among other Mnionopsida—have been described in the present chapter. *Andreaea* of the Andreaeopsida has been considered only briefly.

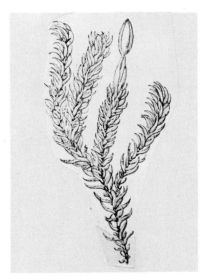

Fig. 16–34. *Andreaea rupestris* Hedw. Branches with dehiscent capsule. X 9. (From *Bryologica Europaea.*)

When one reviews the structure and reproduction of the members of these several groups, the diversities among them appear more striking than the resemblances. Why, then, are they so often grouped together, inasmuch as such grouping implies, at the very least, morphological parallelism, or, to some people, relationship and common origin? The number of characters common to both the Hepatophyta and the mosses are few, in the writer's opinion. All these plants are similar in their life cycle, which involves the regular alternation of a free-living gametophyte and an epiphytic sporophyte. The gametophyte of liverworts, horned liverworts, and mosses is clearly the dominant, longer-lived phase, although the sporophyte in the Mnionopsida perhaps rivals the gametophyte in complexity. While such characteristics as biflagellate sperms, multicellular sex organs, sporic meiosis, aerial spore dissemination, and terrestrial habitat may seem attractive as significant common attributes, one or more of them are found in either the algae or the higher plants. In the final analysis, it is largely the life cycle and the relative balance between the alternating generations upon which the usual concept of the division Bryophyta is based. Whether this is a sufficiently firm foundation is, of course, a matter of opinion. The great German morphologist Goebel[1] wrote more than fifty years ago: "Between Hepaticae (liverworts) and Musci (mosses) there are no transition-forms; as there are none between Bryophyta and Pteridophyta, and as there never were such transitions their absence is not caused by their having died out." No evidence has been educed in the interim to contradict these views. The liverworts and mosses, therefore, have been considered as separate phyletic lines and placed in separate divisions (Hepatophyta and Bryophyta) in this text.

With reference to the origin of the Hepatophyta and Bryophyta, there seems to be universal agreement that this should be sought among algal ancestors. If one recalls the various algal classes described in earlier chapters—the Myxophyceae, Chlorophyceae, Phaeophyceae, Rhodophyceae, and miscellaneous additional groups—certain suggestive parallelisms become apparent. In the first place, in photosynthate and pigmentation the Hepatophyta and Bryophyta (and all the higher plants) are fundamentally similar to the Chlorophyceae, but they differ in these respects from the remaining groups of algae. It is quite possible, however, that the variation in pigmentation and photosynthate among the several groups of algae may represent biochemical mutations from an original common type, so that morphological parallelisms between Hepatophyta and Bryophyta, on the one hand, and groups of algae other than Chlorophyceae, on the other hand, perhaps should not be excluded from discussion.

Certain ecological and morphological attributes also are common to

---

[1] K. Goebel, *Organography of Plants,* Clarendon Press, 1905, Part 2, p. 7.

Chlorophyceae, liverworts, and mosses. Among these may be cited the occurrence of parenchymatous plant bodies, apical growth, terrestrial or amphibious existence, morphological alternation of generations, biflagellate motile reproductive cells (with apical insertion of the flagella), alga-like protonematal stages, and development of anchoring and absorptive organs. Examples of green algae with one or more of these attributes will occur to the reader.

On the other hand, multicellular sex organs having sterile jackets, like the antheridia and archegonia of Hepatophyta and Bryophyta, are absent among Chlorophyceae, as is also an example of morphological alternation of generations with the balance and nutritive relations characteristic of the Hepatophyta and Bryophyta. The Charophyceae furnish a possible exception to these statements, insofar as multicellular sex organs are concerned.

All the criteria of possible relationship so far reviewed belong to the realm of comparative morphology. The student will recall that in such discussions as the present one, evidence from the fossil record usually is evoked. Insofar as Hepatophyta and Bryophyta are concerned, the fossil record is perhaps eloquent in its silence, for very few fossil forms have been described. The few records available are from Pennsylvanian (Fig. 30–1) strata and indicate, in a fragmentary manner, that the Hepatophyta of that era were not markedly different from our extant genera. While liverworts and mosses possess many physiological and morphological attributes in common with green algae, actual intermediate types never have been discovered, although future investigation may reveal them. It is possible that the stimulus of a terrestrial rather than an aquatic habitat evoked sudden large changes which account for the absence of intermediates between the Chlorophyceae and the most primitive land plants.

Finally, there remains the problem of classification of the Bryophyta, with special reference to the illustrative genera described in this chapter. Two classes of the division Bryophyta, the Sphagnopsida and Andreaeopsida, are usually considered to contain but a single order and family. The class Mnionopsida, however, is the largest of the Bryophyta and is composed of a number of diverse types which have occasioned the creation of a number of orders and families (varying between seven and thirteen). These have been delimited on the basis of varying combinations of sporophytic and gametophytic attributes, among them number of rows of leaves, position of the gametophores (erect or prostrate), longevity of the gametophores (annual, biennial, or perennial), and position and structure of the sporophyte and capsule, especially the peristome. Inasmuch as approximately 14,000 species of Mnionopsida have been described, detailed consideration of their classification is outside the scope of this book. The more important illustrative genera described in this chapter may be grouped as follows:

Division Bryophyta
    Class 1. Sphagnopsida (Peat mosses)
        Order 1. Sphagnales
            Family 1. Sphagnaceae
                Genus: *Sphagnum*
    Class 2. Andreaeopsida (Granite mosses)
        Order 1. Andreaeales
            Family 1. Andreaeaceae
                Genus: *Andreaea*
    Class 3. Mnionopsida (True mosses)
        Order 1. Funariales
            Family 1. Funariaceae
                Genus: *Funaria*
        Order 2. Eubryales
            Family 1. Mniaceae
                Genus: *Mnium*
        Order 3. Polytrichales
            Family 1. Polytrichaceae
                Genera: *Atrichum, Polytrichum*

Review of these classes, as illustrated by their representative genera, will reveal the morphological differences on the basis of which the three classes are separated. The Sphagnopsida are distinguished from the Mnionopsida by the unique structure of their gametophores, by their protonema, by the lack of apical growth in the development of their sporophytes, by the formation of the sporogenous tissue from the amphithecium and its dome-like position over the columella, and finally, by the possession of a pseudopodium rather than an active sporophytic seta. Furthermore, all the genera of Mnionopsida discussed in this chapter differ from *Sphagnum* in having a peristome. The Andreaeopsida have certain features in common with each of these groups, such as origin of sporogenous tissue from the endothecium and a pseudopodium which elevates the capsule.

The three orders of Mnionopsida, representatives of which have been emphasized in this chapter, differ as follows: The gametophores of the Funariales are usually annual or biennial inhabitants of soil and are small in stature. The peristome, if present, may be single or double and is composed of sixteen segments; the operculum is not beaked. The gametophores of the Eubryales usually form perennial mats and their stems bear many rows of leaves. The sporophyte is mostly apical and its capsule is usually bent or pendulous. The Polytrichales are distinguished by their angular capsules which have thirty-two to sixty-four *cellular* teeth attached to an epiphragm that closes the capsule orifice. A more complete discussion of the classification of mosses will be found in certain of the reference works listed at the conclusion of Chapter 15.

THEORETICAL ASPECTS OF ALTERNATION OF GENERATIONS

The question of the origin of the alternating generations and their relation to each other has always played a prominent role in discussions of the phylogeny of land plants. This question was alluded to briefly at the end of the preceding chapter. Two somewhat different interpretations of the nature, relation, and origin of the alternating generations have developed since the life cycle of land plants was clarified by Hofmeister in the middle of the nineteenth century. These are known as the **homologous** and **antithetic theories of alternation of generations.** According to the **antithetic theory,** which was developed in large part before the complexity and range of algal life cycles were fully appreciated, the gametophyte generation is the primitive one, and the sporophyte is of secondary origin. Furthermore, according to this theory, the sporophyte is not merely a modified gametophyte but an entirely different phase of the life cycle which has been interpolated between successive gametophyte generations because of a delay in meiosis. Proponents of this "interpolation" theory view the gametophyte of the simpler land plants as having had an algal origin, but they are inclined to the assumption that the first appearance of the sporophyte in the land plants coincided with the inception of the terrestrial habit. Assuming that the sporophyte appeared as a result of delay in meiosis, with the result that a number of diploid cells (rather than one) ultimately produce tetrads of spores, they interpret the primary function of the sporophyte as spore production. With the production of increasingly large numbers of spores, it is postulated that the sporophyte gradually took upon itself nutritional and other vegetative functions by sterilization of some of the sporogenous tissue. According to this theory, the vegetative tissues of the sporophytes of the land plants all have had their origin in the sterilization of potentially sporogenous tissue. Furthermore, it is strongly implied that alternation of generations in the land plants arose independently of that in aquatic algae. Alternation in algae and in land plants is interpreted as an example of **parallel evolution** or **homoplasy**.

In contrast to the antithetic or interpolation theory of the alternation of generations, the **homologous theory,** while agreeing that the gametophyte generation is the more primitive, views the sporophyte as a modified gametophyte. The range of variation in the life cycles described for the various genera of algae in earlier chapters furnishes evidence in support of the homologous theory. Especially strong support is available in the genera in which the alternating generations are almost indistinguishable morphologically, as in *Ulva, Cladophora suhriana, Ectocarpus,* and possibly *Polysiphonia* and *Griffithsia.* In these life cycles, the diploid, spore-producing asexual sporophytes are strikingly similar to their corresponding gametophytes. Furthermore, it should be noted that like the gametophytes, they are photosynthetic throughout their development. There is no evidence that their photosynthetic tissues arose by sterilization of potentially sporogenous tissues. Even in haplobiontic algae like *Chlamydomonas* and *Spirogyra,* the homologue of the sporophyte, namely, the unicellular zygote, is photosynthetic. Further evidence for the homologous theory of alternation of generations is available in the deviations from the normal life cycle observable in certain mosses and vascular plants. In such genera, either naturally or as a result of artificial stimulation, portions of the sporophyte can give rise to gametophytes, or gametophytes may give rise directly to sporophytes in the absence of a sexual process. These phenomena are known as **apospory** and **apogamy,** respectively. This is certainly an indication that sporophyte and gametophyte generations are not as fundamentally different as postulated by the interpolation theory.

While it is possible to assume that alternation of gametophyte and sporophyte originated independently in the land plants at a time when their supposed algal ancestors took up a terrestrial habitat, and to attempt to reconcile the divergence between their sporophytes and gametophytes by this device, quite another view is possible. The algae exhibit types of alternation in which the sporophyte and gametophyte are in as marked contrast (*Laminaria*) as those of the land plants, yet both develop in an aquatic habitat. It seems quite possible that the stimulus which so profoundly modified the sporophyte generation in so many land plants was retention of the zygote and the sporophyte within the nourishing tissues of the gametophyte. The carpospore-bearing generation of such Rhodophyceae as *Griffithsia* and *Polysiphonia* may well indicate the result of such retention among the algae.

It is impossible, of course, to decide which of these two theories regarding alternating generations is correct, for much of the "evidence" on which both are based is speculative rather than verifiable by observation or experiment. Nevertheless, these views have been presented for the consideration of the student to guide him toward a synthesis of his own views on the phylogeny of plants.

DISCUSSION QUESTIONS

1. What attributes distinguish the Bryophyta from the Hepatophyta?
2. What attributes do the Hepatophyta and Bryophyta share in common?
3. Which of the Bryophyta have the most highly developed gametophyte, with reference to size and/or tissue differentiation, in your opinion? Which has the most highly developed sporophyte? In each case, give the reasons for your answer.
4. On what grounds can you support separation of the Sphagnopsida from the Mnionopsida?
5. What evidence can you cite in support of an algal origin for Hepatophyta and Bryophyta?
6. Can you suggest an explanation for the scarcity of liverwort and moss fossils?
7. Describe the modifications related to water absorption in *Sphagnum*.
8. How does *Polytrichum* withstand drought?
9. Of what theoretical significance is the observed fact that wounded moss setae produce protonemata? What mechanism is involved?
10. Can you suggest a procedure for obtaining diploid moss sporophytes? Triploid moss sporophytes?
11. Review your knowledge of the structure and nutritional arrangements in the sporophytes of algae, Hepatophyta, and Bryophyta. Then state whether or not you are of the opinion that the evidence supports the interpolation (antithetic) theory of alternation of generations, especially its doctrine of progressive sterilization. Give the reasons for your answer.
12. Can you suggest an experimental approach for obtaining evidence which might support the homologous theory of alternation of generations?
13. With the aid of labeled diagrams, describe the structure and reproduction of *Sphagnum* and one of the Mnionopsida.
14. Observe mosses in the field and examine various species for the presence of sex organs and sporophytes.

CHAPTER 17

Introduction to Vascular Plants; Division Psilophyta

INTRODUCTION TO VASCULAR PLANTS

The plants which have been discussed in Chapters 2 through 16 have in common the negative attribute of lacking vascular tissues, namely, **xylem** and **phloem.**[1] Those which are to be described in the remaining chapters possess these tissues and are known as **vascular plants.** To many botanists, the possession of xylem and phloem, among other attributes, is considered of sufficient significance to warrant classifying all vascular plants in a single division, Tracheophyta (Table 1, Chapter 31), in spite of their other great divergences. This view is not shared by the writer; he views the widespread occurrence of vascular tissue as a manifestation of parallel development in several otherwise diverse groups. This topic will be discussed again at appropriate points in later chapters.

The vascular plants that lack seeds often are called **vascular cryptogams** (Gr. *kryptos,* hidden + Gr. *gamos,* marriage), an appellation of earlier botanists which, in fact, emphasized their ignorance of reproduction in the plants they were designating. In current usage, the term "vascular cryptogams" is applied to vascular plants which do not produce seeds.

All botanists are in agreement that the most primitive vascular plants are those which lack seeds. These are the ferns and "fern allies" of some systems of classification in which these organisms were classified in a single division, the Pteridophyta (Table 1, Chapter 31). The more ad-

---

[1] The phloem-like cells of kelps may be considered an exception.

vanced vascular plants, the seed plants, were placed in a single division, the Spermatophyta, in such classifications. Augmentation of our knowledge of vascular plants by comparative studies of both extant and extinct types has resulted in radical revisions of earlier classifications. It has become apparent that the old group Pteridophyta harbored an unnatural assemblage, rather than true "allies," among which four distinct series were present. These four series are accorded subdivisional rank by those who group all vascular plants in a single division, Tracheophyta (Table 1, p. 617). In the present text, however, the four series which comprised the old division Pteridophyta are raised to divisional rank. These divisions are the **Psilophyta, Microphyllophyta** (Lycopsida or Lepidophyta of other authors), the **Arthrophyta** (Sphenopsida or Calamophyta of other authors), and the **Pterophyta** (the Filicinae of many other authors). (See Table 1, Chapter 31.)

DIVISION PSILOPHYTA: *PSILOTUM*

Introduction and Vegetative Morphology

The division **Psilophyta,** which contains a single class with living members, the **Psilopsida,** is represented in our extant flora by two genera, namely, *Psilotum* (Gr. *psiloun,* to bare), the **whisk fern,** and *Tmesipteris,* the latter native to Australia and New Zealand. Inasmuch as one species of *Psilotum, P. nudum* (L.) Beauv. (Figs. 17–1, 17–8) occurs in our own country in Florida, it will be described as representative of the extant Psilophyta. *Psilotum* is found in tropical and subtropical habitats where it may occur as an epiphyte among the roots of other vegetation or in humus-rich soil pockets among rocks.

The conspicuous plant body, which is the sporophyte, as is the case in all vascular plants, consists of dichotomously branched aerial axes a foot or more in height, and of subterranean stems called **rhizomes** whose epidermal cells bear unicellular **rhizoids** (Fig. 17–1). The aerial stems are angled, often pentagonal in cross sections of the lower portions of the axis and triangular above. They bear small, scale-like appendages which lack vascular tissue. Certain branches have a nodular, jointed appearance at maturity, because they develop globose **sporangia** on extremely short lateral branches (Fig. 17–1). These also bear two bractlike appendages which subtend the sporangium. True roots are absent.

Both rhizome and aerial branches develop by apical growth which may be traced to the activity of a single tetrahedral apical cell and its derivatives, all of which divide actively. This apical, meristematic region is

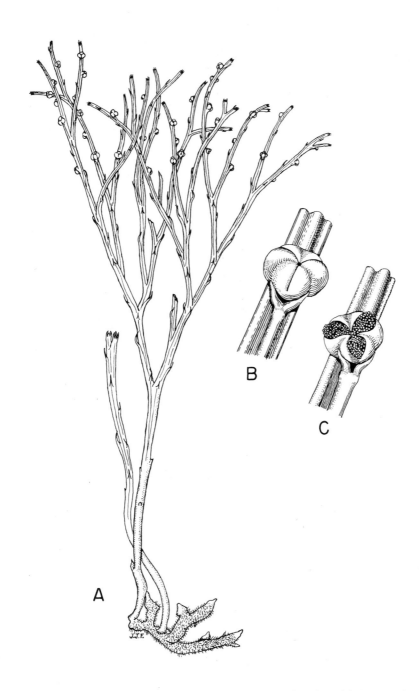

Fig. 17–1. *Psilotum nudum* (L.) Beauv. A, Rhizome and aerial branches of fruiting specimen. X ¾. B,C, Detail of sporangia with bracts; sporangium at C dehiscent. X 9.

called the **promeristem** (Fig. 17–2). A short distance posterior to the promeristem, differentiation becomes apparent (Fig. 17–2) in the meristematic tissues, in which three groups of cells are recognizable. The outermost single layer of cells are prismatic and radially elongate and are known as the **protoderm.** The central mass of elongate cells comprises

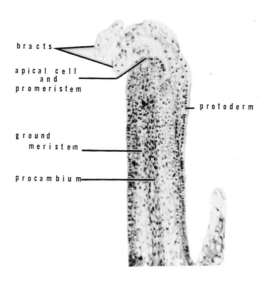

Fig. 17–2. *Psilotum nudum.* Median longitudinal section of tip of aerial axis; note apical cell and promeristem, overlapping bracts, protoderm, ground meristem, and procambium. X 25.

the **procambium;** the cells between the procambium and protoderm are known as the **ground meristem.** These three are sometimes called the **primary meristems,** for their component cells continue to divide.

In slightly older regions of the stem, the procambium cells differentiate into the vascular tissue which is termed the **stele** (Gr. *stele,* a post or rod) (Fig. 17–3A). The vascular tissue is composed of centrally located **xylem** (Gr. *xylon,* wood) surrounded by **phloem** (Gr. *phloios,* bark). Where the xylem forms a central strand surrounded by phloem, the stele is called a **protostele.** In *Psilotum,* the peripheral portion of the xylem is ridged (Fig. 17–3B); such a protostele is called an **actinostele** (Gr. *aktis,* ray + Gr. *stele*). In the differentiation of the mature tissues from the procambium, an orderliness in development is clearly visible (Fig. 17–3B). Certain peripheral procambium cells are the first to metamorphose into mature xylem cells, and this process continues gradually

in a centripetal direction in older portions of the stem increasingly remote from the apex. This first-formed xylem, the **protoxylem** (Gr. *protos*,
first + Gr. *xylon*), is usually composed of annular or spiral **tracheids**
(Fig. 17–4); these are elongate, tapering cells that function early in
water conduction. The centripetal development of the protoxylem is said
to be **exarch** (Gr. *ex*, out + Gr. *arche*, origin). The later-differentiated
xylem cells, the **metaxylem** (Gr. *meta*, beyond + Gr. *xylon*), are more

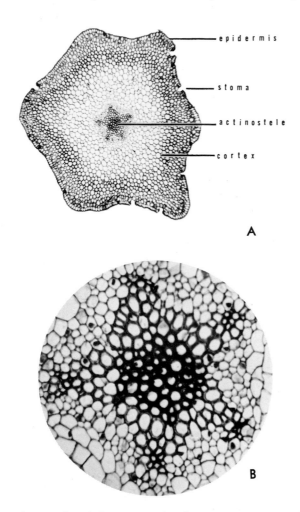

Fig. 17–3. *Psilotum nudum. A,* Transverse section of mature stem; note central actinostele, broad
cortex composed of three tissue types, epidermis, and stomata. X 25. *B,* Enlarged view of stele;
note pentarch xylem surrounded by phloem. X 125.

lignified and are irregularly reticulate or pitted with elongate or circular pits (Fig. 17–4). The tracheids of the metaxylem are usually larger in diameter than those of the protoxylem. The central portion of the stele is composed of thick-walled sclerenchyma (Gr. *skleros*, hard + Gr. *enchyma*, infusion) cells which are usually interpreted as belonging to the xylem. Some of the thinner-walled cells surrounding the xylem are phloem cells. The sieve elements have sieve areas in both their terminal and lateral walls, and they lack nuclei at maturity. A well-developed **endodermis,** readily recognizable by the differentially staining Casparian strips, is present outside the stele. The **cortex** is massive as compared with the stele (Fig. 17–3A) and consists of a parenchymatous storage region adjacent to the endodermis. This is surrounded successively by a zone of sclerenchyma and by several layers of photosynthetic parenchyma cells. The latter represent the major photosynthetic region of the plant, and the increase of the internal surface of the cells by lobing suggests the chlorenchyma in the leaves of certain conifers. The cortical cells of rhizomes frequently contain fungi whose role is not understood. The **epidermis** is heavily cutinized and interrupted here and there, between the ridges of the stem, by **stomata** and **guard cells** (Fig. 17–3A), the latter slightly sunken, as in many xerophytes. A small substomatal chamber is present beneath each stoma.

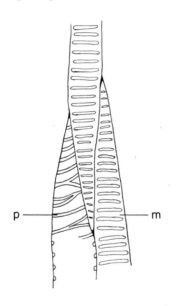

p — — m

Fig. 17–4. *Psilotum nudum.* Portion of three tracheids, one of protoxylem, *p,* and two of metaxylem, *m.* X 770.

In summary, it should be noted that the protoderm differentiates into the epidermis, the procambium differentiates into the xylem and phloem, and the cortex and endodermis arise from the ground meristem. This general pattern of differentiation is repeated, with minor variations, in the stems of a great majority of vascular plants. The bract-like appendages of the stem lack vascular tissue and are made up entirely of photosynthetic tissues covered by an epidermis. Centripetal or **exarch** xylem differentiation is a primitive attribute of vascular plants. **Mesarch** (protoxylem embedded in metaxylem, see Fig. 21–4) and **endarch** (metaxylem centrifugal with reference to protoxylem, see Fig. 27–3B) development of xylem occurs in the higher vascular plants.

Reproduction

Spores are produced in the globose, trilobed sporangia that are borne at the apices of short lateral branches (Fig. 17–1) and therefore

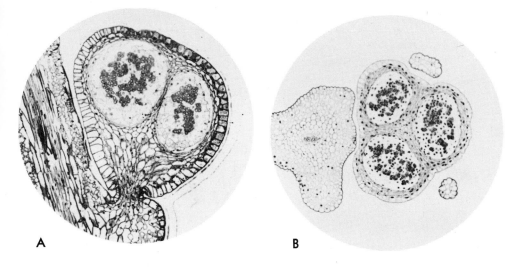

A   **B**

Fig. 17–5. *Psilotum nudum.* A, Longitudinal, and B, transverse section of sporangia in spore mother cell stage. X 30.

are cauline. Two lateral emergences curve about the sporangium. Their subtending branches are traversed centrally by a vascular connection, or **trace,** which is connected with the stele of the main axis. The sporangium originates from the superficial cells of the lateral branch and is **eusporangiate** in development. In this method of sporangium development, which is characteristic of a great majority of vascular plants, a superficial cell or cells divide by periclinal division into an inner and outer cell layer. In subsequent development, the sporogenous tissue arises from the inner products of the initial periclinal divisions, and most of the sporangial wall arises from the outer. It is not entirely clear whether the three-lobed sporangium of *Psilotum* (Fig. 17–5B) represents a single, partitioned sporangium or three single sporangia which have been united. In any case, as development proceeds, both the wall region and the sporogenous

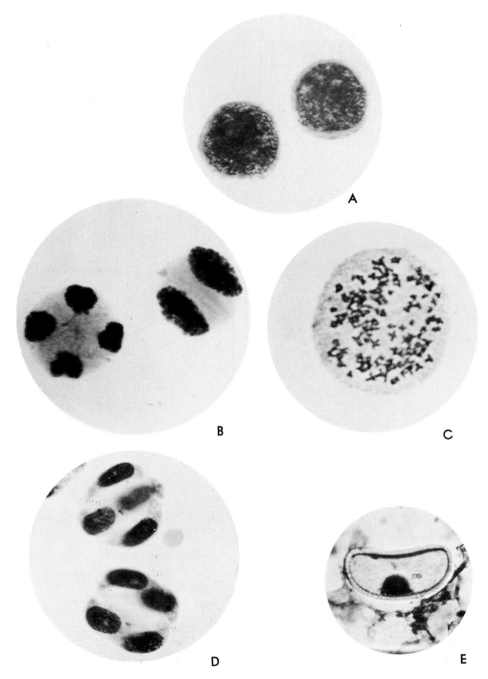

Fig. 17–6. *Psilotum nudum*. Sporogenesis. A, Two spore mother cells, early prophase of division I. B, Telophases of divisions I and II. C, "Squash" of spore mother cell showing numerous diakinetic chromosomes. D, Tetrads of spores. E, Mature spore in section. X 500.

layers increase in thickness by nuclear and cell division. Only a portion of the potentially sporogenous tissue functions as spore mother cells. The remainder disintegrates (Fig. 17–5) at sporogenesis, during which the products of disintegration are absorbed by the spore mother cells. The latter undergo the meiotic process, forming tetrads of spores which ulti-

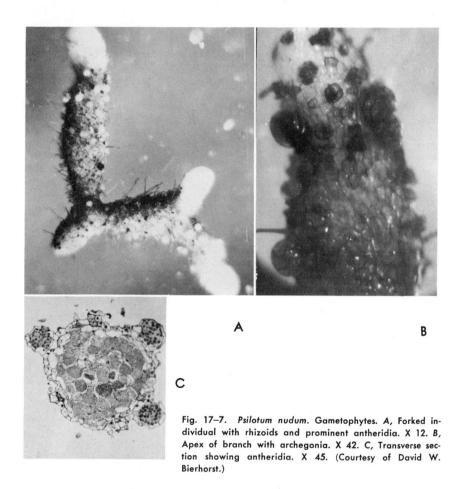

A

B

C

Fig. 17–7. *Psilotum nudum.* Gametophytes. A, Forked individual with rhizoids and prominent antheridia. X 12. B, Apex of branch with archegonia. X 42. C, Transverse section showing antheridia. X 45. (Courtesy of David W. Bierhorst.)

mately separate (Fig. 17–6). The mature spores (Fig. 17–6) are colorless. During sporogenesis, the epidermal layer of the sporangium wall undergoes thickening by additional deposition of wall material. However, a single vertical layer remains thin-walled and, upon drying, serves as the site of dehiscence (Figs. 17–1C, 17–5A).

The spores of *Psilotum* are slow to germinate; none ever have been grown into mature gametophytes under laboratory conditions.[2] The gametophytes (Fig. 17–7) found in nature are cylindrical and sometimes forked and are covered with numerous rhizoids. They are colorless and saprophytic in nutrition, possibly because of their association with an endophytic fungus. They have little internal differentiation. Their cylindrical form, dichotomous branching, and subterranean habitat render

Fig. 17–8.   *Psilotum nudum.* Greenhouse specimen. X 1/6.

them difficult to distinguish from young rhizomes without microscopic examination. The occasional presence of typical xylem cells in the center of the gametophytes, along with their cylindrical form and rhizoids, has been interpreted as support for the homologous theory of alternation of generations, according to which sporophytes and gametophytes are merely different manifestations of a single ancestral plant body. It should be noted that the gametophytes in which xylem tissue has been observed have been shown to be diploid.

The sex organs develop from surface cells of the homothallic gametophytes (Fig. 17–7). The antheridia are hemispherical and slightly protuberant, the single layer of jacket cells enclosing a small number of coiled, multiflagellate sperms (Fig. 17–7C). The archegonia (Fig. 17–7B)

---

[2] Dr. D. W. Bierhorst has recently succeeded in growing gametophytes in the soil of potted greenhouse plants.

are partially sunken within the gametophyte and have necks that are much shorter than those in the Hepatophyta and Bryophyta. The necks are composed of only four rows of neck cells.

Following fertilization, the zygote undergoes transverse division. The outer product of the division gives rise to the embryonic stem; the derivatives of the inner one are organized as an enlarged foot. The primary stem is a branch rhizome which develops rhizoids and becomes infected with a fungus as it emerges from the gametophyte. Some of the branch tips soon become negatively geotropic and produce aerial axes. By this time the embryonic stem usually has separated from the foot, which remains within the gametophyte.

SUMMARY

The more important features of *Psilotum* described above illustrate its anomalous position in comparison with other vascular cryptogams. In its lack of roots and vascularized leaves it is paralleled only by certain fossil genera such as *Rhynia* (Chapter 30). An additional characteristic it shares with them is the terminally cauline position of the sporangia. In this respect it is unlike other living vascular cryptogams, with the possible exception of *Equisetum*. The sporangium itself is primitive in lacking a tapetum, a special tissue for nutrition of the developing spores. The latter obtain metabolites through the distintegration of some of the sporogenous tissue prior to sporogenesis, as noted also in the liverwort, *Sphaerocarpos*. The branched cylindrical gametophytes, similar in some respects to the sporophyte, are almost unique in the plant kingdom. It is possible that *Psilotum* represents a living remnant of members of the Devonian (Chapter 30) flora now extinct, and that it has survived to the present with few modifications from its progenitors. The fossil record sheds no light on this speculation.

DISCUSSION QUESTIONS

1. What is the distinguishing attribute of the division Tracheophyta, as conceived by certain botanists?
2. Define or explain the following: vascular tissue, stele, protostele, actinostele, exarch xylem, protoxylem, metaxylem, promeristem, procambium, protoderm, ground meristem, primary meristems, tracheid, sclerenchyma, parenchyma, chlorenchyma, mycorrhiza.
3. What is meant by eusporangiate sporangium development?
4. The gametophytes of *Psilotum* have never been grown to maturity from spores in laboratory cultures. How would you attempt to accomplish this?

5. What significance has been attached to the occasional occurrence of tracheids in *Psilotum* gametophytes?

6. In what respects is *Psilotum* unusual among vascular plants?

7. Distinguish between rhizoids, rhizomes, and roots.

8. What structural adaptations related to photosynthesis occur in the stems of *Psilotum?*

9. What type of nutrition probably occurs in the *Psilotum* gametophyte?

REFERENCE WORKS ON VASCULAR CRYPTOGAMS[3]

Bower, F. O. *The Origin of a Land Flora,* Macmillan & Co., Ltd., 1908.

Bower, F. O. *Primitive Land Plants,* Macmillan & Co., Ltd., 1935.

Campbell, D. H. *The Structure and Development of Mosses and Ferns,* The Macmillan Company, 1928.

Campbell, D. H. *The Evolution of the Land Plants (Embryophyta),* Stanford Univ. Press, 1940.

Eames, A. J. *Morphology of Vascular Plants,* McGraw-Hill Book Co., Inc., 1936.

Eames, A. J., and MacDaniels, L. H. *An Introduction to Plant Anatomy,* McGraw-Hill Book Co., Inc., 1947.

Esau, K. *Plant Anatomy,* John Wiley and Sons, Inc., 1953.

Jeffrey, E. C. *The Anatomy of Woody Plants,* Univ. of Chicago Press, 1930.

Manton, I. *Problems of Cytology and Evolution in the Pteridophyta,* Cambridge Univ. Press, 1950.

Smith, G. M. *Cryptogamic Botany, Vol. II, Bryophytes and Pteridophytes,* McGraw-Hill Book Co., Inc., 1955.

Verdoorn, F. *Manual of Pteridology,* Martinus Nijhoff, 1938.

Wardlaw, C. W. *Embryogenesis in Plants,* John Wiley and Sons, Inc., 1955.

---

[3] For use with Chapters 17–23.

CHAPTER 18

Division Microphyllophyta

INTRODUCTION

Members of the division **Microphyllophyta** (Gr. *mikros*, small + Gr. *phyllon*, leaf + Gr. *phyton*, plant), a group accorded only subdivisional rank under the title Lycopsida in many schemes of classification (Table 1, p. 617), are readily distinguishable from the Psilophyta by their possession of vascularized leaves and roots and by the intimate association of their sporangia with fertile leaves known as **sporophylls** (Gr. *spora*, spore + Gr. *phyllon*). Some of these plants are known commonly as **club mosses,** because their small stature and their crowded moss-like leaves, closely arranged on the stems, suggest mosses, and the aggregation of sporophylls into terminal groups in certain species has suggested the term "club." Whether they are given class or divisional rank, two series usually are distinguished in the classification of these plants (Table 1, p. 617). In one series, exemplified in this chapter by *Selaginella* (Figs. 18–15 to 18–17) and *Isoetes* (Fig. 18–34), each leaf produces a small, basal, tongue-like protuberance, the **ligule** (L. *ligula*, little tongue). These genera are grouped in the class **Glossopsida** (Gr. *glossa*, tongue + Gr. *opsis*, appearance of); in the other series, **Aglossopsida,** the ligule is absent. The genus *Lycopodium* (Figs. 18–1, 18–4) is classified in the latter category. In addition to these extant plants which are described in the present chapter, a relatively large number of extinct genera usually are included in the same taxa with *Lycopodium* and *Selaginella;* these will be described in Chapter 30.

CLASS 1. AGLOSSOPSIDA: *LYCOPODIUM*

Introduction and Vegetative Morphology

Lycopodium and *Phylloglossum,* the only living genera included in this class, comprise 180 species. Species of *Lycopodium* (Figs. 18–1, 18–4) are widely distributed and are familiarly known as **ground pines, trailing evergreens,** and **club mosses.** Some species are perennials, living

Fig. 18–1.   *Lycopodium complanatum* L. Shoot with two groups of strobili. X 1.

upon the forest floor in temperate climates, but many tropical species are epiphytic in habitat. The plants are rather firm herbs whose stems are dichotomously branched (Fig. 18–4) or monopodial. In the latter case, the branch system consists of a main axis which supports minor branches. The leaves are small and sessile, and spiral in arrangement. In *L. com-planatum* L., the leaves are much reduced and almost scale-like (Fig. 18–2). All species have branching rhizomes from which aerial branches develop. The roots are delicate and dichotomously branched, and are scattered along the underground portions of the stem from which they arise endogenously.

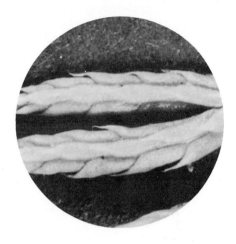

Development of both the stem and root of *Lycopodium* may be traced to an apical group of meristematic cells no one of which is specially differentiated. A central procambium strand develops some distance back from the promeristem in both stem and root

Fig. 18–2. *Lycopodium complanatum*. Detail of leafy axis. X 6.

and ultimately gives rise to an exarch protostele in both (Fig. 18–6). In the stem, the stele is bounded by several layers of pericycle cells and

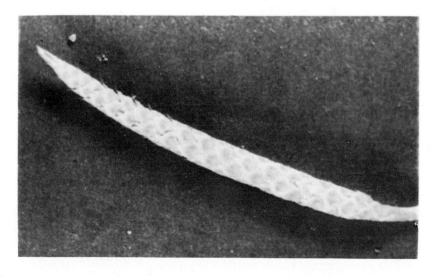

Fig. 18–3. *Lycopodium complanatum*. Strobilus. X 3.

sharply delimited by a well-developed endodermis. The epidermis of the stem contains stomata and guard cells. The arrangement of xylem and phloem in the stem varies in different species, in accordance with the degree of ridging or dissection of the central xylem mass. In the species (Fig. 18–6) in which the xylem seems to consist of discrete

Fig. 18–4. *Lycopodium lucidulum* Michx. X 3/5.

masses in transverse section, serial transverse sections reveal that the *apparently* discrete units are lobes that join each other at different levels of the stem. In species with dissected xylem masses, phloem cells develop between them. In species with continuous xylem, the phloem is present between the lobes of the xylem.

The roots of *Lycopodium* arise deep within the rhizomes from the surface of the stele. They grow down through the cortex and emerge into the soil at points somewhat removed from the level of their origin. Transverse sections indicate that the mature root also contains an exarch protostele with only one protoxylem ridge. Such a root is said to be **monarch** in its xylem arrangement. The tip of the root is protected by a root cap. The root hairs are anomalous in that they develop in pairs from the epidermal cells. Roots of *Lycopodium* usually branch dichotomously; the branches originate through the reorganization of the apical meristematic cells into two groups.

The leaves of *Lycopodium* arise by localized growth of groups of superficial cells near the stem apex. As they grow, each develops a central procambium strand which finally differentiates into a vascular strand of tracheids surrounded by scattered sieve elements and parenchyma. The chlorenchyma of the leaf is rather uniform in structure, small intercellular spaces being present. Depending on the species, the stomata occur either on the epidermis of both leaf surfaces or only on the lower epidermis. The vascular supply of the leaf passes into the stem as a **leaf trace**[1] which is connected with the protoxylem of the stem stele (Fig. 18–6).

Fig. 18–5. *Lycopodium lucidulum.* Detail of fertile zone showing dehiscent sporangia. X 6.

Leaves with a single unbranched vein, whose trace leaves no parenchymatous gap in the stele above its point of departure, are said to be **microphyllous.** It should be emphasized at this point that small size is merely a secondary attribute of many microphyllous leaves; their possession of single, unbranched veins and the absence of leaf gaps near their traces are their distinguishing features.

---

[1] Although leaf traces are said to "pass out" or "pass in" they of course do not move. Vascular connections between stems and leaves, stems and roots, and roots and branch roots are established during ontogeny by the differentiation of procambium strands which are precursors of the vascular connection. The "connection" occurs merely by juxtaposition of conducting elements, not by any sort of cell fusion.

Reproduction

Species of *Lycopodium,* like *L. lucidulum* Michx., in which the sporophylls are not localized in compact aggregations, in many instances produce special mechanisms for vegetative propagation, namely, **gemmae**

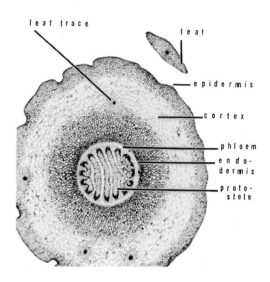

Fig. 18–6. *Lycopodium clavatum* L. Transverse section of axis; note central (partially dissected) protostele, endodermis, cortex with three component tissues, leaf traces, epidermis, and (transverse section) leaves. X 25.

or **bulbils.** These consist of a proximal enlarged base and a distal short axis with several pairs of leaves. The distal portion is abscised and may develop into a young sporophyte under favorable conditions.

The sporophyte of *Lycopodium* at maturity produces spores in rather massive, kidney-shaped sporangia which are borne on short stalks either on the leaf base or in the axil of the leaf and stem (Figs. 18–5, 18–7). In some species—*L. lucidulum,* for example, the fertile, sporangium-bearing leaves, the **sporophylls,** are entirely similar to sterile leaves and occur in zones among them (Figs. 18–4, 18–5); such species are considered primitive. In species like *L. complanatum,* on the other hand, localization of the sporophylls into a terminal cone-like structure, the **strobilus,** is accompanied by their modification into nonphotosynthetic, scale-like structures which are reduced in size (Figs. 18–1, 18–3). This condition is interpreted as the most advanced in the genus. Some morphologists regard the *lucidulum* type as a strobilus comprising an entire plant. According to this view, the sterile leaves represent secondarily sterilized sporophylls. Evidence for this interpretation is based mainly on the occurrence of abortive sporangia on some of the vegetative leaves.

It is clear that the compact type of strobilus is a stem with short internodes bearing sporophylls (Fig. 18–7). The strobilus develops from an apical meristem and its vascular structure is similar to that of the vegetative axis. Each sporophyll is supplied from the stele by a single trace, as are the vegetative leaves of the plant. The individual sporangium arises from a row of superficial cells on the adaxial surface of the leaf base

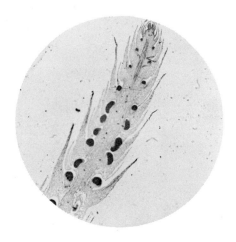

Fig. 18–7. *Lycopodium obscurum* L. Longitudinal section of strobilus showing ontogeny of sporangia. X 12½.

or at the junction of the leaf and stem (Figs. 18–7, 18–10*B*). These cells usually undergo divisions parallel to the leaf surface; hence a single trans-

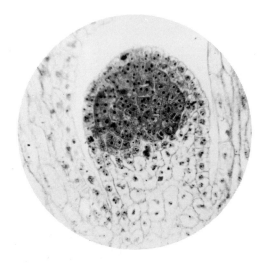

Fig. 18–8. *Lycopodium obscurum*. Longitudinal section of immature sporangium; note stalk, sporogenous tissue, and wall. X 250.

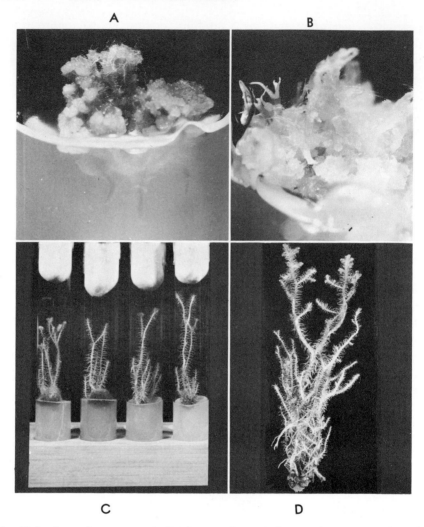

Fig. 18–9. *Lycopodium cernuum* L. Development of gametophytes and young sporophytes in culture. *A*, Prothallus on agar; note club-shaped tips and rhizoids. X 2.3. *B*, Prothallus with several embryos (left) with first leaves or prophylls. X 4. *C*, Young sporophytes arising from prothalli; cultures two months old. *D*, Plants with young strobili, 28 months after spore germination. (Courtesy of Ralph H. Wetmore.)

verse row of cells, three cells deep, extends partially across the leaf base. The central row continues division and ultimately forms the sporogenous tissue (Fig. 18–8). The upper row also undergoes division and develops a three-layered sporangium wall. The innermost wall layer, next to the sporogenous tissue, functions as a nutritive layer, the **tapetum**. The lowermost of the original three cell layers contributes to the lower sporangial wall and stalk. As the sporangium develops, the sporogenous cells become isolated and spherical and ultimately produce a tetrad of spores each. These finally separate and secrete a wall whose ornamentation varies with the species. The spores are yellow at maturity. Dehiscence of the sporangium occurs along a line of cells running across the upper surface of the reniform sporangium (Fig. 18–5). In species with compact strobili,

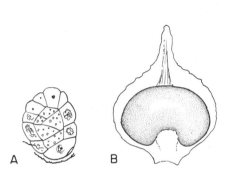

Fig. 18–10. A, *Lycopodium annotinum* L. Spore germination; peripheral cells with mycorrhizal fungus. X 312. (From Bruchmann.) B, *Lycopodium complanatum*. Adaxial view of sporophyll. X 8.

Fig. 18–11. Gametophytes of *Lycopodium,* the first and second (l. to r.) of *L. complanatum* and the third of *L. obscurum.* X ½.

this is preceded by slight elongation of the internodes and by drying and spreading of the sporophylls.

The various species of *Lycopodium* vary in the speed with which their spores germinate and complete their development into mature gametophytes. This process has been followed under controlled conditions in only one species, namely, *L. cernuum* L.;[2] consequently reports of pregermination dormancy periods as long as eight years for some species may be altered as a result of further work. The first divisions of the germinating spore are largely endogenous and in some species are reported to cease early, unless the young gametophyte becomes infected with a mycorrhizal fungus (Fig. 18–10). Mature gametophytes found in nature usually are associated with such a fungus throughout their existence. Among the species thus far investigated, three intergrading types

---

[2] J. A. Freeburg and R. H. Wetmore (in press) recently have succeeded with other species by scarifying the spores thus hastening germination.

of gametophytes (Figs. 18–9, 18–11, 18–12) have been observed: (1) fleshy structures whose lower conical portion is subterranean, the epiterranean portion bearing photosynthetic lobes among whose bases the sex organs are produced (Figs. 18–11, 18–12); (2) completely subterranean, fleshy gametophytes lacking photosynthetic lobes, in which nutrition is entirely saprophytic, and the sex organs are borne on the upper

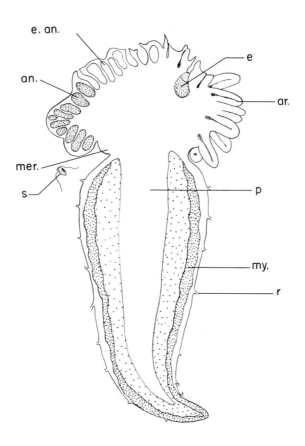

Fig. 18–12. *Lycopodium complanatum*. Median longitudinal section of gametophyte, diagrammatic. X 25. (After Bruchmann.) *an.*, antheridium; *ar.*, archegonium; *e*, embryo; *e.an.*, empty antheridium; *mer.*, meristematic collar; *my.*, mycorrhizal zone; *p*, central pith-like region; *r*, rhizoid; *s*, sperm.

surface of the gametophytes; (3) branching, cylindrical, colorless gametophytes whose elongate branches may become independent as a result of apical growth and posterior decay.

The development of both antheridia and archegonia may be traced to single superficial cells. In each case, these undergo periclinal division; by further division, the inner of the two cells gives rise to the major portion of the antheridium and archegonium. The sex organs therefore are partially embedded. The antheridia (Fig. 18–12) are massive and produce large numbers of biflagellate sperms which are liberated through the ruptured superficial wall cells. The archegonial necks (Figs. 18–12, 18–13) vary among the several species in length and degree of emergence. The necks are composed of four or five rows of neck cells.

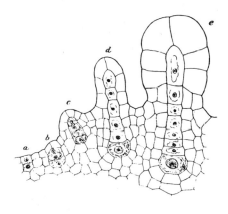

Fig. 18–13. *Lycopodium selago* L. Development of archegonia. X 250. (After Bruchmann.) a-e, successively older stages.

The finding of *Lycopodium* gametophytes, each with several attached sporophytes in various stages of development, indicates not only that the gametophytes are long-lived and active in the nutrition of the embryonic sporophyte, but also that the sex organs may function over long periods. The zygote divides by a transverse wall into an outer, **suspensor cell,** and an inner, **embryo-forming cell** (Fig. 18–14). The latter develops the embryo itself; the former may divide once or twice. The first embryonic leaf may be called the **cotyledon** (Gr. *kotyledon*, socket). The portion of the axis between the cotyledonary node and the root is known as the **hypocotyl.** Its length varies in different species, according to the depth of the gametophyte which bears the embryo. The primary root, the **radicle,** eventually penetrates the soil; the primary axis grows out of the gametophyte and up into the light. Axes and leaves of sporophytes borne on subterranean gametophytes remain colorless until they emerge above the substratum. The gametophyte may persist for a long time attached to the sporophyte (Fig. 18–11), but it ultimately disintegrates as the latter becomes established. It should be noted that the primary root or radicle is relatively ephemeral; all roots of the mature sporophyte are **adventitious.**[3] Furthermore, the first leaves differ from those on the ma-

---

[3] The primary root and its branches develop from the root of the embryonic sporophyte. According to one point of view, *all other* roots are **adventitious.** Other morphologists call roots that are regularly borne on stems, as in the present case, **cladogenous.**

ture plant in their scale-like habit as well as in the absence of vascular tissue and chlorophyll.

Summary

The axis of the sporophyte in many *Lycopodium* species, like that of *Psilotum,* is fundamentally a protostelic structure. Its branching may be dichotomous or monopodial. Although the mature sporophyte has microphyllous leaves and roots, organs that are absent in *Psilotum,* there is evidence that these organs are secondary additions to the axis of

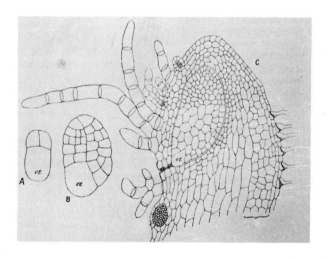

Fig. 18–14. *Lycopodium clavatum.* A,B,C, Stages in development of embryo; *et,* suspensor. X 60. (After Bruchmann.)

Lycopodium. This is suggested by the absence of vascular tissue in the early leaves of the embryonic plant and the lack of a specially differentiated root-forming region in the embryo.

The several species show variation in the distribution of sporogenous tissue, apparently progressing from a scattered, zonate condition in *L. lucidulum* through stages in localization at the stem apex found in *L. innundatum* and *L. complanatum.* For the most part, the massive, short-stalked, reniform sporangia occur on the adaxial surface of the leaf base, but they sometimes originate from the axil of the stem and leaf. Their development can be traced to a row of surface cells which divide periclinally to form a row of cells three tiers deep. The sporangial wall and the tapetum arise from the uppermost layer; the sporogenous tissue may be traced to the intermediate layer, a manifestation of the eusporangiate condition characteristic of a majority of vascular plants.

The spores of most species require long periods to develop mature gametophytes. The latter are of several kinds, either photosynthetic and partially epiterranean, or completely devoid of chlorophyll and subterranean. In the latter case, they may be either tuberous or branching cylindrical structures. Subterranean types are infected with a mycorrhizal fungus and are saprophytic. The sex organs are massive and partially embedded; the sperms are biflagellate. Each gametophyte may produce several sporophytes at inter-

A   B

Fig. 18–15. A, *Selaginella uncinata* Spring. A prostrate species; note strobili and rhizophores. X ½. B, *Selaginella pallescens* Spring. Single "frond" with strobili. X ⅔.

vals as long as a year apart. The gametophytes persist during the slow development of the embryonic sporophyte.

CLASS 2. GLOSSOPSIDA

Selaginella

INTRODUCTION AND VEGETATIVE MORPHOLOGY

Selaginella (dim. of *L. selago,* kind of plant) (Figs. 18–15 to 18–17) is one of two extant genera of the class **Glossopsida,** a group whose members possess ligulate leaves (Fig. 18–24). Although it has such *Lycopodium*-like attributes as small microphyllous leaves, the herbaceous habit,

Fig. 18–16.   *Selaginella pallescens.* Greenhouse specimen. X 1/6.

and strobili composed of sporophylls each bearing a single sporangium on the adaxial surface, *Selaginella* also has features which distinguish it from *Lycopodium.* The most significant of these, the production of two kinds of spores, a condition known as **heterospory,** has evoked profound changes in the morphology and physiology of the gametophyte generation. Furthermore, both the vegetative leaves and the sporophylls of *Selaginella* have small, tongue-like ligules (Fig. 18–24).

The genus *Selaginella,* sometimes called the **spike moss,** is a large one, including approximately 700 species which are developed most abundantly in tropical regions with heavy rainfall. In the United States, S. *apoda* (L.) Fern., an inhabitant of moist soils, is widely distributed, as is the xerophytic S. *rupestris* (L.) Spring, an inhabitant of exposed

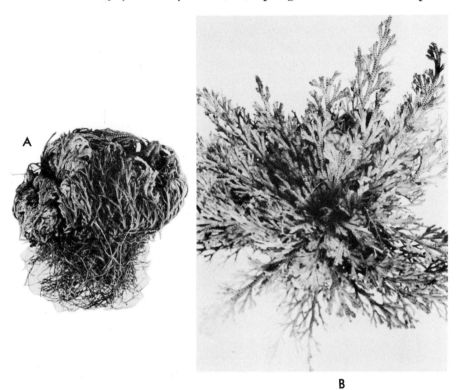

Fig. 18–17. *Selaginella lepidophylla* (Hook. and Grev.) Spring. The "resurrection plant." A, Dry; B, moistened. X ½.

rocks. The so-called **"resurrection plant"** (Fig. 18–17), often sold as a novelty, is S. *lepidophylla* (Hook. and Grev.) Spring, which is native to the southwestern United States. A number of tropical species are cultivated in conservatories and in Wardian cases because of the beauty of their branches and foliage. S. *kraussiana* A. Br. and S. *uncinata* Spring are encountered frequently as a ground cover in greenhouses.

Most species of *Selaginella* exhibit abundant branching, often in a single plane (Fig. 18–15B). The branches are arranged either dichotomously or in monopodial fashion. Branching in some species results in the production of frond-like growths (Figs. 18–15B, 18–16) which may arise from a common center, simulating a fern. Other species are climbers, and still others are prostrate and creeping (Fig. 18–15A).

Development of the stem may be traced either to a single apical cell and its derivatives or to a group of apical meristematic cells, depending on the species. S. kraussiana is typical of those with a single apical cell. Some distance back from the apical meristem, the central region of the

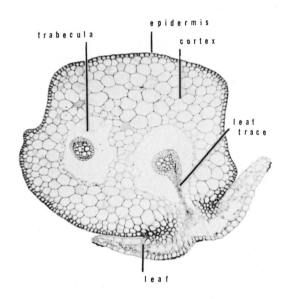

Fig. 18–18. *Selaginella Kraussiana.* Transverse section of stem; note central steles, traces of trabeculate endodermal cells in cavity surrounding stele, cortex, and epidermis. X 25.

stem differentiates as procambium from which the vascular tissues arise. In older regions of the axis (Fig. 18–18) in species like S. *caulescens* Spring, the central portion is separated from the cortex by a cylindrical cavity. The cortex and central tissues are connected by elongate endodermal cells which are called **trabeculae** (*L. trabecula,* little beam). Casparian thickenings are apparent on the walls of these cells. The stele in S. *kraussiana* is a dual structure. In other species there may be one or several steles. Each stele in S. *kraussiana* is surrounded by a single layer of pericycle cells, immediately within which the phloem is located. The central portion of each stele contains the xylem, which is exarch and monarch. The cortex is composed of thin-walled, photosynthetic parenchyma cells, bounded externally by a cutinized epidermis with stomata. It should be noted that in some species of *Selaginella*, series of procambium cells differentiate into **vessels** rather than into tracheids. Vessels are composed of cell segments whose common terminal walls have become

Fig. 18–19.   *Selaginella uncinata.* Leaf arrangement and dimorphism. X 8.

perforate; they are multicellular in origin. Their occurrence in *Selaginella* is surprising, inasmuch as they are usually present only in the vascular tissues of the more advanced seed plants.

The ligulate leaves of *Selaginella* may be arranged either spirally, a primitive attribute, as in *S. rupestris,* or spirally and compressed in four rows, as in *S. uncinata* (Fig. 18–19). In the latter, the two dorsal rows of leaves are smaller than the two rows with ventral insertion. The leaves

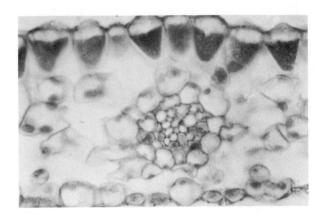

Fig. 18–20. *Selaginella caulescens.* Sector of a transverse section of a leaf at the midrib region; note large plastids in epidermal cells, vein, and two stomata on lower surface of leaf. X 500.

are sessile on the stem, alternately inserted, and each is traversed longitudinally by a single unbranched vein which is connected to the stele by a leaf trace. The leaves, therefore, are microphyllous. Mention has already been made of the basal ligule (Fig. 18–24) on the adaxial surface of each leaf. Transverse sections of the leaf (Fig. 18–20) reveal lower

Fig. 18–21. *Selaginella pallescens.* Enlarged view of strobilus; megasporophylls, megasporangium, and megaspores (circle); microsporophyll, microsporangium (lower ring), and microspores (arrow). X 10.

and upper epidermal cells containing chloroplasts, and between them the mesophyll composed of photosynthetic parenchyma cells with inter-cellular spaces. The mesophyll cells of different species vary in number of chloroplasts from one to several. The plastids are always rather massive, as com-pared with those of other vas-cular plants. Stomata are pres-ent on the abaxial surface of the leaf and are localized near the midrib (Fig. 18–20).

The plants are anchored to the substratum by elongate naked branches which have adventitious roots at their tips; these branches are known as **rhizophores** (Gr. *rhiza*, root + Gr. *phora*, bearer) (Fig. 18–

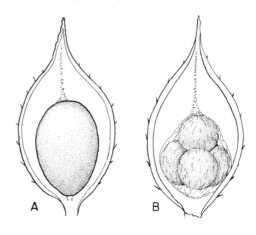

Fig. 18–22. *Selaginella pallescens.* A, Microsporo-phyll and microsporangium. B, Megasporophyll and megasporangium. Both in adaxial view. X 18.

15A). It is not certain whether these organs are morphologically stems or roots; there is some evidence that favors both interpretations. The fact that severed rhizophore tips can develop leaves is cited as evi-dence in support of their stem-like structure. The roots them-selves are delicate structures with an exarch protostele which is usually monarch.

REPRODUCTION

All species of *Selaginella* pro-duce their sporangia in strobili (Figs. 18–15B, 18–21). The spo-rophylls are scarcely different from vegetative leaves, and in some species they are arranged so loosely as to render the strobi-li inconspicuous. The sporo-phylls, like the vegetative leaves, are ligulate (Fig. 18–24). Each

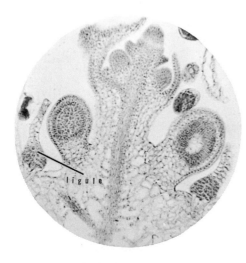

ligule

Fig. 18–23. *Selaginella* sp. Median longitudinal section of apex of strobilus; note sporophylls, lig-ules, young (undifferentiated) sporangia above, young mesgasporangium (right), and young micro-sporangium (left). X 125.

bears a single sporangium near its adaxial base (Figs. 18–21, 18–22). There is evidence that in some species, as in *Lycopodium*, the sporangia may actually originate on the stem in the leaf axil. Growth of the strobilus is apical (Fig. 18–23); hence median sections of a young strobilus show various stages in the eusporangiate development of the sporangia. The sporangium wall is two-layered and separated from the sporogenous tissue by a tapetum (Fig. 18–24).

Fig. 18–24. *Selaginella* sp. Median longitudinal section of immature megasporangium and ligule; note dark-staining, elongate cells of tapetum. X 250.

The sporogenous tissue is segregated into individual cells which function as spore mother cells as development proceeds. It subsequently becomes apparent that there are two types of sporangia. In some, a small percentage of spore mother cells may degenerate, the remainder undergoing meiosis and cytokinesis to produce many tetrads of spores (Fig. 18–25). In others (Figs. 18–25, 18–26), usually all except one of the spore mother cells degenerate. The survivor undergoes meiosis and cytokinesis, producing a single spore tetrad whose members gradually enlarge, apparently by appropriating the soluble organic materials made available by the degeneration of the other spore mother cells. Ultimately the four spores in these sporangia grow large enough to cause bulging of the sporangial wall (Figs. 18–22B, 18–25). This account of the ontogeny of the two types of sporangia indicates that they are fundamentally similar through the spore mother cell stage. The divergence in development begins at that period. The greatly enlarged spores are called **megaspores** (sometimes, macrospores), and the sporangia in which they develop and the sporophylls which subtend the sporangia are known as **megasporangia** and **megasporophylls,** respectively. The smaller spores are called **microspores,** their sporangia are **microsporangia,** and their sporophylls are **microsporophylls.**

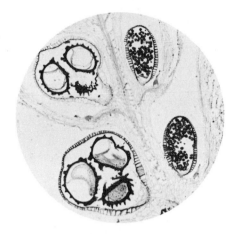

Fig. 18–25. *Selaginella* sp. Longitudinal section of older portion of strobilus; note two megasporangia to the left and microsporangia at the right. X 125.

The spore mother cells that give rise to megaspores are called **megaspore mother cells;** those that form microspores are known as **microspore mother cells.** This dimorphic condition of the spores is known as **heterospory.** Of the living vascular plants so far discussed, *Selaginella* is the first to exhibit it. While the immediate cause of heterospory in *Selaginella* obviously is degeneration of a majority of spore mother cells in certain sporangia and increase in size of the survivors, the factors which evoke this condition are obscure. That the number of degenerating megaspore mother cells is not absolutely fixed is indicated by the presence of as many as twenty-four and as few as one megaspore in megasporangia of certain individuals.

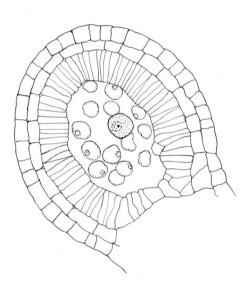

Fig. 18–26. *Selaginella* sp. Median longitudinal section of young megasporangium with functional megaspore mother cell, remainder aborting; somewhat diagrammatic. X 410.

As the microspores and megaspores mature, their walls thicken. Those of the microspores are red in certain species and those of the megaspores cream-colored. The tapetum of the megasporangium seems to play a nutritional role in the thickening of the megaspore walls. Both microspores and megaspores have prominent **triradiate ridges** which mark the lines of cytokinesis of the spores within the spore mother cell walls. Dehiscence of the sporangia is explosive; the spores are ejected through a vertical cleft in the sporangial wall.

The development of heterothallic gametophytes is an invariable result of heterospory in land plants. Microspores develop into male gametophytes, and megaspores into female gametophytes. Unlike *Psilotum* and *Lycopodium,* spore germination in *Selaginella* frequently is precocious,[4] so that at the time of their ejection the spores are found to be in various stages of gametophyte development. These intrasporangial stages are sometimes called **primary germination.** Under certain conditions, the gametophytes may reach maturity, as manifested by their production of sex organs, by the time of their dissemination from the sporangia. In extreme instances, fertilization and embryo development may occur while the megaspores and their contained gametophytes are still within the opened walls of the megasporangium. This has been reported in S. *apoda* and S. *rupestris.* This phenomenon is often cited in discussions of the origin of the seed habit. Further comparative study of a number of species of *Selaginella* is desirable to establish the factors that effect the liberation of the spores in relation to the degree of maturity of their enclosed gametophytes.

The mature microspore is uninucleate at first. Its development of the male gametophyte is initiated by an internal mitosis and cytokinesis that result in the formation of a small, peripheral **prothallial cell** and a large cell, the **antheridial cell** (Fig. 18–27A). The prothallial cell usually is interpreted as the sole remnant of the vegetative tissue of free-living gametophytes; it undergoes no further divisions. The antheridial cell, by anticlinal and periclinal divisions (Fig. 18–27B,C), forms a single-layered jacket enclosing 256 spermatogenous cells, each of which gives rise to a single biflagellate sperm. The microspore of S. *kraussiana* is shed from the microsporangium before the antheridium is fully formed. The latter matures in the microspores that fall into environments which favor

---

[4] The spores of *Pellia* and *Conacephalum* among the Hepatopsida also exhibit a degree of precocity in their endogenous divisions.

further development. The prothallial cell and wall cells of the antheridium ultimately disintegrate; the sperms are liberated by rupture of the microspore wall.

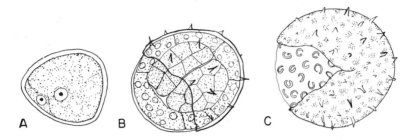

Fig. 18–27. *Selaginella pallescens*. Development of microspore into ♂ gametophyte. A, Section of microspore; note small prothallial cell. B, Partially exposed ♂ gametophyte; note jacket cells and two antheridia. C, Microspore with mature gametophyte ready to liberate sperm. X 770.

The megaspores begin their development into female gametophytes while still grouped together in the tetrad and before they have attained their maximum size. The young megaspore contains a large central vacuole surrounded by a thin peripheral layer of cytoplasm. The single nucleus undergoes mitosis which is not followed by cytokinesis; this process continues, and the cytoplasm, which gradually increases in amount, becomes multinucleate (Fig. 18–28). This process of successive mitoses without ensuing cytokineses is known as **free-nuclear division.** With continued increase in number of nuclei and amount of cytoplasm, the megaspore vacuole is finally obliterated. The nuclei lying in the portion of the megaspore near the triradiate ridge now are gradually separated by cell walls (Fig. 18–29).

Fig. 18–28. *Selaginella* sp. Section of megaspore in free-nuclear condition (somewhat plasmolyzed). X 125.

This process continues until the entire lumen is filled with cellular tissue. This may not occur, however,

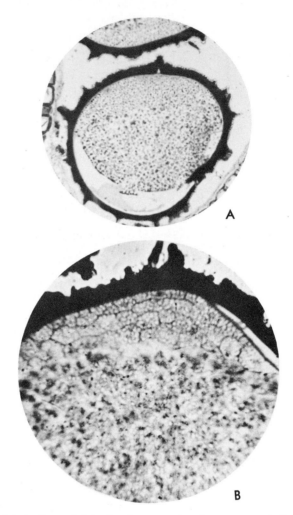

Fig. 18–29. *Selaginella* sp. Cellular female gametophyte in megaspore. A. Entire megaspore. X 125. B, Detail of cellular region beneath triradiate ridge. X 250.

until after fertilization. The megaspore is finally ruptured in the region of the triradiate ridge by the protrusion of the developing female gametophyte (Fig. 18–30). It is in this region that the several archegonia develop. Gametophytes in megaspores that have been shed have been reported to develop chloroplasts and rhizoids if they come in contact with soil in the presence of light. It is probable, however, that the gametophyte derives the bulk of its nutriment from the metabolites freed by degeneration of the spore mother cells and by the activity of the tapetum of the megasporan-

gium, and from the food stored within the megaspores. The female gametophytes of S. *pallescens* (Presl.) Spring remained colorless indefinitely

in the writer's laboratory, although
the cultures were illuminated. A
number of superficial cells of the
exposed portion of the female gametophyte develop into archegonia
(Fig. 18–31). These are largely embedded, except for their short necks,
which are two tiers high and composed of four rows of neck cells.

As noted previously, union of the
sperm and egg may occur either
when the mature gametophytes
have been shed from the strobilus
or by sifting of the microspores
containing male gametophytes into
the open megasporangia. This
transfer is in some respects suggestive of pollination in seed plants.

Fig. 18–30. *Selaginella pallescens*. Germinating megaspore with protruding ♀ gametophyte (living). X 60.

As in *Lycopodium*, the first division of the zygote in *Selaginella* gives
rise to a suspensor initial near the neck of the archegonium; the lower cell
and its derivatives form the embryo proper. In some species the suspensor remains relatively inactive as it does in *Lycopodium*, whereas in
others it undergoes cell division with subsequent elongation, so that the
developing embryos are thrust into the starch-filled vegetative tissue of
the female gametophyte (Fig. 18–32). The portion of the embryo opposite the suspensor becomes organized as a foot, and the remainder develops into an axis consisting largely of primary rhizophore and stem
bearing two cotyledons. As development continues, the embryo, except
for the foot, emerges from the female gametophyte and megaspore. The
primary rhizophore develops roots and the young plant is soon established independently. This embryonic sporophyte, attached to the female
gametophyte within the megaspore, looks strikingly like a minute seedling at this stage (Fig. 18–33).

SUMMARY

Although *Selaginella* is similar to *Lycopodium* in a number of respects,
it differs in the possession of ligulate leaves, frequently polystelic stems,

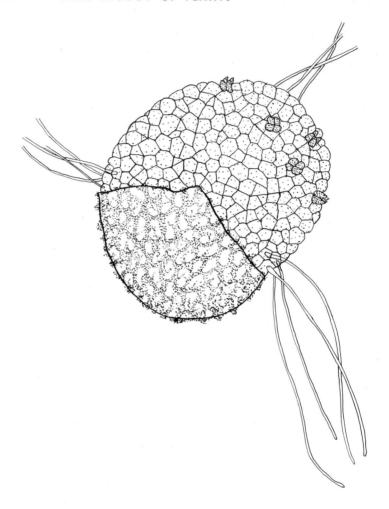

Fig. 18–31. *Selaginella pallescens.* Mature ♀ gametophyte in megaspore; note archegonia. X 50.

vessels in its xylem, special organs known as rhizophores, and especially in its heterospory. In accordance with the latter, the gametophytes are strictly heterothallic. The ontogeny of the spores of *Selaginella* is instructive in providing a clue as to the possible origin of heterospory. In view of the similarity in development of both microsporangia and megasporangia through the spore mother cell stage, along with the variation in megaspore number in certain individuals and species, it seems probable that heterospory here is occasioned by a difference in nutrition during sporogenesis. The ultimate causes of heterospory are not clear.

The precocious germination, and in some instances maturation, of the spores into gametophytes before they are shed from the sporangia is a noteworthy departure from the reproductive cycle of *Lycopodium* and *Psilotum*. Spore dimorphism here has resulted in gametophyte dimorphism. Both male and female gametophytes are much reduced in size, duration of existence, and complexity of structure as compared with free-living gametophytes, the male gametophyte especially so. Although in

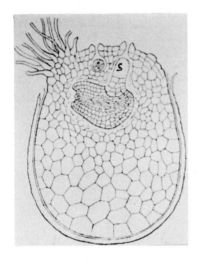

Fig. 18–32. *Selaginella martensii* Spring. Median longitudinal section of megaspore and ♀ gametophyte with developing embryo; s, suspensor. X ⅔. (After Bruchmann.)

Fig. 18–33. *Selaginella* sp. Young germling sporophyte attached to ♀ gametophyte (within megaspore). X 5.

some species the female gametophyte retains its capacity for developing photosynthetic tissues and rhizoids, the major portion of the nutriment for its development, as well as for the developing embryo, is the material stored in the megaspore during its long period of enlargement. The food is sporophytic in origin. While the transfer of microspores containing immature male gametophytes to the opened megasporangia containing megaspores with female gametophytes suggests pollination in the seed plants, there are important differences. The occurrence of fertilization and embryo development within the megasporangium, in some instances, is also of interest in this connection.

Isoetes

INTRODUCTION AND VEGETATIVE MORPHOLOGY

Although morphologists differ in their opinion regarding the relation of *Isoetes* to other plants, there is considerable evidence that its affinities may be with the Microphyllophyta, in which division it is included in the present text. *Isoetes* is a genus containing 64 species familiarly known as "**quillworts**" because of their narrow, elongate leaves, the bases of which are rather spoon-like. Most species of *Isoetes* are either partially sub-

Fig. 18–34. *Isoetes butleri* Engelm. Plant removed from soil; note enlarged leaf bases (white), corm, and roots. X ⅔.

merged aquatics (*I. engelmanni* A. Br.) or amphibious; a few, like *I. butleri* Engelm. (Fig. 18–34), are terrestrial. *I. butleri* is perennial, but active growth occurs only during the early spring rains.

The quill-like leaves are attached in spiral fashion to a subterranean corm-like structure (Fig. 18–34). Their spiral arrangement is readily apparent in transverse sections through the overlapping leaf bases. Although the leaves in some species, as in *I. engelmanni*, attain a length as great as two feet, they are considered to be microphyllous, inasmuch as they

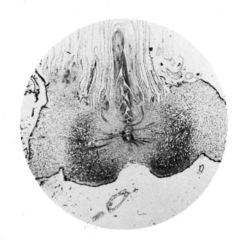

Fig. 18–35. *Isoetes butleri.* Median longitudinal section of corm and leaf bases; note apical region, stele and traces, and dense storage region of corm. X 12½.

have single, unbranched veins and the traces leave no gap in the vascular cylinder of the stem. It is evident, in transverse section, that each leaf contains four longitudinally placed lacunae or air chambers; the vein is located in the solid tissue in the center of these. The tissue external to the air chambers is photosynthetic parenchyma. Leaves of terrestrial species have stomata in their epidermis.

The corm-like structure on which the leaves are borne is difficult to interpret morphologically (Fig. 18–35). Its upper portion is considered to be a much shortened, fleshy, vertical stem with a broad and sunken apex. The nodes are so close together that the internodes are practically obliterated. Elongation of the upper portion of the axis is very slow, most of the derivatives of the apical meristem cells becoming involved in the formation of leaves and the portions of the stem immediately subtending the leaves. The vascular tissue is arranged as a central protostele, the xylem of which consists of a large number of parenchyma cells and relatively few tracheids, a characteristic of aquatic plants in general. The xylem is surrounded by phloem. Outside the phloem there is a meristematic layer whose exact nature is somewhat in dispute. It functions as a cambium in that its divisions add to the tissues of the stem. Apparently the cambium derivatives may develop occasionally as xylem cells next to the primary xylem, or, more frequently, as sieve elements or paren-

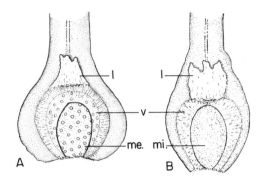

Fig. 18–36. *Isoetes* sp. Adaxial views of A, mega-sporophyll, and B, microsporophyll: *l*, ligule; *me.*, meg-asporangium; *mi.*, microsporangium; *v*, velum. X 3.

chyma cells adjacent to the phloem. The cortex, which is composed largely of starch-storing parenchyma cells, sur-rounds the tissues developed from the cambium. No endo-dermis is present. The surface of the corm is covered by the remains of the leaves of pre-vious seasons. In mature spec-imens the outer cortical tis-sues are constantly sloughing off. The surface layers that re-main become suberized.

The lower portion of the corm is a bilobed or trilobed organ the struc-ture and homologies of which have received various interpretations. It often is referred to as the rhizo-phore, inasmuch as the delicate roots are borne only on this region of the plant. The rhizophore end of the plant develops from its own meristem which is sunken in a groove (Fig. 18–35). The young-est roots, therefore, occur near the deepest portion of the groove, and the older ones arise from the sides of the rhizophore lobes. The roots are endogenous in origin; each is connected to the central vascular tissue of the rhizophore by a trace (Fig. 18–35).

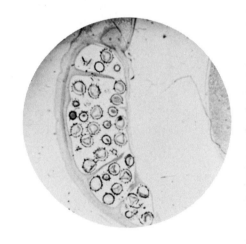

Fig. 18–37. *Isoetes butleri*. Sectional view of megasporophyll and megasporangium; note megaspores and trabeculae. X 12½.

The delicate roots are protected by a root cap beneath which a group of apical cells is present; these add to both the root cap and the root itself. The roots branch di-chotomously as a result of the organization of two groups of apical ini-tials below the root cap. Mature roots contain delicate protosteles which are excentric in position because of the disintegration of the inner cortical cells on one side of the stele to form a lacuna. The stele is bounded by a well-differentiated endodermal layer. The cortex is surrounded by an epidermis.

REPRODUCTION

Every leaf of *Isoetes* is potentially a sporophyll. The first-formed leaves of any season, the outermost, are frequently sterile, however. The next older leaves mature as megasporophylls (Fig. 18–36A) and are followed by microsporophylls (Fig. 18–36B) within. The last-formed leaves of the season frequently bear abortive sporangia. Microsporophylls and megasporophylls are indistinguishable at first. In each case, the single sporangium arises from superficial cells near the adaxial surface of the spoon-shaped leaf base; these cells undergo a series of periclinal divisions. Development of the sporangium is eusporangiate. The sporangium is massive and larger than that in *Lycopodium* and *Selaginella*. It may attain a length up to 7 mm. A small ligule arises just above the apex of the sporangium, and other superficial cells in that region grow down to form an

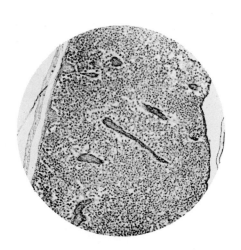

Fig. 18–38. *Isoetes butleri.* Sectional view of portion of microsporangium; note microspores and trabeculae. X 30.

indusium-like covering, the **velum** (L. *velum,* veil) (Fig. 18–36). The sporangia are incompletely chambered by plates of sterile tissue which extend from the walls partially across the sporangial lumen (Figs. 18–37, 18–38); these are known as **trabeculae.** The sporangial walls and trabeculae are lined with a two-layered tapetum.

As in *Selaginella,* development of both microsporangia and megasporangia is similar through the spore mother cell stage. Practically all of the microspore mother cells undergo meiosis and form tetrads of microspores; hence tremendous numbers of spores, estimated to be between 150,000 and 1,000,000, develop in each microsporangium. Certain of the megaspore mother cells enlarge, but only a small number divide and form tetrads; the remainder disintegrate. Megasporangia of the several species produce between 50 and 300 megaspores. Both microspores and megaspores have walls with ornamentation that varies from species to species. There is no special mechanism of sporangial dehiscence, at least in aquatic species. The spores are liberated as the sporophylls and sporangial walls disintegrate at the end of the growing season.

Unlike *Selaginella*, the spores of *Isoetes* do not begin their development into gametoyphtes until they have been set free from their sporangia. The

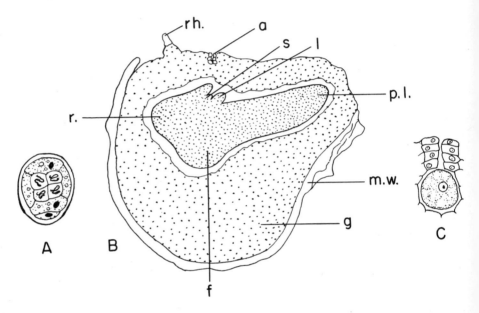

Fig. 18–39.   *A, Isoetes lacustris* L. Section of microspore containing mature ♂ gametophyte; note prothallial cell, jacket cells, and four spermatogenous cells. (After Liebig.) *B, Isoetes lithophila* Pfeiffer. Sectional view of megaspore with mature ♀ gametophyte and young embryo; *a*, archegonial neck; *f*, foot; *g*, ♀ gametophyte; *l*, ligule, *m.w.*, megaspore wall; *p.l.*, primary leaf or cotyledon; *r*, root; *rh.*, rhizoid; *s*, stem apex. X 120. *C*, Single archegonium, median longitudinal section. X 300. (*B,C*, after LaMotte.)

male gametophyte, as in *Selaginella*, is entirely enclosed within the microspore wall (Fig. 18–39A). It arises by internal divisions of the microspore protoplast to form a single prothallial cell and a single antheridial cell. The latter develops into an antheridium consisting of a single-layered wall enclosing four spermatogenous cells. Each of these gives rise to a single multiflagellate sperm at maturity.

Development of the female gametophyte of *Isoetes*, as of *Selaginella*, involves a series of free-nuclear divisions of the megaspore nucleus and its descendants. Cell wall formation occurs first in the region of the tri-radiate ridge and gradually extends through the remainder of the female gametophyte. It may still be incomplete in the basal portion of the game-tophyte for some time after fertilization. The megaspore wall cracks open, exposing the cellular apex of the developing gametophyte. Certain super-ficial cells undergo division to form archegonia which are largely em-bedded (Fig. 18–39B,C). Their necks, composed of three or four tiers of four cells, are longer than those of *Selaginella.*

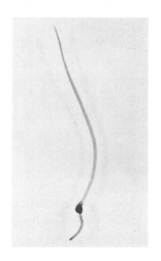

Usually only one zygote in each fe-male gametophyte develops into a sporophyte (Fig. 18–39B). Nuclear and cell division by the zygote and its derivatives produce a spherical mass of tissue which later differentiates into the embryonic regions of the sporo-phyte. These include a rather massive foot in contact with the starch-filled cells of the female gametophyte, an embryonic root, and a leaf or cotyle-don. The stem develops secondarily in the region between the leaf and the

Fig. 18–40. *Isoetes* sp. Young sporophyte emerging from ♀ gametophyte in mega-spore; primary root below, cotyledon above. X 4.

root (Fig. 18–39B). Although the young sporophyte soon becomes es-tablished as an independent plant, it remains attached to the female gametophyte and megaspore for a considerable period (Fig. 18–40). It should be noted that no suspensor is present in the embryo of *Isoetes.*

SUMMARY AND CLASSIFICATION

Although the leaves of *Isoetes* are markedly larger than those of *Selaginella* and *Lycopodium,* they are microphyllous, as indicated by their single unbranched veins and the absence of gaps in the stele. All organs of the plant show evidences of adaptation to an aquatic habitat in their anatomical structure. Among these are air lacunae and the paucity of lignified xylem tissue. The leaves of *Isoetes* are ligulate and spirally inserted on a short, underground corm-like stem. Each leaf is potentially a sporophyll. Although growth in length of the corm is very limited, the presence of a cambium-like layer contributes to its increase in girth. The cortex of the corm is composed of starch-filled cells, an indication that the perennial corm is primarily a storage organ. The stele of the stem is a protostele with few tracheids, most of the xylem cells maturing as parenchyma. The lower portion of the corm is called a rhizophore. This is a lobed structure on which the delicate roots are borne in orderly fashion. Both stem and root develop from a group of apical meristematic cells rather than one. Root branching is dichotomous.

The sporangia are massive and heterosporous. A variable number of megaspores matures in the megasporangium. The number is always larger than in *Selaginella,* and unlike the latter, the spores do not initiate development until they have been shed from their sporangia. Evidences of further reduction of the gametophytes, as compared with those of *Selaginella,* are present in *Isoetes.* Among these, the reduction of spermatogenous cells to four and the failure of the female gametophyte to project from the megaspore wall are noteworthy. Unlike both *Selaginella* and *Lycopodium,* the sperms of *Isoetes* are multiflagellate. The development of the embryo differs from these genera in the complete absence of a suspensor and in the long-delayed development of the stem. In spite of the differences just cited, there are many evidences of similarity in morphology between *Isoetes* and *Selaginella* and *Lycopodium.* Some morphologists, however, on the basis of the multiflagellate sperms and anatomical considerations, are of the opinion that *Isoetes* is more closely related to certain ferns. This view seems to ignore such a fundamental attribute as the microphylly of *Isoetes* as contrasted with the macrophylly of ferns.

The genera described in this chapter may be classified as follows:

Division Microphyllophyta
    Class 1. Aglossopsida
        Order 1. Lycopodiales
            Family 1. Lycopodiaceae
                Genus: *Lycopodium*
    Class 2. Glossopsida
        Order 1. Selaginellales
            Family 1. Selaginellaceae
                Genus: *Selaginella*
        Order 2. Isoetales
            Family 1. Isoetaceae
                Genus: *Isoetes*

DISCUSSION QUESTIONS

1. What attributes distinguish the Microphyllophyta from the Psilophyta?
2. Compare *Psilotum* and *Lycopodium* with respect to vegetative structure and reproduction.
3. Define or explain strobilus, leaf trace, microphyllous leaf, suspensor, sporophyll.
4. What is meant by eusporangiate sporangium development?
5. Suggest the composition of a culture medium suitable for the cultivation of saprophytic *Lycopodium* gametophytes.
6. What significance may be attached to the absence of vascular tissue from the first-formed leaves on the young sporophytes of *Lycopodium*?
7. On what basis is dichotomous branching considered to be a primitive attribute in vascular plants?
8. Can you suggest a biological advantage of the strobiloid arrangement of sporophylls in certain *Lycopodium* species as compared with the scattered, zonate arrangement?
9. Although the stems of *S. kraussiana* are distelic in the mature plants, the embryonic and juvenile stems are monostelic. Of what significance is this?
10. How does the xylem of *Selaginella* differ from that of *Psilotum* and *Lycopodium*?
11. What evidence is there that rhizophores are stem-like organs?
12. How do the leaves of *Selaginella* differ from those of *Lycopodium*?
13. What is the origin of the thick megaspore wall in *Selaginella*?
14. What light does ontogeny shed on the possible origin of heterospory? Explain.
15. Why are the gametophytes of *Selaginella* said to be "reduced"?
16. Distinguish between the terms primitive, advanced, specialized, generalized, simple, and reduced, as they are used in comparative morphology.
17. How do *Selaginella* megaspores with attached embryonic sporophytes differ from dicotyledonous seedlings?
18. Why are both *Selaginella* and *Lycopodium* considered to be microphyllous?
19. With the aid of labeled diagrams, illustrate the reproductive cycle in *Selaginella*.
20. Define or explain heterospory, homospory, prothallial cell, free-nuclear division.
21. What attributes do *Selaginella* and *Lycopodium* have in common?
22. List the attributes shared by *Isoetes* and other Microphyllophyta.
23. What anatomical evidences of aquatic habitat are present in *Isoetes*?
24. In what respects does the development of the gametophytes in *Isoetes* differ from that in *Selaginella*?

25. On what basis are the leaves of *Isoetes* said to be microphyllous?
26. How do the sporangia of *Isoetes* differ from those of other Microphyllophyta?
27. Describe the structure of the corm of *Isoetes*.

CHAPTER 19

Division Arthrophyta

INTRODUCTION AND VEGETATIVE MORPHOLOGY

Members of the third group of vascular cryptogams, the **Arthrophyta** (Gr. *arthros*, jointed + Gr. *phyton*, plant), are at once distinguishable from other seedless vascular plants by the whorled or verticillate arrangement of their stem branches and appendages (Fig. 19–1). Although the group was well represented in the Paleozoic period, only a single genus, *Equisetum* (L. *equus*, horse + L. *saeta*, bristle), with 25 species, has survived in our present flora. *Equisetum* is widely distributed, and the various species are familiarly known as **"pipes," "horsetails,"** and **"scouring rushes."** Some species, like the common *E. arvense* L., grow both in moist and in somewhat xeric habitats, whereas others, like *E. sylvaticum* L. and *E. hyemale* L., frequently flourish in marshy situations. Temperate-zone species are relatively small in stature, rarely exceeding four feet in height.

The stem is the dominant organ of the plant body in the genus *Equisetum*, for the minute leaves, although photosynthetic for a short period after their formation, soon become dry and scale-like (Figs. 19–1, 19–5B). In *E. arvense* and other species, the plant consists of a subterranean, deep-growing rhizome and an erect aerial stem (Fig. 19–1). Rhizome systems of *E. arvense* have been observed growing horizontally six feet below the surface of the soil. The aerial stem may be richly branched, as in *E. arvense*, or branching may be absent, as in *E. hyemale* (Figs. 19–1, 19–2). The fact that unbranched species, under such stimulation as injury, develop branches at the nodes is often cited as evidence that branching is a primitive attribute in the genus.

Both the aerial stems and rhizomes have well-defined **nodes** and **internodes** (Figs. 19–1, 19–2). The surface of the stem is ribbed or ridged, the ribs of successive internodes being arranged in alternate fashion. The bases of the leaves are fused and give the appearance of a scalloped collar. A few rudimentary stomata are present near the tips of

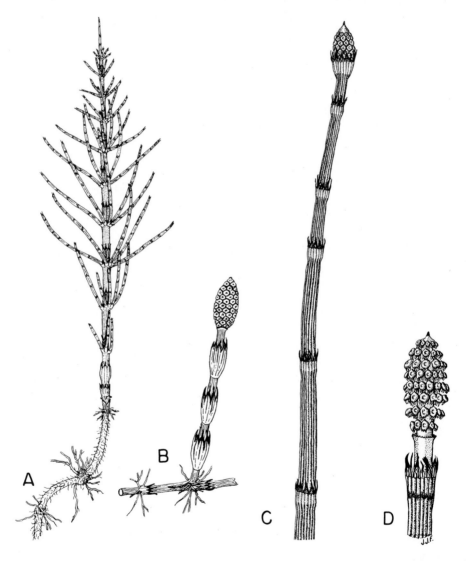

Fig. 19–1. *Equisetum arvense* L. A, Portion of rhizome and aerial shoot. B, Portion of rhizome bearing fertile shoot and strobilus. X ¾. C, *E. hyemale* L. Vegetative shoot with terminal strobilus. X ¾. D, Strobilus shedding spores. X 1.

the adaxial surface of the leaves of *E. arvense*. Stomata are present in two or three rows on both sides of the projecting midrib on the abaxial leaf surface. The central region of each leaf is photosynthetic when the leaves first appear. The relation between the branches and leaves in *Equisetum* differs from that in all other vascular plants. In the latter, stem branches originate from the axils of the leaves, whereas in *Equisetum* they emerge from the region of the node between the leaves. As the branches elongate, they pierce the nodal leaf sheath (Fig. 19–1).

Fig. 19–2. *Equisetum hyemale*. Colony of plants. X 1/12.

Development of the stem originates in a single, pyramidal apical cell which divides regularly in three directions (Fig. 19–3). The derivatives of the apical cell divide in an anticlinal direction soon after they are delimited. One of the cells thus formed, in each case by further division, contributes to the internodal and the other to the nodal portion of the axis. The leaves originate as superficial, ring-like outgrowths of the nodal cells. A short distance back from the apical region, tissue differentiation is initiated in the axis. The surface cells form an epidermis the cells of which are silicified. Certain of the epidermal cells undergo two successive

Fig. 19–3. *Equisetum hyemale.* Median longitudinal section of apex of vegetative shoot. X 60.

divisions to form guard cells and their more superficial accessory cells. The latter are thickened, with siliceous ribs. Stomata are present most abundantly on the slopes of the ridges of the fluted stem surface.

Fig. 19–4 shows a sector of a transverse section of the vegetative stem of *E. arvense* taken from an internode where differentiation has been completed. The central region of the stem is hollow at maturity and is surrounded by the remains of the parenchymatous pith. Outside the pith there is a ring of circular canals whose position is directly internal to the surface ridges of the stem. These, therefore, are known as **carinal** (L. *carina*, keel) **canals,** and they mark the position of discrete strands of xylem and phloem. Development of the xylem is **endarch,** for the first-formed annular and spiral protoxylem cells arise near the inner limit of each procambium strand (Fig. 19–4B). With the subsequent formation of the carinal canals, the position of the protoxylem elements is disturbed. The phloem, which lies directly outside each carinal canal, is bordered laterally by two groups of several metaxylem cells. The **pericycle** is represented by a single layer of cells just within a rather prominent **endodermis**. The **cortex** consists internally of parenchyma cells which are interrupted by large **vallecular canals** whose position corresponds with the

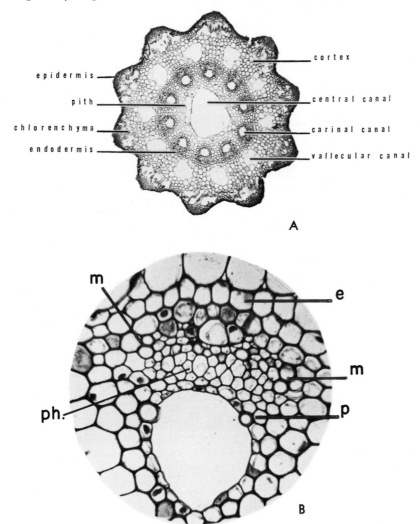

Fig. 19–4. *Equisetum arvense.* A, Transverse section of vegetative stem; note (in centrifugal direction) central canal surrounded by remains of pith; vascular bundles associated with carinal canals and separated from the cortex by the endodermis; cortex with vallecular canals; epidermis. X 30. B, Single carinal canal and vascular bundle, enlarged; note protoxylem cells, *p,* adjacent to canal and metaxylem, *m,* phloem, *ph.,* and endodermis, *e.* X 250.

depressions of the stem surface. Groups of outer cortical cells contain abundant chloroplasts. The walls of the cortical cells beneath the surface ridges are markedly thickened and contribute to the support and rigidity of the stem. The **epidermal cells** are heavily thickened and the stomata are sunk beneath the surface.

Although the xylem and phloem are present as discrete strands in the internodes of *Equisetum*, serial sections through the nodes reveal that they join there to form a short, hollow cylinder called a **siphonostele**. The vascular strands above and below the nodal region are joined to the

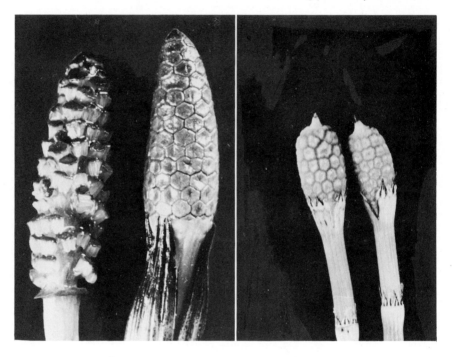

A   **B**

Fig. 19–5. *A, Equisetum arvense.* Strobili, the one at the left about to shed spores. X 2. *B, E. hyemale.* Strobili. X 1.

siphonostele in alternate fashion. A ring of small, protoxylem leaf traces leaves the stele at each node; branch traces originate between the leaf traces. The absence of leaf gaps indicates that the leaves are probably to be interpreted as **microphyllous.**[1] The internodal stele is known as a

---

[1] That the unbranched vein of *Equisetum* leaves may be derived rather than primitive is suggested by the presence of dichotomously branched veins in the leaves of the arthrophytan fossil *Sphenophyllum* (see Chapter 30).

eustele because the parenchymatous gaps between the internodal bundles are neither leaf nor branch gaps. It is worthy of note that the stem of the embryonic sporophyte is at first a protostele; the eustele differentiates in later development of the axis.

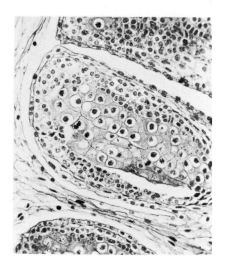

Fig. 19–6. *Equisetum hyemale.* Longitudinal section of young sporangium. X 125.

Roots of mature plants are nodal, endogenous, and adventitious in origin. The root grows as a result of the activity of a single apical cell and its derivatives and is protostelic and exarch.

REPRODUCTION

The sporogenous tissue in all species of *Equisetum* is localized in a strobilus, but the relation of the strobilus to the vegetative branches varies. In some species—*E. hyemale,* for example—the strobili develop at the tips of vegetative axes (Figs. 19–1*C,* 19–5*B*). In *E. arvense,* however, the strobilus is usually borne on a nonchlorophyllous fertile branch which develops from the rhizome as a unit (Fig. 19–1*B*). The latter later produces green vegetative branches after the strobilate branches have withered away. *E. sylvaticum* is intermediate between these two extremes, in that the unbranched axis which bears the strobilus lacks chlorophyll at first. It becomes green and branched after the spores have been discharged.

In *E. arvense,* the strobilus and its subtending branch are formed in the autumn preceding the spring in which they will appear above the soil. As in the vegetative stem, growth of the strobilus is apical. Its axis produces a series of surface enlargements each of which grows into a spore-

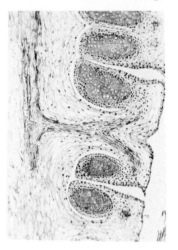

producing appendage called a **sporangiophore.** Mature sporangiophores typically are hexagonal in surface view (Figs. 19–1, 19–5) because of mutual pressure. Between five and ten superficial and equidistant cells on the periphery of each sporangiophore function as sporangium initials; development of the sporangium is eusporangiate. Growth of the central portion of each sporangiophore is in a radial direction and inverts the young sporangia, so that their position at maturity is adaxial. The mature sporangia are elongate and finger-like (Figs. 19–5A, 19–7).

Fig. 19–7. *Equisetum arvense.* Longitudinal section of portion of strobilus; sporangiophores and sporangia with mature spores. X 12½.

The sporogenous tissue of the young sporangium (Fig. 19–6) is surrounded by a tapetum and a wall several cells in thickness. As development progresses, the cell walls of the tapetum disintegrate. There is thus

formed a tapetal plasmodium which contributes to the nutrition of the sporogenous tissue. A number of the spore mother cells abort, but those that remain undergo meiotic division, each producing a tetrad of spores. The haploid chromosome number is approximately $n = 108$ in *E. arvense* and *E. hyemale.* The outermost layer of sporangial wall cells thickens spirally, and those beneath disintegrate. Dehiscence of the sporangium

Fig. 19–8. *Equisetum arvense.* Spore and "elaters." X 420.

is longitudinal along a vertical line which lies toward the axis of the sporangiophore stalk. The wall structure of the mature spores is complex, the outermost wall layer consisting of four spirally arranged portions

(Fig. 19–8). These separate at the time of sporangial dehiscence, so that each spore bears four somewhat spoon-like appendages sometimes called "elaters." The "elaters" are hygroscopic and quickly affected by slight changes in humidity. When the spores are ready for dissemination, the internodes of the strobilus elongate slightly, thus separating the sporangiophores. The stalk of each now increases in length on its lower side,

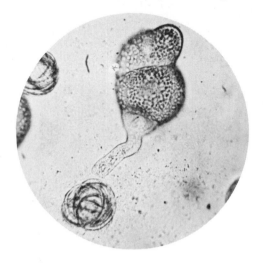

Fig. 19–9.   *Equisetum arvense.* Germinating spore; note rhizoid and "elaters." X 250.

so that the apex of the sporangiophore is brought into such a position that the sporangia are approximately perpendicular to the soil surface (Fig. 19–5A).

The green spores of *Equisetum* germinate rapidly after their dissemination, provided that they are carried to suitable substrata. In the case of *E. arvense,* which frequently is found in rather xeric situations, it is doubtful that any considerable number of spores produce mature gametophytes in such conditions. Vegetative multiplication by means of the rhizomes probably accounts for the formation of extensive colonies. Germinating spores and mature gametophytes of several species have been found on moist soil in nature. Naturally occurring gametophytes of *E. arvense* varied in size from a pinhead to 8 mm. in diameter. The spores of *E. arvense* and *E. hyemale,* among others, germinate rapidly in laboratory cultures on suitable media and on moist *Sphagnum* (Fig. 19–9). The developing gametophytes are extremely sensitive to such unfavor-

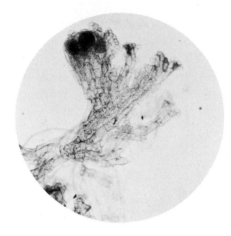

Fig. 19–10. *Equisetum arvense.* Young gametophyte with antheridia. X 30.

able environmental conditions as crowding, and their form is modified accordingly. However, well-isolated spores form rather disc-like or cushion-like green gametophytes several millimeters in diameter (Figs. 19–10,

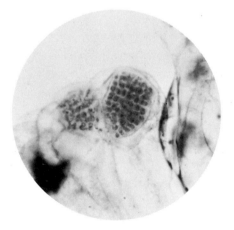

Fig. 19–11. *Equisetum arvense.* Antheridia with mature sperms. X 125.

19–16). They are anchored to the substratum by numerous unicellular rhizoids. The superficial cells of the gametophyte develop lamellar lobes of photosynthetic cells which densely cover the mound-like basal portion.

Under laboratory conditions, the antheridia may be produced on very young gametophytes, in which they occur at the apices of the surface lobes (Fig. 19–10). In nature, however, the sex organs seem to develop

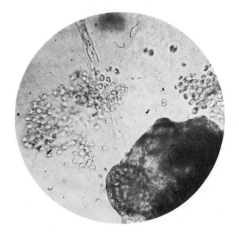

Fig. 19–12.   *Equisetum arvense.* Discharge of sperms. X 125.

regularly on the surface of the mound-like portion of the gametophyte between and at the bases of the lobes. The gametophytes of *E. arvense*

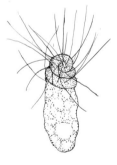

Fig. 19–13.   *Equisetum arvense.* Recently liberated sperm. X 600.

are reported to be homothallic, but this was not true of the author's cultures, which were not at all crowded. However, other conditions of culture may have evoked a preponderance of antheridia.

Each antheridium originates from a single superficial cell which undergoes division into an outer cell and an inner cell. The outer cell forms the wall of the upper portion of the antheridium; the inner, by successive divisions, forms the spermatogenous tissue (Fig. 19–11). Each antheridium produces a large number of multiflagellate sperms which are liber-

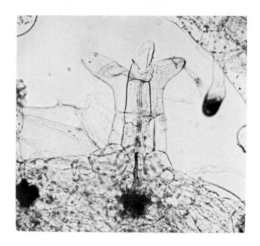

Fig. 19–14. *Equisetum arvense.* Overmature archegonium. X 125.

ated when the mature antheridia are moistened (Fig. 19–12). The sperms of *Equisetum* are relatively large (Fig. 19–13). They are explosively discharged. When first liberated, they are surrounded by a spherical sur-

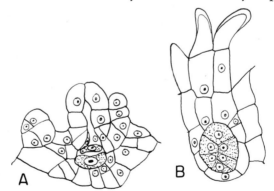

Fig. 19–15. A, *Equisetum arvense.* Immature archegonia. B, *E. hyemale.* Longitudinal section of archegonium with young sporophyte. (From Jeffrey.)

face layer (Fig. 19–12) which swells and ultimately bursts, liberating the sperm protoplast which becomes actively motile.

The archegonia (Figs. 19–14, 19–15A) also arise from superficial cells. At maturity, their short necks, consisting of four vertical rows of neck cells, are protuberant; the venter is buried in the thallus. The eggs of several archegonia of a single gametophyte may be fertilized and may develop embryonic sporophytes.

Growth of the sporophyte is initiated by transverse division of the zygote, followed by divisions to form a quadrant. The two upper (outer)

Fig. 19–16. *Equisetum arvense.* Young sporophyte developing on gametophyte. X 12½.

cells are often smaller than the two lower (inner) cells, and develop the first leaf sheath and stem in *E. arvense.* The lower cells develop the foot and the root, no suspensor being present. In some species the primary axis (Fig. 19–16) ceases development after it has formed a limited number of nodes and internodes. In such forms, secondary axes are successively formed, one of which ultimately gives rise to the mature axis. The embryonic root grows through the gametophyte into the soil, thus establishing the independence of the young sporophyte.

SUMMARY AND CLASSIFICATION

Equisetum, the only extant member of the Arthrophyta, differs from other seedless vascular plants in the whorled arrangement of its leaves and branches. Furthermore, its alternate arrangement of leaves and branches is anomalous among vascular plants. The leaves are reduced to scale-like appendages; each, however, receives a vascular trace and is provided with stomata. The burden of photosynthesis is borne by the axis. Except for the primary root, the roots are adventitious and arise at the bases of the lateral branches or their primordia. Both roots and stems develop as a result of the activity of apical cells and their derivatives. The root is protostelic, and the stem is eustelic at the internodes and siphonostelic at the nodes; the xylem is endarch in the stem. The parenchymatous gaps in the internodal steles are not related to either leaf or branch traces.

The sporogenous tissues of *Equisetum* always are localized in strobili; the relation of the latter to the vegetative branches is variable in the several species. The sporangium-bearing appendages are called **sporangiophores**; each has from five to ten sporangia. The sporangiophores differ from sporophylls, which are foliar, in being whorled branches of the strobilus axis. Sporangium development is eusporangiate and the spores are homosporous. The spores are anomalous in their possession of four hygroscopic appendages called "elaters." The gametophytes of *Equisetum* are mound-like, chlorophyllous structures which have numerous erect, plate-like lobes. The sex organs arise at the meristematic margin of the cushion between the bases of the lobes. In young gametophytes, however, antheridia may be borne upon the lobes. The sperms are multiflagellate. Suspensors are absent from the developing embryos, a number of which may be borne on a single gametophyte. *Equisetum* may be classified as follows:

Division Arthrophyta
    Class 1. Arthropsida
        Order 1. Equisetales
            Family 1. Equisetaceae
            Genus: *Equisetum*

DISCUSSION QUESTIONS

1. What attributes distinguish *Equisetum* from other vascular cryptogams?
2. Why are the parenchymatous regions between the vascular bundles in *Equisetum* not considered to be leaf or branch gaps?
3. Define or explain carinal canal, vallecular canal, central canal.
4. What does the paucity of xylem in a stem, leaf, or root usually indicate?
5. How does the arrangement of branches with reference to the leaves mark *Equisetum* as unique?
6. Summarize the methods of nutrition of the gametophyte in *Lycopodium, Selaginella, Psilotum, Isoetes,* and *Equisetum.*
7. Describe the process of spore dissemination from the strobilus of *Equisetum.*
8. Can you give other examples, among the vascular plants, in which the stems are the chief photosynthetic organs?
9. What evidence can you cite to support the claim that the branched condition is primitive in *Equisetum?*

CHAPTER 20

Division Pterophyta—Part I

INTRODUCTION

The division **Pterophyta,** the final group of vascular cryptogams to be considered, includes the plants commonly known as **ferns.** The members of this alliance may be distinguished at once from the preceding divisions of seedless vascular plants by their possession of **macrophyllous leaves.** Macrophyllous leaves are usually (but not always) markedly larger than microphyllous leaves, but their distinguishing attributes are the presence of branched veins in their blades and of parenchymatous gaps in the stem stele (when it is a siphonostele) above the point of departure of their leaf traces (Fig. 21–15). It will be recalled that traces of microphyllous leaves do not leave parenchymatous gaps in the stele. As a group, the Pterophyta have as highly developed and complex an external leaf form as occurs among the vascular plants. In a majority of genera, the leaf seems to have become the dominant organ of the sporophyte, the stems being correspondingly inconspicuous.

Survey of living members of the Pterophyta indicates that the group may be divided into two series on the basis of method of sporangium development. The first series, the class **Eusporangiopsida,** have a type of sporangium development essentially similar to that of the Psilophyta, Microphyllophyta, and Arthrophyta. Furthermore, the sporangia are massive and entirely or partially embedded, and they contain an indefinitely large number of spores surrounded by a many-layered sporangial wall. In the second series, the **Leptosporangiopsida** (Gr. *leptos,* fine or small), the sporangia develop from single cells which undergo periclinal divisions. Here the outer cell forms the major portion of the protuberant sporangium which is small in size, thin-walled (one-layered), and few-spored, the number usually definite and a multiple of two. A vast majority of familiar cultivated and field ferns are members of the Leptosporangiopsida.

CLASS 1. EUSPORANGIOPSIDA

The Eusporangiopsida include two series of living plants, each represented by two genera in the present text, namely, *Ophioglossum* and *Botrychium*, and *Marattia* and *Angiopteris*. The first two genera are found in both the temperate zone and the tropics; the last two are entirely tropical. For this reason, only brief mention will be made of *Marattia* and *Angiopteris*. A total of 10 genera and 280 species of ferns are included in the Eusporangiopsida.

Ophioglossum and Botrychium

INTRODUCTION AND VEGETATIVE MORPHOLOGY

The genera *Ophioglossum* (Gr. *ophis*, serpent + Gr. *glossa*, tongue), the adder's tongue fern (Fig. 20–1), and *Botrychium* (Gr. *botrychos*, grape), the grape fern (Fig. 20–2), are rather widely distributed in temperate North America. The former occurs in old fields and meadows, and the latter is frequently an inhabitant of the forest floor where it thrives in partial shade.

The leaves in both genera arise from a rather short, fleshy subterranean stem which bears fleshy, adventitious roots. The roots of some species of *Ophioglossum* produce adventitious buds that may develop new plantlets, a phenomenon which results in the formation of rather extensive colonies. Both *Botrychium* and *Ophioglossum* usually elevate only a single leaf from the perennial stems each growing season (Fig. 20–1). The leaves are annual in activity. Serial transverse sections of the axis of *O. engelmanni* Prantl reveal that the leaves arise in spiral order in five vertical rows, although usually only one is present at a time. In *Botrychium virginianum* (L.) Sw. (Fig. 20–2), the leaf blade is large and dissected, but in other species of the genus the leaves are smaller and simpler. The leaf of *Ophioglossum engelmanni* is simple and entire. There is good evidence that simple leaves are reduced rather than primitive in these ferns.

Inasmuch as the leaf is the dominant and most conspicuous organ of these plants, its structure will be described first. The young leaves are rolled up and protected by the remains of the sheathing base of the pre-ceding leaf as they emerge from the soil. The leaflets of *Botrychium* are characterized by open dichot-omous venation; the leaf blade in *Ophioglossum* is traversed by a reticulate system of veins which are mostly united at the leaf margins. Open dichotomous venation is con-sidered to be a primitive attribute of leaves on the basis of the fossil record. The leaves appear as pri-mordia near the slow-growing stem tip several years before they are raised above the ground, and their development is extremely slow. The vascular tissue of the leaf is connected to that in the stem through the petiole. In *O. engel-manni*, the double leaf trace branches into four or more strands soon after it enters the petiole. The petiole of *Botrychium virgianum* contains an undivided trace. The leaf blade in *Ophioglossum* is cov-ered by epidermal cells above and

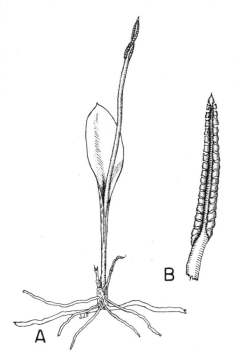

Fig. 20–1. *Ophioglossum engelmanni* Prantl. A, Single plant and detail of fertile spike. X ½; B, Dehiscent fertile spike. X 1.

below (Fig. 20–3); the central portion is composed of photosynthetic parenchyma cells which are not differentiated into palisade and spongy layers. Stomata occur abundantly on both surfaces of the leaf. The guard cells, alone among the epidermal cells, contain chloroplasts.

The underground stems of both *Ophioglossum* and *Botrychium* are slow-growing and fleshy. They are covered with the remains of previous seasons' leaves at their summits, and with rather closely arranged, fleshy roots below (Fig. 20–1A). Development of the stem in both genera is localized in the division of single apical cells and their derivatives. These differentiate in older portions of the stem into stelar, cortical, and epi-dermal regions. The vascular tissue in the primary (embryonic) stems of some species is protostelic, but as the stem grows older the vascular

Fig. 20–2. *Botrychium virginianum* (L.) Sw. Single plant with fertile spike. X ½.

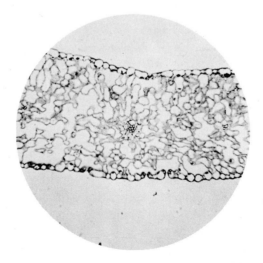

Fig. 20–3. *Ophioglossum engelmanni.* Transverse section of leaf blade; note upper and lower epidermis, both with stomata, spongy mesophyll, and transverse section of veins. X 60.

tissue formed later is arranged as a **siphonostele.** The siphonostele, how-ever, is much dissected (Fig. 20–4) into discrete strands because of the close proximity to each other of the roots, the nodes, and the points of departure of leaf traces, which in these macrophyllous plants, leave parenchymatous gaps in the stele above the point of their departure (Fig. 20–4). The shortness of the internodes and the overlapping of leaf gaps result in the arrangement of vascular tissue as a **dictyostele,** with **endarch** maturation of the xylem. The phloem is external to the xylem.

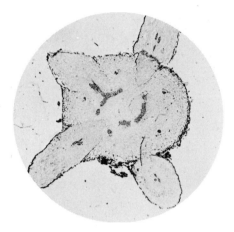

Fig. 20–4. *Ophioglossum engelmanni.* Transverse section of stem; note emergent roots and dissection of siphonostele by gaps to form dictyostele. X 12½.

Endodermis and pericycle are absent in mature stems of *O. engelmanni.* In the stems of *Botrychium,* a cambium adds secondary vascular tissues to the primary ones. The cortex is parenchymatous and starch-filled. The stem surface is suberized in older portions by the formation of a periderm layer.

The roots in both genera also develop through the activity of single apical cells. They arise endogenously in the rhizome in association with the leaves and below them. The vascular tissue is protostelic, an almost universal condition in the roots of vascular plants. In *Ophioglossum,* the root (Fig. 20–5) may be monarch, diarch, or tetrarch; it is most often tetrarch in *Botrychium virginianum.* The phloem alternates with the xylem, and both are surrounded by one or more layers of pericycle cells. The stele is delimited from the cortex by a well-differentiated endodermis. The cortex is extensive and serves as a storage region. The epidermis is devoid of root hairs; in older regions of the root, the surface is suberized. Mycorrhizal fungi usually are present in these genera.

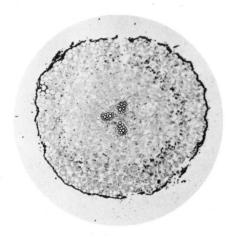

Fig. 20–5. *Ophioglossum engelmanni.* Transverse section of root; note triarch xylem and extensive cortex for storage. X 30.

REPRODUCTION

Both *Ophioglossum* and *Botrychium* are at once distinguishable from other Pterophyta by the arrangement of their sporogenous tissue, which is localized in a branched or unbranched **fertile spike** (Figs. 20–1, 20–2). The latter emerges at the junction of the leaf blade and petiole. Anatomical evidence has been interpreted as indicating that this structure represents a pair of fertile, lateral pinnae (leaflets) in *Ophioglossum*. The fertile axis is unbranched in *O. engelmanni* (Fig. 20–1) but compound in *B. virginianum* (Fig. 20–2). In the former it has two longitudinal rows of deeply sunken sporangia (Fig. 20–1B) which arise in eusporangiate fashion (Fig. 20–6). Their walls are composed of several layers of cells. A branch of vascular tissue runs to the base of each sporangium. There is a one- or two-layered tapetum between the central sporogenous tissue and the wall (Fig. 20–6). As the sporangium develops, the walls of the tapetal cells disintegrate and give rise to a tapetal plasmodium. A few of the sporogenous cells also disintegrate, but the remainder undergo meiosis and give rise to tetrads of spores. It has been reported recently that the haploid number of chromosomes in *O. vulgatum* L. is approximately 256. The cells of the sporophyte, therefore, contain more than 500 chromosomes; a tropical species, *O. petiolatum*, with over 1000 chromosomes, has the largest number yet observed in a naturally occurring vascular plant. The sporangia dehisce at maturity along a line predetermined by the formation of several rows of thin-walled cells (Fig. 20–1*B*). Each sporangium may contain as many as 15,000 spores in some species.

Development of the gametophyte from the spores has never been followed completely in laboratory cultures; hence our knowledge of it is

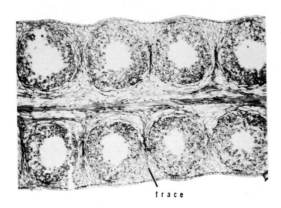

Fig. 20–6. *Ophioglossum* sp. Median longitudinal section of apex of fertile spike; note seriate eusporangiate sporangia and vascular traces. X 25.

based largely on specimens collected in the field. In both *Ophioglossum* and *Botrychium*, the gametophyte is fleshy, subterranean, and colorless and usually is infected with the hyphae of a mycorrhizal fungus. *Ophioglossum* gametophytes are cylindrical (Fig. 20–7), up to two inches in length, and branched in some individuals. The diameter of the largest is about one-eighth of an inch. The nutrition of the gametophyte here, as in *Psilotum* and many species of *Lycopodium*, apparently is saprophytic. However, small amounts of chlorophyll may develop in exposed portions of the gametophyte, the growth of which is apical.

Ophioglossum is homothallic, the antheridia and archegonia occurring together in various stages of development (Fig. 20–7). Both sex organs arise from cells on the surface of the gametophyte, but at maturity they are largely sunken within it. The antheridia are massive and contain

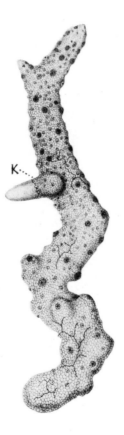

Fig. 20–7. *Ophioglossum vulgatum* L. Branching, cylindrical gametophyte with antheridia and archegonia and young embryo at k. X 20. (After Bruchmann.)

large numbers of multiflagellate sperms. Only the tips of the archegonial necks protrude above the gametophyte surface. Fertilization has been observed to occur in the summer months in the northern hemisphere.

Development of the zygote into an embryonic sporophyte progresses slowly in various species of *Ophioglossum* (Fig. 20–8). A small spherical mass of tissue is formed within the archegonial venter. This becomes differentiated into foot, root, and leaf primordia. The apical initial of the stem appears later, and this perhaps foreshadows the inconspicuous state of that organ in the mature sporophyte. Several years are required, in most species, for the production of a leaf with a fertile spike.

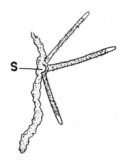

Fig. 20–8. *Ophioglossum vulgatum.* Gametophyte showing roots and minute stem, s, of young sporophyte. X 2. (After Bruchmann.)

Marattia and Angiopteris

With the exception of *Ophioglossum* and *Botrychium,* the eusporangiate Pterophyta are exclusively tropical in distribution and are known in the temperate zone only through herbarium and conservatory specimens. For these reasons their treatment in this text is abbreviated. *Angi-*

Fig. 20–9. *Angiopteris evecta* Hoffm. (From Wettstein.)

opteris (Gr. *angion*, vessel + Gr. *pteris*, a fern) and *Marattia* (after J. F. Maratti, a Tuscan botanist) often are cultivated in the fern houses of large conservatories (Fig. 20–9). The leaves in these genera are large and frequently elaborately compound; they arise from tuberous, partially subterranean stems that are covered with persistent leaf bases, between which the rather large fleshy roots emerge. Unlike *Ophioglossum* and *Botrychium*, the young leaves in *Angiopteris* and *Marattia* are coiled circinately (Fig. 20–9), as in the leptosporangiate Pterophyta. In this type of vernation, growth of the lower leaf surfaces during ontogeny is more rapid than that of the upper. As a result, the leaves are coiled, with

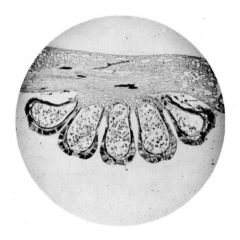

Fig. 20–10. *Angiopteris evecta.* Eusporangiate sporangia on ventral surface of leaf. X 30.

the upper surfaces concealed. They are elevated through the soil or from the stem in this coiled condition and unfold after they have emerged by growth of the upper leaf surfaces.

These genera are like *Ophioglossum* and *Botrychium* in their production of massive eusporangiate sporangia but differ in that the latter occur not on a fertile spike but on the margin or ventral surface of the pinnae (Fig. 20–10), in groups or **sori.** The sporangia of a single sorus may unite during development, forming massive **synangia** (Gr. *syn*, together + Gr. *angeion*, vessel), as in *Marattia*. The sporangia are partially sunken in their receptacles, and all those in a single synangium or on a single receptacle mature simultaneously.

The gametophytes of *Marattia* and *Angiopteris* (Fig. 20–11) are dorsiventral, green, surface-growing thalli. Large specimens resemble such liverworts as *Pellia*. The gametophytes are long-lived and may be perennial. The thallus is many layers of cells thick except at the margins, and the sex organs are borne on the ventral surface in the midrib region. The antheridia occur on both the upper and lower surfaces of the gametophyte, the cells of which usually contain an endophytic fungus. The sex

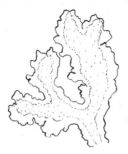

Fig. 20–11. *Marattia sambricina* Bl. Gametophyte 27 months after spore germination. X 4. (From Stokey.)

organs are sunken in the thallus, as in *Ophioglossum* and *Botrychium*. A suspensor has been described in the embryo of certain individuals of *Angiopteris*.

SUMMARY

The eusporangiate Pterophyta include two groups of living ferns exemplified in the preceding account by *Ophioglossum* and *Botrychium*, on the one hand, and by *Marattia* and *Angiopteris*, on the other. The first two genera bear their massive, individual eusporangiate sporangia on fertile spikes, whereas in the latter they occur in united (synangial) or unfused groups on the lower surface or margins of vegetative leaf blades. In both cases, development and maturation of all the sporangia are synchronous, and each sporangium produces an indefinitely large number of spores.

The gametophytes of *Ophioglossum* and *Botrychium* are fleshy, subterranean saprophytic structures. That of the former is cylindrical and radially organized, with sex organs well distributed over the surface. In *Botrychium virginianum*, the gametophyte has some degree of dorsiventrality, with the sex organs limited to the upper surface. The gametophytes of *Marattia* and *Angiopteris*, on the other hand, are epiterranean, green and *Pellia*-like, although they also contain a mycorrhizal fungus. The archegonia are confined usually to the lower surface; the antheridia may occur on both surfaces.

These genera possess macrophyllous leaves which are the dominant organs of the sporophyte. This is attested by the profound disturbance of the stem stele by leaf gaps and the relatively slow development of the stem itself. The latter is especially apparent in the development of the embryonic sporophyte, in which leaf development far outstrips that of the stem. Discussion of the significance of macrophyllous leaves is deferred to Chapter 23.

DISCUSSION QUESTIONS

1. Distinguish between macrophyllous and microphyllous leaves.
2. Distinguish between protosteles, siphonosteles, dictyosteles, and eusteles.
3. How does the venation of *Ophioglossum* differ from that of *Botrychium*? Which is considered to be more primitive, and on what basis?
4. Are microphyllous and macrophyllous leaves homologous in your opinion? Explain.
5. Can you suggest a reason for the relatively small size of the stems in *Botrychium* and *Ophioglossum*?
6. Does the approximately simultaneous maturation of the spores in these genera occur in vascular plants previously studied? Can you suggest a biological disadvantage of this habit?
7. Can you suggest similarities between the gametophyte of *Ophioglossum* and that of other seedless vascular plants? Explain.
8. How does spore production in *Marattia* and *Angiopteris* differ from that in *Ophioglossum* and *Botrychium*?
9. In what respects are the gametophytes of these genera different?
10. Where would you search for *Botrychium* and *Ophioglossum* in nature?

CHAPTER 21

Division Pterophyta—Part II

CLASS 2. LEPTOSPORANGIOPSIDA

Introduction

As stated at the beginning of Chapter 20, the division **Pterophyta** contains two classes of living ferns, the **Eusporangiopsida**, described in the preceding chapter, and the **Leptosporangiopsida**, to be considered in the present one. The Leptosporangiopsida include all the ferns which have leptosporangiate sporangium development. In this type of sporangium ontogeny, the sporangium arises from a single surface cell whose derivatives protrude from the surface of the plant. An apical cell functions in sporangium development. Leptosporangiate sporangia are small, produce a definite number of spores (frequently 48 to 64), and have a wall one layer of cells in thickness. Other attributes, in addition to sporangial characters, serve to distinguish the Eusporangiopsida from the Leptosporangiopsida. These will be cited in the following account.

In number of genera, species, and individuals, the leptosporangiate ferns far outnumber the eusporangiate types. Some 250 genera and 9000 species have been described. Leptosporangiopsida are most abundant in the tropics, but they are also well represented in the temperate zone. In habit, they vary from small, delicate filmy plants to large tropical tree ferns with upright stems and enormous leaves; a number are climbers. The Leptosporangiopsida have been classified into a number of families, many of which are inhabitants of the tropics and therefore not readily available for study except in collections in herbaria and conservatories. For this reason, the treatment of the group in this text will be restricted to a brief discussion of representatives that are readily available.

The illustrative leptosporangiate genera will be treated under the following headings: *Osmunda;* **Polypodiaceous ferns;** *Marsilea,* and **additional types.** The last two are discussed in Chapter 22.

Osmunda

VEGETATIVE MORPHOLOGY

In most classifications of leptosporangiate ferns, *Osmunda* (*Osmunder,* Saxon equivalent to the god Thor) and its relatives are placed at the beginning of the series of genera in recognition of certain attributes which are interpreted as intermediate between the eusporangiate and leptosporangiate Pterophyta. The genus *Osmunda* is cosmopolitan in distribution. Three species are distributed widely in the United States, namely, *O. regalis* L. (Fig. 21–1), the **royal** or **flowering fern;** *O. cinnamomea* L., the **cinnamon fern,** and *O. claytoniana* L., the **interrupted fern** (Fig. 21–2).

Fig. 21–1. *Osmunda regalis* L. The royal fern or flowering fern; single frond with distal pinnae fertile. X 1/6.

These perennial ferns are found usually in rather hydric habitats in which the magnificent ascending fronds attain a large size, often reaching six feet in length. In the northeastern part of the United States, the several species of *Osmunda* are planted as ornamentals in semishaded locations. The striking leaves of *Osmunda* are either once or twice pinnately compound, depending on the species. Compound leaves, it will be recalled, are so designated because of their divided blades. In pinnately compound leaves, the leaflets are distributed along an axis called the **rachis.** The latter merges below with the petiole. The ultimate segments of pinnately compound leaves are called **pinnules,** and the entire leaf is spoken of as a **frond.** Each growing season, the underground stem (called a "stock," in this case) produces a group of circinately coiled fronds which unfold, photosynthesize, and produce spores. The leaves are annual and die at the end of the season; but the long-persistent leaf bases surround the stem and, together with the wiry roots, form prominent mounds. Mature pinnae are rather leathery in texture. Their venation is open-dichotomous, as in *Botrychium*.

Fig. 21–2. A, *Osmunda claytoniana* L. The interrupted fern; note fertile pinnae among vegetative ones. B, *Osmunda cinnamomea* L. The cinnamon fern; note fertile frond at left, vegetative frond at right. X 1/10. (After Waters.)

The dense covering of wiry roots and persistent leaf bases, noted above, effectively protects the vertical underground stem of *Osmunda* (Fig. 21–3). The roots, leaf bases, and stem are so intimately associated that sections of all are usually available for study in a single preparation (Fig. 21–3). The vascular tissue of the mature *Osmunda* stem, as viewed in transverse section, is composed of a circle of strands separated by narrow parenchymatous leaf gaps. Leaf traces which have occasioned the gaps may be observed in section at various points in the cortex, through which they pass into the leaf bases. Three-dimensional and longitudinal views of the stele indicate that it is a siphonostele dissected by leaf gaps, and therefore a dictyostele, as in *Ophioglossum*. The xylem strands are **mesarch** (Fig. 21–4), with the protoxylem surrounded by metaxylem, the latter composed largely of scalariform-pitted tracheids. A prominent endodermis delimits the stele from the cortical region of the stem. Within

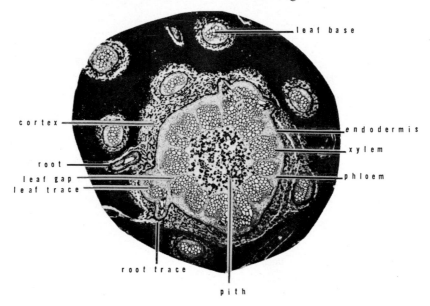

Fig. 21–3. *Osmunda* sp. Transverse section of rhizome; note circle of leaf bases and associated roots surrounding the central rhizome with its massive pith and dictyostele. X 18.

it there are several layers of parenchyma cells, the pericycle, the phloem cells, and the mesarch xylem. An inner endodermis which separates the stele from the central pith is sometimes visible. The cortex of the stem is composed of parenchyma and dark-stained sclerenchyma tissue. The spirally arranged leaves are connected to the stele by C-shaped traces. Near each leaf base, two roots, with their vascular supply derived from the leaf trace, originate endogenously and grow between the leaf bases into the soil. The roots contain exarch protosteles which are diarch or triarch. The development of both root and stem is localized in single apical cells. In certain individual roots, however, as many as four apical cells may be present, an attribute suggestive of ferns of the *Marattia* group.

REPRODUCTION

Further striking modifications of leaf structure are associated with sporangium production in *Osmunda*. The location of the sporangia varies in the several species. In *O. regalis*, only the most distal pinnae and pinnules are fertile (Figs. 21–1, 21–5). In *O. claytoniana* (Fig. 21–2A), on the other hand, certain intermediate pairs of pinnae bear sporangia, whereas the proximal and distal ones are sterile. Finally, in *O. cinnamomea* (Fig. 21–2B), the sporangia are borne only upon special spore-

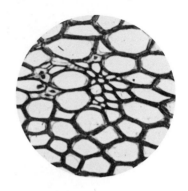

Fig. 21–4. *Osmunda* sp. Mesarch xylem from stele shown in Fig. 21–3; note protoxylem surrounded by metaxylem. X 250.

bearing leaves, usually called **sporophylls**, whose vegetative tissues and functions are greatly restricted. Intermediate stages in these dimorphic phenomena are readily observable on examination of several individuals

Fig. 21–5. *Osmunda regalis*. Enlargement of fertile tip of frond; note transition between blade-like and nonblade-like segments. X 3.

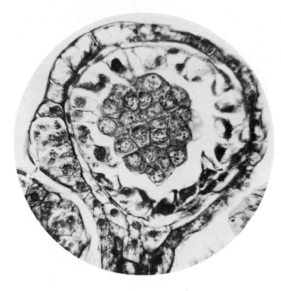

Fig. 21–6. *Osmunda regalis*. Median longitudinal section of sporangium in spore mother cell stage; note two-layered wall, tapetum, spore mother cells, and unilateral annulus at the left. X 125.

(Fig. 21–5). The sporangia themselves originate superficially on the pinna surface. Although prominent single initial cells may be present in each sporangial precursor, adjacent cells also contribute to the formation of the sporangium, which becomes protuberant and rather massive, in comparison with that in other leptosporangiate ferns. Furthermore, the sporangial stalk is also thicker (Fig. 21–6) than in other leptosporangiate ferns, and the wall is two-layered. A central sporogenous cell in each sporangium undergoes repeated divisions until approximately 128 sporogenous cells are produced. The outermost layer of these functions somewhat as a tapetal plasmodium during sporogenesis. The large and prominent chromosomes, relatively

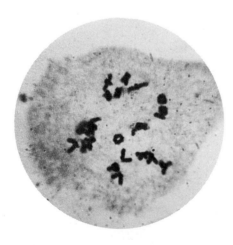

Fig. 21–7. *Osmunda regalis*. Squashed spore mother cell in meiosis, showing 22 diakenetic chromosomes (aceto-carmine preparation). X 500.

few in number ($n = 22$) as compared with other ferns, are counted readily in the meiotic divisions associated with sporogenesis (Fig. 21–7). Each sporangium produces between 256 and 512 spores. These are green at maturity and are shed by dehiscence of the sporangium along a vertical line running between a unilateral group of thick-

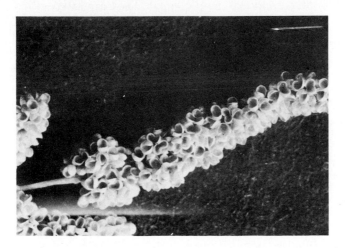

Fig. 21–8. *Osmunda regalis.* Mature sporangia at dehiscence. X 5..

walled cells, the **annulus,** and the stalk of the sporangium (Fig. 21–8). As is the case with the chlorophyllous spores of *Equisetum,* those of *Osmunda* do not remain viable very long if stored. They germinate very readily, however, if transferred to agar, soil, or other environments with adequate moisture (Figs. 21–9, 21–10).

The young gametophyte at first consists of a short chain of cells with a basal rhizoid, but an apical cell is organized soon by successive oblique

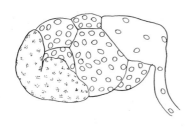

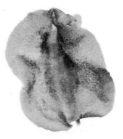

Fig. 21–9. *Osmunda regalis.* Spore germination, two weeks after spores were planted on agar. X 315.

Fig. 21–10. *Osmunda regalis* L. Mature gametophyte growing on agar. X 2.

divisions of the terminal cell. This gives rise to a spatulate gametophyte at whose apex several apical cells may function later. Their derivatives build up a relatively massive green gametophyte, suggestive of *Marrattia* and *Angiopteris* (Figs. 21–10, 21–11C). Prominent, ventrally projecting midribs are present in the gametophytes of *Osmunda,* which are liverwort-like and long-lived and may be perennial. They are often called **prothallia.** Vegetative propagation of the gametophytes by separation of marginal lobes has been observed.

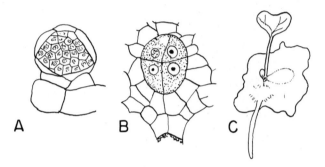

Fig. 21–11.   A, *Osmunda cinnamomea,* mature antheridium, X 215. B, *O. claytoniana* L. Section of eight-celled embryo in archegonium. C, *O. claytoniana.* Gametophyte with young sporophyte emerging. X 4. (From Campbell.)

There is some evidence that the prothallia are protandrous; well-separated individuals are always homothallic. The antheridia (Fig. 21–11A) are borne on the under side of the gametophyte near the margins, and the archegonia (Fig. 21–12) are on or near the midrib. The protuberant antheridia have a single layer of jacket cells, one of which, near the apex, is thrown off as the antheridium dehisces. Approximately 100 spermatogenous cells fill the antheridium; each gives rise to a single, coiled, multiflagellate sperm. The archegonial venters are sunk in the superficial tissue on the ventral surface of the gametophytes (Fig. 21–12). The single binucleate neck canal cell is surrounded by four rows of neck cells about six to eight tiers high.

The zygote undergoes two successive vertical divisions parallel in direction to the axis of the archegonium but perpendicular to each other. The next divisions are transverse, so that an octant stage develops (Fig. 21–11B). The outermost four cells (nearest the neck) gradually develop the stem, leaf, and primary root of the embryo, and the four basal cells form a foot. Growth of the embryo is relatively slow in

Osmunda as compared with other leptosporangiate ferns. The arche-gonium functions as a calyptra during early embryogeny, but it is ulti-mately ruptured by the developing embryo which protrudes from the gametophyte and becomes established as an independent plant (Fig. 21–11C).

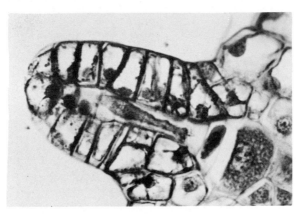

Fig. 21–12. *Osmunda* sp. Median longitudinal section of immature archegonium; note egg cell, ventral canal cell, neck canal cell, and neck cells. X 500.

The primary embryonic leaf and those which follow it during the early phases of development are much simpler than those of the adult plant (Fig. 21–11C). The stem of the young sporophyte is protostelic at first, and the dictyostelic condition does not arise until considerable develop-ment has occurred.

Polypodiaceous Genera: *Adiantum, Dryopteris,* and Others

VEGETATIVE MORPHOLOGY

A majority of the most familiar, naturally occurring, and widespread ferns of the temperate zone, as well as many cultivated varieties, are members of a vast assemblage of polypodiaceous ferns, so named from the genus *Polypodium* (Gr. *polys,* many + Gr. *pous,* foot). Among these are *Dryopteris* (Gr. *drys,* tree + Gr. *pteris,* fern), *Adiantum* (Gr. *adi-antos,* maidenhair), *Polystichum* (Gr. *polys* + Gr. *stichos,* row), *Wood-sia* (after Joseph Wood, an English botanist), *Pteris* (Gr. *pteris,* fern), *Pteridium* (Gr. *pteris*), and *Nephrolepis* (Gr. *nephros,* kidney + Gr. *lepis,* scale). Most of these genera are plants of moist, mesic woodlands. *Adiantum capillus-veneris* L. (Fig. 21–13), the Venus maidenhair, however, is an example of a rather hydrophytic species; *Pellaea atropurpurea* (L.) Link., the cliff brake, and *Polypodium polypodioides* (L.) Watt. are xerophytes. All temperate-zone members of this alliance are perennial and a few are evergreen.

Fig. 21–13.   *Adiantum capillus-veneris* L. Venus maidenhair, greenhouse specimen. X 1/7.

Dryopteris dentata (Forsk.) C. Chr. (Fig. 21–14) and *Adiantum capillus-veneris* L. (Fig. 21–13) will be emphasized as illustrative types in the following account. In both of them the stem is subterranean, although in the latter it may be exposed in part as it clings tenaciously to dripping limestone cliffs or other substrata. The bases of the preceding seasons' leaves persist indefinitely and form a sort of jagged armor about the stems. The stem in *Dryopteris dentata* is relatively slow-growing, but in *Adiantum* it is a horizontal, rapidly elongating rhizome. Branching of the stem is abundant in *Adiantum* and results in colonization of the area around the original plant. The stems of both genera are clothed with a dense mass of adventitious roots which emerge from the stem between the leaf bases.

Growth of the stem in each case may be traced to the activity of single apical cells and their derivatives; these occur at the stem tip, often concealed by a dense growth of superficial multicellular scale-like organs known as **paleae.** The apical cell of the stem is triangular in transverse section, but actually tetrahedral, and it gives rise to three ranks of deriva-

Fig. 21–14. *Dryopteris dentata* (Forsk.) C. Chr. A species of shield fern. X 1/12.

tive cells. Although the vascular tissues in the embryonic stems of all leptosporangiate ferns are reported to be arranged in protostelic fashion, there is a gradual transition in older stems to a siphonostelic or dictyo-stelic condition. In both *Adiantum* (Fig. 21–15) and *Dryopteris* the vascular tissue is completely surrounded by a well-differentiated endodermis which separates it from the parenchymatous pith and cortex. Portions of both of these may become sclerotic. The xylem is mesarch in development and composed chiefly of large tracheids with abundant, transversely elongate bordered pits. In a few genera (*Pteridium*) the closing membranes of the pits of the sloping terminal tracheid walls are dissolved at maturity, resulting in direct continuity between adjoining elements. This condition

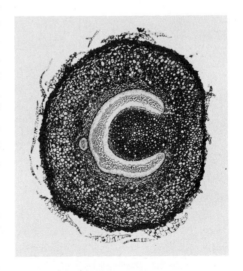

Fig. 21–15. *Adiantum* sp. Transverse section of rhizome; note amphiphloic siphonostele with leaf gap and root trace. X 25.

results in the organization of primitive **tracheae** or **vessels,** previously noted in *Selaginella* and characteristic of the xylem of higher seed plants. The sieve elements are elongate, lack companion cells, and have numerous sieve areas in their vertical walls.

All roots, with the exception of the embryonic radicle, are adventitious and arise endogenously from the stem. They emerge between the leaf bases. Development of the root originates in a single apical cell; in this case, however, the latter cuts off derivatives in a direction perpendicular to the long axis of the root, thus adding cells to the root cap. The cells of the central procambium differentiate into an exarch protostele, the arrangement characteristic of the roots of most vascular plants. The roots of *Dryopteris dentata* are diarch. The stele is surrounded by a narrow pericycle, a prominent endodermis, cortex, and epidermis, the latter with root hairs. The inner portion of the cortex is often sclerotic. Branch roots originate from endodermal cells opposite the protoxylem groups. Secondary growth is absent in both stems and roots of leptosporangiate ferns.

As in the eusporangiate ferns and *Osmunda*, the leaves of *Dryopteris* and *Adiantum* and other Leptosporangiopsida are the dominant organs of the sporophyte. The large compound leaves, circinately coiled in the bud (Fig. 21–16), may be extremely elaborate when mature. The petiole

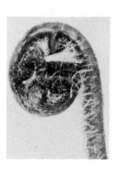

of each leaf in these genera is connected to the stem stele by one or more traces; these run throughout the rachis, giving rise to branches which traverse the pinnae and pinnules. In *Adiantum* the venation is dichotomous (Fig. 21–20) and therefore more primitive than the reticulate arrangement of the veins in *Dryopteris*. Internally, the leaf blade consists of an upper and lower epidermis, the latter with abundant stomata enclosing a relatively undifferentiated mesophyll

Fig. 21–16.   Cyathea sp. Circinate leaf bud or "fiddle-head." X ½.

(Fig. 21–17). The mesophyll of *Adiantum* is limited in extent; the abundant chloroplasts in the epidermal cells in this genus undoubtedly play a major role in photosynthesis. The veins are collateral in arrangement of xylem and phloem. The leaves arise close to the growing point of the stem and develop through the activity of an apical cell; a new group of

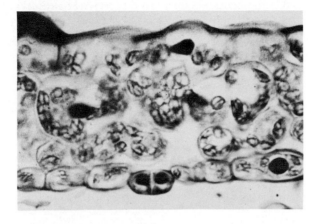

Fig. 21–17. *Dryopteris dentata*. Transverse section of leaf blade; note upper epidermis, mesophyll cells with starch in plastids, lower epidermis, and a stoma. X 500.

leaves is produced each season. The simple leaves of the **walking fern,** *Asplenium rhizophyllum* L., function in propagation (Fig. 21–19).

REPRODUCTION

After a series of entirely vegetative leaves has been produced from the stem of a young plant, all the leaves which develop subsequently in *Dryopteris* and *Adiantum* are usually both vegetative and fertile. In both genera, groups of sporangia known as **sori** (Gr. *soros,* heap) develop on the under surface of ordinary leaves (Figs. 21–20, 21–21, 21–22). Some segregation of vegetative and reproductive functions is apparent in the distribution of sporogenous tissue in several other genera of polypodiaceous ferns. In the Christmas fern, *Polystichum acrostichoides* (Michx.) Schott (Fig. 21–18), for example, only the distal pinnae of each frond are fertile. *Ono-*

Fig. 21–18. *Polystichum acrostichoides* (Michx.) Schott. Portion of frond showing distal fertile pinnae. X ½.

clea sensibilis L., the sensitive fern, and *Pteretis Struthiopteris* Nieuwl., the ostrich fern, superficially suggest *Osmunda cinnamomea* in that they produce sporangia on markedly modified fronds, the remaining leaves being purely vegetative.

Fig. 21–19. *Asplenium rhizophyllum* L. The walking fern; note simple leaves developing new plantlets at their apices. X ¼. (Courtesy of Dr. Ilda McVeigh.)

In *Adiantum* (Fig. 21–20) and *Pteris* (Fig. 21–21), the sori are almost marginal and are covered during development by a revolute leaf margin known as a **false indusium.** The sporangia are actually borne on this false indusium in *Adiantum.* In *Dryopteris dentata* (Fig. 21–22), the sori lie over the veins of the pinnules, and each is covered by a shield-like

A   B

Fig. 21–20.   *Adiantum capillus-veneris.* Fertile leaf segments. A, Sorus covered by false indusium. B, Mature sori. X 6.

flap of tissue, the **true indusium** (L. *indusium,* tunic), a single layer of cells in thickness. The sporangia in both genera arise from the lower leaf surface (Fig. 21–22C) and the region of their origin is known as the

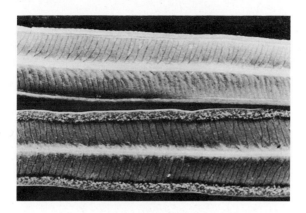

Fig. 21–21. *Pteris* sp. Immature sporangia covered by false indusium, above; mature sporangia exposed, below. X 2½.

receptacle. The order of development in both cases is said to be **mixed,** inasmuch as sporangial development follows no definite order with relation to the receptacle, in contrast to the simultaneous maturation of the sporangia in the Eusporangiopsida and *Osmunda.*

The details of sporangium development are illustrated in Fig. 21–23. Each sporangium arises from a single surface cell of the receptacle which projects above the surface and undergoes transverse division. The entire sporangium usually develops from the outer product of this division. This cell becomes divided by three somewhat anticlinal walls that cut out a central apical cell (Fig. 21–23C,D). The apical cell undergoes division in three directions, forming a stalk-like outgrowth. The apical cell now divides in a direction perpendicular to the stalk to form an apical wall initial, beneath which lies the **primary archesporial cell** (Fig. 21–23E). The latter gives rise, by periclinal divisions, to the **four primary tapetal cells** (Fig. 21–23F) which subsequently undergo division, forming a two-layered **tapetum** (Fig. 21–23G). The central sporogenous cell now divides repeatedly and forms the spore mother cells, which vary in number from 12 to 16. Each of these separates slightly from the others, becomes spherical, and undergoes the meiotic process, forming a tetrad of spores which ultimately separate and thicken their walls (Fig. 21–24). The

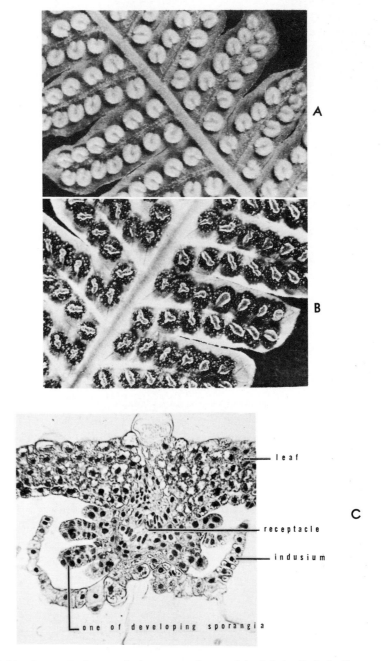

Fig. 21—22. *Dryopteris dentata.* A, Immature sori covered by indusia. X 5. B, Mature sori, indusia retracted. X 5. C, Transverse section of young leaf segment, receptacle, developing sporangia, and indusium. X 175.

chromosome number of the Venus maidenhair, A. *capillus-veneris* L., has been determined to be $n = 30$, a rather low number among the Leptosporangiopsida. The tapetal cells elongate radially during sporogenesis and finally become disorganized.

During sporogenesis, the cells of the sporangial jacket divide by anticlinal division and the products increase in size, as do the cells of the

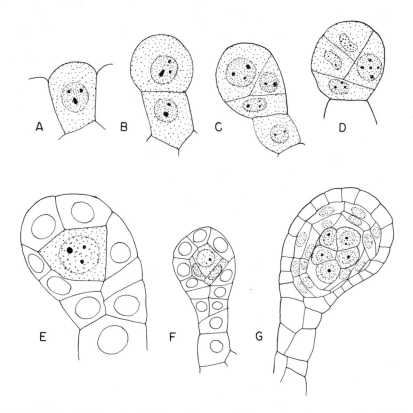

Fig. 21–23.   *Dryopteris dentata.* A-G, Successive stages in leptosporangiate sporangium development. A-E, X 770; F, X 410; G, X 190.

stalk. At maturity the sporangium is a somewhat flattened spheroid or ellipsoid (Fig. 21–25). The wall cells on the flattened faces are large and have undulate walls. A vertical row of specially differentiated cells, the **annulus,** forms an incomplete ring about the sporangium (Fig. 21–25). The radial and inner tangential walls of these cells are markedly thickened. Between the last cell of the annulus and the base of the stalk there are a number of thin-walled cells, the **lip cells** or **stomium.**

As the spores mature, they become invested with a dark, brown-black-ish epispore coat, and the entire sorus changes from a delicate whitish-green to dark-brown in appearance. When the spores on a majority of the sporangia are mature, the indusium in *Dryopteris* contracts (Fig. 21–22B), exposing them to the air. In *Adiantum* (Fig. 21–20B) and *Pteris* (Fig. 21–21) the revolute leaf edge unfolds slightly when the spores are

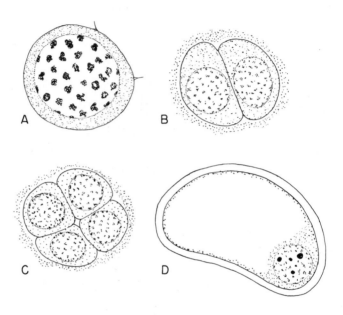

Fig. 21–24. *Dryopteris dentata*, sporogenesis. A, Spore mother cell, prophase of meiosis I. B, End of division I. C, Spore tetrad. D, Mature spore, sectioned. X 1700.

mature. Spore dissemination in both genera is accomplished by a rather explosive dehiscence of the sporangia which depends on loss of water. The annulus and lip cells are directly concerned in the process. The loss of water through the thin outer tangential walls of the cells of the annulus shortens its length, so that the sporangium wall is rup-tured in the region of the lip cells (Fig. 21–25B); the wall cells of the sporangium are also ruptured. As the annulus continues to shorten, the outer tangential walls become increasingly concave because they are ad-herent to the water within the annulus cells, the amount of which is less-ening through evaporation. Ultimately a point is reached (Fig. 21–25C) at which the tensile resistance of the water within the annulus cells is no longer sufficient to prevent the separation of the outer tangential walls from its surface; at this point the cells fill with air or water vapor or both, and the shortened annulus elongates suddenly, snapping back to its original position, thus ejecting the spores. It is not entirely clear

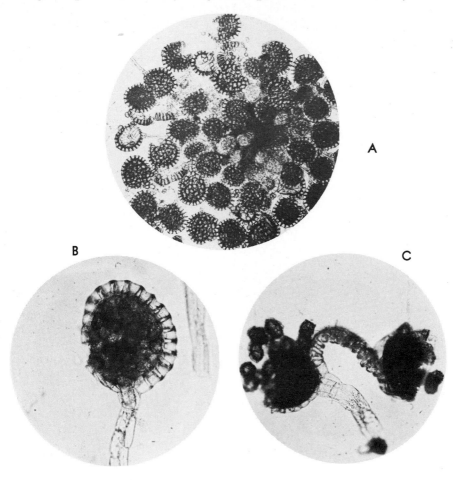

Fig. 21–25. A, *Polypodium* sp., sorus with mature and dehiscent sporangia; note annuli. X 30. B, *Dryopteris dentata*, mature sporangium. X 125. C, The same sporangium in dehiscence. X 125.

whether this disjunction of the outer tangential walls from the water in their lumina occurs in all the cells of the annulus simultaneously. Resaturation of the annulus with water would explain the observed fact that a given sporangium may open and close more than once when in water. The latter occurs also in air, however.

Although the number of spores produced by a single sporangium in most leptosporangiate ferns is small, frequently 48 to 64, as compared with those of *Osmunda* (256 to 512) and the eusporangiate genera (1500 to 2000 in *Botrychium*), the large number of sporangia in a sorus, along

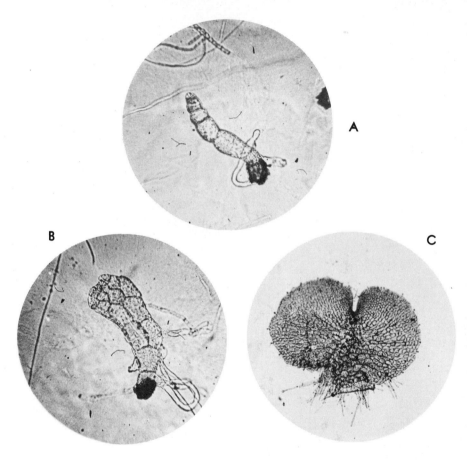

Fig. 21–26. *Dryopteris dentata.* Spore germination and development of gametophyte. A, Gametophyte 10 days old. X 250. B, Gametophyte 20 days old. X 250. C, Gametophyte 61 days old. X 35.

with the enormous number of sori on the pinnules of a single mature plant, results in the production of a surprisingly large number of spores by a single individual. It has been estimated that one mature plant of a species of *Dryopteris* produces 50,000,000 spores each season.

In spite of this enormous number of spores, relatively few complete their development into mature gametophytes, because so many are borne by air currents to places unfavorable for germination. The process of spore germination and gametophyte development may be followed readily in laboratory cultures of spores of *Dryopteris, Adiantum,* and other leptosporangiate ferns planted on agar or moist soil, or on the surface of moist flower pots or other crockery. Some stages in their development are illustrated in Fig. 21–26. In crowded cultures, the developing gametophytes remain irregularly filamentous, but where there is sufficient space, they become typically cordate. Gametophytes are usually present on moist soil or in rock crevices in the vicinity of fern colonies growing in nature.

Spore germination frequently results in the formation of a small, protonema-like chain of bulbous cells rich in chloroplasts (Fig. 21–26A). Under favorable conditions, oblique divisions in the terminal cell of the filament result in the production of an apical cell which cuts off segments in two directions (Fig. 21–26B). The derivatives continue to divide, forming a spatulate plant body (Fig. 21–26C) one layer of cells in thickness except in the central region near the apical notch. Abundant unicellular rhizoids emerge from the ventral surface and penetrate the substratum.

The **prothallia,** as the gametophytes often are designated, are usually homothallic but usually somewhat protandrous (Fig. 21–27A). This is especially noticeable in crowded cultures in which minute filamentous gametophytes tend to develop antheridia precociously. In uncrowded cultures, the sex organs appear in laboratory cultures on agar in about forty-five days. Both types are normally borne on the ventral surface, although deviations may appear in the moist atmosphere of petri dish cultures.

In general, the antheridia (Fig. 21–27) are produced nearer the posterior portion of the gametophyte than the archegonia, which are borne on the thickened, central apical cushion. Like the sporangia, the antheridia are protuberant, whereas only the necks of the archegonia project from the thallus surface (Fig. 21–27A). Both antheridia and archegonia originate from single cells of the prothallium. The antheridial initial protrudes to form a hemispherical cell which undergoes transverse division. The outer product of division develops the antheridium, as shown in Fig. 21–27B. At maturity each antheridium contains about 32 spermatogenous cells, each of which gives rise to a single sperm. The latter is largely composed of the coiled nucleus of the spermatocyte and is multiflagellate

(Fig. 21–28*B,C*). Liquid water is necessary for antheridial dehiscence, which is effected by the swelling of the component cells and rupture of the cap cell. The extruded spermatogenous mass undergoes disintegration, the individual sperms separating, becoming motile, and subsequently sloughing off their spheres of attached cytoplasm.

The archegonia arise from surface cells close to the growing point of the prothallium (Fig. 21–27*A*). Each initial undergoes periclinal division

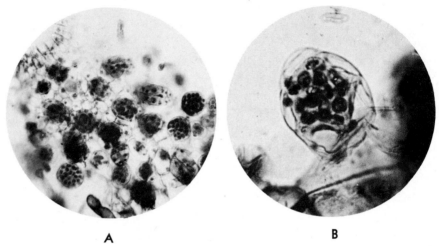

A   B

Fig. 21–27. *Dryopteris dentata.* A, Ventral view of mature gametophyte near apical notch, showing antheridia and archegonia. X 125. B, Antheridium, enlarged. X 500.

into a superficial and a hypogenous cell, the latter dividing only once. The outermost cell undergoes two successive perpendicular anticlinal divisions, forming initials of the four rows of neck cells which arise by division of these initials. The hypogenous cell divides periclinally to form the neck canal initial and the central cell. The neck canal initial undergoes nuclear division to form two neck canal nuclei, but cytokinesis is often suppressed. The central cell divides, forming the basal egg and ventral canal cell. On immersion in water, the distal tiers of neck cells are ruptured, apparently by the swelling of the disintegrated neck and ventral canal cells which are extruded and leave a canal-like passageway to the egg (Fig. 21–28*A*).

It was demonstrated long ago that the movement of sperms toward archegonia is not fortuitous but the result of a chemotactic response. The chemical stimulant secreted from the archegonium can be replaced by malic acid in laboratory experiments. The moist habitat of the prothallia, along with the ventral position of the sex organs, enhances the opportunities for fertilization (Fig. 21–28A). Further growth of the prothallium

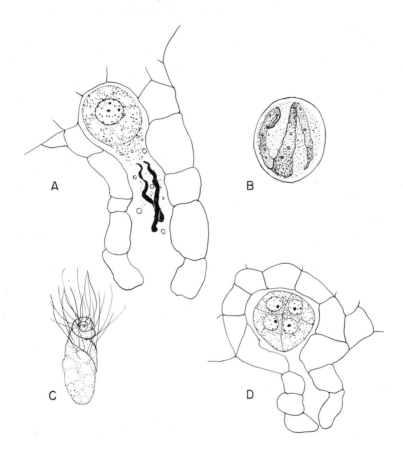

Fig. 21–28. *Dryopteris dentata.* A, Median longitudinal section of mature archegonium showing sperms in neck. X 770. B, Sperm in spermatogenous cell (aceto-carmine preparation). X 1700. C, Free-swimming sperm, X 770. D, Median longitudinal section of archegonium with 8-celled embryo. X 190.

ceases after its archegonia have been fertilized. Although it seems probable that more than one egg is fertilized on each gametophyte, only one zygote normally completes its development into an embryonic sporophyte (Fig. 21–31).

The zygote secretes a cell membrane soon after fertilization and quickly undergoes cytokinesis in a direction parallel to the neck of the archegonium. Two cell divisions at right angles to the original direction of division and to each other result in the formation of an octant stage (Fig. 21–28*D*). Subsequent development of the cells of this octant indicates that already at this stage provision has been made for the organs of the older embryo. The origin and development of these organs are depicted in Fig. 21–30 and explained in its labeling. The archegonial venter keeps pace for a short time with the developing embryo (Fig. 21–29), but soon the root and cotyledon burst forth, the former penetrating the substratum and the latter emerging usually through the apical notch (Fig. 21–31). The gametophyte persists in some cases until several leaves have been formed, but it ultimately turns brown and the embryonic sporophyte initiates an independent existence. The early embryonic leaves are simpler in form than the mature leaves of the parent species, but gradually leaves are produced which are characteristic of the mature plant of the

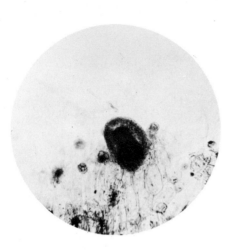

Fig. 21–29. *Dryopteris* sp. Ventral view of gametophyte with young sporophyte within calyptra among sex organs. X 12½.

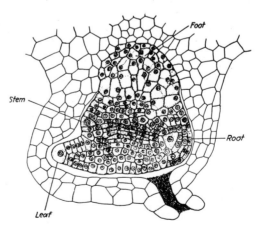

Fig. 21–30. Median longitudinal section of fern embryo, similar to that in Fig. 21–29. X 160. (From Haupt.)

species. Once established, the young sporophyte embarks on a perennial existence in leptosporangiate ferns.

The genera *Dryopteris* and *Adiantum,* just described, have been chosen to serve as representatives of the more advanced leptosporangiate ferns. Their distinctive characters are their method of sporangium development from a single cell; the size, structure, protrusion, and dehiscence of the sporangium; and the small number of spores produced in each. The gametophytes of these genera, as compared with those of the eusporangiate ferns and *Osmunda,* differ in their more delicate structure, less massive form, absence of a midrib, and protuberant and smaller antheridia. Furthermore, they are more rapid in their development and more ephemeral in their existence.

Fig. 21–31. *Adiantum capillus-veneris.* Ventral view of gametophyte with young sporophyte. X 1⅔.

Their dorsiventrality is marked. The precocity with which the organs of the embryo are organized in the early divisions of the zygote is also unlike the embryogeny of the eusporangiate ferns and *Osmunda,* in which differentiation appears later.

Deviations from the Life Cycle

The life cycle of *Adiantum* and *Dryopteris* is fundamentally similar to that of other vascular cryptogams in that it involves a regular alternation of a diploid, asexual, spore-producing generation and a haploid, sexual, gamete-producing one. However, deviations from this type of life cycle occur in these and a number of other genera. These deviations have been grouped together under the terms **apogamy** and **apospory.** Apogamy, sometimes called **apomixis,** denotes a deviation from the usual life cycle in which the transition from the gametophyte phase to the sporophyte is accomplished without sexual union of cells and nuclei. By apospory, on the other hand, is meant the transition from sporophyte to gametophyte in a manner other than through the medium of spores.

Apospory is known to occur among both Hepatophyta and Bryophyta, as well as in the vascular cryptogams and seed plants. Injured sporophytes of *Anthoceros* develop gametophytic thalli, and injured moss setae and capsules may develop protonemata. In certain fern varieties, prothallia may develop at the leaf margins or from transformed sporangia. Examples of apogamy are best known from certain varieties of ferns. In most of these, the gametophytes do not produce archegonia, although antheridia may be developed abundantly. The thickened central region of the gametophyte develops directly into a sporophyte without sexual union. This phenomenon occurs spontaneously in certain species and may be induced in normally sexual ones by preventing fertilization over long periods.

The phenomena of apogamy and apospory have an important bearing on such fundamental questions as the nature and relation of the alternating generations and the chromosome cycle. Are apogamously produced sporophytes haploid or diploid? If the former is the case, what is the nature of chromosome behavior during sporogenesis? In the latter case, are the prothallia diploid, and, if so, what is the origin of the diploid condition? In spite of the investigations of numerous cytologists, the chromosome cycle in apogamous and aposporous ferns has not been clarified until recently. It has been shown for the holly fern, *Cyrtomium falcatum* Presl. (Fig. 21–32), for example, that the chromosome number of both sporophytes and gametophytes is the same. Furthermore, only the spores from certain types of sporangia in a sorus develop into gametophytes. Spores from other types of sporangia abort. In the sporangia that produce fertile spores, the first three divisions of the primary archesporial cell are normal; hence 8 cells are produced. When these undergo nuclear division in preparation for the formation of 16 spore mother cells, nuclear division is arrested at prophase or metaphase, with the result that in all 8 sporogenous cells the nuclei are precociously reorganized. These contain double the chromosome complement of the original cells. These 8 cells (second eight-celled stage) now function directly as spore mother cells, undergoing meiosis with regular chromosome pairing and production of 32 spores, each of which, however, contains a nucleus with the chromosome number char-

Fig. 21–32. *Cyrtomium falcatum* Presl. The holly fern, an apogamous species. X 1/9.

acteristic of the sporophyte. This temporary doubling, in the abortive fourth nuclear division, makes normal meiosis possible and also explains the similarity of chromosome number in gametophyte and sporophyte. A number of other ferns have been shown to have a similar chromosome cycle.

The apogamous production of sporophytes and the aposporous development of gametophytes, together with the deviations in the chromosome cycle noted above, have been interpreted by some as strong evidence in support of the **homologous theory of alternation of generations.** The facts that sporophytes can directly transform some of their tissue into gametophytes (apospory), that gametophytes can directly transform their tissues into sporophytes (apogamy), and that the same chromosome complement may be present in both phases without modifying their fundamental morphology, all seem to indicate that the two alternating generations are fundamentally similar.

DISCUSSION QUESTIONS

1. How do eusporangiate and leptosporangiate sporangium development and sporangia differ?
2. Define or explain sorus, indusium, false indusium, annulus, lip cells, circinate vernation.
3. Define apogamy and apospory. What is the phylogenetic significance of these phenomena?
4. How would you go about inducing apogamy in *Adiantum* and *Dryopteris?*
5. What is the nature of the stele in *Adiantum* and *Dryopteris?* Discuss the types of steles found in vascular cryptogams.
6. Why are the sori of *Dryopteris* and *Adiantum* said to be "mixed"?
7. How do the gametophytes of *Dryopteris* and *Adiantum* differ from those of *Ophioglossum* and *Botrychium?* From those of *Osmunda?* From those of *Angiopteris* and *Marattia?*
8. Why is the fern gametophyte called a "prothallus" or "prothallium"?
9. Where would you look for fern gametophytes in nature?
10. How would you go about propagating ferns from spores?
11. What genera of ferns grow in the vicinity of your home or campus?
12. What is meant by the "octant" stage in the embryogeny of leptosporangiate ferns?
13. To what group of nonvascular cryptogams does the fern gametophyte show some similarity? How does it differ?

14. Comment on the significance of the location of sporangia in various species of *Osmunda*.

15. What features of *Osmunda* suggest eusporangiate ferns?

16. How do the gametophytes of *Osmunda* differ from those of *Dryopteris* and *Adiantum?*

CHAPTER 22

Division Pterophyta—Part III

INTRODUCTION

The occurrence of heterospory in the division Pterophyta, in the genera *Marsilea, Regnellidium, Pilularia, Salvinia,* and *Azolla,* as well as in *Selaginella* and *Isoetes* among the Microphyllophyta, suggests that this condition evolved independently in microphyllous and macrophyllous plants. Of the heterosporous Pterophyta, a detailed account will be presented only of *Marsilea; Salvinia* and *Azolla* will be described briefly in the final section of this chapter.

MARSILEA

Vegetative Morphology

Most species of *Marsilea* (after Count F. L. Marsigli, an Italian naturalist) are inhabitants of the borders of ponds and marshy places, but one occurs in xeric conditions. The related genera *Pilularia* and *Regnellidium* also grow in hydric habitats. *Marsilea* at first glance is decidedly unfern-like in appearance (Fig. 22–1); its compound leaves frequently suggest four-leaved clovers to the uninitiated. *Marsilea* is worldwide in distribution but most abundant in warm climates. It grows readily under greenhouse conditions and is fairly hardy in colder climates, where it perennates by means of its stems which are embedded in mud.

The plant body consists of an elongate, stolon-like stem (Fig. 22–2) which grows either on the surface of the mud or slightly below it. The stem is somewhat branched, the branches originating in association with leaf bases. The leaves are in two rows, alternately inserted on opposite sides of the stem, from which they arise in circinate fashion. The inter-

421

nodes are frequently very long; much-branched adventitious roots emerge at the nodes and penetrate the substratum. In submerged plants, the petioles are relatively flaccid and the leaflets float on the surface of the water. The petioles of aerial leaves, however, are sufficiently rigid to sup-

Fig. 22–1. *Marsilea* sp. Habit of growth of vegetative plants. X 1/6.

port the leaflets in an erect position. The four leaflets of each leaf do not actually arise at one locus from the petiole; two are slightly higher than the others and are inserted in alternate fashion. The leaflet veins are dichotomously branched, but laterally and marginally united to some ex-

Fig. 22–2. *Marsilea vestita* Hook. and Grev. Habit of fertile branch with vegetative leaves and sporocarps. X 1/7.

tent to form a loose reticulum. A transverse section of the leaf (Fig. 22–3) reveals the presence of an upper and lower epidermis, both with slightly sunken stomata. The mesophyll is differentiated into palisade and spongy areas. Each petiole is traversed by a V-shaped vascular trace which leaves a gap above the place of its departure from the stem stele.

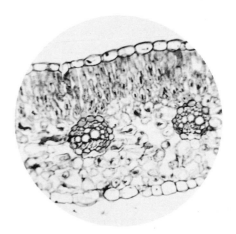

Fig. 22–3. *Marsilea* sp. Transverse section of leaf blade. X 125.

Growth of leaves, stem, and root originates in apical cells and their derivatives. The vascular tissue of the mature stem (Fig. 22–4) is arranged in the form of a siphonostele which is **amphiphloic**, that is, with phloem on both surfaces of the xylem. Both inner and outer phloem are covered by a single layer of pericycle cells, which, in turn, are covered by a single endodermal layer. The pith may be parenchymatous or sclerotic, usually the latter, in rhizomes growing in nonsubmerged soil. The continuity of the cortex is interrupted by large air chambers, and it is outwardly bounded by an epidermis. Stem branches always arise at the base of leaves.

The roots are monarch or diarch protosteles with exarch arrangement (Fig. 22–5). Here, too, the stele is surrounded by a single layer of pericycle and an endodermis. The inner cortex is sclerotic; the outer contains air chambers.

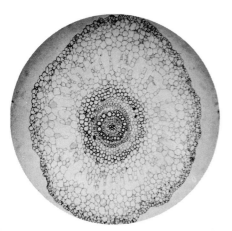

Fig. 22–4. *Marsilea* sp. Transverse section of rhizome; note epidermis, cortex with air chambers, siphonostele, and sclerotic pith. X 60.

Reproduction

The sporangia of *Marsilea* are borne in specialized structures known as **sporocarps**, which occur on short lateral branches of the petioles (Fig. 22–2). These appear after a long period of vegetative development and are thought to represent modified fertile pinnae. The sporocarps at first are relatively soft and green, but they become hard, brown, and nut-like at maturity. They may be borne singly or in clusters, depending on the species. Anatomical and ontogenetic evidence indicate that the

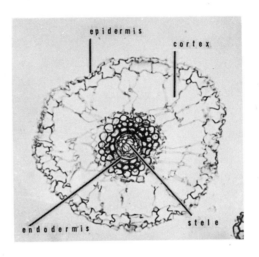

Fig. 22–5. *Marsilea* sp. Transverse section of root; note epidermis, cortex with air chambers, prominent endodermis, and diarch protostele. X 125.

sporocarp probably represents a fertile pinna which has become folded with the margins united, thus enclosing the fertile (abaxial) surface of the leaflet. Each lateral half of the sporocarp bears a row of elongate sori (Fig. 22–6) with ridge-like receptacles. The sori of one half alternate with those of the other, but all are close together and there is overlapping. Each sorus is covered with a delicate indusium; the indusia of adjacent sori are partially fused together, so that each receptacle and its sporangia lie in a cavity (Fig. 22–6).

Sporangial initials develop first at the apex of each ridge-like receptacle; subsequently, additional initials on the flanks initiate sporangium development. The oldest sporangia, therefore, are at the apex, and the younger at the base of the receptacle. This is known as a **gradate** condition and is considered to be more primitive than the **mixed** type of sorus which occurs in such homosporous leptosporangiate ferns as *Dryopteris* and *Adiantum*.

The sporangia develop according to the leptosporangiate method, and all produce between 32 and 64 spores. In the sporangia at the apex of the receptacle, however, all the spores except one degenerate, their contents mingling with those of the tapetal cells which have formed a plasmodium late in sporogenesis. The surviving spore, probably as a result of absorbing large quantities of nutriment, increases to many times its original size, becoming somewhat ellipsoidal. A single megaspore, therefore, matures in each of the sporangia at the apex of the linear receptacle (Fig. 22–6). The mature megaspore has a rounded protuberance at one end on which the triradiate ridges remain visible. The wall in this region is delicate, but over the remainder of the spore protoplast it is extremely thick. The megaspores are sufficiently large to be readily visible to the unaided eye. The single nucleus of the megaspore lies in dense cytoplasm in the region of the protuberance. The bulk of the spore cavity is filled with starch grains; only a small amount of cytoplasm is present.

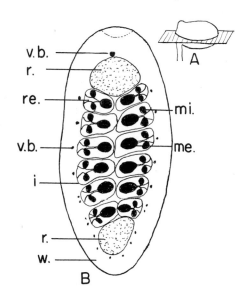

Fig. 22–6. *Marsilea* sp. A, Diagram indicating plane of section. B, Section of sporocarp; note *i*, indusium; *me.*, megasporangium; *mi.*, microsporangium; *r.*, gelatinous ring; *re.*, receptacle; *v.b.*, vascular bundle; *w.*, wall of sporocarp. (Adapted from Eames.)

All the spores in the sporangia on the flanks of the receptacle mature; hence they are many times smaller than the megaspores. Each of these microspores has a single central nucleus and rather dense cytoplasm containing starch grains. Hence *Marsilea* is heterosporous, as are *Selaginella* and *Isoetes* among microphyllous plants.

As the spores mature, changes occur in the sterile tissues of the sporocarp. The outer layers become stony, and their cell walls greatly thicken. The other tissues, except for the sori and indusia, disintegrate and gelatinize. Both microsporangia and megasporangia lack a highly differentiated annulus, an indication of the fact that the spores are not discharged explosively from the sporangia.

Fig. 22–7. *Marsilea vestita.* Petri dish with dehiscent sporocarps; note emergent gelatinous rings bearing sori. X 3/5.

In nature, the sporocarps persist in the water and soil after the vegetative portions of the plants which produced them have disappeared. It is probable that bacterial action plays a role in rotting the sporocarp wall and in thus effecting spore dissemination. This process may be hastened

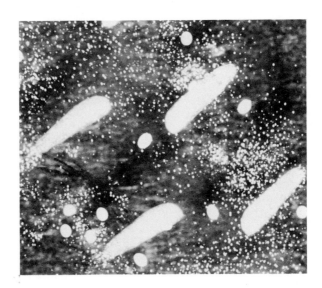

Fig. 22–8. *Marsilea vestita.* Sori and liberated megaspores and microspores. X 3½.

in the laboratory by cutting away a small portion of the stony wall and immersing the sporocarps in water. After such treatment, water is imbibed by the hydrophilic colloids in the sporocarp. Within a short time, the attendant swelling forces the two halves of the sporocarp apart and a

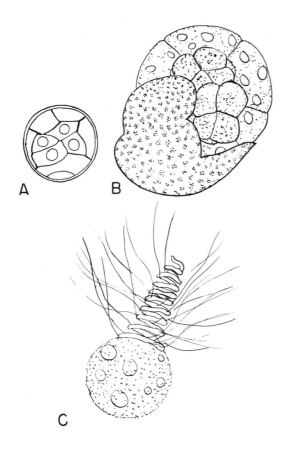

Fig. 22–9. *Marsilea vestita.* Development of the ♂ gametophyte. A, Section of the microspore with male gametophyte; note prothallial cell and two rudimentary antheridia. X 260. (Adapted from Sharp.) B, Microspore with emergent ♂ gametophyte. X 430. C, Living sperm. X 2266.

gelatinous ring bearing the sori emerges (Fig. 22–7). Several hours after their emergence, the sporangial walls become gelatinous, with the result that large numbers of free microspores and megaspores are shed into the common soral cavity still enclosed by the indusium. The latter disintegrates ultimately, and the microspores and megaspores are liberated into the water (Fig. 22–8).

Unlike those of *Selaginella* but like those of *Isoetes,* the spores of *Marsilea* do not germinate until they have been shed from the sporocarp. Development into gametophytes is then very rapid. Formation of the

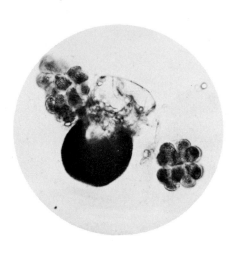

male gametophyte by the microspore is initiated by a nuclear and cell division to form unequal cells within the microspore wall; the smaller cell is the prothallial cell. As in *Isoetes* and *Selaginella,* this cell fails to divide again and is interpreted as the sole remnant of vegetative tissue in the male gametophyte. The larger cell divides in two, and each of the resulting cells by further division (Fig. 22–9A) forms an antheridium which is covered with jacket cells that surround the sixteen spermatogenous cells. The microspore wall now ruptures and the mature

Fig. 22–10. *Marsilea vestita.* Mature ♂ gametophyte; note microspore wall, remains of jacket cells, and two groups of sperms. X 250.

antheridia protrude (Fig. 22–9B). The disintegrated prothallial cells and jacket cells undergo hydrolysis and the large sperms, which have previously developed singly in each spermatogenous cell, become actively motile and swim away (Fig. 22–10). The sperms are tightly coiled and have a number of flagella on the apical nuclear portion (Fig. 22–9C, 22–11B). The development of the male gametophyte and liberation of the sperms may take place in as short a time as 12 hours.

In the development of the female gametophyte by the megaspore, a limited number of nuclear and cell divisions occurs within the hemispherical protuberance, resulting in the formation of a small amount of vegetative tissue bearing a single apical archegonium (Fig. 22–11A). Enlargement of these cells ruptures the megaspore wall, which is delicate in the region of the protuberance. The megaspore that bears the mature female gametophyte becomes surrounded by a gelatinous matrix which is usually thickest in the region of the female gametophyte (Fig. 22–11). The liberated sperms, apparently attracted chemotactically, swarm into the matrix in the vicinity of the archegonium (Fig. 22–11). One of them makes ·its way to the egg cell and fertilization occurs.

Development of the embryo is initiated several hours after fertilization by nuclear and cell division of the zygote (Fig. 22–12A). Cytokinesis is usually in a direction parallel to the long axis of the archegonium and megaspore, which are typically horizontal. A second division, also par-

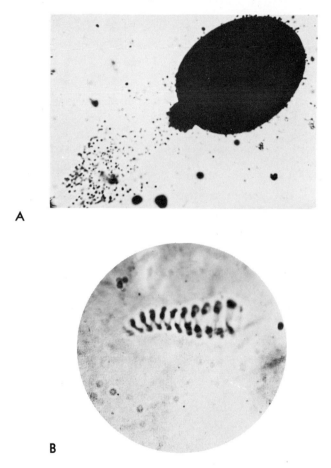

A

B

Fig. 22–11. *Marsilea vestita.* A, Megaspore with protuberant ♀ gametophyte surrounded by sperms. X 60. B, Single living sperm. X 1200.

allel to the archegonial axis but in a plane perpendicular to that of the first division, results in the formation of four cells. These by further division develop the foot, leaf (cotyledon), stem, and root of the embryonic sporophyte, as indicated· in Fig. 22–12B. The vegetative cells of the gametophyte are stimulated to divide as the embryonic sporophyte develops

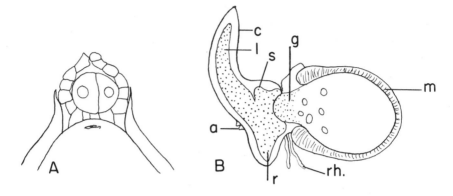

Fig. 22–12. A, *Marsilea vestita*. Median longitudinal section of ♀ gametophyte, archegonium with early embryo. X 280. (From Campbell.) B, *Marsilea sp.* Median longitudinal section of megaspore, ♀ gametophyte and embryo: *a*, archegonium; *c*, calyptra-like sheath; *g*, ♀ gametophyte; *l*, primary leaf or cotyledon; *m*, megaspore wall; *r*, root; *rh.*, rhizoid; *s*, stem. (From Sachs.)

(Fig. 22–13), and they form a sheathing calyptra around the latter. The surface cells of this gametophytic tissue develop rhizoids; both rhizoids and other gametophytic cells develop chloroplasts. The calyptra is relatively persistent but disappears about the same time that the embryonic root penetrates the substratum. Growth of the embryonic sporophyte is rapid (Figs. 22–13 to 22–15). One series of germling sporophytes of *M. vestita* planted in April produced mature plants bearing sporocarps by the following October.

Fig. 22–13. *Marsilea vestita*. Mature ♀ gametophyte with embryo within; note archegonial neck. X 60.

Summary

Although decidedly not fern-like in appearance, the vegetative structure and sporangial development of *Marsilea* are very similar to those of other leptosporangiate ferns. The clover-like leaves represent sterile pinnae whose dichotomous venation is closed at the margins and to some extent laterally. Vernation of the leaves is circinate. The

stems are amphiphloic siphonosteles, interrupted by leaf gaps
which usually do not overlap because of the great length of the internodes. The leaves arise alternately in two rows from the stolon-
like stems. Both roots and stems afford anatomical evidence of aquatic
habitat in the form of air chambers;
the vascular tissue, however, is un-
usually abundant for a hydrophytic
plant. *Marsilea* is representative of
the leptosporangiate ferns in which
heterospory has been developed.
With it have appeared such concomitant attributes as heterothal-

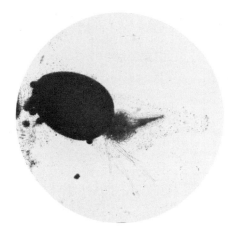

Fig. 22–14. *Marsilea vestita.* Megaspore, ♀ gametophyte and embryo, the cotyledon well developed. X 30.

Fig. 22–15. *Marsilea vestita.* Megaspore, ♀ gametophyte and emergent embryo; note cotyledon and root. X 30.

lism, reduction in vegetative functions, and duration of the gametophytes. Gametogenesis and embryogeny are extremely rapid in *Marsilea*.

OTHER LEPTOSPORANGIOPSIDA

The treatment of the Leptosporangiopsida in this and the preceding chapters comprises merely a résumé of representatives of the more

Fig. 22–16. *Lygodium japonicum* Sw. Portions of climbing leaves, the upper vegetative and the lower spore-bearing. X ⅔.

commonly encountered genera. Space is not available for a more extensive treatment of the diversities in form, habitat, and reproduction in the group, but brief mention of certain leptosporangiate genera which the student may observe in the field, in the conservatory, or in aquatic gardens will be made in the following paragraphs.

Lygodium japonicum Sw. (Fig. 22–16), the climbing fern, is frequently cultivated in greenhouses as a curiosity. *L. palmatum* (Bernh.) Sw. is native to wooded areas with acid soil in the eastern part of the United States. The underground stem is not extensive, but it bears leaves which are characterized by apical growth of long duration. The leaves climb by means of their extended rachises which become entwined about supports during development. The lower pairs of pinnae are sterile; the more distal ones are greatly contracted and fertile (Fig. 22–16). The sporangial jackets of *Lygodium* develop apical annuli and their dehiscence is longitudinal.

Hymenophyllum and *Trichomanes,* also sometimes cultivated under glass, are members of the filmy fern alliance, so called because of the extremely thin and delicate texture of their leaves (Fig. 22–17). Most species of these genera are tropical, but *Trichomanes boschianum* Sturm occurs on wet cliffs in restricted areas of the southeastern United States and a minute species of *Hymenophyllum* has been collected in a gorge in South Carolina. The leaves of many species are only a single cell in thickness except in the region of the veins at the ends of which the sporangia develop. The annulus is slightly oblique and sporangial dehiscence is approximately transverse.

In such respects as stature, leaf size and form and aesthetic appeal, the tree ferns

Fig. 22–17. *Trichomanes boschianum* Sturm. A filmy fern. X ½.

are the most spectacular members of the leptosporangiate series. All are tropical and available in temperate regions only in conservatory collections. *Dicksonia* and *Cyathea* (Fig. 22–18) are widely cultivated in such collections. In their native habitat, specimens of *Cyathea* may attain a height of 80 feet. The stems are usually unbranched and bear a crown of enormous leaves which are circinate in the bud. The leaves may be three or four times pinnate and thus extremely finely divided. The trunks of tree ferns may be covered by a densely tangled mass of wiry, adventitious roots which frequently support a rich flora of epiphytes. The vertical annulus incompletely encircles the sporangial wall. Tree ferns, of course,

Fig. 22–18.   *Cyathea* sp. Tree fern at Xalapa, Mexico.

are unsuitable as a source of lumber because they lack secondary xylem and are entirely primary in development, in spite of their great stature.

Finally, three other genera of aquatic ferns are cultivated widely in pools and aquatic gardens. These are *Ceratopteris, Salvinia,* and *Azolla.*

Of the three, only *Ceratopteris* (Fig. 22–19) is at all fern-like in appearance. Furthermore, it alone is homosporous like typical ferns. It is grown extensively in small fish pools and aquaria and is **annual** in habit, a rare attribute in ferns, which as a group are **perennial**. *Ceratopteris*, a floating plant, exhibits dimorphism in its leaves. The lower leaves are recumbent

Fig. 22–19. *Ceratopteris* sp. An annual aquatic fern; note vegetative propagation at leaf margins, and contracted, spore-bearing fronds. X 1/6.

and spreading and broad-bladed. The fertile leaves are narrower and more erect. The plants multiply vegetatively by adventitious leaf buds. One species of *Ceratopteris* is native to Florida.

Salvinia and *Azolla*, formerly grouped with *Marsilea* because of their common heterospory, are decidedly unfern-like in appearance (Fig. 22–20). Both are floating aquatics. *Salvinia* is native to Mexico but widely cultivated in lily pools and aquaria. *Azolla caroliniana* Willd., which is found in quiet waters in the eastern United States, also is frequently cultivated. The leaves of these genera are much modified, in accordance with the floating habit. The spores are borne in sporocarps which, unlike those of *Marsilea,* represent indusia. *Salvinia* is rootless, the root-like appendages representing filiform leaf segments. In *Azolla,* however, delicate roots extend down into the water. Under certain conditions, plants of *Azolla* are red instead of green.

A   B

Fig. 22–20.   A, *Azolla caroliniana* Willd. X 3. B, *Salvinia* sp. X 5.

While this somewhat disconnected account gives no really detailed insight into the morphology of these miscellaneous leptosporangiate genera, it provides some indication of the diversity of the group and may serve as a stimulus to further reading and laboratory studies of these more uncommon plants.

CLASSIFICATION AND SUMMARY OF PTEROPHYTA

Classification

The ferns discussed in this and the two preceding chapters may be classified as follows:

Division Pterophyta
    Class 1. Eusporangiopsida
        Order 1. Ophioglossales
            Family 1. Ophioglossaceae
                Genera: *Ophioglossum, Botrychium*

Order 2. Marattiales
    Family 1. Marattiaceae
        Genera: *Marattia, Angiopteris*
Class 2. Leptosporangiopsida
    Order 1. Filicales
        Family 1. Osmundaceae
            Genus: *Osmunda*
        Family 2. Polypodiaceae
            Genera: *Polypodium, Dryopteris, Adiantum, Onoclea, Pteretis, Pellaea,*
                Polystichum, Pteris, Pteridium, Woodsia, Nephrolepis
        Family 3. Marsileaceae
            Genus: *Marsilea*
        Family 4. Schizaeaceae
            Genus: *Lygodium*
        Family 5. Hymenophyllaceae
            Genera: *Hymenophyllum, Trichomanes*
        Family 6. Cyatheaceae
            Genera: *Cyathea, Dicksonia*
        Family 7. Parkeriaceae
            Genus: *Ceratopteris*
        Family 8. Salviniaceae
            Genera: *Salvinia, Azolla*

The division Pterophyta is here conceived to include all macrophyllous vascular cryptogams. This definition of the scope of the division is at variance with that of many other botanists who, in a broader definition of its limits, classify all macrophyllous plants, both spore-bearing and seed-bearing, together in a single taxon. Discussion of the reasons for excluding the seed plants from the same division as the spore-bearing plants cannot be summarized profitably until one has become familiar with the seed plants, and accordingly it is deferred to a later chapter.

A comparative and orderly review of the various genera of Pterophyta may be instructive at this point, not only as a recapitulation but also as a prelude to the discussion of the entire group of vascular cryptogams and their phylogeny which follows in the next chapter. The comparison is based on discussion of the following topics: **the sporophyte** and its vegetative and reproductive features, **the gametophyte,** and **embryogeny.**

The Sporophyte

The plant bodies of the Pterophyta exhibit a remarkable range in habit and complexity. At one extreme, perhaps, are the minute sporophytes of the hydrophytic genera *Salvinia* and *Azolla*, which are dwarfed by such plant bodies as those of *Dicksonia* and *Cyathea*, the tree ferns. The remaining genera, for the most part, are intermediate between these extremes and rarely exceed 6 to 8 feet in stature, with the exception of tropical species of *Lygodium*, a climber, the leaves of which may attain a length of 100 feet! It is of interest to note that in spite of the great stature of certain of these genera, secondary growth by cambial activity is absent from members of the division, except for the relatively abortive fashion in which it occurs in *Botrychium*. With rare exceptions (*Ceratopteris*), the ferns are perennial and long-lived.

The dominant organ of the sporophyte is the macrophyllous leaf. In no group of vascular plants other than the Pterophyta has the leaf attained such predominance and elaborate form. In many cases, the leaves rival the stems of other plants in duration of development and regular ontogeny from apical initials. In almost all the genera except *Ophioglossum*, vernation is typically circinate. The dominant role of the leaf is reflected further in the large trace or traces which pass into the petioles and the profound disturbances they occasion in the stelar tissues of the stem. Leaf form varies from such simple types as those of *Ophioglossum* and certain species of *Polypodium*, through pinnately once-divided leaves like those of *Polystichum acrostichoides* (Michx.) Schott., to such extreme division of the blade as is evident in *Lygodium, Trichomanes*, and *Hymenophyllum*. There is evidence that in some forms (*Botrychium*) the leaves have become secondarily simplified, although the juvenile, embryonic leaves of most genera are also simple. Both open dichotomous (*Angiopteris, Osmunda, Adiantum*) and closed reticulate venation (*Ophioglossum, Dryopteris*) are present in the leaves of Pterophyta.

The form of the stem varies from the minute, poorly developed type observable in *Ophioglossum, Lygodium*, and *Ceratopteris*, through the rather massive erect or ascending types in *Osmunda*, the horizontal rhizomes and rootstocks of such genera as *Adiantum* and *Dryopteris*, to the erect trunks of tree ferns. The range of stelar structure in fern stems is extensive. Most genera have protostelic stems in the juvenile stages, evidence that the protostele is truly primitive. The protostelic condition persists in the adult in such genera as *Lygodium*, but in a great majority of ferns the stems contain siphonosteles (*Adiantum*) which may be dissected into dictyosteles (*Dryopteris*), depending on the proximity of the nodes to each other. In a number of genera there has taken place a proliferation of the vascular tissues to form a complex system, polystelic in arrangement (*Pteridium*). Ontogeny of the stem, with few exceptions, originates in a single prominent apical cell. In *Pteridium*, as in *Selaginella* among the Microphyllophyta, perforation of the terminal walls of tracheids has resulted in the development of a primitive type of trachea or vessel, a xylem element otherwise absent in the vascular cryptogams. The dominance of the leaves, the relatively great size of the vascular traces passing into their petioles, and the resulting dissection of the cauline steles have impelled some morphologists to suggest that the stem in such genera as *Ophioglossum* is composed largely of overlapping leaf bases.

Except for the primary root (radicle) of the embryonic sporophyte, the root system of ferns is entirely adventitious. The thin, often blackish or brownish wiry roots arise at and between the leaf bases, usually endogenously. The roots, and for that matter, the plant bodies of the Ophioglossales differ in their fleshiness from those of other Pterophyta, except *Ceratopteris*. Ontogeny of the root is also localized in a single apical cell or several such cells (*Osmunda*) and results in the development of an exarch protostele. The root, therefore, is thought to be a conservative organ. The roots (and stems) of a number of ferns (*Ophioglossum* and *Botrychium*) become infected with a fungus which invades the cortical cells and functions in mycorrhizal fashion. *Salvinia* is one of the few rootless genera.

The sporogenous tissue of the fern sporophytes varies in its distribution. *Ophioglossum* and *Botrychium*, of the genera discussed in this text, are unique in the localization of their sporogenous tissues on an organ known as the "fertile spike." A physiologically similar but morphologically dissimilar dimorphism occurs, however, in varying degrees in several species of *Osmunda, Onoclea, Pteretis*, and *Ceratopteris*. In genera with sporangia distributed abaxially on the foliage leaves, the sporangia may be uniformly arranged (*Dryopteris*) or restricted to the apical pinnae (*Polystichum acrostichoides*). The receptacular regions which give rise to the sporangia may be marginal or amarginal, and the sori bear varying relationships to the leaf veins.

Two series on the basis of sporangium development, the class Eusporangiopsida and the class Leptosporangiopsida, are apparent among the Pterophyta. The development of the sporangium of *Osmunda* suggests an intermediate condition. It is noteworthy that leptosporangiate sporangium development is restricted to the pterophyte series, a point of great importance in discussions of the phylogeny of seed plants, in which it is frequently disregarded. Leptosporangiate and eusporangiate sporangia differ in respects other than origin in ontogeny. These include size, wall thickness, spore number, and degree of projection from the plant surface. Among the Pterophyta, the sporangia may develop simultaneously, the simple type (*Ophioglossum*); in basipetal succession, the gradate type (*Marsilea*); or in no special order, the mixed type (most Polypodiaceae).

Heterospory is present in the Leptosporangiopsida only in *Marsilea* (and its related genera), *Salvinia*, and *Azolla*. In all of these genera, the early stages in ontogeny of the megasporangia and microsporangia are similar. However, following meiosis, only one spore survives, enlarges, and functions in the megasporangium. Spore germination in all these genera occurs only ofter the spores have been shed, as in the microphyllous genus *Isoetes*.

The Gametophyte

Review of the genera of Pterophyta which have been described reveals a great range in the organization and physiological attributes of the gametophyte generation. The gametophytes of most species of *Ophioglossum* and *Botrychium* are long-lived, slow-growing, subterranean, and, with few exceptions, entirely lacking in photosynthetic tissues. Their saprophytic nutrition is probably connected with the presence of a mycorrhizal fungus in the gametophyte tissues. The gametophytes of the heterosporous genera also are saprophytic, but in this case the ultimate source of the nutriment is the parent sporophyte which has stored it in the microspores and megaspores. It is true, however, that photosynthetic tissue appears late in the development of the female gametophyte of *Marsilea* and also in that of *Salvinia*. The gametophytes of *Marattia* and *Angiopteris* and those of the homosporous leptosporangiate ferns are photoautotrophic. Those of *Marattia* and *Osmunda* are relatively massive, long-lived and hepatopsidan as compared with the delicate, rather ephemeral cordate genera like *Adiantum* and *Dryopteris*. The antheridia of the eusporangiate genera are partially embedded and massive and contain large numbers of sperms. The antheridia of most homosporous leptosporangiate forms are smaller and protuberant and they contain fewer sperms. *Osmunda*, again, is intermediate in these respects.

The Embryo

The development of the embryonic sporophyte varies in the several groups of Pterophyta. Embryo development in *Ophioglossum* and

Botrychium is of relatively long duration as compared with that in the polypodiaceous series. Furthermore, the first division of the zygote is transverse with reference to the long axis of the archegonium in *Ophioglossum* and *Botrychium,* whereas a suspensor functions in some species of *Botrychium.* Finally, the primary organs of the sporophyte cannot be traced back as clearly to early derivatives of the zygote in eusporangiate ferns as they can regularly be in the development of the embryo of many Leptosporangiopsida. The embryogeny of *Marattia* and *Angiopteris* is similar in many respects to that of *Ophioglossum* and *Botrychium,* but the embryos of the former lack a foot. *Osmunda,* again, is somewhat intermediate between the eusporangiate and leptosporangiate ferns with respect to its embryogeny. Although quadrant and octant stages of equal-sized cells are formed, the primary organs of the sporophyte cannot be referred back to one of these with certainty. Emergence of the primary leaf is slow, as compared with that in other Leptosporangiopsida, and the leaf grows laterally around the gametophyte in *Osmunda* rather than anteriorly upward through the apical notch. In conclusion, it should be noted that detailed knowledge of the morphology of a more extensive series of genera than has been described in this and the preceding two chapters is a necessary precursor to a more complete discussion of the variation and phylogeny of the Pterophyta.

DISCUSSION QUESTIONS

1. How does venation in *Marsilea* differ from that in *Adiantum?* Which do you consider more primitive and for what reason?
2. Describe the structure of the sporocarp of *Marsilea.*
3. What evidence indicates that the sporocarp of *Marsilea* is a folded pinna?
4. What is meant by the terms "simple," "gradate," and "mixed" as applied to sporangium development? Illustrate with examples from the genera described above.
5. How does the ontogeny of the functional megaspores differ in *Selaginella* and *Marsilea?*
6. A student argued that inasmuch as heterospory is obviously an advanced condition derived from homospory, *Selaginella, Isoetes,* and *Marsilea* should be classified together, as distinct from other extant vascular cryptogams. Give reasons against supporting such a classification.
7. Would you consider the male gametophyte of *Selaginella* or that of *Marsilea* to be more primitive? Give the reasons for your answer.
8. Sporocarps of *Marsilea,* stored in alcohol for twenty years, have germinated when placed in water. How do you explain this?
9. A layman, observing the sporocarps of *Marsilea* for the first time, referred to them as "seeds." How do they differ from seeds?

10. Why are the trunks of tree ferns unsuitable for lumber?

11. How do the sporangia of *Lygodium* differ from those of *Dryopteris* and *Adiantum?*

12. In what conservatories of the United States are there living specimens of tree ferns?

13. Cite examples of hydrophytic, mesophytic, and xerophytic Pterophyta.

CHAPTER 23

The Vascular Cryptogams: Recapitulation

INTRODUCTION

Chapters 17 through 22 have presented a discussion of the structure and reproduction of representatives of the divisions **Psilophyta, Microphyllophyta, Arthrophyta,** and **Pterophyta.** The present chapter presents a brief comparative summary of the more important features of these organisms, **the vascular cryptogams.**

THE LIFE CYCLE

In some schemes of classification other than the one used in this book, the seedless vascular plants are grouped together in a single division, **Pteridophyta.** Although the plants so classified have been re-grouped as four separate phyletic lines (divisions) in the present volume, it should be emphasized that they do have in common the same balance between the alternating generations in their life cycles. In all vascular cryptogams, the sporophyte is the dominant phase in the life cycle; the gametophyte is clearly simpler and more ephemeral. In all cases, however, the latter is separated ultimately from the parent sporophyte, unlike the female gametophyte in the seed plants, in which it is permanently retained. In the Hepatophyta and the Bryophyta, on the other hand, the gametophyte is dominant. That the life cycle is not entirely inflexible and obligate is evidenced by numerous examples of apogamy and some of apospory. **Apogamy,** the development of a sporophyte from a gametophyte in which no fertilization took place, occurs regularly in certain species of polypodiaceous ferns, and there is evidence of its presence in species of *Marsilea* and *Selaginella* as well. Furthermore, apogamy has been induced in normally sexual genera by withholding water when their sex organs mature. **Apospory,** the development of a gametophyte directly from sporophytic tissue and not from a spore, is less widespread. These phenomena have focused attention on the question of the origin and relation of the two alternating phases.

There seems to be rather general agreement that primitive plants were at least potentially sexual and hence gametophytic and haploid. The Myxophyceae and Euglenophyceae usually are interpreted in this manner. The initiation of the sexual process would obviously result in the existence of a diploid cell, the **zygote.** In organisms with **zygotic meiosis,** the diploid zygote was and is but a transitory phase which is obliterated in the meiotic process. It seems clear that the inception of sexuality and the first occurrence of meiosis must have been closely related in time, if not simultaneous, in view of their complementary functions. An extensive diploid sporophyte generation appears to have been a secondary adjunct to the life cycle with sexuality. Its origin is postulated to have been occasioned by a delay in meiosis in the zygote and the interpolation of a more or less extensive series of mitoses and cytokineses between fertilization and meiosis, with the result that diploid cells other than the zygote arose for the first time. Meiosis then occurred in all these diploid cells, however numerous. This, of course, represents the type of life cycle present in all organisms with **sporic meiosis.** Finally, gradual extension of the duration and importance of the diploid sporophytic phase, concomitant with the suppression of the haploid phase, is thought to have resulted in the type of life cycle in which **gametic meiosis** occurs. It should be emphasized that the preceding statements are mere conjectures, none of which are verifiable experimentally. The optimism and abject credence with which they frequently are received and repeated might well be tempered by this consideration and others, among them the following: The great majority of animals are diploid organisms with gametic meiosis. It is scarcely conceivable that their present life cycles have evolved from genera with zygotic and sporic meiosis, especially in the absence of any examples of the latter among living animals. Furthermore, that diploidy of zygotes, resulting from failure of meiosis, might of itself have been insufficient to explain the origin of a sporophyte, especially of the type in heteromorphic alternation, is suggested by polyploidy and the phenomena of apogamy and apospory noted above.

In addition to these speculations concerning the *origin* of the alternate phases, there have been many conjectures regarding the fundamental *relationship* between them. Speculations about the relation of the sporophyte and gametophyte to each other often are summarized as two theories, namely, the **antithetic** and the **homologous,** referred to briefly in Chapters 8 and 16. According to the antithetic theory, the gametophyte and sporophyte are essentially different manifestations of a single organism. The sporophyte is looked upon not as a modified or changed gametophyte but rather as a phase *sui generis,* which has been interpolated between successive gametophytic phases through delay in meiosis, as suggested above. Furthermore, by some adherents of this theory the sporophyte is thought to have been entirely a reproductive phase originally, in which asexual spores in large numbers were produced as a result of delayed meiosis. Assumption by sporophytes of such vegetative functions as photosynthesis and translocation, among others, is viewed as secondary. These are interpreted as acquired functions taken up by primarily sporogenous tissues. It should be emphasized that this view of the sporophyte was originally proposed by a student of the land plants long before the complexity of algal life cycles was appreciated fully. This theory, perhaps in somewhat modified form, is much in evidence at present in many morphological discussions. It is sometimes called the **interpolation theory.**

In opposition to the antithetic theory, the proponents of another point of view hold that alternating gametophytes and sporophytes are fundamentally similar. The sporophyte is looked upon as a somewhat modified or transformed gametophyte, modified in accordance with its function of spore production. According to the homologous theory, vegetative and reproductive functions coexisted in primitive sporophytes, although the balance between them may be variable. Certainly algal sporophytes are photosynthetic. Conceding that the alternants among the land plants are indeed heteromorphic, possibly because of the stimulus of a terrestrial environment, proponents of this theory also point to the algae, in which numerous cases of both isomorphic and heteromorphic alternation of generations in a uniform aquatic habitat are known. It has been suggested that one important factor effecting heteromorphism is the permanent retention of the sporophyte in the gametophyte, as in the diploid carposporophyte of the Rhodophyta and the sporophytes of Hepatophyta and Bryophyta, and its retention during embryogeny in the vascular cryptogams. However, marked heteromorphism is present in the kelps

(*Laminaria*) in which the two generations are entirely independent of each other. This discussion of alternation of generations is presented not with the purpose of settling the matter but rather to indicate the complexity of the problems involved. It seems quite possible that alternating generations may have arisen as a result of different circumstances and different stimuli in different organisms and that a comprehensive explanation may be unattainable.

VEGETATIVE ORGANS OF THE SPOROPHYTE

Comparison of the several divisions into which the vascular cryptogams have been classified indicates that the stem is certainly the dominant organ of the sporophyte, except in the Pterophyta in which it may be equaled or surpassed in stature and anatomical complexity by the macrophyllous leaves. In the living Psilophyta, Microphyllophyta, and Arthrophyta, examples of erect and ascending, vine-like, rhizomatous, and stolon-like stems occur. With the exception of the tree ferns, the stems of the Pterophyta are mostly subterranean, vertical or horizontal, or at the surface of the ground. Dichotomous branching of the stems, by the equal division of single apical cells or groups of meristematic cells, is considered primitive as compared with monopodial and sympodial types. *Equisetum,* with its whorls of branches and leaves, the latter alternating in origin with the former, is unique among vascular plants.

A considerable range in disposition of the vascular tissues is apparent in the members of the several divisions. The most primitive genera and the juvenile stages of most others have stems that contain **protosteles.** Examples of increasingly complex types of steles—namely, **siphonosteles,** both **amphiphloic** and **ectophloic, dictyosteles, eusteles,** and **polysteles**— have been described. Branch gaps occur in all the groups, but foliar gaps are present only in the Pterophyta. Thickening of the stem by addition of secondary tissues through the activity of a cambium is rare among living vascular cryptogams, and where it occurs (*Isoetes, Botrychium*) it does not result in any considerable increase in girth. The unicellular tracheid is the conducting element of the xylem of all these forms. In *Selaginella* and *Pteridium,* however, perforation of the terminal walls of tracheids has resulted in the formation of vessel-like xylem tubes.

It is clear that the structures designated by the term "leaf" are not morphologically equivalent in the vascular plants. Inasmuch as the fundamental nature of the macrophyllous leaf has an important bearing on discussions of the phylogeny of vascular cryptogams, a review of its attributes is relevant at this point. It will be recalled that in contrast with the microphyllous leaves of such plants as *Lycopodium* and *Selaginella*, which are relatively small, determinate in growth, and traversed by unbranched veins that leave no leaf gaps in the stem steles, macrophyllous leaves are typically larger, their development is more extended if not indeterminate (*Lygodium*), their vascular system is richly branched, and their traces profoundly modify the stem stele from which they depart by leaving parenchymatous gaps. Because both these structures are called "leaves," are we therefore to consider them homologous? Some morphologists have answered this question in the negative. It is agreed by them that microphyllous leaves are to be interpreted as localized, superficial enations of stems, and that macrophyllous leaves are to be interpreted as branches of stems which have undergone flattening by limitation of branching to one plane and webbing by extension of parenchymatous tissues between the branching steles. The evidence for this interpretation of the macrophyllous leaf is based on its extensive, much-branched vascular supply, on the fact that its trace, like the branch trace of microphyllous plants, effects a break in the stele where it originates,[1] and, finally, on its relatively large size and indeterminate development, all supported by study of the fossil record (Chapter 30). According to this view, at least the main branching veins even of an undivided fern leaf represent the direction of the branching of a primitive axis which has become webbed between the vein branches. These views regarding leaves are in accord with the **telome theory** which emphasizes the shoot or axis as the fundamental unit in the organization of plants. Microphyllous and macrophyllous leaves are therefore not homologous.

Roots are present in all the divisions of vascular cryptogams save the Psilophyta, in which the underground rhizomes, provided with rhizoidal appendages, carry on the function of absorption with sufficient efficiency to support the aerial portions of the plant. That the root is probably an organ of the vascular cryptogams which developed later than leaves and stems is suggested by its tardy appearance in the embryogeny of such genera as *Lycopodium* and *Selaginella* and by the minor and relatively transitory role of the primary root or radicle in other genera. The root system of the vascular cryptogams is almost exclusively adventitious in origin. Internally the roots are **exarch** and **protostelic** without exception, and they develop entirely from primary meristems. It has been suggested

---

[1] Macrophyllous leaves do not leave gaps in protosteles.

that the root arose as a modified rhizome branch which became covered with a root cap.

SPOROGENOUS TISSUE

Review of Chapters 17 through 22 reveals considerable variation in the disposition and nature of the sporogenous tissues in the extant vascular cryptogams. Examples of little or no segregation of vegetative and sporogenous tissues are available in such instances as *Lycopodium lucidulum* and many polypodiaceous and marattiaceous ferns. Even in the primitive *Psilotum*, however, the sporogenous tissue is restricted to special, determinate lateral branches. The dimorphism observable in such plants as *Lycopodium complanatum*, species of *Osmunda*, the fertile spike of the *Ophioglossum-Botrychium* type, and the strobili of the Microphyllophyta and *Equisetum* is a manifestation of segregation of vegetative and reproductive functions. Furthermore, examples of both cauline (*Psilotum*) and foliar (Microphyllophyta, polypodiaceous ferns) sporangia are present.

With reference to method of sporangium ontogeny, all the vascular cryptogams (and seed plants) are **eusporangiate,** with the exception of the Leptosporangiopsida among the Pterophyta. There is good evidence that **heterospory** developed independently in the Microphyllophyta, the Arthrophyta (fossil forms), and the Pterophyta. Spore ontogeny in the heterosporous genera indicates that the immediate cause of heterospory lies in discrepancies in spore number and nutrition and that these are expressed ultimately by spore size.

THE GAMETOPHYTE

Considerable morphological and physiological variation is apparent among the gametophytes of the vascular cryptogams. Cylindrical form, radial symmetry, and saprophytism characterize the gametophytes of *Psilotum*, of certain species of *Lycopodium*, and of *Ophioglossum*. Dorsiventral and photosynthetic gametophytes are present in *Equisetum* and in marattiaceous and homosporous leptosporangiate ferns. The presence of heterospory is associated with marked reduction in the morphological complexity and duration of the gametophyte, as is evident in *Selaginella, Isoetes,* and *Marsilea.* The nutrition in these gametophytes is based largely on metabolites stored by the parent sporophyte in the spores. Although the gametophytes of *Psilotum* and species of *Lycopodium, Ophioglossum,* and *Botrychium* are relatively long-lived, as compared with those of other genera, the gametophyte generation in general is of lesser duration and complexity than are the persistent perennial sporophytes of the vascular cryptogams.

The archegonia of the female gametophytes produced in heterosporous ferns are in general smaller and less complex than those in homosporous types. Both biflagellate (*Lycopodium, Selaginella*) and multiflagellate sperms (*Isoetes, Equisetum,* Pterophyta) occur among vascular cryptogams.

THE EMBRYO

The embryogeny of the vascular cryptogams exemplifies both slow-growing (*Lycopodium, Psilotum, Ophioglossum*) and relatively rapid (*Selaginella, Equisetum,* polypodiaceous ferns) types. Nutrition of the embryo in heterosporous forms is based on metabolites of the parent sporophyte.

In concluding this brief summary, it seems clear that comparison of the living genera of the divisions Psilophyta, Microphyllophyta, Arthrophyta, and Pterophyta offers little evidence for close relationship of these plants. Their diversities seem clearly to overshadow the combination of attributes which they share in common, namely, presence of vascular tissue, absence of seeds, and similarity of balance in the alternating generations.

DISCUSSION QUESTIONS

1. a. What is meant by the term cryptogam, in current usage?
   b. What did it mean originally?
   c. What is meant by the term vascular cryptogam?
   d. What are nonvascular cryptogams?
   e. What did the term phanerogam mean originally?
   f. How is the term used currently?
2. Define or explain the terms apogamy and apospory. Where do these phenomena occur in the plant kingdom?
3. Briefly summarize and distinguish between the antithetic and homologous theories regarding the nature and origin of alternating generations.
4. Explain the following statement: "It seems clear that the initiation of sexuality and meiosis must have been closely related if not simultaneous, in view of their complementary functions."
5. Why are the phenomena of apogamy and apospory interpreted as evidence in support of the homologous theory of alternation?
6. What bearing does the observed presence of chlorophyll and starch in liverwort sporophytes have on the question of the relation between the alternating generations and their origin?

7. Why is the stem often said to be the dominant organ of the sporophyte in Psilophyta, Microphyllophyta, and Arthrophyta? Why not in the Pterophyta?

8. Distinguish between protosteles, siphonosteles, dictyosteles, eusteles, and polysteles. Give examples of each from among the vascular cryptogams.

9. On what evidence are macrophyllous leaves considered to be homologous with branch systems?

10. Speculate regarding the possible origin of the root as an organ of the sporophyte.

11. Discuss the distribution of sporogenous tissue in the vascular cryptogams, citing illustrative examples.

12. Distinguish between cauline and foliar sporangia, giving examples. How do you interpret those of *Equisetum*?

13. What evidence can you cite as to the origin of heterospory?

14. Compare the gametophytes of vascular cryptogams as to habitat, form, and nutrition, giving examples.

CHAPTER 24

Introduction to Seed Plants; Division Cycadophyta

INTRODUCTION TO SEED PLANTS

The members of the plant kingdom described as representative morphological types in Chapters 2 to 18 all are seedless plants whose *apparently* obscure reproductive organs and life cycle suggested to Linnaeus the name **Cryptogamae** (Gr. *kryptos,* hidden + Gr. *gamos,* marriage). He called the seed-bearing plants **Phanerogamae** (Gr. *phaneros,* visible + Gr. *gamos*), an allusion to the prominence of their supposed sexual organs, which in fact are spore-bearing organs.

The seed plants are vascular plants in whose bodies abundant xylem and phloem are present, except in secondarily reduced aquatics. This attribute they share with the vascular cryptogams with which they sometimes are grouped in a single division, **Tracheophyta** (Table 1, Chapter 31). This designation has not been adopted in the present text, because in the author's opinion such a grouping places too much weight on one attribute. The habit of producing seeds formerly was considered to be such an important indication of relationship that all seed-bearing plants were classified in a single division, **Spermatophyta** (Table 1, Chapter 31). However, this division has been replaced in many modern classifications by a still more inclusive taxon, the **Pteropsida,** under the division Tracheophyta. In spite of its lower rank, the subdivision (subphylum) Pteropsida includes a wider assemblage of plants, namely, the macrophyllous ferns as well as the seed plants. This arrangement reflects the views of those who see in the extinct seed ferns (Chapter 30) a possible bridge between the ferns and the living seed plants. In most systems of classification, the seed plants in which the seeds are not enclosed in a sporophyll are usually grouped in a taxon, **Gymnospermae** (Table 1, Chapter 31), a practice also not followed in the present text for reasons to be explained more fully in a later chapter.

The classification of the seed plants here tentatively suggested emphasizes the important diversities apparent in the several types often included in the taxon Gymnospermae. The seed habit is considered to occur in several *divisions* of living plants (as well as fossil plants, Chapter 30), namely, the divisions **Cycadophyta, Ginkgophyta, Coniferophyta, Gnetophyta** and **Anthophyta.** The remainder of the present chapter is devoted to a consideration of the first of these.

DIVISION CYCADOPHYTA

Introduction

The **Cycadophyta,** commonly called the **cycads,** include a small group of 9 genera and 100 species of tropical plants which superficially

Fig. 24–1. *Zamia floridana* A. DC. Potted plant with megastrobilus. X 1/9.

suggest both ferns and palms, insofar as the general form of the plant body is concerned (Fig. 24–1 to 24–3). They are sometimes regarded as "living fossils," and it has been predicted that they will be extinct by the next geological era. Once widely distributed and important components of the earth's vegetation, they now are reduced in number of genera, species, and individuals. Only one genus, *Zamia* (L. *zamiae*, erroneous reading in Pliny for *azaniae*, pine nuts), is represented in the flora of the

Fig. 24–2. *Cycas revoluta* Th. Greenhouse specimen showing new crown of leaves with circinate pinnae. X 1/48. (Courtesy of Dr. Elsie Quarterman.)

United States, in Florida, although the other eight genera are cultivated in conservatories. The genus *Cycas* (Fig. 24–2) is widely planted as an ornamental in warmer portions of the country. *Zamia* has been selected as representative of the cycads in the present book because it usually is to be found in university greenhouses or it may be obtained readily. Furthermore, the small stature of the plants makes it feasible to maintain a supply of fruiting specimens.

Fig. 24–3. *Dioon edule* Lindl. Apex of plant with microstrobilus. X ¼. (Courtesy of Chicago Natural History Museum.)

Two or more species of *Zamia* occur in Florida. Of these, Z. *floridana* A. DC. and Z. *umbrosa* Small have been studied with respect to reproduction.

Vegetative Morphology

The plant body of *Zamia* (Figs. 24–1, 24–9) consists of a relatively short, vertical, approximately conical stem which tapers toward the base; the latter bears a number of somewhat fleshy roots. Remains of leaves of former seasons are visible on the upper portions of the tuberous stem, and the apex supports a crown of spirally arranged, leathery, dark-green leaves. The latter are decidedly fern-like in appearance. The leaves of *Cycas* (Fig. 24–2) are even more fern-like because of the circinate vernation of the young pinnae.

As in the Pterophyta, the leaves of cycads are the most striking and dominant organs of the plant. They are arranged spirally on the axis,

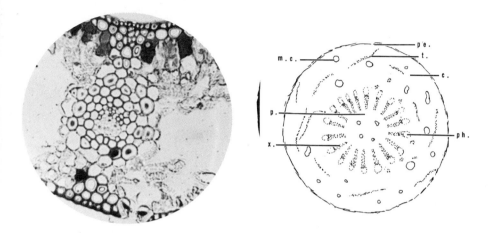

Fig. 24–4. *Zamia* sp. Transverse section of pinna; note thickened epidermis and hypodermis, sunken stomata, vein, and mesophyll. X 120.

Fig. 24–5. *Zamia* sp. Transverse section stem; c., cortex; m.c., mucilage canal; p., pith; pe., periderm; ph., phloem; t., leaf trace; x., xylem. X ½.

and under usual greenhouse conditions both *Zamia* and *Cycas* produce a new crown of leaves annually. Leaf crowns of preceding seasons may persist but they finally become reflexed and abscised. The pinnae are parallel-veined. Internally (Fig. 24–4), the leaflets of *Zamia* display markedly xerophytic attributes. The epidermis of both surfaces is thickened heavily on the outer walls. Stomata are present only on the lower surface of the pinnae and are sunken. A thick-walled **hypodermis,** an additional protective layer, lies beneath the upper epidermis. The mesophyll is differentiated into palisade and spongy zones.

The apex of the cycad stem is occupied by a dome of meristematic cells rather than by the single apical initial that is characteristic of so many vascular cryptogams. The meristematic zone differentiates into permanent tissues during the formation of strobili, and new apical meristems arise successively from mature cells lateral to the original meristem. A transverse section of the mature stem of *Zamia* (Fig. 24–5) reveals a surprising paucity of xylem. The latter is composed largely of scalariform-pitted tracheids whose pits lack toruses. A large part of the stem is occupied by the extensive cortex, the cells of which are full of stored metabolites. The stem surface is protected by an impermeable periderm layer. Mucilage canals are abundant in the cortex and pith. The cortex is traversed by leaf traces whose path is unusual. Each leaf of *Zamia* receives from seven to nine traces which depart from different points in the stele and girdle it, rising slightly as they approach the leaf base, which may be 180° from the point of origin of some of the traces.

The stele is an ectophloic, endarch siphonostele in mature plants. Its vascular cylinder is interrupted by numerous leaf gaps formed in association with the traces. Although a cambium is present between the xylem and phloem, it is relatively inactive, so the amount of vascular tissue remains small, and clearly defined growth rings are absent from the xylem of *Zamia*. The center of the stem is a parenchymatous pith.

The roots of cycads are fleshy, although considerable secondary xylem is produced. Those of *Zamia* usually are diarch in primary growth. In some genera, *Cycas*, for example, certain root branches are negatively geotropic, growing upon and above the soil. Such roots develop tubercular nodules which contain bacteria at first and later filaments of the myxophycean alga, *Anabaena*. The relationships of the bacteria and *Anabaena* with the host have not been ascertained.

Reproduction

In *Zamia* and in all the seed plants the gametophytic phases are strictly heterothallic. The male and female gametophytes arise from different types of spores which usually are designated microspores and megaspores. This designation has not gone unchallenged, however, because of several considerations which will be reviewed at this point.

The most important of these is the fact that the so-called microspores and megaspores of seed plants scarcely differ in size. Furthermore, the so-called megaspores have membranes only slightly thickened, if at all, and they never are shed from the sporangia in which they are produced. It has been suggested that these so-called microspores and megaspores of seed plants may well be homosporous, in spite of the heterothallism of the gametophytes which they generate. The names androspores (for microspores) and gynospores (for megaspores) have been suggested, but assignment of prefixes denoting sex to spores cannot be supported, in the writer's opinion. The terms microspore and megaspore will be used in the discussion of the several groups of seed plants in this text, but the student should remember that their heterosporous nature has been questioned.

The microsporangia and megasporangia of *Zamia* are segregated in different strobili which are produced by different individuals. This segregation is known as **dioecism** (Gr. *di*, two + Gr. *oikos*, house). The **microstrobili** (Fig. 24–6) are borne among the leaves at the stem apex in *Zamia floridana*. They appear in summer (July) at first as small, somewhat conical emergences and gradually enlarge, finally becoming as long

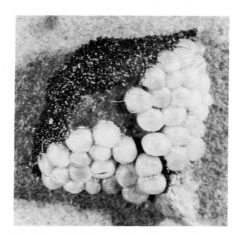

Fig. 24–6. *Zamia* sp. Mature microstrobilus at pollination. X ½.

Fig. 24–7. *Zamia* sp. Abaxial view of microsporophyll and microsporangia, some of the latter dehiscent. X 1¾.

as 10 cm. They are brown and rather fleshy throughout development, and are composed of a central axis to which the spirally arranged microsporophylls are attached. Each microsporophyll has two groups of microsporangia on its abaxial surface (Fig. 24–7), a total of between 28 and 50. Each microsporangium is subtended by a short thick stalk and its development is eusporangiate (Fig. 24–8). The number of spores is large and the sporangial wall is composed of several layers. A tapetum functions in nutrition during microsporogenesis, the cells disintegrating to form a tapetal plasmodium. The microspore mother cells undergo meiosis, each giving rise to a tetrad of microspores which finally separate from each other. The walls of mature microspores are composed of several layers.

The **megastrobili,** which appear among the leaves of plants other than those that bear the microstrobili, are massive in construction (Fig. 24–9).

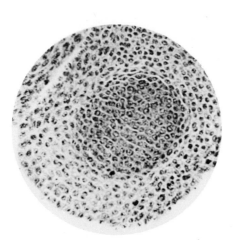

Fig. 24–8. *Zamia* sp. Section of single immature microsporangium with sporogenous tissue. X 125.

The megasporophylls are dark-brown peltate structures attached to the axis of the strobilus by stipes (Fig. 24–10). Each megasporophyll bears two ovoidal white bodies, the **ovules** (Fig. 24–10), which are attached to the adaxial surface of the megasporophyll by extremely short stalks. A median longitudinal section of a young ovule shortly after the appearance of the megastrobilus is shown in Fig. 24–11. The central cells of the young ovule contain dense protoplasmic contents. These cells comprise the young megasporangium in which the megaspore mother cell has not yet differentiated. The megasporangium tissue is surrounded by a multicellular covering, the **integument,** which is incompletely closed, leaving a minute passageway, the **micropyle.** This is at the pole opposite the point of attachment of the ovule. The ovule of *Zamia* and other seed plants is a megasporangium surrounded by an integumentary layer or layers. The ovule of *Zamia* is about 1 cm. long at the time of pollination.

Somewhat later in its development, one of the deeper cells of the megasporangium enlarges and undergoes two successive nuclear and cell divisions during which the meiotic process takes place. The products of these divisions are arranged in linear fashion (Fig. 24–11B). They are interpreted usually as four **megaspores** arranged as a **linear tetrad.** The cell which gives rise to the linear tetrad is known as the **megaspore mother cell.** The name megaspore has been assigned to the cells of the linear tetrad on the basis of comparison with the heterosporous cryptogams in which the megaspores are markedly larger than the microspores. It may be that the permanent retention of the megaspores within the megasporangium in the seed plants, with the related differences in mode of nutrition, has been the stimulus which effected their reduction in size.

Soon after the formation of the linear tetrad, three of the four megaspores degenerate. The survivor, usually the one farthest from the micropyle, appears to appropriate the products of the degeneration of the nonfunctional megaspores and it increases in size as a result. This increase in size also depends on the transfer of nutriment from the fleshy megasporangial tissues to the megaspore. The latter never contains large amounts of stored metabolites, as is the case in megaspores of the heterosporous cryptogams. This surviving megaspore, which gives rise to the female gametophyte, is known as the **functional megaspore.**

As in *Selaginella,* the microspores begin their development into male gametophytes, and the megaspores theirs into female gametophytes, while still enclosed by their respective sporangia. The early stages of the male gametophyte are intrasporal, and those of the female are permanently so in seed plants. As the microspore (Fig. 24–12A) separates from the tetrad, it is uninucleate.

Fig. 24–9. *Zamia floridana.* Portion of plant showing stem, leaf bases, and megastrobilus. X ¼. (Courtesy of the Chicago Natural History Museum.)

A single nuclear division and cytokinesis then take place within the microspore (Fig. 24–12B). This results in the formation of a small **prothallial cell** and a larger cell. A second nuclear and cell division in the large cell forms a small **generative cell** and a large **tube cell** (Fig. 24–12C). When the male gametophytes have attained this stage of development, the microsporophylls separate slightly, apparently by elongation of the internodes of the strobilus axis, thus exposing the microsporangia to the air.

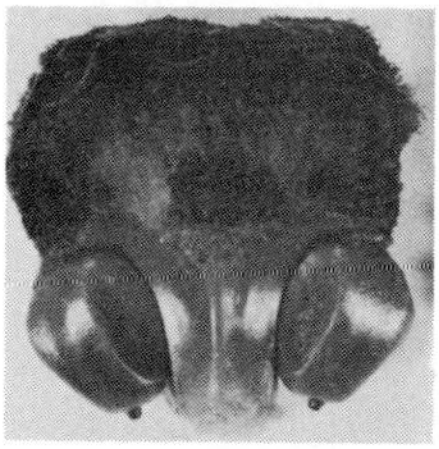

Fig. 24–10. *Zamia floridana.* Megasporophyll and ovules. X 1¼.

During microsporogenesis and subsequently, the surface cells of the microsporangium thicken, except for a vertical belt over the summit of the sporangium. When the microsporangia are exposed, drying effects their rupture into two valves along a vertical line of dehiscence (Fig. 24–7). The microspores containing the immature male gametophyte thus are shed from the microsporangium. They are known as **pollen grains** at the time of shedding. In the vicinity of Miami, Florida, this occurs between December and February each year.

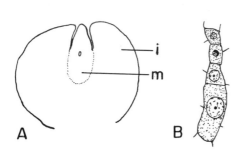

Fig. 24–11. *Zamia floridana.* A, Median longitudinal section of ovule showing integument, *i,* and megasporangium, *m,* with single megaspore mother cell, diagrammatic. B, Linear tetrad of megaspores, the lowermost the functional megaspore. X 620. (From F. Grace Smith.)

During pollination, changes take place in the megastrobili and the ovules within them. A slight elongation of the internodes, beginning at the base of the megastrobilus and extending gradually to the higher nodes, separates the hitherto contiguous sporophylls by ¼- to ⅛-inch crevices. It is through these that the wind-borne pollen grains sift into the megastrobilus. During this period, the cells at the apex of the megasporangium (sometimes called the nucellus) disintegrate, forming a droplet of colloidal material known as the **pollination droplet.** The breakdown of these cells results in the formation of a small depression, the **pollen chamber,** at the apex of the megasporagium. A number of pollen grains come to rest in the pollination droplet when it protrudes through the micropyle, the latter a tubular passageway through the integument (Fig. 24–13). As the pollination drop dries, it contracts, carrying the pollen grains into the pollen chamber. The observation, in living material, that pollen grains of pine float through the pollination droplet into the pollen chamber suggests that a similar mechanism may operate in both the cycads and *Ginkgo.* The actual transfer of the immature male gametophytes contained in the microspores, from the microsporangia to the micropyle of the ovule is known as **pollination.**

When the pollen grains have come to rest on the walls and near the base of the pollen chambers, their protoplasts protrude from the pointed (tube cell) pole through predetermined fissures to form tube-like haustoria into which the tube nuclei migrate in each case (Fig. 24–12*D*). These **pollen tubes** digest their way through the sterile tissue of the megasporangium, at first in a radial direction, but then curving toward the base of the ovule (Figs. 24–12E, 24–14A). That they accumulate some of the substance digested from the megasporangium tissue is indicated by the appearance of starch grains in the elongating pollen tubes. The

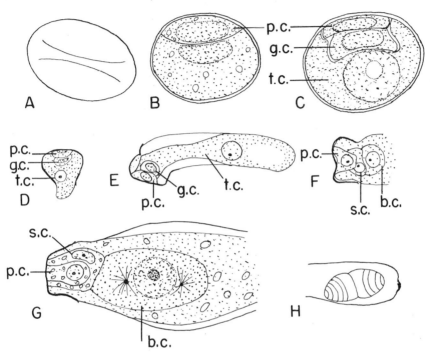

Fig. 24–12. *Zamia* sp. Development of ♂ gametophyte. A, Surface view of microspore. B, Sectional view of microspore showing prothallial cell. C, Sectional view of microspore (pollen grain) at shedding; note immature ♂ gametophyte consisting of prothallial cell, generative cell, and tube cell. D,E, Germination of pollen grain to form tube-like haustorial protuberance, migration of tube nucleus. F, Pollen grain end of ♂ gametophyte some time after pollination, with prothallial cell, stalk cell, and body cell. G, Pollen grain end of ♂ gametophyte; note prothallial cell, stalk cell, and body cell nucleus in prophase. H, Two sperm cells in pollen tube, b.c., body cell; g.c., generative cell; p.c., prothallial cell; s.c., stalk cell; t.c., tube cell. A-C, X 1030; D,H, X 400. (From Webber.)

tubes are unbranched or sparingly branched. As many as fourteen pollen tubes may be present within the apical tissues of a single ovule. The tubes may attain a length of 2 to 4 mm. Shortly after the pollen tube has been initiated, about a week after pollination, the generative cell divides to form a **stalk** and **body cell** (Fig. 24–12F). The latter enlarges gradually as the pollen tube lengthens. The prothallial, stalk, and body cells all remain at the pollen grain region of the elongating pollen tube (Fig. 24–12F,G).

Meanwhile, the functional megaspore within the megasporangium has begun to enlarge. The tissue immediately surrounding it becomes vacuolated, forming a so-called **spongy layer.** The latter seems to function like a tapetum whose protoplasmic contents contribute to the enlargement and subsequent development of the functional megaspore. The nucleus of the megaspore now begins a period of repeated free-nuclear divisions. This results, at first, in the formation of a number of nuclei which lie in a peripheral layer of cytoplasm just within the membrane of the original megaspore; the center of the latter is occupied by a large vacuole (Fig. 24–13). As free-nuclear divisions continue, however, additional cytoplasm is synthesized, so that the vacuole is obliterated gradually, and the megaspore lumen, which has been increasing constantly by absorption of the surrounding megasporangial tissues, is ultimately filled with large numbers of nuclei and watery cytoplasm. Wall formation is then initiated, at first between the peripheral nuclei, and it continues in a centripetal direction until the female gametophyte is entirely cellular (Fig. 24–15). Four (sometimes fewer) cells at the micropylar pole of the female gametophyte now function as archegonial initials. Each of them, by cell and nuclear division, forms an extremely large archegonium (Fig. 24–14B) consisting of two neck cells and a large central cell. Just before maturation, the nucleus of each central cell undergoes mitosis, forming the egg and ventral canal nuclei which usually are separated by cytokinesis.

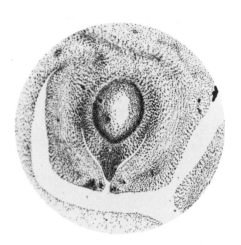

Fig. 24–13. *Zamia* sp. Median longitudinal section of young ovule; note integument enclosing megasporangium, the inner portion of which is being digested by the young free-nuclear ♀ gametophyte. X 30.

The vegetative cells of the female gametophyte which surround each archegonium form a **jacket layer,** the cells of which are especially involved in the transfer of nutriments to the developing egg and proembryo. The egg cytoplasm projects into these cells through small pit-like apertures. The egg cell may attain dimensions of 3.0 by 1.5 mm. and is readily

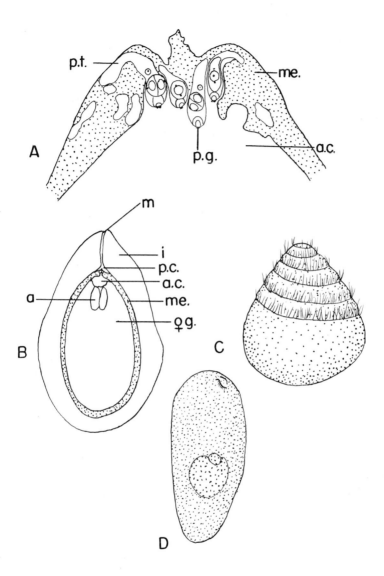

Fig. 24–14. *Zamia* sp. *A,* Longitudinal section of apex of megasporangium showing four maturing pollen tubes elongating at their pollen grain ends and protruding into archegonial chamber; clear spaces in megasporangium are segments of other pollen tubes. X 10. *B,* Median longitudinal section of ovule before fertilization. X 2. *C,* Single sperm cell. *D,* Egg cell at karyogamy, remains of the blepharoplast near apex. X 18. *a,* archegonium; *a.c.,* archegonial chamber; *i,* integument; *m,* micropyle, *me.,* megasporangium; ♀*g.,* female gametophyte; *p.c.,* pollen chamber; *p.g.,* pollen grain end; *p.t.,* pollen tube. (Modified from Webber.)

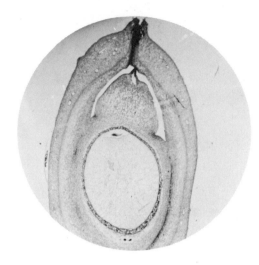

Fig. 24–15. *Zamia* sp. Longitudinal section of ovule some time after pollination; note, in centrifugal order, immature ♀ gametophyte within megasporangium, the apex of which shows part of a pollen tube, all the preceding surrounded by the massive integument with an apical micropyle. X 12½.

visible to the naked eye. The egg nucleus may attain a diameter of 550 microns.

Megasporogenesis and the maturation of the female gametophyte occupy about five months in *Zamia floridana*. During this period, all the component tissues of the ovule increase greatly by cell division, as do the megasporophylls and the strobilus axis. It has been demonstrated that the epidermis of the integument of the ovule has stomata and that stomata also may be present on the surface of the megasporangium. The significance of these observations remains to be explained. Median sections of ovules containing mature female gametophytes are shown in Figs. 24–14B and 24–16.

During the development of the

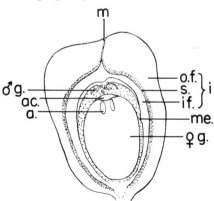

Fig. 24–16. *Zamia* sp. Median longitudinal section of ovule at fertilization: *a.*, archegonium; *ac.*, archegonial chamber; *i*, integument composed of *o.f.*, outer fleshy layer, *s.*, precursor of stony layer, and *i.f.*, inner fleshy layer; *m.*, micropyle; *me.*, megasporangium, ♂ g. and ♀ g., ♂ and ♀ gametophytes. X 2.

female gametophyte, the haustorial pollen tubes have progressively digested away the tissues of the megasporangium. As the archegonia mature, the cells of the apex of the female gametophyte increase slightly in size and number so that the group of archegonia comes to lie in a slight depression, the **archegonial chamber** (Fig. 24–16), which is about 2 mm. in diameter and 1 mm. deep. Soon after this the pollen tubes complete digestion of the megasporangium and enter the archegonial chamber (Fig. 24–14A).

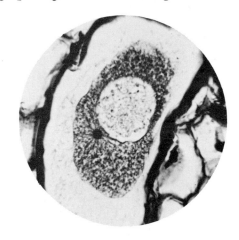

Fig. 24–17. *Zamia* sp. Section of pollen tube within megasporangium, showing body cell with nucleus at early prophase; note blepharoplast and radiations. X 250.

Just prior to this, usually late in May, the body cell nucleus divides to form two **sperm nuclei** which are segregated by delicate cell membranes (Figs. 24–12G, H, 24–18). These cells are composed of very large nuclei invested with a delicate layer of cytoplasm. During the enlargement of the body cell and its nuclear division, two

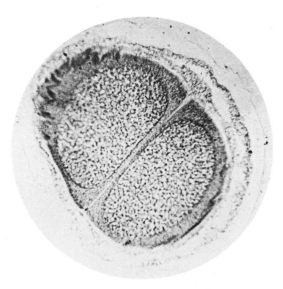

Fig. 24–18. *Zamia* sp. Transverse section of pollen tube and body cell containing two sperm cells; note segments of spiral blepharoplast near plasma membrane. X 250.

bodies with astral radiations appear in the body cell and one becomes associated with each sperm. After the division, each of these bodies, the **blepharoplasts,** disintegrates into a mass of granules which are arranged in spiral fashion about part of the sperm nucleus. Each of these spirals ultimately generates a great many short flagella (cilia) (Figs. 24–14C, 24–18).

The mature sperms now are liberated from the body cell, become motile, and swim actively within the pollen tube. The sperms may attain a diameter of 300 microns, the largest known in the plant kingdom. The pollen tubes are extremely turgid, probably because of the high osmotic value of the substances which have been digested and absorbed. This is evidenced by the fact that the sperms continue their motility in a 10 percent solution of cane sugar.

There is no liquid water in the archegonial chamber at fertilization. Observations of living material indicate that the pollen tubes burst and discharge the sperms into the archegonial chamber, that the neck cells shrink, and that a portion of the egg cytoplasm protrudes into the archegonial chamber, drawing the sperm or sperms into the egg cytoplasm. This process is of sufficient violence to sever the blepharoplast from the surface of the sperm in some cases (Fig. 24–14D). A sperm nucleus migrates to the vicinity of the egg nucleus, now of tremendous size, and nuclear union occurs (Fig. 24–14D). It should be emphasized at this point that **pollination,** the transfer of the immature male gametophyte to the micropyle of the ovule, and **fertilization,** nuclear union and the culmination of sexuality, are very different processes. In *Zamia,* they are separated by an interval of five months. Fig. 24–16 shows a median longitudinal section of an ovule at the time of fertilization. The archegonia are readily visible to the unaided eye at this stage.

In the development of the zygote into the embryo in *Zamia* and other cycads, the zygote nucleus enters a period of free-nuclear mitoses which is variable in extent. In *Zamia,* approximately 256 nuclei are formed in the egg cell (Fig. 24–19A). Development of the embryonic sporophyte has recently been studied in *Zamia umbrosa.* Wall formation here is initiated among the free nuclei near the base of each archegonium and extends gradually toward the neck end. Some free nuclei may remain unenclosed by walls (Fig. 24–19B). The lowermost cells of this intra-archegonial **proembryo** function as a meristematic zone which is covered by a cap-like layer. An intermediate layer of meristematic cells to-

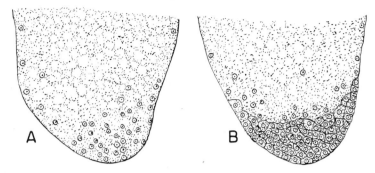

Fig. 24–19. *Zamia umbrosa* Small. Early embryogeny. A, Base of archegonium with free nuclei
of proembryo. X 50. B, Cellular proembryo. X 46. (From Bryan.)

ward the neck region of the archegonium ceases to divide; its component
cells increase in length and force the basal meristematic cells and their cap
out through the base of the egg cell into the vegetative tissues of the female gametophyte (Fig. 24–20). This elongating zone of the proembryo,
the **suspensor,** is augmented from the meristematic zone below.

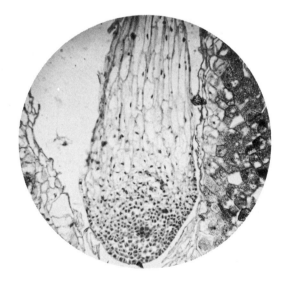

Fig. 24–20. *Zamia* sp. Later stage in embryogeny; suspensor and cellular embryo. X 60.

Although the zygotes of all the archegonia of one female gametophyte
may initiate embryo formation, only one embryo normally is present in

the mature seed, the others having aborted. The embryo grows at the expense of the female gametophyte tissues which are gradually digested. The uppermost cells (those nearest the archegonial neck) of the pro-embryo function as a sort of buffer zone which resists the pressure of the elongating suspensor sufficiently to cause it to become coiled.

The terminal, embryo-forming cells of the proembryo organize two **cotyledons** between which is a minute terminal bud, the **plumule.** The axis of the embryo consists of a **hypocotyl** which extends from the cotyle-donary node to the **radicle,** the embryonic root. The latter is covered with a special sheath, the **coleorhiza.** During the development of the embryo within it, the entire ovule increases in size, and changes occur in the massive integument in which three layers are more clearly dif-ferentiated (Fig. 24–21). The outermost of these becomes fleshy and bright yellow-orange in color. The middle layer is hard and stony, and the innermost remains soft. A median longitudinal section of the seed (Fig. 24–21) reveals that it contains an embryonic sporophyte embedded in vegetative tissue of the female gametophyte, the latter surrounded by the remains of the megasporangium and an integument. This statement regarding the seed of *Zamia* will serve to define seed structure in all gymno-sperms.

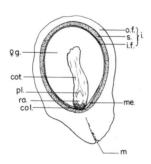

Fig. 24–21. *Zamia* sp. Median longitudi-nal section of recently shed seed: *i,* in-tegument (layers as in Fig. 24–16): *col.,* coleorhiza; *cot.,* cotyledons; ♀ *g.,* ♀ ga-metophyte; *m.,* micropyle; *me.,* megaspo-rangium remains; *pl.,* plumule; *ra.,* radicle or embryonic root. X 5/12.

As the seeds ripen, the megaspo-rophylls separate and the seeds are abscised. Germination may follow immediately. The first manifestation of it is the protrusion of the coleo-rhiza and enclosed root through the micropyle. The coleorhiza soon grows downward and is penetrated by the enclosed primary root. The tips of the cotyledons remain embedded within the seed, where they function in absorbing food stored in the female gametophyte cells. After some weeks the cotyledons emerge and ultimately the first foliage leaf appears. Further growth and development of other foliage leaves are very slow in *Zamia.* A number of years are required for the young sporophyte to develop strobili.

Although *Zamia* has been chosen as representative of the cycads, several other genera may be available for observation in tropical regions or in conservatory collections. *Cycas,* native of the eastern hemisphere, and *Dioon,* from Mexico, usually are represented. *Cycas* is of phylogenetic interest because its megasporophylls are woolly, modified, pinnately compound structures, loosely aggregated at the crown of the plant, and not borne in strobili. The microsporophylls of *Cycas* and both types of sporophylls in the remaining genera of cycads are localized in strobili.

SUMMARY AND CLASSIFICATION

In general appearance, *Zamia, Cycas, Dioon,* and other cycads are suggestive of *Marattia*-like ferns. The tuberous, often petiole-armored, sparingly branched stems and pinnately compound and circinate leaves contribute to this similarity. The stems are characterized by relative paucity of vascular tissue in spite of the presence of a cambium, and by their girdling leaf traces. The primary stele is an endarch siphonostele interrupted by large and persistent leaf gaps.

All cycads are dioecious, microsporangia and megasporangia being produced on separate strobili (loosely grouped megasporophylls in *Cycas*) which occur on separate individuals. Sporangial development is of the eusporangiate type. The megasporangia are covered by a massive protective layer, the integument, which surrounds them completely except for a minute passageway, the micropyle. Such covered megasporangia are known as ovules. The megasporangium wall is not specially differentiated. The single megaspore mother cell gives rise to a linear tetrad of megaspores, only one of which is functional. The megaspore does not contain large amounts of stored metabolites, is not markedly larger than the microspore, is thin-walled and permanently retained within the megasporangium, in contrast to the megaspores of nonseed plants. As a result, the female gametophyte also develops within the megasporangium, and fertilization and development of the embryonic sporophyte also take place within the megasporangium and its integument. The permanent retention of these structures within the megasporangium has resulted in the seed habit. It will be recalled that a tendency toward such retention was noted in *Selaginella;* partial retention occurred in certain extinct Microphyllophyta (Chapter 30). That the seed habit probably arose independently in more than one group of plants is suggested by the study of paleobotany.

The male gametophyte of *Zamia* and other cycads also reveals innovations not present among the vascular cryptogams. Foremost among these is the development of a pollen tube whose primary function seems to be nutritive, inasmuch as it serves as a haustorial organ which digests the tissues of the megasporangium. Its elongation at the pollen grain end just prior to fertilization brings the male gametes into close proximity to the archegonia. The sperms of *Zamia* are multiciliate and actively motile, although their movement is confined to the pollen tubes. The number of sperms produced by each male gametophyte of *Zamia* is reduced, as compared with the vascular cryptogams, 2 being produced in all the cycads except the genus *Microcycas*, which is said to produce 16 to 22.

In addition to the permanent retention of the female gametophyte within the megasporangium, there are two adaptive modifications, the pollen chamber and the archegonial chamber. Another departure in *Zamia* is the free-nuclear phase in embryogeny, an attribute of several groups of seed plants not paralleled in the vascular cryptogams. Finally, the abscission of the ovule containing the embryonic sporophyte within the female gametophyte, all covered by the integument, produces the characteristic structures known as seeds.

The classification of cycad genera discussed in the present chapter is as follows:

Division Cycadophyta
  Class 1. Cycadopsida
    Order 1. Cycadales
      Family 1. Cycadaceae
        Genera: *Cycas, Dioon, Zamia, Microcycas*

DISCUSSION QUESTIONS

1. What vegetative attributes of cycads suggest *Marattia*-like ferns?
2. In what respect are the leaf traces of *Zamia* anomalous?
3. How do the stem and root apex of *Zamia* differ from those of many vascular cryptogams?
4. What evidence can you cite to indicate that cycad leaves are macrophyllous?
5. Define or explain the terms endarch siphonostele, periderm, dioecism, ovule, seed, micropyle, pollen grain, free-nuclear embryo development, pollination, linear tetrad.
6. What conditions must prevail for seed formation to occur?
7. A possible approach to the seed habit is cited in certain Microphyllophyta, which are heterosporous. Would you search for the origin of the seed plants in that group? Explain.
8. Compare the female gametophyte of *Zamia* with that of *Dryopteris, Sela-*

ginella, and *Isoetes* with reference to both vegetative and reproductive aspects.

9. Compare the male gametophyte of *Zamia* with that of heterosporous cryptogams.

10. What biological advantages accrue to the plant from the seed habit?

11. Where would you seek cycads in nature?

12. Distinguish between the pollen and archegonial chambers. Cite as many differences in these structures as you can.

REFERENCE WORKS ON SEED PLANTS[1]

Arnold, C. A. Origin and Relationship of the Cycads, *Phytomorphology,* 3:51–65, 1953.

Campbell, D. H. *The Evolution of the Land Plants (Embryophyta),* Stanford Univ. Press, 1940.

Chamberlain, C. J. *The Living Cycads,* Univ. of Chicago Press, 1919.

Chamberlain, C. J. *Gymnosperms: Structure and Evolution,* Univ. of Chicago Press, 1935.

Coulter, J. M., and Chamberlain, C. J. *Morphology of Gymnosperms,* Univ. of Chicago Press, 1917.

Eames, A. J., and MacDaniels, L. H. *An Introduction to Plant Anatomy,* McGraw-Hill Book Co., Inc., 1947.

Esau, K. *Plant Anatomy,* John Wiley and Sons, Inc., 1953.

Haupt, A. W. *Plant Morphology,* McGraw-Hill Book Co., Inc., 1953.

Jeffrey, E. C. *The Anatomy of Woody Plants.* Univ. of Chicago Press, 1930.

Johansen, D. A. *Plant Embryology,* Chronica Botanica Company, 1950.

Lawrence, G. H. M. *Taxonomy of Vascular Plants,* The Macmillan Company, 1951.

Maheshwari, P. *An Introduction to the Embryology of Angiosperms,* McGraw-Hill Book Co., Inc., 1950.

Seward, A. C. The Story of the Maidenhair Tree, *Smithsonian Report,* 1938, pp. 441–460.

Wardlaw, C. W. *Embryogenesis in Plants,* John Wiley and Sons, Inc., 1955.

---

[1] These references may be consulted as supplementary to Chapters 24–29.

CHAPTER 25

Division Ginkgophyta

INTRODUCTION

Whereas the Cycadophyta, discussed in the preceding chapter, had comparatively small, sparsely branched stems and large, pinnately compound leaves, *Ginkgo* (Chinese *yin*, silver + *hing*, apricot), the sole extant genus of the Ginkgophyta, is characterized by large, richly branched stems and smaller simple leaves. Furthermore, the extensive pith, scanty xylem, and large cortex of cycadean stems are in marked contrast to the small pith, abundant xylem, and narrow cortex in stems of *Ginkgo*.

Ginkgo biloba L., the maidenhair tree (Fig. 25–1), has often been called a living fossil. There is considerable doubt whether it still occurs in habitats where it has not been cultivated, although there are reports of specimens in the wild in certain forests in remote western China. The fossil record indicates that *Ginkgo* and related genera were distributed widely, especially in the northern hemisphere, in earlier geological periods, some records extending back to the Permian (Fig. 30–1).

The name "maidenhair tree" is an allusion to the similarity in appearance between certain leaves of *Ginkgo* trees and the leaflets of the maidenhair fern, *Adiantum*. The tree is widely cultivated in the United States and readily grown from seed. In Washington, D.C., a large number of trees have been planted along some of the streets. The leaves are of a beautiful yellow-golden color in the autumn. Many oriental peoples have cultivated *Ginkgo* in their temple grounds. The Japanese once believed that *Ginkgo* exuded water during a fire, probably because these trees are more resistant than others to the disastrous effects of fire.

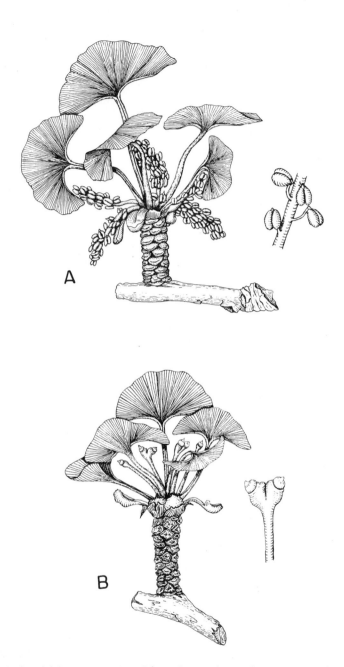

Fig. 25–1. *Ginkgo biloba* L. *A,* Portion of long shoot and spur shoot in spring, showing numerous terminal bud scale scars, bud scales, emerging leaves, and microstrobili; detail of axis and four microsporophylls at the right. *B,* Similar portion of ovulate plant, showing paired pedunculate ovules; detail of latter at the right. X 1.

VEGETATIVE MORPHOLOGY

Mature specimens of *Ginkgo* in cultivation may attain a height of more than a hundred feet. The form of young trees is narrowly conical, with the branches ascending; but in older specimens, especially ovule-bearing trees, the form is rounded, with the branches somewhat spreading and drooping.

Growth and development of the aerial portions of *Ginkgo,* as in all woody plants of the temperate zone, are marked by seasonal periodicity. *Ginkgo* trees are deciduous, producing entirely new leaves each year; these persist for only one growing season. During the fall and winter, the delicate growing tips of the stems are enclosed by leaf primorida which will emerge the following spring, and these, in turn, are covered by the resistant bud scales characteristic of woody plants. With the renewal of growth each spring, the bud scales are shed, and the embryonic stem tips undergo rapid cell division and enlargement, thus exposing the rudimentary leaves.

Examination of branches in the leafy condition reveals that there is a dimorphism of branching (Fig. 25–1). The elongate main axes are known as **long shoots.** These produce a series of spirally arranged leaves on widely separated nodes during their first year of growth. Older portions of the long shoots bear a large number of short lateral branches, the **spur shoots.** These develop from the lateral buds of long shoots after the first season. Each spur shoot produces a terminal cluster of as many as sixteen leaves every season. Growth of the spur shoots in length is extremely slow. However, on proper stimulation, such as injury to the terminal bud of a long shoot, spur shoots may metamorphose into long shoots.

Development of both spur shoots and long shoots may be traced to the activity of a group of meristematic cells and their derivatives, the promeristem. The young leaves are initiated very close to the stem apex in *Ginkgo.* The vascular system is arranged in the form of a cylindrical network, a **dictyostele,** in primary growth. The primary xylem is endarch, and the stele is interrupted by the departure of traces, two to each leaf.

As in stem development in all woody perennial plants, the completion of primary differentiation is followed early by the initiation of activity by the **cambium.** The latter is a zone of meristematic cells of the procambium, between the primary xylem and phloem, which has remained undifferentiated. Frequently if not always, cambial activity, with resulting differentiation of secondary xylem and phloem, commences before primary differentiation has been completed. The secondary tissues (Fig. 25–2) which have developed from cambium derivatives can usually be recognized by their orderly radial arrangement, in contrast to that of the primary xylem and phloem. Cambial activity is seasonal; hence in older stems the annual zones of secondary xylem are readily distinguishable. Comparison of transverse sections of spur and long shoots of the same age indicates that considerably more secondary xylem (wood) is produced by the cambium of the long shoots. The pith and cortex of the spur shoots are persistent and more extensive than those of the long shoots. With the addition of secondary vascular tissues and expansion of the inner portion of the stem, the outermost cells of the cortex become organized into **phellogen,** a cork cambium. This is a meristematic cylinder whose derivatives augment the cortex and replace the epidermis of the primary stem with **phellem** or cork cells. Abundant **lenticels,** which facilitate gaseous interchange, develop in the stems after the

Fig. 25–2.   *Ginkgo biloba.* Transverse section of segment of a long shoot early in its second year; note central pith, primary xylem, two rings of secondary xylem, cambium, phloem, cortex with large mucilage canal, and periderm; torn outermost part is remains of epidermis. X 30.

phellogen becomes active.

A number of meristematic cells also comprise the promeristem of the root, which is covered by a protective cap. Each root contains an exarch protostele which is diarch in arrangement of the protoxylem. The primary tissues of the root also are supplemented by secondary tissues developed by cambial activity.

The leaves of *Ginkgo* are perhaps its most distinctive attribute that is readily observable. Leaves of seedlings and those of long shoots are deeply bilobed. Those

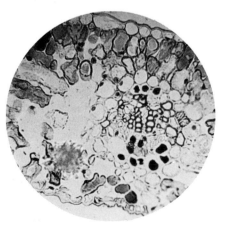

Fig. 25–3.   *Ginkgo biloba.* Transverse section of leaf. X 125.

of spur shoots are entire or obscurely lobed (Fig. 25–1). The two vascular traces of the petiole fork as they enter the blade, where they undergo repeated dichotomies. Internally (Fig. 25–3), the mesophyll cells are differentiated into palisade and spongy layers in the leaves of long shoots but are less differentiated in leaves of the spur shoot. Stomata occur almost exclusively on the abaxial surfaces of the leaves. All the organs of *Ginkgo* are traversed by a series of mucilage canals in which a sticky substance is secreted.

REPRODUCTION

Like the cycads, which are dioecious, the microsporangia and ovules of *Ginkgo* are borne on separate individuals (Fig. 25–1). The microsporangia develop in lax strobili; the ovules occur in pendulous pairs at the tips of short, petiole-like stalks. Both arise among the vegetative leaves of spur shoots and emerge with the latter in the spring. The

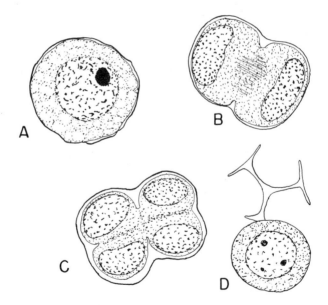

Fig. 25–4. *Ginkgo biloba.* Microsporogenesis (aceto-carmine preparations). A, Microspore mother cell. B, End of meiosis I. C, Formation of tetrad of microspores. D, Single microspores and remains of common tetrad walls. X 1030.

microstrobili of a given season develop during the summer preceding their emergence from the meristem of the spur shoot and attain considerable size by late autumn. They may pass the winter in the microspore mother cell stage, meiosis and microsporogenesis (Fig. 25–4) occurring the following spring. Each microstrobilus is composed of an axis which bears spirally arranged microsporophylls, the latter stalked and humped (Fig. 25–1A). Each microsporophyll has two elongate microsporangia. The development of the latter is eusporangiate. The wall of the microsporangium is composed of five or six layers of cells within which there is a tapetum. Dehiscence of the microsporangia is by a vertical fissure.

The ovules are not borne in strobili but occur in pairs, terminally, at the tips of stalks or **peduncles** which emerge among the leaf bases of the spur shoots in early spring (Fig. 25–1B). Two vascular bundles traverse both the stalk of the microsporophyll and the peduncle which bears the ovules. The vascular bundles terminate at the base of the sporangia. An enlarged, collar-like rim is present at the base of each ovule (Fig. 25–1B). In certain abnormal individuals the collar may be expanded and blade-like. This suggests that the collar may represent the remnant of an expanded sporophyll. The ovule itself consists of a massive integument

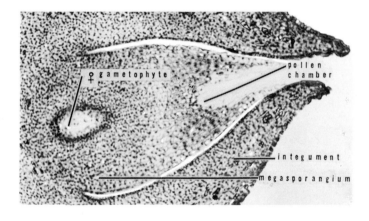

Fig. 25–5. *Ginkgo biloba*. Median longitudinal section of young ovule; note micropyle, pollen chamber, megasporangium, and early free-nuclear ♀ gametophyte. X 125.

which rather loosely surrounds the elongate megasporangium except at its tip, where it leaves a micropyle (Fig. 25–5). As in *Zamia*, a single megaspore mother cell is differentiated deep within the megasporangium. The sterile cells of the megasporangium which surround the megaspore mother cell are somewhat different in appearance from the more peripheral cells and form a spongy tissue. Soon after the ovules emerge from the buds of the spur shoots, certain of the apical cells of the megasporangia degenerate into mucilaginous masses, forming a pollen chamber in each ovule (Fig. 25–5). Meiosis and megasporogenesis, in which a linear tetrad of megaspores is formed, occur at the time of pollination or soon after.

Development of the uninucleate microspores (Fig. 25–6A) into male gametophytes is initiated, as in *Zamia*, soon after the completion of

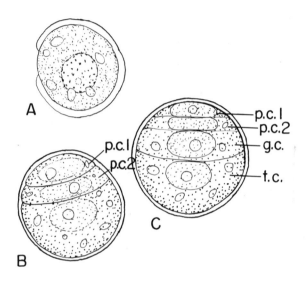

Fig. 25–6.   *Ginkgo biloba*. Intrasporangial stages of ♂ gametophyte development (I_2–KI preparations). A, Microspore. B,C, later stages; C, at shedding. g.c., generative cells; p.c.1, p.c.2, first and second prothallial cells; t.c., tube cell. X 1033.

microsporogenesis and before the microspores are shed. The mature microspores are slightly protuberant at one pole, which is covered by a delicate wall, the intine (Fig. 25–6A). The outer exine is absent from this portion of the microspore surface. Development of the male gametophyte begins with an intrasporal nuclear and cell division which delimits a small cell, the prothallial cell, from a larger cell. The latter undergoes a second nuclear and cell division to form a second prothallial cell and an antheridial initial (Fig. 25–6B). The first prothallial cell sometimes degenerates promptly, but the second is more persistent. The antheridial cell now divides again, forming a small generative cell adjacent to the second prothallial cell, and a tube cell (Fig. 25–6C). The immature male gametophyte or pollen grain is shed in this four-celled condition.

The pollen, which is light and wind-borne, is produced in large amounts by the microsporangiate trees. In the vicinity of Nashville, Tennessee, pollination takes place about April 15 each year, although there is variation in accordance with the temperature. Some of the pollen grains reach the apex of each megasporangium and become lodged in the mucilaginous material at the mouth of the pollen chamber. It has been reported that as this material dries, it contracts and draws the pollen grains into the pollen chamber in contact with the megasporangial cells. The region of the pollen grains covered only by the intine digests its way into the tissues of the megasporangium, much as in *Zamia,* apparently also serving in an haustorial capacity. Maturation of the male gametophyte is completed as the pollen tube grows through the tissues of the megasporangium.

It will be recalled that each ovule contains either a megaspore mother cell or a linear tetrad at the time of pollination. As in *Zamia,* usually only one of the megaspores functions in developing a female gametophyte. It also will be recalled that the interval between pollination and fertilization in *Zamia* is about five months, and that during this period the functional megaspore develops into the female gametophyte. Similarly, in

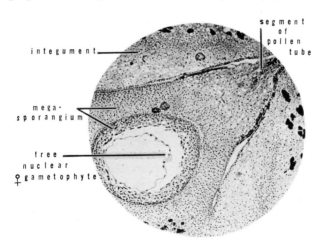

Fig. 25–7. *Ginkgo biloba.* Longitudinal section of apex of ovule, with later free-nuclear ♀ gametophyte than that in Fig. 25–5; note evidences of pollen tubes in megasporangium, inner disintegrating tissue of megasporangium, and ♀ gametophyte (somewhat plasmolyzed). X 30.

Ginkgo, it takes from early April until August (in the vicinity of Nashville) for the megaspore to produce a mature female gametophyte.

Development of the female gametophyte involves an extended period of free-nuclear division (Figs. 25–5, 25–7, 25–8), during the early stages of which the nuclei are arranged around the periphery of the enlarging megaspore. The latter increases in size at the expense of the surrounding megasporangial tissue, which becomes spongy in the portion immediately surrounding the megaspore. The period of free-nuclear division is about two months, during which all the tissues of the ovule enlarge. Wall forma-

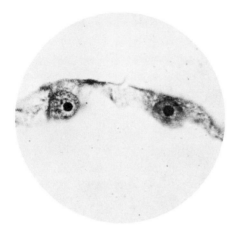

Fig. 25–8. *Ginkgo biloba*. Segment of free-nuclear ♀ gametophyte in Fig. 25–7, enlarged. X 500.

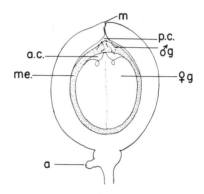

Fig. 25–9. *Ginkgo biloba*. Diagrammatic median longitudinal section of entire ovule at the time of fertilization: *a,* aborted ovule; *a.c.,* archegonial chamber; *m,* micropyle; *me.,* megasporangium; ♂ *g,* ♂ gametophyte in megasporangium; ♀ *g,* ♀ gametophyte with archegonium; *p.c.,* pollen chamber.

tion begins at the periphery of the female gametophyte, near the megasporangium membrane, and gradually extends centripetally. Inasmuch as the innermost nuclei near the center of the gametophyte are finally completely surrounded by their individual walls, the mature cellular gametophyte may be split readily into two halves (Fig. 25–9). Although surrounded by the remains of the megasporangium as well as by the massive integument, the vegetative cells of the female gametophyte are green. Whether or not extensive photosynthesis occurs has not been ascertained. It is probable that nutrition of the female gametophyte of *Ginkgo,* as in *Zamia* and other seed plants, is based largely on material derived from the parent sporophyte.

Two archegonia develop at the micropylar pole of each female gametophyte, but occasionally there are three (Figs. 25–9 to 25–11). The archegonia are large but not as large as those of *Zamia.* Each has two neck cells and a jacket layer. However, in *Ginkgo,* the division of the central cell nucleus into egg and ventral canal nuclei generally is followed by cytokinesis, so that a ventral canal *cell* is formed. The latter disintegrates before fertilization. At that time, the archegonia are sunk in a

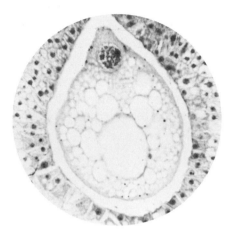

Fig. 25–10. *Ginkgo biloba.* Archegonium with central cell nucleus in prophase of division to form egg and ventral canal nuclei. X 125.

somewhat circular groove, the archegonial chamber (Figs. 25–9, 25–11). The vegetative tissue between the archegonia elongates, forming a short

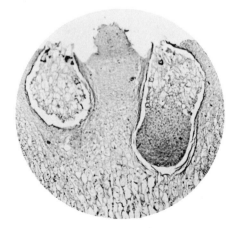

Fig. 25–11. *Ginkgo biloba.* Apex of ♀ gametophyte; note "tent pole"-like protuberance and two archegonia, the one at the left abortive, the one at the right with a cellular proembryo. X 125.

column the apex of which extends to the megasporangial tissues (Figs. 25–9, 25–11).

During the development of the female gametophyte, the male gametophyte has been digesting its way through the apical portion of the enlarging megasporangium. Early in this process, the generative cell divides into two cells, the stalk and body cell, as in *Zamia*. Division of the body cell into two sperms does not occur until shortly before fertilization. After the nuclear division that forms the sperms, blepharoplasts, which appear prior to the division of the body cell, move to the surface of the sperm cells where they form elongate, spirally coiled bands of cilia over a small portion of the sperm surface (Fig. 25–12). All the

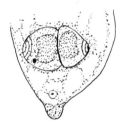

Fig. 25–12. *Ginkgo biloba.* Pollen grain end of mature ♂ gametophyte; note prothallial cell nucleus (second) and two sperm cells. X 300. (From Hirase.)

nuclei of the male gametophyte, excepting sometimes the tube nucleus, remain at the pollen grain end of the tube until just before fertilization. The function of the pollen tube, therefore, is primarily haustorial.

Details of fertilization are not as well known for *Ginkgo* as they are for the cycads.[1] A report that the archegonial chamber may be filled with fluid at the time of fertilization requires further confirmation, especially that based on living material. Soon after nuclear union, the zygote nucleus enters upon a period of free-nuclear division, the division products being uniformly distributed throughout the cytoplasm of the egg. Eight successive nuclear divisions occur, so approximately 256 proembryonic nuclei are formed. Cell walls then segregate the nuclei, and the entire embryo becomes cellular (Fig. 25–13). The cells of the embryo in the region of the base of the archegonium divide rapidly; those in the neck region elongate slightly but do not divide. The cells in the intermediate zone then enlarge somewhat, but a highly organized suspensor, such as is found in *Zamia*, does not occur in *Ginkgo*. The actively divid-

---

[1] C. L. Lee, "Fertilization in *Ginkgo biloba*," *Botanical Gazette*, Vol. 117, pp. 79–100, 1955, has recently augmented our knowledge.

ing basal portion of the embryo grows through the base of the archegonium, digesting the vegetative tissues of the female gametophyte (Fig.
25–13) as it develops. The zygotes of both archegonia may initiate
embryos, but usually only one is present in the mature seeds. Relatively
early in development, the surviving embryo is differentiated into a root,

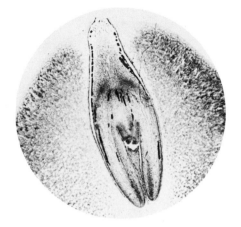

Fig. 25–13. *Ginkgo biloba.* Median longitudinal section of apex of ♀ gametophyte and of
embryo; note radicle, hypocotyl, plumule, cotyledons, and surrounding starch-filled cells of ♀
gametophyte. X 30.

a short hypocotyl, two cotyledons, and a short epicotyl terminated by the
primordia of approximately the first five foliage leaves (Fig. 25–13).

During the development of the embryo, the integument increases
greatly and its three component layers are clearly differentiated. The
outermost and most extensive becomes fleshy and a mottled green-purple.
The innermost layer is rather dry and papery, and the middle layer is
stony, as in the cycads. The mature seeds have the appearance of small
plums (Fig. 25–14). A median section of a seed is shown in Fig. 25–15.
The fleshy layer has a foul odor and may cause nausea and skin eruptions
in certain individuals. The embryo and female gametophyte, however, are
edible.

In seed germination, *Ginkgo* is **hypogean,** the cotyledons remaining
within the seed; from it they absorb the remains of the female gametophyte, translocating it in soluble form to other parts of the developing
seedling. The primary root emerges early and functions as a tap root.
The seedling leaves are deeply bilobed like those at the tips of the long
shoots in the mature trees.

Fig. 25–14. *Ginkgo biloba.* Spur shoot and single mature seed; the latter with outer fleshy layer removed shown in the specimen at the right. X ⅔.

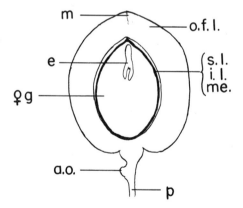

Fig. 25–15. *Ginkgo biloba.* Median longitudinal section of mature seed (diagrammatic): *a.o.,* aborted ovule; *e,* embryo; ♀ *g,* ♀ gametophyte; *m,* micropyle; *me.,* megasporangium remains; *o.f.l.,* outer fleshy, *i.l.,* inner layer, and *s.l.,* stony layer of integument; *p.* peduncle.

SUMMARY AND CLASSIFICATION

Although the reproductive processes in *Ginkgo* are similar in many respects to those in *Zamia* and other cycads, its vegetative structure is in marked contrast. *Ginkgo* plants are large, richly branched trees, with an active vascular cambium that functions in stems and roots throughout the life of the plant in adding secondary xylem and phloem. The leaves are either almost entire or bilobed, never compound as in the cycads. The spur shoots superficially resemble the cycad stems in their armored surfaces and leaf crowns as well as in their extensive pith and cortex and the paucity of xylem.

Next to those of the cycads, the sperms of *Ginkgo* are the largest in the plant kingdom, and, with those of the cycads, the only ciliate sperms among the living seed plants. The male gametophyte of *Ginkgo*, with its two prothallial cells, is considered to be more primitive than *Zamia*'s, which has one. The occurrence of cytokinesis to form a ventral canal cell in the archegonium of *Ginkgo*, as in *Zamia*, is also a feature more primitive than seen in other seed plants. An actively functioning suspensor is absent in the developing embryo of *Ginkgo*. It also differs from cyads and vascular cryptogams in its extremely woody and deciduous habit.

Ginkgo may be classified as follows:

Division Ginkgophyta
    Class 1. Ginkgopsida
        Order 1. Ginkgoales
            Family 1. Ginkgoaceae
            Genus: *Ginkgo*

DISCUSSION QUESTIONS

1. Why is *Ginkgo* sometimes called a "living fossil"?
2. What is the origin of the common name for *Ginkgo*?
3. Where does *Ginkgo* grow natively? Where is the tree nearest to your campus?
4. Of what possible significance are the collars at the bases of the ovules?
5. What structures are visible in a median longitudinal section of the ovule made at pollination?
6. Describe the development of the male and female gametophytes and fertilization in *Ginkgo*. Make labeled drawings to illustrate these phenomena.
7. Compare the embryogeny of *Ginkgo* with that of *Zamia*.
8. In what respects are the gametophytes of *Ginkgo* more primitive than those of *Zamia*? On what assumptions do you base your answer?
9. Why is it so easy to split the mature female gametophyte of *Ginkgo* into two portions?
10. What significance do you attach to the green color of the female gametophyte of *Ginkgo*? Describe procedures to demonstrate whether the pigment is a complex of chlorophylls.

11. Draw and label a mature seed of *Ginkgo* as it would appear in a median longitudinal section.

12. Devise a definition of a seed as you have observed its structure.

13. Define the terms epigean, hypogean, epicotyl, hypocotyl, radicle, cotyledons, coleorhiza.

14. How do the archegonial chambers of *Zamia* and *Ginkgo* differ?

CHAPTER 26

Division Coniferophyta

INTRODUCTION

Whereas the cycads are represented by only nine living genera, and *Ginkgo* by a single living species, the genus *Pinus* (L. *pinus* from L. *picinus,* pitch) with its many species is selected here as reasonably representative of a large group of related genera of conifers or cone-bearing seed plants. Of the latter, some 50 genera and 550 species have been described. Among the genera of Coniferophyta are such familiar trees as *Tsuga* (hemlock), *Abies* (fir), *Picea* (spruce), *Juniperus* (juniper, red cedar), *Sequoia* (redwood, big tree), and other widely cultivated forms. Although the genera just listed are evergreen in habit, others, like *Larix* (larch, tamarack) and *Taxodium* (cypress), are deciduous. Certain Coniferophyta from the southern hemisphere—among them *Araucaria* and *Podocarpus*—are often cultivated in conservatories and botanical gardens. Members of the Coniferophyta form extensive forests in western North America and in parts of Europe and Asia. Many are large trees, but a few—some of the junipers (*Juniperus*), for example—are shrub-like in habit. In the southern hemisphere, conifers are abundant in temperate South America, New Zealand, and Australia.

Pinus and its relatives may be the dominant type in many forested regions. The great value of these trees as lumber, in the manufacture of paper, and for naval stores and other commercial enterprises has markedly reduced the extent of naturally occurring stands in areas readily accessible to transportation. *Pinus* has been chosen as the representative genus of Coniferophyta because of the great detail in which its structure and reproduction are known and because of its widespread distribution in the northern hemisphere.

A relatively large number of species of *Pinus* occur in North America and in the United States. *Pinus strobus* L., the white pine, is a familiar species in the northeastern part of the country and at high altitudes in the Appalachian chain. *Pinus virginiana* Miller, the scrub pine, is abundant in the eastern part of the country; *P. palustris* Miller, the long-leaved pine, is restricted to the coastal plain in the southeast. *Pinus ponderosa* Dougl., the western yellow pine, is one of the largest species of the genus. *P. cembroides* Zucc. var. *edulis* Voss., the piñon of the western states, produces large edible seeds. The student no doubt will discover other species, either native or introduced, in the locality where he is studying. The following account is based largely on *Pinus virginiana* as it occurs in the southeastern United States.[1]

VEGETATIVE MORPHOLOGY OF *PINUS*

The habit of *Pinus* is sufficiently familiar to permit dispensing with extensive description. The trees are freely and excurrently branched and evergreen, and therefore conspicuous elements of the areas where they occur during the winter months when the surrounding deciduous trees are leafless. Like all woody perennials of the temperate zone, growth is seasonal and periodic. In the winter months, the delicate growing points of the stems and the young leaf primordia are protected by impermeable bud scales. The latter are shed early during renewal of growth in the spring.

Two kinds of branches and two kinds of leaves are produced in *Pinus*. In addition to the familiar needle leaves, less conspicuous leaves, the scale leaves, occur on the main branches and at the bases of the branches that bear the needle leaves (Fig. 26–1). Only the needle leaves are photosynthetic. They occur singly or in groups that vary from one to eight in number in the several species. The short lateral branches on which the leaves arise are known as spur shoots, as in *Ginkgo*. These occur in the axils of scale leaves of the long shoots, the latter increasing rapidly in length during the growing season.

The needle leaves of species of *Pinus* have been observed to persist on the trees for periods varying between two and fourteen years, after which they are abscised with the spur shoots which bear them. They are

---

[1] The writer is indebted to Dr. Ruth B. Thomas for use of her microscopic preparations of *Pinus virginiana*.

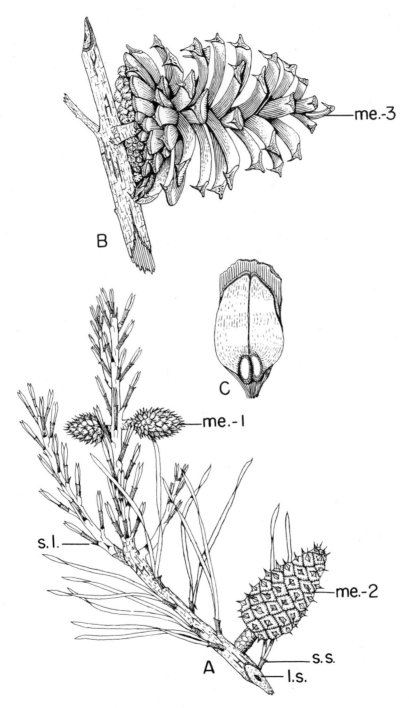

Fig. 26–1. *Pinus virginiana* Miller. A, Long shoot with megastrobili in spring, just after pollina
tion. B, Megastrobilus shedding seed. C, Adaxial view of ovuliferous scale and two winged seeds.
l.s., long shoot; *me.*-1, megastrobilus of the season, just after pollination; *me.*-2, megastrobilus
which was pollinated one year earlier; *me.*-3, megastrobilus pollinated two years previously; *sl.*,
scale leaf; *s.s.*, spur shoot. X 1.

shed gradually, so that their fall is not as striking as leaf fall is in deciduous plants. Although the needle leaves are small—in some species they
have only a single unbranched vein—they are macrophyllous, as evidenced by the foliar gaps in the stem stele.

The needle leaves of *Pinus* exhibit striking xerophytic attributes (Fig.
26–2). The leaf surface is covered by a heavily cutinized epidermis within

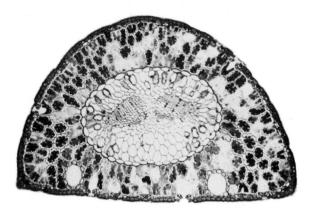

Fig. 26–2. *Pinus nigra* Arnold. Transverse section of leaf; note heavily cutinized epidermis and
hypodermis, sunken stomata, mesophyll cells with resin canals, prominent endodermis surrounding two veins. X 30.

which there are one or more thick-walled hypodermal layers. The stomata are sunk beneath the leaf surface. The mesophyll is compact, with
few air spaces; each mesophyll cell has trabecular projections on the
walls on the surfaces of which numerous chloroplasts are arranged. Resin
canals are present in the mesophyll. The central portion of the leaf is
delimited by a conspicuous endodermis within which, depending on the
species, one or two vascular groups are embedded in transfusion tissue.
The latter sometimes is interpreted as secondarily simplified, hence
reduced, xylem.

The multicellular apical meristem of the stem is active only during the
spring and summer months, when the buds are developing the season's
branches. The procambium differentiates into an endarch siphonostele
which encloses the pith and is surrounded by pericycle, cortex, and
epidermis. Young stems are green and photosynthetic. The vascular
cylinder is interrupted by gaps above the points of departure of the
traces which connect with the spur shoots. The cambium becomes
active even before primary differentiation has been completed, and
it adds abundant derivatives which mature internally into secondary

xylem and externally into secondary phloem (Fig. 26–3). The xylem of *Pinus* is very homogeneous, being composed mostly of elongate tracheids whose prominent bordered pits (Fig. 26–4) occur in linear se-

Fig. 26–3. *Pinus* sp. Portion of a transverse section of a five-year-old stem; note central pith, primary xylem, leaf gap, five annual zones of secondary xylem, cambium, phloem, cortex, and periderm; cavities in xylem and cortex are resin canals. X 30.

ries on the radial walls. Narrow rays extend centrifugally through the xylem (Fig. 26–3). Well-marked annual zones of secondary xylem are present in older stems; sieve elements of the primary and secondary phloem are crushed, except for those most recently added by the cambium (Fig. 26–3). As the vascular cylinder is augmented by the cambium, a phellogen or cork cambium arises in the outermost layers of the cortex. Phellem (cork cells) and phelloderm (cork parenchyma or "secondary cortex") are added by this meristematic layer (Fig. 26–3). In older stems phellogen strips are progressively deeper in the cortex and finally in the secondary phloem; hence the bark of older limbs is composed largely of alternating layers of dead secondary

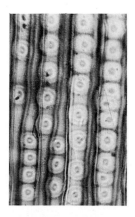

Fig. 26–4. *Pinus* sp. Radial section of xylem showing tracheids with bordered pits. X 125.

phloem and periderm. Resin canals occur in the secondary xylem and in the cortex of the stem as well as in the root and leaf.

The root of *Pinus* is protostelic (Fig. 26–5) and may be diarch, triarch, or tetrarch. The stele is surrounded by a narrow pericycle, a

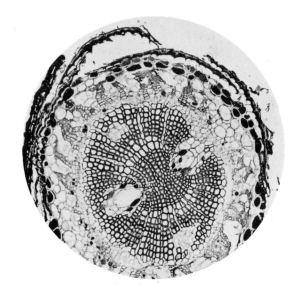

Fig. 26–5. *Pinus virginiana.* Transverse section of root in early secondary growth; note diarch primary xylem, the almost complete cylinder of secondary xylem, cambium, phloem, periderm, and outer primary tissues being shed. X 60.

prominent endodermis and extensive cortex, and an epidermis with root hairs. The root hair zone is very short in *Pinus.* The roots also undergo secondary growth and become extremely woody (Fig. 26–5). The younger portions of the root system frequently are infected with mycorrhizal fungi.

REPRODUCTION IN *PINUS*

The microsporangia and megasporangia of *Pinus* occur in separate strobili, but both are borne on the same individual. Pine therefore is **monoecious,** in contrast with the cycads and *Ginkgo.* The microstrobili develop in clusters around the base of the terminal buds of most branches on mature individuals and are recognizable all through the winter preceding the spring in which they emerge. During the dormant season, the microstrobili are covered with brown bud scales which are shed early in the spring as the strobili enlarge (Figs. 26–6, 26–7). The micro-strobilus is composed of an axis bearing spirally arranged micro-sporophylls. To the abaxial surface of each of these are attached two

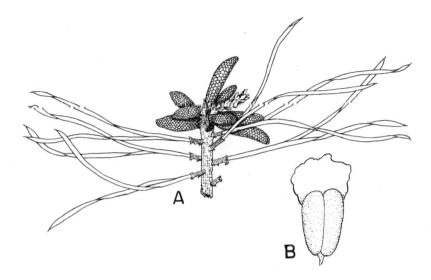

Fig. 26–6.   *Pinus virginiana.* A, Shoot with microstrobili at base of expanding terminal bud of the season, spring condition, X 1. B, *Pinus* sp. Abaxial view of single microsporophyll and microsporangia. X 5.

elongate microsporangia (Fig. 26–6B). The microsporangia are euspo-rangiate in development (Fig. 26–8); the sporangial wall is about four layers of cells thick, and a prominent tapetum is present. Dehiscence takes place by a longitudinal fissure along a region of thin-walled cells. The spore mother cell stage is attained early in the spring and micro-sporogenesis occurs as the strobili enlarge. In *P. virginiana,* the micro-sporophylls become purple-red in color as they protrude from the bud scales and it is during this period that meiosis occurs. In the vicinity of Nashville, Tennessee, the meiotic process (Fig. 26–9) takes place between March 15 and April 1 each year. The microspore mother cells contain abundant starch which is digested during sporogenesis. Cytoki-nesis is accomplished by furrowing at the conclusion of two successive nuclear divisions. The individual microspores (Fig. 26–9D) are liberated from the microspore mother cell walls through predetermined thin areas. As the microspores enlarge and mature, they develop a two-layered wall

Fig. 26–7. *Pinus strobus* L. Shoot with microstrobili and vegetative bud (Woods Hole, Mass., early June). X ¾.

composed of an **intine** and **exine.** The two layers subsequently separate at two points on the surface of the microspores, thus forming the characteristic winged cells (Fig. 26–14A). The haploid number of chromosomes in all species of *Pinus* so far investigated is $n = 12$.

In *Pinus*, the megastrobili are borne on short lateral branches near the apices of some of the younger branches of the current season (Figs. 26–1A, 26–10). They are not visible clearly, therefore, until the terminal bud of such a branch has unfolded and elongated. When they first emerge, they are green and soft in texture. They begin to harden after pollination.

The ovules are not borne directly on the bract-like appendages which emerge from the strobilus axis (Fig. 26–11). Instead, they develop on

Fig. 26–8. *Pinus virginiana*. Sagittal section of microsporophyll and microsporangium (early March) with premeiotic sporogenous tissue. X 125.

ovuliferous scales (Fig. 26–11), which, in turn, are borne on the bracts. Each ovuliferous scale has two ovules on its adaxial surface (Fig. 26–1C). The ovuliferous scales are larger than their supporting bracts and have

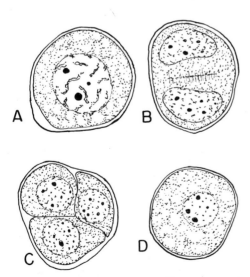

Fig. 26–9. *Pinus virginiana*. Microsporogenesis (late March). A, Microspore mother cell. B, End of meiosis I. C, Tetrad of microspores. D, Microspore liberated from tetrad. X 1030.

Fig. 26–10. *Pinus rigida*. Shoot showing season's growth and part of preceding season's growth: 1, megastrobilus at pollination; 2, one pollinated a year earlier (Woods Hole, Mass., early June). X ½.

been homologized with spur shoots. The megastrobilus of *Pinus*, therefore, is a compound structure.

Each ovule is an ovoidal structure composed of a massive integument surrounding a small megasporangium (Figs. 26–11, 26–12). The integument is rather widely flaring at the apex where it surrounds the micropyle. As in *Zamia* and *Ginkgo*, a single cell of the megasporangium differentiates as a megaspore mother cell (Figs. 26–11, 26–12), enlarging somewhat before it undergoes meiosis to form a linear tetrad of megaspores. In some ovules, one of the daughter nuclei of the first division fails to divide a second time, so that a linear triad results (Fig. 26–13A). In either case, however, only one of the megaspores functions, always the one farthest from the micropyle (Fig. 26–13B). The remainder degenerate and their remnants are resorbed. Occasionally, more than one megaspore in a given ovule may function, with the result that two female gametophytes develop.

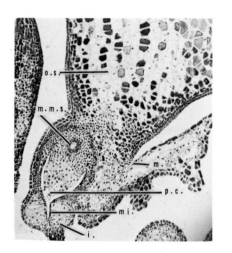

Fig. 26–11. *Pinus virginiana*. Median longitudinal section of megasporophyll, ovuliferous scale, and ovule soon after pollination; *i;* integument; *m.,* megasporophyll; *mi.,* micropyle; *m.m.c.,* megaspore mother cell; *o.s.,* ovuliferous scale; *p.c.,* pollen chamber. X 45.

The microspores begin their development into male gametophytes before they are shed from the microsporangia. As in *Zamia* and *Ginkgo*, the first stages in this process involve a series of intrasporal nuclear and cell divisions in which first and second prothallial cells, generative cell, and tube cell are produced, as shown in Fig. 26–14. The prothallial cells disintegrate rapidly, and their remains are incorporated in the wall as it thickens. The immature male gametophytes, the pollen grains, are shed in this four-celled condition (Fig. 26–14D) by the elongation of the internodes of the microstrobilus and the drying and longitudinal dehiscence of the microsporangia. The pollen grains are produced in enormous numbers and are carried great distances by air currents.

Pollination occurs during April in *Pinus virginiana* in the vicinity of Nashville, Tennessee, although the date varies within a period of approximately two weeks, depending on the temperature. At the time of pollination, the distal portions of successive ovuliferous scales are slightly separated. The wind-borne pollen grains thus are carried readily

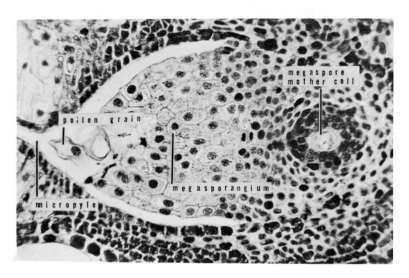

Fig. 26–12. *Pinus virginiana*. Enlarged view of ovule of Fig. 26–11; note pollen grains at apex of megasporangium (late April).

into the fissures. The pollen grains sift between the scales into the axillary chamber formed where the megasporophyll is attached to the axis of the strobilus. After pollination, the surface cells on adjacent ovuliferous scales undergo cell division and bridge the fissures between them, thus sealing the megastrobili. Observation of living ovules at the time of pollination has revealed that a prominent pollination droplet is present at the orifice of the micropyle at this time and that the pollen grains which make contact with the droplet float through it into the pollen chamber. The latter

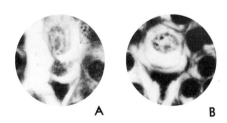

Fig. 26–13. *Pinus virginiana*. A, Linear triad, the functional megaspore above. B, Enlargement of the functional megaspore, abortion of the remainder. X 600.

(Fig. 26–12) has been formed by disintegration of some of the apical cells of the megasporangium. After the pollen grains have made contact with megasporangium tissue, the integumentary cells lining the micropyle elongate in a radial direction (Fig. 26–11) and decrease the diameter of the micropylar canal.

At the time of pollination and germination of the pollen grains, the

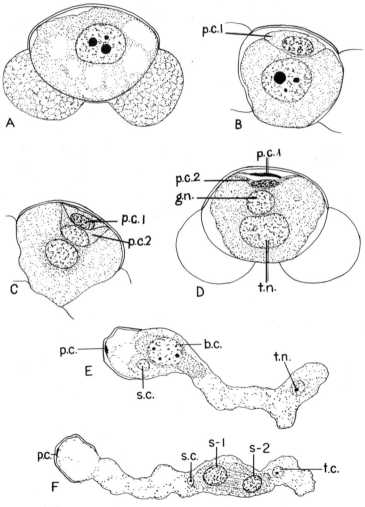

Fig. 26–14. *Pinus virginiana.* Stages in development of the ♂ gametophyte. A, Microspore with bladder-like exine. B,C, Delimitation of first and second prothallial cells. D, Microspore (pollen grain) with enclosed ♂ gametophyte at shedding (pollination); note two aborting prothallial cells, small generative cell, and large tube cell. E, ♂ gametophyte within megasporangium fourteen months after pollination (compare with Fig. 26–18); note stalk, body and tube cells and nuclei. F, Almost mature ♂ gametophyte; note division of body cell nucleus to form two sperm nuclei. b.c., body cell; g.c., generative cell; g.n., generative nucleus; p.c. prothallial cell; S, sperm; s.c., stalk cell; t.c., tube cell; t.n., tube nucleus and cell. A-D, X 1030; E,F, X 410.

megasporangium of *P. virginiana* has arrived at the megaspore mother cell stage. Megasporogenesis follows about a month after pollination (mid-May), but the functional megaspore does not begin development into the female gametophyte for some months, often not until the following October or November. Both the megaspore mother cell and the functional megaspore apparently secrete substances that diffuse into the tissues of the megasporangium which forms a nutritive, tapetum-like spongy tissue, as in *Ginkgo* (Fig. 26–12). Development of the female gametophyte is extremely slow and is effected by a long-continued process of free-nuclear division which occupies approximately six months in *P. virginiana*. As the number of free nuclei increases, additional cytoplasm is produced. The large central vacuole of the early female gametophyte (Fig. 26–15) is in this way replaced by watery cytoplasm. Meanwhile, the entire ovule and megastrobilus increase in size, and the exposed distal portions of the ovuliferous scales harden (Figs. 26–1, 26–10).

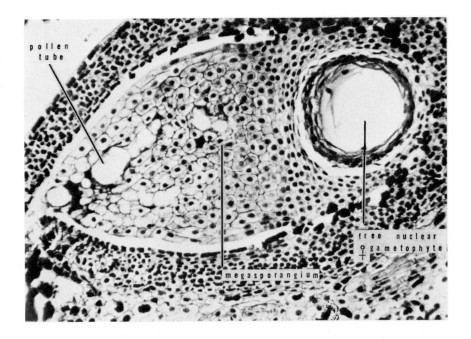

Fig. 26–15. *Pinus virginiana.* Longitudinal section of ovule a year after pollination; note free-nuclear ♀ gametophyte surrounded by disintegrating cells of megasporangium, pollen tubes within the latter. X 150.

Early in May of the following year, about thirteen months after pollination, the female gametophyte becomes cellular by the formation of delicate walls between the numerous nuclei. The process of wall formation begins at the periphery of the gametophyte and gradually extends in a centripetal direction. A much thickened megaspore wall is not demonstrable around the female gametophyte in *Pinus virginiana*. The thickened layer frequently visible on the surface of the female gametophyte is made up, for the most part, of disintegrating cells and nuclei of the megasporangium.

As the gametophyte becomes cellular, several cells at its micropylar end function as archegonial initials (Fig. 26–16). There are usually

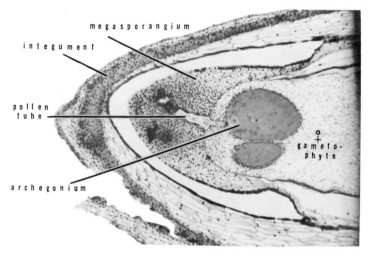

Fig. 26–16. *Pinus virginiana*. Longitudinal section of apex of ovule at fertilization (fourteen months after pollination); note course of pollen tubes through megasporangium to archegonia. X 30.

two or three in *Pinus virginiana*. As these initials enlarge, the vegetative cells of the gametophyte immediately surrounding them become somewhat modified in form and are organized to form a **jacket layer** around each archegonium. Prior to extensive enlargement of the archegonial initials, each divides into a neck initial at the surface of the gametophyte, and a central cell. The neck initial divides to form a short neck (Fig. 26–17) which may consist of as many as two tiers of four cells each; but frequently fewer neck cells are formed, the number varying. The central cell and its nucleus enlarge tremendously, as in *Zamia* and *Ginkgo*. Soon after they have attained their maximum size, early in June, the central cell nucleus migrates to the neck region of the archegonium and there divides, forming a ventral canal nucleus and an egg nucleus. These usually, but not always, are separated by a wall. The cell containing the

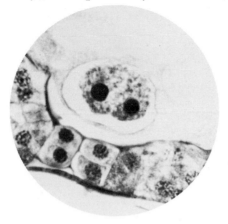

Fig. 26–17. *Pinus virginiana.* Apex of archegonium showing central cell nucleus (which will divide to form egg and ventral canal nuclei) and neck cells. X 500.

ventral canal nucleus is very small and promptly disintegrates. The female gametophyte is now mature and ready for fertilization. A section of an ovule at this stage is shown in Fig. 26–16.

It will be recalled that the pollen grain or immature male gametophyte reached the micropyle and pollen chamber (Fig. 26–12) of the ovule in a four-celled condition (Fig. 26–14D) and that the pollination of the ovule occurs more than a year before the ovule will contain a mature female gametophyte. In the middle of April, twelve months after pollination, the generative nucleus divides; this is followed by cytokinesis, forming a stalk and body cell (Figs. 26–14E, 26–18). During the intervening year, the pollen tube, initiated soon after pollination, has developed into a branched haustorial organ (Figs. 26–14E,F, 26–15, 26–16) which has digested its way through the elongate megasporangium. The pollen tube nucleus lies near the tip of the pollen tube during its growth. Although the pollen tube is branched and haustorial, as in *Zamia* and *Ginkgo,* it also serves as a conveyor which carries the male nuclei to the archegonium. This is in contrast with the pollen tubes of *Zamia* and *Ginkgo,* which are solely haustorial. Several days before the pollen tube reaches the female gametophyte, the nucleus of the body cell divides to form two sperm nuclei which lie close together in the common cytoplasm of the body cell (Fig. 26–14F). No centrosomes or blepharoplasts appear during this division in *Pinus*, and the sperms consist largely of nuclear

Fig. 26–18. *Pinus virginiana.* Pollen grain at apex of megasporangium, tube not shown; note small stalk nucleus, large body nucleus. X 600.

material without differentiated cytoplasm. Some time before fertilization, the two sperm nuclei and the stalk cell move nearer the tip of the pollen tube.

As the tube makes contact with the female gametophyte in the vicinity of an archegonium, it discharges some of its cytoplasm and generally all of its nuclei into the egg cell. One of the sperm nuclei migrates toward the egg nucleus with which it unites (Fig. 26–19); the mechanism of this movement is not understood. The remaining nuclei of the male gametophyte disintegrate in the cytoplasm of the egg.

Usually the egg nuclei of all the archegonia of a single gametophyte are fertilized by sperms. In such cases, each zygote initiates embryo development and several embryos may begin to grow, although the mature seed usually contains only one. The development of several zygote nuclei into embryos is known as **simple polyembryony.** Soon after fertilization the zygote nucleus undergoes two successive nuclear divisions, forming four diploid nuclei of the proembryo (Fig. 26–20). These nuclei, which correspond to the first four free nuclei in the em-

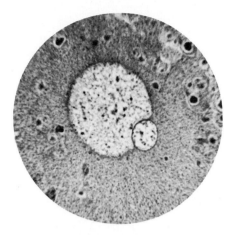

Fig. 26–19. *Pinus virginiana.* Fertilization (karyogamy); union of large egg nucleus and small sperm nucleus. X 250.

bryogeny of *Zamia* and *Ginkgo,* migrate to the base of the egg cell where they arrange themselves in a tier of four, then undergo mitosis and cytokinesis. Successive nuclear and cell divisions result in the formation of

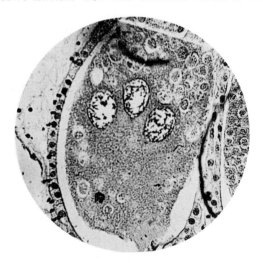

Fig. 26–20. *Pinus virginiana.* Archegonium after fertilization with three of four free nuclei of proembryo (smaller bodies are ergastic). X 125.

sixteen cells arranged in four tiers (Fig. 26–21). The tier of nuclei nearest the neck cells may or may not remain in continuity with the cytoplasm of the egg cell.

In further development, the lowermost tier of four cells is directly involved in the formation of the embryo. The next upper tier of four cells elongates markedly, functioning as a **primary suspensor** which pushes the

Fig. 26–21. *Pinus virginiana.* Median longitudinal section of archegonium with sixteen-celled (only eight visible) proembryo at the base (diagrammatic). X 40.

cells of the lowermost tier into the vegetative tissue of the female gameto-phyte (Fig. 26–22). The four primary suspensor cells and the lowermost tier, the embryo-forming cells, often separate along their longitudinal

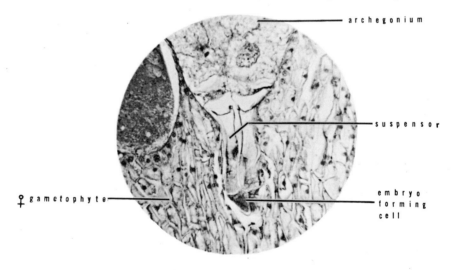

Fig. 26–22. *Pinus virginiana.* Base of archegonium, showing elongation of suspensor cells and resultant projection of embryo-forming cells into tissue of the ♀ gametophyte. X 125.

walls (Fig. 26–23). Inasmuch as each of the embryo-forming cells can initiate an embryo, this phenomenon is known as **cleavage polyembryony.** The lowermost embryo-forming cells cut off cells between themselves and the primary suspensors, often called embryonal tubes, which function as secondary suspensors. These with the primary suspensors exert pressure on the developing embryos in the direction of the vegetative cells of the female gametophyte which have become filled with stored metabolites.

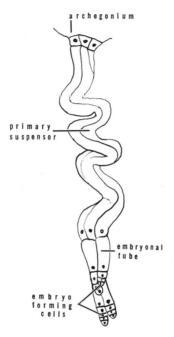

Fig. 26–23. *Pinus banksiana* Lamb. Base of archegonium (above) and further elongation of suspensors and divisions in embryo-forming cells. X 60. (From Buchholz.)

The gametophyte is digested and liquefied by the advancing embryos which lie in a cavity into which they have been thrust by the coiled suspensor system. One of the developing embryos outstrips the others, and by rapid nuclear and cell divisions organizes an embryo which occupies a major part of the central portion of the gametophyte (Fig. 26–24).

The embryo, as it enters the dormant period, has a radicle which lies in the region originally occupied by the archegonia. The remains of the latter and suspensors and embryonal tubes are compressed at the tip of the radicle. The remainder of the axis is the hypocotyl, which in some species of *Pinus* bears as many as eight needle-like cotyledons. Among their bases is the apex of the embryonic stem. The peripheral cells of the

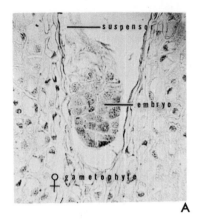
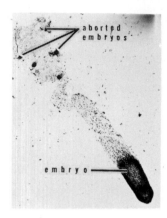

A

B

Fig. 26–24. *Pinus virginiana*. A, Successful embryo at base of suspensor, digesting cells of the ♀ gametophyte, X 30. B, Still older embryo (six weeks after fertilization); note aborted embryos, suspensor, and well-developed embryo. X 20.

female gametophyte continue nuclear and cell divisions during the development of the embryo, so that, as the latter enters dormancy, considerable female gametophyte tissue remains (Fig. 26–25). Although

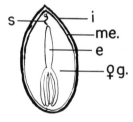

Fig. 26–25. *Pinus cembroides* Zucc. var. *edulis* Voss. Bisection of mature seed: e, embryo; i, integument; me., megasporangium; ♀g., ♀ gametophyte; s, suspensor. X 2.

three layers are distinguishable in the integument of the immature seed, the innermost and outermost are disorganized and vestigial by the time the seed is shed. The middle layer becomes hard and stony and actually serves as the seed coat.

In *Pinus virginiana*, the seeds are mature and are shed in the autumn of the second year following the appearance of the megastrobili. Similar intervals occur among other species. During this period the megastrobilus, which was soft and green at pollination, increases in size from approximately a half-inch to a hard, woody cone many times larger (Fig. 26–1B). The ovuliferous scales become separated and recurved, making possible the dissemination of the winged seeds (Fig. 26–1C).

Germination of the pine seed is **epigean**. The cotyledons remain within the seed some time after germination, absorbing the metabolites still present in the female gametophyte. Ultimately they emerge, shed the remains of the seed, and function as photosynthetic organs.

OTHER CONIFERS AND CLASSIFICATION

Although *Pinus* has been chosen here to serve as material for an introduction to the Coniferophyta, a number of related genera are familiar either through cultivation or through widespread distribution in nature. Some of these were mentioned in the opening paragraphs of this chapter. The members of the Coniferophyta may be grouped in a single class, the Coniferopsida, with a single order, the Coniferales. This order is often divided into six or seven families. Some of the more familiar genera are classified as follows:

Division Coniferophyta
    Class 1. Coniferopsida
        Order 1. Coniferales
            Family 1. Abietaceae
                Genera: *Pinus, Cedrus* (true cedar), *Larix* (larch or tamarack), *Picea* (spruce), *Tsuga* (hemlock), *Pseudotsuga* and *Abies* (fir)
            Family 2. Taxodiaceae
                Genera: *Sequoia* (including S. *gigantea* Decke, big tree, and S. *sempervirens* Endl., redwood tree) and *Taxodium* (*T. distichum* Rich., bald cypress)
            Family 3. Cupressaceae
                Genera: *Thuja, Cupressus,* and *Juniperus* (common and red cedar)
            Family 4. Araucariaceae
                Genera: *Agathis* and *Araucaria*
            Family 5. Podocarpaceae
                Genus: *Podocarpus*
            Family 6. Taxaceae
                Genera: *Taxus* (yew) and *Torreya*

Of these families, the Abietaceae, Taxodiaceae, and Taxaceae are almost exclusively northern hemisphere in their distribution, while most Podocarpaceae and Araucariaceae are southern-hemisphere genera. The Cupressaceae occur in both hemispheres.

More than half of all the coniferous genera are members of the family Abietaceae, a family whose members are well represented in North America, especially in the western part of the continent. The Douglas fir, *Pseudotsuga taxifolia* Britt., is one of the larger conifers of this family. The evergreen needle leaves of the true cedar, *Cedrus,* are borne in fascicles of 30 to 40. The leaves of *Larix,* larch (Fig. 26–26), are also

Fig. 26–26.   *Larix* sp. Long and spur shoots. X ½.

fasciculate but are deciduous. *Pinus* is the largest genus in number of species. *Tsuga, Picea,* and *Abies* are in widespread cultivation.

The largest and longest-lived of the cone-bearing trees, if not among all plants, are members of the family Taxodiaceae, namely, the genera *Sequoia* and *Taxodium. Sequoia sempervirens,* the redwood tree, is native to California, where specimens more than 300 feet in height have been reported. *S. gigantea* of the Sierra Nevadas is a related species. Large specimens of these trees are thought to be between 3000 and 4000 years old. *Taxodium distichum*, the bald cypress, is deciduous and is a familiar tree in swamps in the southern United States.

Of the Cupressaceae, the genera *Thuja* (eastern white cedar), *Cupressus* (*C. macrocarpa* Hartw., Monterey cypress), and *Juniperus* (cedar, juniper) are perhaps the most familiar. In these genera, needle leaves occur only in the seedling stages, the mature branches being clothed with scale-like leaves. The ovulate cones usually are fleshy when mature, as in *Juniperus virginiana* L. The wood of the latter is used extensively for chests, closet lining, and lead pencils.

Araucaria and *Podocarpus* are cultivated widely in conservatories in the north temperate zone. *Podocarpus* is treated as an ornamental shrub in certain cities of the southern United States. The leaves of *Podocarpus* may be needle-like or broader. The trees are dioecious, with winged pollen; the microsporophylls are in strobili and the ovules solitary. One species of *Araucaria*, *A. araucana* Koch, is known as the monkey-puzzle tree because its branching is very bizarre. The genus *Araucaria* is of special interest because as many as forty prothallial cells may develop in the male gametophyte.

The Taxaceae contain two interesting genera, one of which, *Taxus*, is cultivated as an ornamental in this country and in Europe. *Taxus*, the yew, has branches with dark-green, flattened needle leaves. The solitary ovules are terminal and cauline and are surrounded at maturity by fleshy, red, berry-like cups. The male gametophytes of this alliance lack prothallial cells. *Torreya* includes species native to Florida and California.

Finally, mention must be made of the great economic importance of many conifers. Certain species of spruce are especially important in the manufacture of paper. In addition to the value of many genera as a source of lumber, the resinous secretions of certain species of *Pinus* are the basis of the naval stores industry. The beauty of the evergreen foliage of many conifers, together with the impressive stature and graceful branching of others, have enhanced the favor with which this group of plants is regarded by horticulturists.

SUMMARY

Unlike the Cycadophyta and Ginkgophyta, the former with nine living genera and the latter with only one, the Coniferophyta appear to be a flourishing group in which more than forty living genera are known. Furthermore, many species of Coniferophyta grow in dense aggregations, forming vast forested areas in which they are the dominant organisms. Like *Ginkgo*, the stems of most genera are strongly branched and are either tree-like or shrubby in habit. In the needle-leaved genera, long shoots and spur shoots are present. Strong secondary growth of the stems is characteristic of the group, as is the homogeneity of the xylem, which is composed largely of tracheids, as in *Pinus*.

Pinus is monoecious. The microstrobili occur on the old wood in clusters at the base of the current season's expanding stems, and the megastrobili are on short lateral branchlets of the season's growth. The megastrobili are compound structures in which the ovules are borne on ovuliferous scales; these in turn are supported on megasporophylls. As in the cycads and *Ginkgo*, a number of months intervene between pollination and fertilization. The male gametophytes of *Pinus* and all Coniferophyta produce nonciliate sperms, in contrast with the cycads and *Ginkgo*. Their pollen tubes perform a dual role; in addition to their haustorial function, they convey the sperms to the archegonia. An archegonial chamber is absent. The early embryogeny, although free-nuclear, is restricted, in comparison with that of the cycads and *Ginkgo*. Sixteen cells, arranged in four tiers of four, are organized at the conclusion of free-nuclear division in *Pinus*. Both simple polyembryony (development of more than one zygote) and cleavage polyembryony (vertical dissociation of the tiers of each proembryo) are of common occurrence in *Pinus*, but only one embryo is present in the mature seed, which is winged. Germination is epigean.

DISCUSSION QUESTIONS

1. With the aid of labeled diagrams, summarize reproduction in *Pinus*, giving careful attention to the time factor.
2. If you were to examine trees of pine as the terminal buds were unfolding, what types of strobili would be present, and where?
3. What functions can you ascribe to the pollen tube in *Zamia, Ginkgo*, and *Pinus?*
4. Why are the needles of pine, hemlock, and spruce not microphyllous?
5. Why are the megastrobili of pine considered to be compound?
6. How do the sperms of pine differ from those of *Zamia* and *Ginkgo?*
7. Distinguish between simple and cleavage polyembryony.
8. Diagram a median longitudinal section through a pine seed.
9. In what respects do the archegonia of *Pinus* differ from those of *Zamia* and *Ginkgo?*

10. What is the fate of the nuclei, other than the successful sperm, which are discharged into the archegonium by the pollen tube of *Pinus*?

11. Do you consider it appropriate to call microstrobili "male" and megastrobili "female"? Explain.

12. How does embryogeny in pine differ from that in *Zamia* and *Ginkgo*?

13. Describe the process of primary and secondary development in the pine stem, using labeled diagrams of successively older transverse sections.

14. What are resin canals? How are they distributed in the plant? Do corresponding cavities occur in *Zamia* and *Ginkgo*?

15. Ovules containing two female gametophytes occur with considerable frequency in *Pinus virginiana*. How do you explain their presence?

16. The megaspores of *Pinus, Zamia,* and *Ginkgo* are not markedly larger than microspores of the same plants. On what grounds are they called megaspores? Suggest possible reasons for their size relationship.

17. The megaspores of *Selaginella* and *Isoetes* possess thick walls at maturity. Those of the seed plants lack thick walls. Can you suggest an explanation for this?

CHAPTER 27

Division Gnetophyta

INTRODUCTION

The final representative of the gymnospermous seed plants to be considered in this text is the genus *Ephedra* (L. *ephedra,* horsetail) (Fig. 27–1), which, with the genera *Gnetum* (Malay, *gnenom*) and *Welwitschia* (after F. Welwitsch, its discoverer), is sometimes considered to comprise a single order, the Gnetales, which includes 71 species. Careful morphological comparisons of these three genera, however, indicate that there are a number of important divergences among them. This is reflected in a recent classification in which each of the genera is placed in a separate order. *Ephedra* is chosen as representative of the group because it usually is more readily available for study than the other two genera.

Ephedra is xerophytic. Approximately forty species of the genus have been described, all of them shrubby or trailing plants. *E. antisyphilitica* Meyer (Fig. 27–1) has the habit of a small tree, attaining a height of 9 to 15 feet in the Rio Grande valley. Approximately six species occur in the southwestern United States, among them *E. trifurca* Torr. and *E. antisyphilitica.* The following account is based on these and on *E. foliata* Boiss., an Indian species.

In the arid regions of the southwest, *Ephedra,* known as the **joint fir,** sometimes is important as a range plant and is grazed. The American and Mexican Indians used decoctions of the roots and stems of these plants for genitourinary ailments and as a cooling beverage, and they used the fruits (seeds) to make a bitter bread. The alkaloid, **ephedrine,** is prepared from *E. sinica* Stapf, a Chinese species. The Chinese name of the drug is "**Ma Huang.**" The medicinal properties of species of *Ephedra* were known in China as early as 2737 B.C.

VEGETATIVE MORPHOLOGY OF *EPHEDRA*

The younger, green branches of *Ephedra* plants (Fig. 27–1A) superficially resemble species of *Psilotum* and *Equisetum* because of the

Fig. 27–1. *Ephedra antisyphilitica* Meyer. A, Habit of woody branch with photosynthetic shoots bearing microstrobili shedding pollen. X 1. B, Enlarged view of node with microstrobili. X 5. C, Detail of megastrobili at pollination; note micropylar tube. X 5. D, Megastrobilus with two ovules, X 5.

minuteness and ephemeral photosynthetic activities of the leaves. Many of the lateral branches arise in fasciculate whorls (Fig. 27–1A). In *E. foliata,* the branching is quite variable. On the main excurrent leaders, the branching may be either opposite or alternate. In older portions of the axes where they have become woody, the green shoots are fasciculate, and many of them are shed during dry periods by abscission layers which extend across the pith and wood. The minute leaves are either opposite or in whorls of three (Fig. 27–2). The younger branches are delicately ribbed and carry the main burden of photosynthesis in these plants. The older stems are hard and woody because of secondary growth and are anchored to the substratum by a deep tap root and abundant adventitious roots.

Fig. 27–2. *Ephedra foliata.* Boiss. Node. X 4.

The apices of the young axes are occupied by meristem cells which differentiate into primary meristems from which the primary, permanent tissues develop. The younger shoots of *E. foliata* contain an extensive parenchymatous pith surrounded by vascular bundles with endarch xylem (Fig. 27–3). Sclerenchymatous pith cells may be associated with the xylem groups. Thick-walled sclerenchyma cells are present among the phloem cells (Fig. 27–3B). The cortex is composed of patches of photosynthetic parenchyma into which groups of sclerenchymatous cells beneath the ridges of the stem surface intrude as supporting areas. The stomata occur on the slopes of the ridges, as in *Equisetum,* and are sunken and overarched by accessory cells. The epidermis is heavily thickened. The presence of such an abundance of sclerotic tissue renders even the younger portions of *Ephedra* axes relatively hard and resistant.

Annual zones of secondary xylem are added by the activity of a continuous cambium. The wood is extremely hard and is traversed by multiseriate rays in older axes. The most significant feature in the

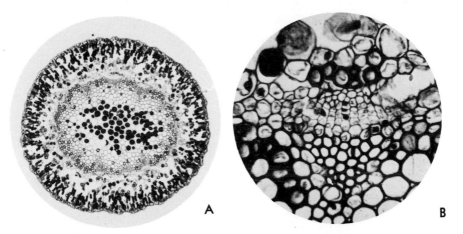

A   B

Fig. 27–3. *Ephedra* sp. A, Transverse section of young stem with endarch siphonostele. X 30. B, Portion of stele enlarged; note endarch xylem, cambium, primary phloem capped by fibers. X 250.

secondary xylem of *Ephedra* is the perforation of the terminal walls of some of the tracheids (Fig. 27–4) to form continuous conducting tubes known as **vessels** or **tracheae.** It will be recalled that these are absent from the xylem of cryptogams, the genera *Selaginella* and *Pteridium* (a fern) being notable exceptions. The wood of the Cycadophyta, Ginkgophyta, and Coniferophyta also lacks vessels, so that *Ephedra* (also *Gnetum* and *Welwitschia*) is unique in possessing them. Vessels are present in the xylem of many flowering plants. The tracheids are pitted

Fig. 27–4.   *Ephedra antisyphilitica.* Slanting terminal wall of two tracheid-like vessel elements, showing perforations. X 325.

with bordered pits on both the radial and tangential walls in *Ephedra*. Although the vessels for the most part are larger in diameter than tracheids, they are linked by a series of elements intermediate in size. Many stages transitional between tracheids and vessels may be observed in the xylem of *Ephedra*. The young seedling contains only tracheids at first.

The primary steles of *Ephedra* roots are diarch. They increase by secondary thickening to form woody tap roots.

The rudimentary leaves of *Ephedra* are histologically simple; they are composed of a thickened midrib region and thin wings which soon lose their chlorophyll and turn brown. Two unbranched veins traverse the leaves, which are macrophyllous in spite of their small size, as evidenced by the gaps above the points of departure of their traces from the stele. Stomata are present on the abaxial surface. The seedling leaves and those of younger branches are less reduced than those in mature specimens.

REPRODUCTION IN *EPHEDRA*

Both monoecious and dioecious species are known in *Ephedra*. *E. antisyphilitica* is strictly dioecious (Fig. 27–1). The microsporangiate strobili have rounded apices (Fig. 27–1*B*); those of the ovulate strobili (Fig. 27–1*C*) are acute. The strobili of *E. antisyphilitica* are already visible and well developed in the late autumn in the vicinity of Abilene, Texas,[1] at the nodes among the fasciculate, photosynthetic axes.

The ovulate strobilus (Fig. 27–1*C,D*) consists of between four and seven pairs of decussate **bracts** attached to an axis. The lowermost pairs are sterile, but in the axil of one or occasionally both of the terminal pairs of bracts a short-stalked ovule occurs. Sometimes two ovules are present, but one of these may be abortive. The ovule is surrounded by a cup-like involucre, sometimes called an outer integument, which is attached at the ovule base and free above. It probably represents a united pair of bracteoles on the ovule axis. A more delicate inner integument also surrounds the ovule and is prolonged at the time of pollination into a tubular process which projects beyond the bracts and involucre of the ovule (Fig. 27–5). The inner integument is chlorophyllous at the time of pollination. Comparative study of a number of species of *Ephedra* indicates that the *apparently* terminal ovules are borne on lateral appendages of the strobilus axis.

The microsporangiate strobilus also is compound. It consists of an axis that bears about seven pairs of decussate **bracts** (Fig. 27–1*B*), most of which subtend a short axis on which microsporangia are borne. Each microsporangiate axis is enclosed early in development by two overlapping, transparent **bracteoles** (Fig. 27–6). The microsporangiate axis is composed of several united microsporophylls, as indicated by anatomical evidence, to form a sterile portion, the **column.** In *E. antisyphilitica*, five two-chambered microsporangia are typically present at the apex of the column (Fig. 27–6). When the pollen is about to be shed, the column elongates, carrying the microsporangia free of the bracteoles and surrounding bracts (Fig. 27–1*B*).

---

[1] The writer is indebted to Mr. and Mrs. Donald T. Knight for numerous excellent collections of fruiting material of *E. antisyphilitica*.

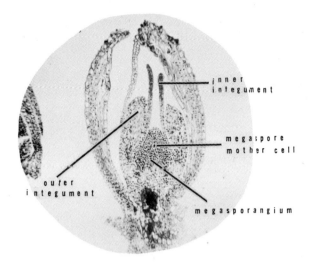

Fig. 27–5. *Ephedra antisyphilitica.* Median longitudinal section of apex of very young megastrobilus; note megasporangium, megaspore mother cell, inner integument prolonged as a tube, and fleshy outer integument. X 30.

The young microsporangia have two-layered walls and a prominent tapetal layer surrounding the sporogenous tissue. The tapetal cells become binucleate during sporogenesis. At maturity, the biloculate micro-

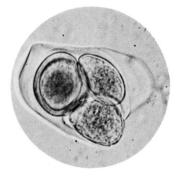

Fig. 27–6. *Ephedra antisyphilitica.* Two microsporophylls emerging from their transparent bracteoles. X 12½.

Fig. 27–7. *Ephedra antisyphilitica.* Microspore mother cell containing tetrad of microspores, one being liberated. X 500.

sporangium (Fig. 27–6) is covered only by a single layer of epidermal cells because of the degeneration of the remaining wall cells. Dehiscence of the microsporangium by an apical fissure (Fig. 27–1B) occurs at maturity. During microsporogenesis, the microspore mother cells separate from each other, become almost spherical, and undergo the meiotic process, which culminates in the usual tetrad of microspores (Fig. 27–7). Microsporogenesis is not simultaneous in all the microsporangia of a given strobilus, those within the distal bracts being retarded. Microsporogenesis in *E. antisyphilitica* continues over a long period during January and early February in west Texas. After the microspores have been liberated from the microspore mother cell walls, they increase considerably in size and their walls become thickened with ribbed exines (Fig. 27–10C).

A single megaspore mother cell differentiates within the megasporangium of the ovule (Fig. 27–5). A linear tetrad is produced as a result of meiosis, and the chalazal megaspore alone usually is functional. Development of the female gametophyte is free-nuclear as in all seed plants. The number of nuclei so formed varies in the several species of *Ephedra*. In one, *E. trifurca*, wall formation occurs when approximately 256 free nuclei have formed, in *E. foliata* after 500 nuclei have appeared, and in *E. distachya* after 1000 nuclei have developed. Two or three archegonia are organized at the micropylar pole of the female gametophyte (Fig. 27–8). The necks of the archegonia are the most massive of any among

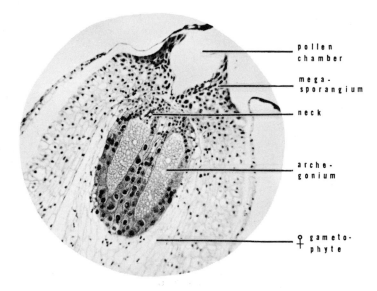

Fig. 27–8. *Ephedra antisyphilitica.* Median longitudinal section of ovule apex just before fertilization; note pollen chamber in megasporangium, two archegonia with prominent jacket layers and necks, vegetative tissue of ♀ gametophyte. X 125.

the gymnosperms; they may consist of 40 or more cells at maturity (Fig. 27–8). The neck cells are arranged in tiers of four or more. The ventral canal nucleus and the egg nucleus are rarely separated by cytokinesis in the developing archegonium. The chalazal cells of the female gametophyte are dense and filled with stored metabolites, and those at the micropylar pole are watery and vacuolate. In *E. antisyphilitica,* polynucleate cells are present, particularly at the chalazal portion of the female gametophytes. The walls of the cells of the archegonial jacket are extremely delicate and the cells may be binucleate. As the female gameto-phyte develops, the cells at the apex of the megasporangium degenerate to form a deep pollen chamber (Fig. 27–8), which, unlike that in other gymnosperms described in earlier chapters, extends to the female game-tophyte and archegonia. A prominent pollination droplet is visible at the subterminal orifice of the micropyle (Fig. 27–9) at the time of pollina-tion.

Fig. 27–9. *Ephedra antisyphilitica.* Pol-lination droplet at orifice of micropyle. X 125.

As in all gymnosperms, the microspores begin their development into male gametophytes before they are shed from the microsporangia. The process may be followed readily in material collected during the winter and forced in laboratory or greenhouse (Fig. 27–10). The microspore nucleus divides first to form a prothallial cell nucleus which is delimited from a larger cell by cytokinesis. The prothallial cell lies near one of the poles of the microspore (Fig. 27–10A). A small second prothallial nucleus and a larger nucleus then arise by mitosis of the nucleus of the large cell, but usually these are not segregated by a cell wall (Fig. 27–10B). The second prothallial nucleus is more persistent than the first, which gradu-ally shrinks into oblivion. The large nucleus now divides to form the generative and tube nuclei (Fig. 27–10C), which are separated by cytokinesis to form a generative cell which is ovoidal in shape. The gen-erative nucleus is reported to form a stalk and body nucleus in several species of *Ephedra,* but conclusive evidence of this has not been observed in *E. antisyphylitica.* On the contrary, the generative nucleus seems to form the two sperm nuclei directly (Fig. 27–10D,E), but further study is

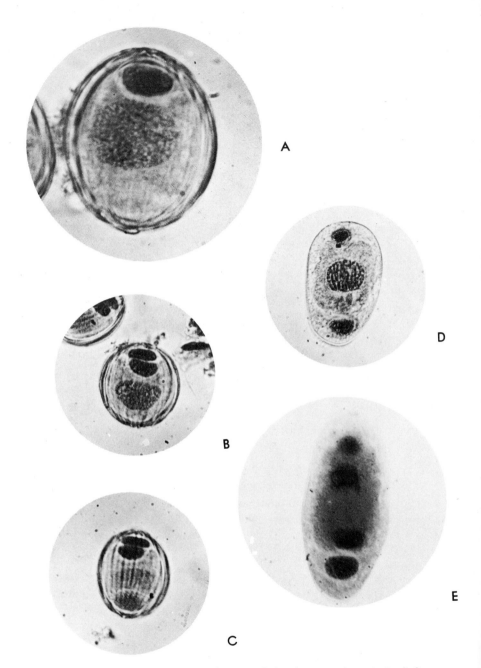

Fig. 27–10. *Ephedra antisyphilitica.* Development of the ♂ gametophyte. *A,* Small first prothallial cell and large cell. X 1200. *B,* Two prothallial cells and antheridial cell. *C,* Two prothallial cells, generative cell, and tube cell (polar). *D,* Prophase of division of generative nucleus, second prothallial nucleus above, tube nucleus below. *E,* Telophase of division of generative nucleus, second prothallial nucleus above, tube nucleus below. *B-E,* X 600.

necessary to settle the point. In other species, of course, the body cell is said to give rise to the two sperm nuclei.

Pollination occurs through the agency of wind, a number of pollen grains usually being present in the pollen chamber of each ovule. Adequate data on pollination and the interval between it and fertilization are lacking in *Ephedra*. Pollination in *E. trifurca* occurs about the time the archegonia are being organized and are maturing. The interval between pollination and fertilization in that species may be as short as ten hours, one of the briefest among the gymnosperms.

Within the pollen chamber, the pollen grain protoplast emerges from the exine and the two male nuclei are formed (Fig. 27–10E). These may be slightly unequal in size. The pollen tube (Figs. 27–11, 27–12A) de-

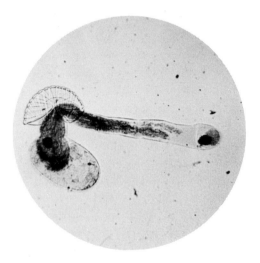

Fig. 27–11. *Ephedra antisyphilitica.* Rupture of exine and formation of pollen tube on 10 percent cane sugar agar; note distal tube nucleus and second prothallial nucleus; other nuclei not visible. .X 250.

velops from the region of the male gametophyte to which the tube nucleus migrates. The tube grows down between the cells of the archegonial neck into the apex of the egg cell, into which it discharges its nuclei. One of the sperm nuclei moves toward the egg nucleus with which it unites, and the other nuclei of the pollen tube remain at the apex of the archegonium in the vicinity of the ventral canal nucleus (Fig. 27–12B).

Development of the embryo of *Ephedra* involves free-nuclear divisions

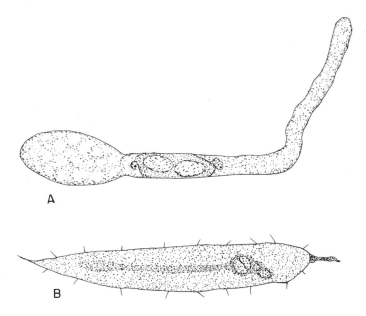

Fig. 27–12. *Ephedra antisyphilitica.* A, Mature ♂ gametophyte; note cell with two sperm nuclei, small second prothallial nucleus, and tube nucleus. X 315. B, Archegonium of *Ephedra trifurca* Torr. at fertilization; note pollen tube above, small ventral canal nucleus, supernumerary sperm nucleus, and union of sperm and egg nuclei. X 125. (From Land.)

as in other gymnosperms. In *E. trifurca*, the zygote nucleus usually undergoes three successive divisions to form eight nuclei which may be somewhat unequal in size and scattered in the egg cytoplasm. Several of these, usually those near the lower pole of each egg cell, become surrounded by delicate walls (Fig. 27–13A) by free-cell formation with residual cytoplasm; they are called proembryos. The small dividing nuclei observed in the neck region of the egg cell (Fig. 27–13A) have been interpreted as dividing nuclei descended from the second sperm nucleus and/or the ventral canal nucleus. The cells of the archegonial jacket break down after fertilization and their nuclei may mingle with the egg cytoplasm.

All of the proembryonic cells descended from the zygote may begin to develop into embryos, but those at the lower region of the egg cell develop more rapidly. Embryogeny is initiated by a nuclear division and the formation of a tube into which both nuclei migrate. They are separated later by a septum (Fig. 27–13B). The upper cell functions as a primary suspensor, and the lower forms the embryo by further nuclear

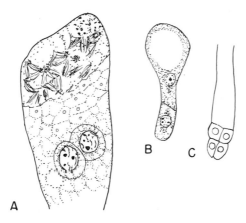

Fig. 27–13. *Ephedra trifurca.* Embryogeny. A, Two (of eight) cells of proembryo near neck end of egg cell. X 250. B, Later stage in development of embryo. C, Suspensor and early embryo. X 125. (From Land.)

and cell division. The several embryos of each archegonium are thrust into the vegetative tissue of the female gametophyte by elongation of the primary suspensors (Fig. 27–13C). Secondary suspensors are organized by the cells at the micropylar pole of the embryo. The developing embryos (Fig. 27–14) gradually appropriate the delicate tissue in the

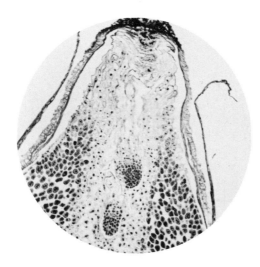

Fig. 27–14. *Ephedra antisyphilitica.* Median longitudinal section of micropylar end of ovule; note twisted suspensors bearing two embryos, vegetative tissue of ♀ gametophyte, and remnant of megasporangium. X 30.

center of the female gametophyte and grow at its expense, finally digesting and absorbing all but the most peripheral cells of the female gametophyte. Only one embryo is present in the mature seed (Fig. 27–15), the others having disintegrated.

Just after fertilization, when the proembryos are developing, certain

Fig. 27–15. *Ephedra antisyphilitica*. Median longitudinal section of seed, outer integument removed; note radicle, hypocotyl, plumule, and two cotyledons embedded in the ♀ gametophyte surrounded by the remains of the megasporangium. X 12½.

cells at the micropylar region of the female gametophyte are stimulated to divide and they form a plug which closes the pollen chamber of the megasporangium (Figs. 27–14, 27–15). It is interesting to note that although some binucleate cells are present in the vegetative tissue of the female gametophyte of *E. antisyphilitica* at the time of fertilization, the cells of this tissue contain from two to four or five nuclei when the embryo enters the dormant period. The significance of this phenomenon has not been ascertained as yet.

As the embryo becomes dormant (approximately mid-April in west Texas), the inner integument forms a hard seed coat. The seeds require about five months to reach maturity after the strobili are first recognizable. The fleshy bracts of the ovulate strobilus become scarlet as the seeds ripen, and the latter become black. Germination follows immediately, under favorable conditions. It is epigean and the two cotyledons are long-persistent and photosynthetic.

SUMMARY AND CLASSIFICATION

Ephedra is a genus of xerophytic seed-bearing plants which differ from other gymnosperms described in earlier chapters in a number of important attributes. First among these may be cited the occurrence of vessels or tracheae in the secondary xylem. These arise by perforation of the pits of the sloping terminal walls of tracheids. The leaves are reduced to minute bract-like organs which function only early in development. The leaves are macrophyllous, however. The delicate fasciculate branches are the chief photosynthetic organs of the *Ephedra* plant.

Furthermore, both the microstrobili and the megastrobili of *Ephedra* are compound structures in which the sporogenous organs are borne on lateral axes in the axils of bracts. The axis on which the microsporangia are produced is itself a compound structure, as evidenced by its vascular supply. The male gametophytes are primitive in their production of two prothallial cells, but may be advanced, as compared with other gymnosperms, if further study indicates that the generative cells form sperm nuclei directly, without dividing to form a stalk and body cell. Development of the male gametophytes of *Ephedra*, as compared with those of *Zamia*, *Ginkgo*, and *Pinus*, is very rapid. The ovule of *Ephedra* is composed of the megasporangium surrounded by two envelopes. The inner envelope is delicate, membranous, photosynthetic, and prolonged into a micropylar tube through which pollination is effected. The outer envelope consists of two united bracts. Breakdown of the apical cells of the megasporangium gives rise to a pollen chamber, which, unlike that in the genera described in earlier chapters, is in direct contact with the female gametophyte and archegonia. The latter are primitive in having the largest number of neck cells known among gymnosperms, namely, 40 or more. The pollen tube performs no obviously haustorial function. Embryogeny includes a more limited free-nuclear period than in other gymnosperms.

Brief mention must be made at this point of two other genera of seed plants, namely, *Gnetum* and *Welwitschia*, which formerly were considered to be closely allied to *Ephedra*. On the basis of gradually accumulating knowledge of these genera, it now appears that they represent three independent lines of development. It is regrettable that, because of their geographical distribution and the difficulties involved in cultivating them, these imperfectly known plants are unavailable for wider study, for what is known of them suggests that in some respects they are similar to the flowering plants.

Gnetum is a genus which contains some thirty species of mostly vine-like woody plants that have broad leaves like dicotyledonous angiosperms. The vessels of *Gnetum* xylem are more highly developed than those of *Ephedra* in that they have single terminal perforations between the segments. The male gametophyte is more reduced than that of *Ephedra* in lacking prothallial cells. The upper portion of the female gametophyte remains in a free-nuclear condition until fertilization. No archegonia are organized, but one of the free nuclei serves as an egg nucleus to which the pollen tube grows, discharging its sperm nuclei. Some of these features have inspired speculations that *Gnetum* and the flowering plants are related.

Welwitschia is a truly remarkable plant. The enlarged, woody-fleshy inverted conical stem, which may attain a diameter of four feet, is extended below the soil as a long tap root. The mature plants bear only two enormous leaves which persist throughout the life of the plant through the activity of basal meristems. The mature female gametophyte also is free-nuclear and no archegonia are organized. *Welwitschia* is endemic in the coastal region of southwest Africa where the annual rainfall approximates one inch. The plants are slow-growing and markedly xerophytic in structure.

Of the three genera, it is clear that *Ephedra* is the most primitive in its vegetative and reproductive features. A recent discussion of the relationship of *Ephedra, Gnetum,* and *Welwitschia* emphasizes that they are not closely related and recommends that they be classified in separate orders and families. In accordance with this, these genera are classified as follows:

Division Gnetophyta
  Class Gnetopsida
    Order 1. Ephedrales
      Family 1. Ephedraceae
        Genus: *Ephedra*
    Order 2. Gnetales
      Family 1. Gnetaceae
        Genus: *Gnetum*
    Order 3. Welwitschiales
      Family 1. Welwitschiaceae
        Genus: *Welwitschia*

DISCUSSION QUESTIONS

1. What vascular cryptogams are suggested superficially by the vegetative attributes of *Ephedra?* In what respects are they similar?

2. In what habitats would you seek *Ephedra?*

3. Discuss the medicinal uses of species of *Ephedra.*

4. By what macroscopically visible criteria could you distinguish the microstrobili from the megastrobili of *Ephedra?*

5. Describe the development of the male gametophyte of *Ephedra.*

6. In what genera, other than *Ephedra,* are long micropylar tubes present?

7. How does the pollen chamber of *Ephedra* differ from that in the seed plants discussed in earlier chapters?

8. What functions are ascribable to the pollen tube of *Ephedra?* How does it compare in function with that of *Zamia, Ginkgo,* and *Pinus?*

9. On the basis of supplementary reading, list features which the genera *Ephedra, Gnetum,* and *Welwitschia* share in common.

10. There is evidence that the sperm nuclei of certain gymnosperms differ in size. Can you cite any other examples of dimorphism in reproductive cells in the plant and animal kingdoms?

11. In what respects is the archegonium of *Ephedra* primitive?

CHAPTER 28

Gymnosperms: Recapitulation

INTRODUCTION

The plant types discussed in Chapters 24 through 27 all have in common the attribute of producing seeds. As was stated in the opening paragraphs of Chapter 24, in earlier classifications the seed habit served as a sufficiently important criterion for uniting a vast assemblage of plants into a single division, the **Spermatophyta.** This taxon often was divided further into two classes, the **Gymnospermae** (Gr. *gymnos,* naked + Gr. *sperma,* seed), and the **Angiospermae** (Gr. *angeion,* vessel + Gr. *sperma*). The Gymnospermae were delimited from the class Angiospermae because the seeds of the former usually are exposed on the appendages which bear them, while those of the Angiospermae develop within their subtending structures. In the present book, the plants formerly grouped in the class Gymnospermae have been interpreted as four independent phyletic series, namely, the Cycadophyta, Ginkgophyta, Coniferophyta, and Gnetophyta. It should be emphasized that this tentative classification is based largely upon a consideration of only living genera. The present chapter has been written in an effort to summarize comparatively the vegetative morphology and the reproductive processes of the living gymnospermous seed plants described in earlier chapters.

COMPARISON OF VEGETATIVE ATTRIBUTES

When one considers such genera as *Zamia* and *Cycas, Ginkgo, Pinus,* and other conifers, and the genera *Ephedra* and *Gnetum,* the striking divergences among them forcefully crowd their more subtle common attribute of gymnospermy almost into oblivion. The vegetative features of these plants are markedly diverse, although all are macrophyllous. In the cycads, the plant bodies are relatively small, never large trees; they are strongly suggestive of the ferns, especially in their pinnately compound leaves. The sparingly branched stems are armored with old leaf bases and contain little xylem tissue, although they have active cambium layers. The leaves in at least some genera of cycads (*Cycas*) exhibit circinate vernation, another fern-like attribute. *Ginkgo* and *Pinus* and its relatives stand in strong contrast to the cycads with respect to their vegetative organs. All are richly branched, usually large trees, in which the leaves are simple and broad-leaved and deciduous, as in *Ginkgo,* or scale-like, needle-like, or narrow and leathery as in the conifers. In these trees, the cambium becomes active in both stem and root during the first season of growth and adds cylinders of secondary xylem each growing season, so that the stems and roots are woody, not fleshy as in the cycads. The stems are protected not by the remains of the leaf bases but by periderm layers generated by cork cambiums. Furthermore, the leaves of these trees often are borne in fasciculate fashion on short lateral shoots, the spur shoots, which increase very slowly in length.

Finally, in the genera *Ephedra, Gnetum,* and *Welwitschia,* the vegetative organization is extremely diverse and in each case is different from that in cycads, *Ginkgo,* and the conifers. *Ephedra,* the representative of the Gnetophyta described in this text, is a shrubby or trailing xerophyte in which the leaves are reduced to scales that function only temporarily in photosynthesis. The ribbed internodes and the absence of well-developed leaves suggest the arthrophytan genus *Equisetum,* and the presence of vessels in the secondary xylem is unique (except for *Gnetum* and *Welwitschia*) among living gymnosperms.

Additional evidence of diversity among the living gymnosperm types is not wanting, of course, but the features cited above should be sufficient to indicate the heterogeneity of the group with respect to vegetative attributes. It seems clear, therefore, that a polyphyletic relationship is indicated.

REPRODUCTION IN THE GYMNOSPERMS

A comparative review of the reproductive features of gymnosperms reveals more uniformity. The sporogenous tissues of all the representative genera are localized in cones or strobili. Conspicuous exceptions to this are the ovules of the genus *Cycas,* which are borne on pinnately divided sporophylls, and those of *Ginkgo,* which occur in terminal pairs on a branching peduncle. The strobili which produce the microspores are said to be simple because the spore-bearing appendages are borne directly on the axis of the strobilus, except in *Ephedra*. In the latter, the microstrobili are compound, the connate sporophylls being produced in the axils of lateral bracts. The megastrobili in *Zamia* are simple, but in *Pinus* and *Ephedra* they are compound. The sporangia themselves are in all cases eusporangiate in development, the sporangial walls being relatively massive; the output of microspores in each sporangium is enormous. In all the representative gymnosperms (and in all seed plants), a single megaspore mother cell undergoes meiosis to form potential megaspores, three of which usually degenerate. Whether or not the spores of the gymnosperms are truly heterosporous was alluded to briefly in Chapter 24; this topic will be discussed again in the final chapter.

The location, nutrition, and course of development of the megaspores into female gametophytes are quite uniform. In all seed plants, the permanent retention of the megaspore within the megasporangium and its intimate connection with the surrounding tissues (sterile megasporangium) make possible the seed habit. The megaspore of each genus develops into the female gametophyte after passing through a period of free-nuclear division. The nutriment for the developing gametophyte diffuses gradually into it by the dissolution of the surrounding sporophytic tissues. Wall formation at the end of the free-nuclear period (except in *Gnetum* and *Welwitschia*) results in the organization of a completely cellular gametophyte. Archegonia, all reduced and less complex than those of the cryptogams, are organized in all genera except *Gnetum* and *Welwitschia*. In *Gnetum,* as in the flowering plants (Chapter 29), one or more of the nuclei of the free-nuclear gametophyte function directly as eggs, and archegonia are lacking. In all the representative gymnosperm genera, breakdown of the apical tissues of the megasporangium results in the formation of a chamber for the reception of pollen and in the secretion of a pollination droplet which facilitates the transfer of pollen to a point deep within the ovule. *Ephedra* is unique, among the types described, in that its pollen chamber extends to the tissues of the mature female gametophyte.

The development of the microspores into male gametophytes in the gymnosperms is quite uniform except for certain deviations, such as number of prothallial cells and motility of male gametes. In all cases, the process begins before the microspores have been shed from the microsporangia. Motile sperms are produced in the cycads and *Ginkgo* but are absent in the other genera. In all but the Gnetophyta, the growth of the pollen tube is slow and prolonged and the pollen tube is obviously both haustorial and nutritive in function. In the Gnetophyta, however, the proximity of the pollen grain to the archegonia eliminates the circumstance which results in haustorial activities, and the pollen tube accordingly is short in length and ephemeral.

The development of the gymnosperm embryo is unlike that of the vascular cryptogams, on the one hand, and of the flowering plants, on the other, for it always involves a period of free-nuclear division of variable duration. In the cycads and *Ginkgo*, approximately 256 nuclei arise in the proembryo before wall formation occurs. In *Pinus*, the proembryo consists of only sixteen free nuclei, and the number is lower in *Ephedra*. In these genera, except *Ginkgo*, the embryo is thrust into the nutritive tissue of the female gametophyte by an active system of suspensors. In *Ginkgo*, a suspensor is absent, but the embryo itself grows into the female gametophyte through the base of the egg cell. Both simple polyembryony (the development of more than one zygote into an embryo within a single female gametophyte) and cleavage polyembryony (the division of the cellular progeny of a single zygote into several embryos) occur among the gymnosperms. Cleavage polyembryony, however, is confined to *Pinus* (of the genera discussed in this text). Normally, the mature seed contains only one functional embryo.

Both hypogean and epigean germination are represented in the gymnosperms. The two cotyledons in *Zamia* and *Ginkgo* remain within the seed at germination and serve as absorptive organs. *Pinus*, which is polycotyledonous, and *Ephedra*, which has two or three cotyledons, are both epigean.

Thus, in spite of the diversities in vegetative structure among the gymnospermous genera discussed in Chapters 24 to 27, there is considerable uniformity in the reproductive process. Whether these vegetative divergencies should be minimized in the light of the uniformity in reproduction, and whether or not the similarities in the reproductive process represent evidences of relationship or merely of parallelism, can best be discussed after a consideration of the fossil gymnosperms (Chapter 30).

DISCUSSION QUESTIONS

1. Explain the term "gymnosperm." How do the terms "gymnosperm" and "Gymnospermae" differ?

Questions 2 to 4 refer to *Zamia, Ginkgo, Pinus,* and *Ephedra.*

2. Compare the vegetative features of these plants.
3. Compare the disposition of sporogenous tissue in these genera.
4. Discuss the ontogeny of the male gametophyte in these genera comparatively. What divergences are apparent in structure, function, and longevity?
5. List the evidence sometimes cited in support of the theory that spores of seed plants are homosoporous.
6. On what basis have they been considered heterosporous?
7. How does the embryogeny of gymnosperms differ from that of vascular cryptogams?
8. If the formal class "Gymnospermae" is abandoned, may one still refer to a plant as a "gymnosperm"?

CHAPTER 29

Division Anthophyta

INTRODUCTION

The division **Anthophyta,** the flowering plants, comprises the most recent and successful plants which have colonized the earth. It is the largest of the groups of vascular plants in number and in diversity of genera and species, approximately 200,000 species of 12,000 genera having been described. The range of these plants in both habit and habitat is extreme. They are represented by such diverse types as trees, shrubs, herbs, vines, floating plants, epiphytes, and even colorless parasites. They have populated a wide variety of xeric, mesic, and hydric habitats and they form the major portion of the vegetation of many areas. With respect to longevity, they include annual, biennial, and perennial types. They perennate either as woody trees, shrubs, and vines, deciduous or evergreen, or as herbaceous types which survive seasons of dormancy by means of corms, bulbs, rhizomes, or other subterranean organs.

The flowering plants may be subdivided into two groups, the **monocotyledons** and the **dicotyledons,** terms which describe the structure of their embryos. Associated with monocotyledony, however, are such additional attributes as trimerous floral organs, parallel venation of leaves, stems with scattered vascular bundles (in many, not all), and absence of secondary thickening by cambial activity. *Yucca, Agave,* and certain other genera do have a mechanism for increase in stem diameter. In the dicotyledons, on the contrary, the floral organs are indefinite in number or pentamerous or tetramerous, leaves have netted venation, stems are siphonostelic, dictyostelic, or eustelic, and there is widespread occurrence of woody genera.

Because of the diversities outlined above, it is not feasible to give an adequate description of the morphology of their vegetative organs in a volume of limited size which includes an account of plants other than Anthophyta, as well as of the latter. Indeed, in practice, such considerations have come to form much of the subject matter of a separate field of plant science, namely, plant anatomy. The present chapter therefore will deal largely with the reproductive process in the flowering plants. This phenomenon occurs in the structure familiarly known as the "flower."

GROSS MORPHOLOGY OF THE FLOWER

In spite of the *apparently* limitless variation of floral structure observable in the numerous genera of flowering plants, a remarkable uniformity of structure pervades the group. This becomes clear on careful analysis, which reveals that the individual flower always is an axis that has as many as four types of appendages (Fig. 29–1), two of which are fertile. Flowers may occur separately or in groups. The stalk of an individual flower is known as a **peduncle.** When flowers are grouped in **inflorescences,** the stalk of the individual flower is called a **pedicel.** In the center of the flower and at the apex of the axis tip, the **receptacle** or **torus,** are one or more ovule-bearing structures, the **pistil** or pistils (L. *pistillum,* pestle) (Fig. 29–1). The fact that the ovules are enclosed in this structure during their development is recognized in the term **angiospermy** (Gr. *angeion,* a vessel + Gr. *sperma,* seed), as distinct from gymnospermy. Surrounding the pistil or pistils, a number of **stamens** (Fig. 29–1) emerge from the receptacle or from the **hypanthium,** the latter a tubular fusion product, or they may arise from the corolla tube. The stamen is composed of a stalk-like portion, the **filament,** and of sporangia which compose the **anther.** The stamens and pistils are spore-bearing, and therefore are essential organs of the flower. The great majority of flowers have sterile appendages on the floral axis, the **petals** (Gr. *petalon,* leaf) and **sepals,** collectively known as the **corolla** (L. dim. of *corona,* crown) and the **calyx** (Gr. *kalix,* cup), respectively (Fig. 29–1). The petals and sepals usually but not always are distinguishable in both color and place of origin. Petals generally are colored other than green. Sepals arise lower on the floral axis than do petals. The calyx and corolla together comprise the **perianth** of the flower. In a number of flowers, both the petals and sepals are inconspicuous, green, or almost colorless.

In a great majority of flowering plants, both stamens and pistils are present in the same flower, which therefore is said to be **perfect.** However, in such flowers as those of corn, *Zea mays* L., (Fig. 29–2), willow,

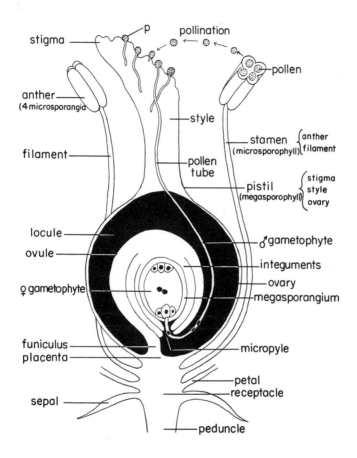

Fig. 29–1.   Diagram of median longitudinal section of a flower; component structures labeled.

Salix sp. (Figs. 29–3, 29–4), and cattail, *Typha* sp., the stamens and pistils occur in separate flowers, which are then said to be **staminate** or **pistillate** and **imperfect.** In both corn and cattail, furthermore, staminate and pistillate flowers are borne on the same individual plant; this condition is known as **monoecism.** In the willow, on the other hand, staminate and pistillate flowers are distributed on different individuals; hence a state of **dioecism** prevails.

Discussion of the various types of inflorescences into which flowers may be aggregated is outside the scope of the present text. One of these, however, is especially noteworthy, namely, the composite **head** (Fig. 29–5). In such an inflorescence the axis is shortened in the form of a

Fig. 29–2.   *Zea mays* L. Corn. A, Pistillate inflorescence. X 2/3. B, Staminate inflorescence. X 1/6. C, Detail of segment of staminate inflorescence. X 2.

convex or flattened head on which many minute flowers are closely arranged. The structural details are shown in Fig. 29–5 and described in its legend.

The floral organs are supplied with vascular tissues in the form of traces which depart from the receptacle. Study of the number, path, and arrangement of these traces has contributed much to our understanding

A   B   C

Fig. 29–3. *Salix* sp. Willow. *A*, Branch with staminate inflorescence in bud and covered by bud scale, winter condition. *B*, The same, expanded and shedding pollen. *C*, Pistillate inflorescence. X 2.

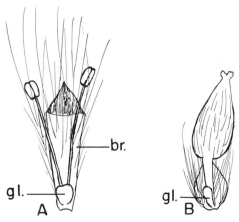

Fig. 29–4. *Salix* sp. *A*, Single staminate flower. *B*, Single pistillate flower. *gl.*, gland; *br.*, bract. X 8.

of the fundamental patterns and variations of flower structure. It is apparent that a flower is an axis of limited growth with shortened internodes, and that it always bears spore-producing appendages and may bear sterile ones in addition. The extreme brevity of the floral axis in many flowers complicates analysis of their floral organization. The several sets of floral organs are supplied by traces which leave gaps in the

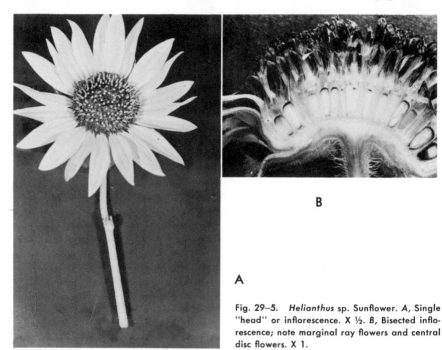

B

A

Fig. 29–5.   *Helianthus* sp. Sunflower. A, Single "head" or inflorescence. X ½. B, Bisected inflorescence; note marginal ray flowers and central disc flowers. X 1.

stele of the receptacle just as the traces of foliage leaves do. The sepals are leaf-like and usually receive the same number of traces as the foliage leaves of the species, three being a common number. Petals and stamens frequently receive only single traces. Stamens with three traces occur in certain families such as the *Magnolia* group. The pistil (carpel) also receives three traces in many plants which are considered to be primitive. Fewer than three traces is interpreted as evidence of reduction, and more than three as a specialized condition.

The several floral organs exhibit variation in their arrangement on the receptacle and in relation to each other. In many flowers, a median longitudinal section or bisection of the flower (Figs. 29–1, 29–6A, 29–7) reveals that the pistil or pistils are borne at the apex of the receptacle, and that the stamens, petals, and sepals occur on it at lower levels. Such an arrangement exemplifies **hypogyny** (Gr. *hypo,* under + Gr. *gyne,* female). Epipetalous flowers, in which the stamens arise from a corolla tube, are still considered as hypogynous, inasmuch as the tube arises below the pistil on the receptacle. In many other flowers, however, it can be observed in longitudinal sections that the pistil, although borne at the apex of the floral axis, has its basal portion, the ovary, partially or wholly united with tissues which represent the bases of sepals, petals, and

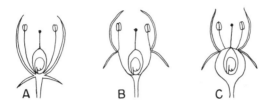

Fig. 29–6. Median longitudinal section of A, a hypogynous, B, a perigynous, and C, an epigynous flower; diagrammatic.

stamens (Fig. 29–6C). Such a flower is said to be **epigynous** (Gr. *epi,* upon + Gr. *gyne*). In many flowers of the rose alliance, the pistil or pistils occur at the base of a cup-like structure (Fig. 29–6B) upon whose rim the stamens, petals, and sepals are borne. This type of organization is called **perigyny.**

Further attention will be devoted at this point to the structure and structural variations which occur in the organs of the flower. The individual floral organs may be approximately similar in size and arranged about the axis in radial fashion, a condition called **actinomorphy;** or they may vary in form and insertion so that the flower is **zygomorphic** (Fig. 29–7). The petals and sepals may be separately inserted on the floral axis (polypetaly and polysepaly), or they may be united at their bases (sympetaly and synsepaly). In flowers considered to be primitive, the stamens and pistils are indefinite in number, spirally inserted, and individually attached to the floral axis. In contrast with this is the cyclic type of flower in which the several organs appear to arise from the axis in whorls of definite number, members of a whorl alternating with those of succeeding whorls.

The pistil is enlarged at the base to form an **ovary** which encloses the ovule or ovules (Figs. 29–1, 29–7B,C). From the apex of the ovary arise the **style** and **stigma** (Figs. 29–1, 29–7B). The style may be either solid or hollow. The stigma may be simple or branched, and variously modified as a receptive surface for pollen (Fig. 29–7B). Each pistil may have

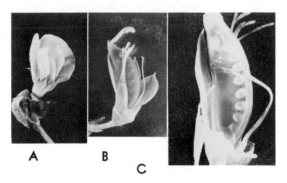

A   B   C

Fig. 29–7. *Lathyrus odoratus* L. Sweet pea. A, A single flower; note peduncle, sepals, large posterior petal (the "standard"), two lateral petals (the "wings"), and fused pair of petals within (the "keel"). X ½. B, A flower soon after pollination, petals mostly removed; note hypogyny; also peduncle, pistil (ovary, style, and pollinated stigma), and stamens. X ¾. C, Dissection of ovary showing the single locule of the simple ovary and parietal placentation. X 1.

a single, undivided style and stigma, or both styles and stigmas may be multiple. The multiple condition is often an indication that the pistil is compound rather than simple. A **simple pistil** is one that is composed of

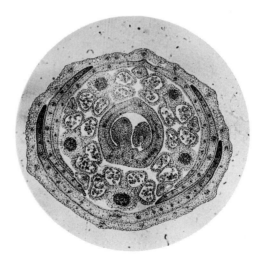

Fig. 29–8. *Pisum sativum* L., garden pea. Transverse section of flower bud; note petals, anthers of five stamens and filaments of the other five, simple ovary with two ovules visible, one showing its parietal placentation. X 125.

a single ovule-bearing unit, generally known as the **carpel** (Gr. *karpos,* fruit) (Figs. 29–7*C,* 29–8). Evidence from external form and internal anatomy indicates that in many flowers a number of carpels have united

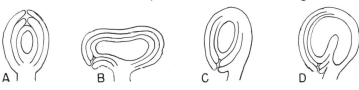

Fig. 29–9. Structure of ovules in median longitudinal section, diagrammatic. A, Orthotropous; B, campylotropous; C, anatropous; D, amphitropous.

and function as a unit, the **compound pistil.** A transverse section of the ovary usually indicates the number of carpels involved (Fig. 29–11).

The portion of the ovary to which the ovules are attached is known as the **placenta** (Fig. 29–1). The point of attachment varies in different flowers. In many, the ovules are attached to the ovary wall, a condition known as **parietal placentation** (Figs. 29–1, 29–8). In other flowers, the ovules are borne on the central axis of the compound ovary, a condition known as **axile placentation** (Fig. 29–11). In still others, the floral axis at maturity is free from the upper portion of the ovary but attached at its base. In this case, the ovules may be borne on the distal portion of the axis as well as on its flanks. This last arrangement is described as **free central placentation.**

The ovules themselves exhibit variations in form and in relation to their stalk, the **funiculus** (Fig. 29–1). **Orthotropous, amphitropous, anatropous,** and **campylotropous** types are common (Fig. 29–9). Orthotropous ovules are those in which the micropyle and funiculus lie on the same longitudinal axis. Anatropous ovules are those in which greater growth of one surface of the funiculus, during development, inverts the body of the ovule so that the micropyle and base of the funiculus are adjacent and parallel. In amphitropous ovules, the body of the ovule itself is strongly curved. In campylotropous ovules, the funiculus is attached near the equator of the ovule body (Fig. 29–9).

Stamens have a stalk-like axis, the **filament,** at whose tip the **anther** is borne (Figs. 29–1, 29–10). The latter is composed of four chambers, the **microsporangia,** supported by a zone of sterile tissue, the **connective,** which contains vascular tissue extending from the filament (Figs. 29–1, 29–11). As the spores mature, the two microsporangia on either side of the connective usually become confluent, so that only two **pollen sacs** are demonstrable in the dehiscent anther. The anthers may dehisce by longitudinal fissures or, less commonly, by apical pores.

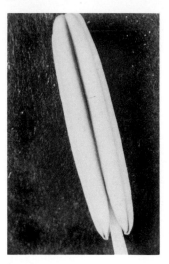

Fig. 29–10. *Lilium* sp. Apex of filament and anther; note four microsporangia. X 2½.

Before entering into a discussion of the details of reproduction in the flowering plants, the student should familiarize himself with the gross aspects of floral morphology summarized in the preceding paragraphs. Examination of a number of types of living flowers will be helpful in this connection. It will be shown below that the spores that arise in the anther become pollen grains which contain immature male gametophytes. Similarly, each ovule produces a spore which develops into a female gametophyte. In the light of comparisons with other seed plants, the stamen of flowering plants often is regarded as a **microsporophyll** which bears four microsporangia that produce microspores, and the pistil as a **megasporophyll** enclosing one or more ovules, megasporangia surrounded by integuments. These terms, of course, are unacceptable to those who regard seed plants as homosporous.

THE REPRODUCTIVE PROCESS

The process of reproduction in the flowering plants may be discussed conveniently under the following topical headings: **microsporogenesis, megasporogenesis, development of the male gametophyte, development of the female gametophyte, pollination and fertilization,** and **development of the embryo, seed, and fruit.**

Microsporogenesis

The earliest stages in the development of the stamen (microsporophyll) may be found by dissecting or sectioning very young flower buds (Fig. 29–11). In these, transverse sections of the anthers exhibit a rudimentary lobing into four parts, but the anther tissue is homogeneous except for slightly differentiated epidermal cells. Development of the microsporangia is eusporangiate. One or more deeply located cells in each

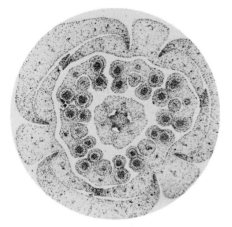

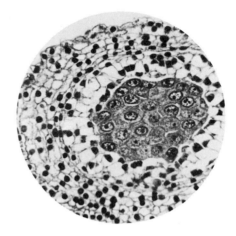

Fig. 29–11. *Lilium* sp. Transverse section of flower bud; note two whorls of trimerous perianth parts, stamens, and compound ovary with three carpels (ovules not shown). X 12½.

Fig. 29–12. *Lilium* sp. Transverse section of single anther lobe or microsporangium; note sporangial wall, tapetum, and microspore mother cells. X 120.

lobe functions in generating sporogenous tissue. In older anthers (Fig. 29–12), the wall is composed of several layers of cells, as in typical eusporangiate sporangia, the outermost of which differentiates as an epidermis. The layer of cells immediately within the epidermis is known as the **endothecium.** As the anther matures, the endothecial cells may develop fibrous bands on their walls. The innermost layer of the microsporangium wall functions as a well-differentiated **tapetum** (Fig. 29–12). The nuclei of tapetal cells frequently undergo either normal or modified mitoses, not followed by cytokinesis; hence binucleate cells result. The tapetum may disintegrate during microsporogenesis, or in some genera it may be organized as a tapetal plasmodium, as is the case in a number of vascular cryptogams.

As development proceeds, the sporogenous cells become differentiated as microspore mother cells which ultimately separate from each other, become spherical, and suspended in fluid (Fig. 29–13A). The meiotic process follows, and tetrads of microspores are organized (Fig. 29–13B,C). Cytokinesis may be by successive bipartition with the formation of cell plates after each division of the nuclei, or it may be by centripetal cleavage furrows which are initiated after the second nuclear division in the mother cell. The tetrads of uninucleate microspores are arranged in tetrahedral or quadrilateral fashion; occasionally they exhibit linear arrangement. Shortly after their formation, the tetrads separate into indi-

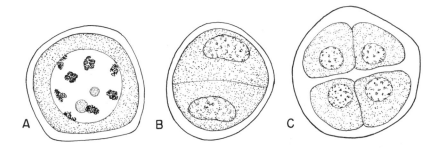

Fig. 29–13. *Lilium* sp. Microsporogenesis. A, Microspore mother cell. B, End of meiosis I. C, Tetrad of microspores. X 770.

vidual microspores. Each microspore contains a single haploid nucleus. The microspores enlarge as they separate from the tetrad and become sculptured by deposition of more or less highly ornamented surface layers

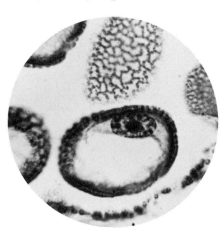

Fig. 29–14. *Lilium* sp. Microspores, in section and in surface view. X 600.

(Fig. 29–14). In a few plants— *Rhododendron,* for example—the microspores remain permanently in the tetrad condition like the spores of some species of the liverwort, *Sphaerocarpos.* In certain orchids and members of the milkweed family, the spores adhere in a waxy mass, the **pollinium.**

Megasporogenesis

The ovule, a megasporangium surrounded with integuments, develops by cell division from its placenta (Figs. 29–1, 29–11). The number of ovules in each ovary varies with the genus. There may be one, as in corn (*Zea mays* L.), buckwheat (*Fagopyrum esculentum* Gaertn.), sunflower (*Helianthus* sp.), or a small number as in pea (*Pisum sativum* L.) and sweet pea (*Lathyrus odoratus* L.) (Fig. 29–7C), or they may be very numerous and minute as in the orchids, begonias, and snapdragons (*Antirrhinum majus* L.). Each ovule is attached to its placenta by the funiculus, as noted above. The megasporangium tissue is covered with either one or two integumentary layers except for a minute passageway, the micropyle (Figs. 29–1, 29–20C).

Early in the development of each ovule, a subepidermal cell in the micropylar region differentiates into a primary archesporial cell. This may form several sporogenous cells or it may function directly as a megaspore mother cell (Figs. 29–15A, 29–20A). The latter is readily recognizable because of its large size as compared with the sterile cells of the megasporangium. In a great majority of the flowering

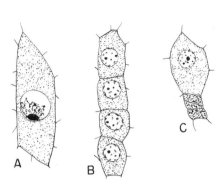

Fig. 29–15.   *Oenothera* sp. Megasporogenesis. A, Megaspore mother cell. B, Linear tetrad. C, Functional megaspore and three aborting. X 770.

plants, the megaspore mother cell undergoes two successive nuclear and cell divisions, during which meiosis occurs. The products of these divisions are the four megaspores arranged in linear fashion (Fig. 29–15B). Several deviations from this process are known. One of the daughter cells of the megaspore mother cell may fail to undergo division, so three instead of four cells result. Furthermore, the megaspores are not always arranged in a strictly linear fashion. Normally, as in the gymnosperms, the three megaspores nearest the micropyle degenerate, and the chalazal megaspore persists and functions (Fig. 29–15C). This is permanently retained within the megasporangium, where it continues its development into the female gametophyte.

Development of the Male Gametophyte

As in other seed plants, the uninucleate microspore (Fig. 29–14) begins its development into the male gametophyte before it is shed from the microsporangium, by undergoing nuclear division and cytokinesis. The two daughter nuclei differ in size, and often in form as well; the larger represents the **tube nucleus** and the smaller the **generative nucleus.** The latter becomes surrounded by dense cytoplasm. In many flowering plants the generative cell may be elliptical, lens-shaped, or somewhat elongate in form (Fig. 29–16). It should be noted that a prothallial cell is not formed in the male gameto-phyte. The generative nucleus may divide to form two **sperm nuclei** before the pollen is shed, or this division may occur in the pollen tube. In that event, the sperm nuclei usually are surrounded by specially differentiated cytoplasm so they are, in fact, sperm cells (Fig. 29–17).

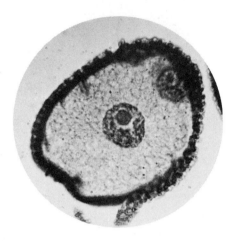

Dehiscence of the anther results in dissemination of the immature male gametophytes or **pollen** (L. *pollen,* fine flour) grains. Depending on the species, some of these reach the receptive stigmatic surface of the pistil by means of gravity, wind, insects, or water currents (Fig. 29–1). The ornamentation of the surface of the pollen grain is a feature of taxonomic value.

Fig. 29–16. *Lilium* sp. Intrasporal development of ♂ gametophyte; note large tube cell and small lenticular generative cell. X 1200.

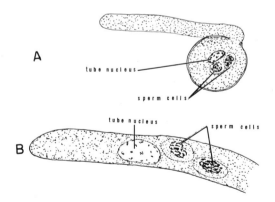

Fig. 29–17. *Polygonatum* sp. A, Mature ♂ gametophyte, tube nucleus, and two sperm cells in microspore. X 515. B, Tip of pollen tube showing detail of tube nucleus and two sperm cells. X 1030.

Development of the Female Gametophyte

The functional megaspore normally gives rise to a single female gametophyte. This process is usually accompanied by a series of three consecutive free-nuclear divisions within the functional megaspore, which enlarges during this period (Fig. 29–18). At the conclusion of these divisions, the developing female gametophyte contains a quartet of nuclei at each pole. Rearrangement, cell membrane formation, and differentia-

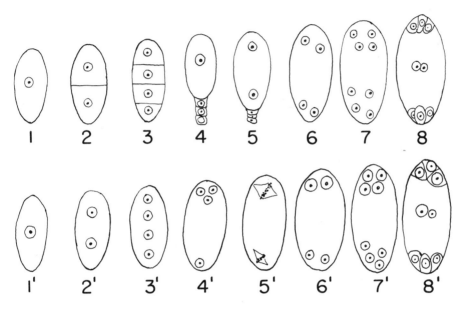

Fig. 29–18.   Megasporogenesis and ontogeny of the ♀ gametophyte: 1–8, the "normal type"; 1′–8′, Lilium (Fritillaria) type; diagrammatic.

tion of the resulting cells effect the maturation of the female gametophyte (Fig. 29–19A), whose size, duration, and organization are obviously much reduced, as compared with those of gymnospermous female gametophytes. Differentiated archegonia are entirely lacking.

Three of the four nuclei at the micropylar pole differentiate as the "egg apparatus," consisting of an **egg cell** and two **synergids** (Fig. 29–19). Three of the four nuclei at the chalazal pole develop cell membranes and are known as **antipodal cells.** The remaining two nuclei, one from each pole, migrate toward each other away from the poles. These, therefore, are known as **polar nuclei.** The mature female gametophyte of most angiosperms thus is a seven-celled structure (Figs. 29–1, 29–19) consisting of three uninucleate cells at each pole with a larger binucleate cell between them.

The process of female gametophyte development just described is essentially that which occurs in more than 70 percent of the flowering plants. It should be noted, however, that a great many regularly recurring deviations characteristic of specific genera have been described. The genus *Lilium,* usually used to illustrate reproduction in angiosperms

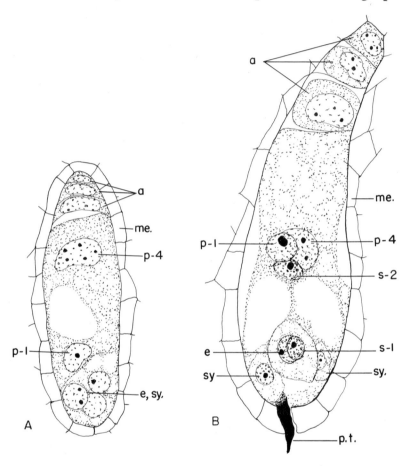

Fig. 29–19. *Lilium* sp. A, Immature eight-nucleate ♀ gametophyte. B, Mature ♀ gametophyte and double fertilization. X 315. a, antipodal cells; e, egg nucleus; me., megasporangium; p-1, haploid polar nucleus; p-4, triploid polar nucleus; p.t., pollen tube; s-1, s-2, sperm nuclei; sy., synergids.

because of the large size of its nuclei and female gametophyte, exhibits one of these deviations. Inasmuch as this plant is still used in most laboratories and because the process of female gametophyte development can be readily demonstrated, the divergent ontogeny will be described at this point (Figs. 29–18, 29–20).

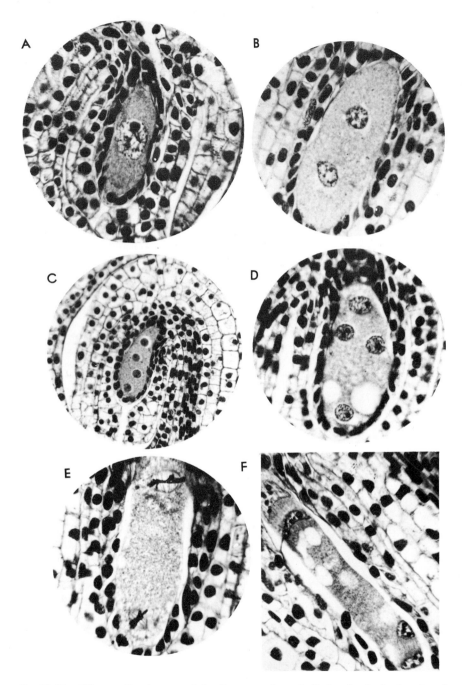

Fig. 29–20. *Lilium* sp. Development of the ♀ gametophyte. *A,* Median longitudinal section of ovule showing integuments, micropyle, megasporangium, and megaspore mother cells. *B,* End of meiosis I. *C,* Four haploid megaspore nuclei ("first four-nucleate stage"). *D,* Migration of three haploid nuclei to chalazal pole, prophases of division. *E,* Metaphase of triploid division above, metaphase of haploid division nearer micropyle. *F,* Two triploid nuclei above, two haploid nuclei nearer micropyle ("second four-nucleate stage"). *A,* X 125; *B-F,* X 250.

The first point at which the lily differs from the normal type of female gametophyte development is during the division and meiosis of the megaspore mother cell (Fig. 29–20A). Two successive nuclear divisions occur as usual, but these are not followed by cytokineses (Fig. 29–20B,C). As a result, the four linearly arranged megaspore nuclei are embedded in common cytoplasm of the megaspore mother cell. A second deviation is that in *Lilium,* three of the four megaspore nuclei do not degenerate and, furthermore, all four are involved in the formation of the female gametophyte (Fig. 29–18). The latter, therefore, is tetrasporic in origin. The linear arrangement of the megaspore nuclei is followed by a change in position in which one remains near the micropylar pole of the developing female gametophyte and three migrate to the other (chalazal) end (Fig. 29–20D). At this point, a third deviation becomes apparent, namely, as the three chalazal nuclei enter mitosis, either in late prophase or in metaphase, they join together, making a single large division figure (Fig. 29–20E). Inasmuch as each of the haploid nuclei had undergone chromosome reduplication in preparation for this mitosis, the single large spindle includes three haploid sets of dual chromosomes. The result is that two large triploid nuclei are organized at telophase (Fig. 29–20F). The megaspore nucleus at the micropylar pole, meanwhile, has divided to form two haploid nuclei (Fig. 29–20F). This "second four-nucleate stage" is readily recognizable by the presence of two large (triploid) nuclei at the chalazal pole and two smaller (haploid) nuclei at the micropylar pole of the female gametophyte. Following this, a fourth mitosis takes place, resulting in the formation of four triploid nuclei and four haploid nuclei (Fig. 29–18). Further development is normal, one triploid nucleus and one haploid nucleus functioning as polar nuclei (Fig. 29–19A). In the mature female gametophyte of *Lilium,* the antipodal cells are triploid and the egg and synergids are haploid. One polar nucleus is triploid and one is haploid.

Pollination and Fertilization

In many angiosperms, the maturation of the female gametophyte occurs just as the flower opens or just prior to its opening. Each ovule in the ovary contains a single mature gametophyte. The pollen grains, in reality immature male gametophytes, are transferred to the receptive surface of the stigma after the flower has opened, in the process of **pollination** (Figs. 29–1, 29–21). Pollination here differs from that in gymnosperms in that in the latter the pollen is transferred directly to the vicinity of the micropyle of the ovule. A few flowering plants—many species of *Viola*, for example—produce **cleistogamous** flowers which do not open. These are regularly self-pollinated; in *V. odorata* L. it has been shown that the pollen grains germinate within the anther and grow through its walls to the stigma.

Pollen grains germinate on the stigmatic surface (Figs. 29–1, 29–21). In many cases, germination occurs through a predetermined germ pore,

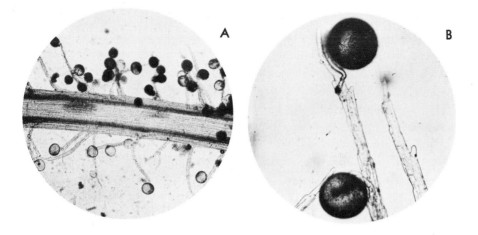

Fig. 29–21. *Zea mays.* Corn. A, Corn "silk" (stigma) with hairs and attached pollen. X 30. B, Hairs and germinating pollen, enlarged. X 250.

a thin place in the wall of the grain. A tubular process emerges from the pollen grain and grows into the stigma and through the style into the ovary (Fig. 29–1). There can be little doubt that part of the nutriment of the pollen tube and male gametophyte is absorbed from the stigma and style. Germination of the pollen grains in most angiosperms is relatively rapid, occurring within a few minutes after the pollen has reached the stigma. In some cases, pollen grains germinate readily in sugar solutions, the optimum concentration varying with the species. Normally, only one tube emerges from each pollen grain. However, in some species as many as fourteen tubes have been observed developing from a single pollen grain. The style through which the pollen tube grows may be hollow, as in *Viola,* or solid, as in cotton (*Gossypium*). In the latter case, the pollen tube forces its way through the intercellular spaces of the stylar tissue.

In most cases, the pollen tube enters the ovule through the micropyle

(Figs. 29–1, 29–19B), but it also may penetrate other points on the surface of the ovule. In ovaries containing more than one ovule, each is penetrated by a single pollen tube if pollination has been sufficiently heavy. The tip of the pollen tube enters through the wall of the female gametophyte. The synergids may disintegrate as it enters. Shortly after its contact with the female gametophyte, the pollen tube discharges the sperm cells, and sometimes the tube nucleus also, into the female gametophyte.

In spite of the great amount of study devoted to the process of reproduction in angiosperms, the details of nuclear union are not well known in most cases. This may indicate that once the sperm cells are discharged into the female gametophyte, nuclear union follows rapidly. One of the sperm cells approaches the egg and unites with it, while the other moves toward the two polar nuclei and unites with them (Fig. 29–19B). In plants in which the polar nuclei have united to form the so-called **secondary nucleus** prior to fertilization, the second sperm unites with it. Thus it is obvious that in the flowering plants, both sperms of a given male gametophyte are functional and involved in nuclear unions within the female gametophyte. These phenomena comprise **double fertilization;** it seems to be limited to angiosperms in which it was discovered in 1898. It is clear, in the female gametophytes that have developed in the "normal" fashion from one haploid megaspore, that union of the two haploid polar nuclei with one sperm nucleus or of a secondary nucleus with a sperm nucleus, results in the formation of a triploid nucleus. The latter is called the **primary endosperm nucleus** because of its subsequent activity. In such a plant as *Lilium*, however, it will be recalled that one of the polar nuclei is triploid and one haploid. Union of these with the sperm nucleus produces a pentaploid primary endosperm nucleus.

Development of the Embyro, Seed, and Fruit

In most cases, the zygote, enclosed by a delicate membrane, remains undivided for some interval after fertilization. The primary endosperm nucleus, in contrast, soon enters upon a period of rapid division which may be free-nuclear (Fig. 29–22), or the mitoses may be followed by successive cytokineses after each nuclear division. If free-nuclear division has occurred, walls are usually but not always developed between the free nuclei, and the tissue which contains them is called **endosperm.** The endosperm of *Lilium* passes through a free-nuclear period before cell walls are laid down (Fig. 29–22). When the first and subsequent divisions of the primary endosperm nucleus are followed by cytokineses, the endosperm is cellular from its inception. This occurs in many plants, among them *Adoxa, Lobelia,* and *Nemophila.* The descendants of the primary endosperm nucleus give rise to a more or less extensive **endosperm** within the enlarging lumen of the female gametophyte, now perhaps most appropriately called the **embryo sac.** The endosperm cells are often filled with starch grains or other stored metabolites which have diffused into them from the parent sporophyte. The endosperm is a storage tissue which provides readily available nutriment to the developing embryo. It is a triploid tissue in a great majority of angiosperms, but a number of exceptions are known, such as the pentaploid type in *Lilium.* The origin

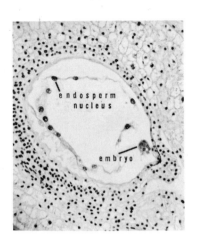

Fig. 29–22. *Lilium* sp. Section of postfertilization ovule; note embryo near micropyle and ring of endosperm nuclei. X 60.

and development of the endosperm and phenotypic attributes residing in it are involved in the phenomenon of **xenia.** This term denotes the direct influence of the male parent as expressed in endosperm characteristics, an influence readily observable in certain corn hybridizations.

Some time after the initiation of endosperm formation, the zygote begins the nuclear and cell divisions which result in the formation of the embryonic sporophyte. The cytokinesis which follows the first nuclear division forms a two-celled embryo. The division product that lies more deeply within the female gametophyte is known as the **terminal cell,** and the other is called the **basal cell.** Considerable variation exists in the subsequent stages of development. The following account is based largely on the process as it occurs in the "shepherd's purse," *Capsella bursa-pastoris* (L.) Medic., a weed with amphitropous ovules (Fig. 29–23).

This species is widespread in distribution, and microscopical preparations of the stages of embryogeny are readily obtainable. After the first division of the zygote, the basal cell divides in a transverse plane, and

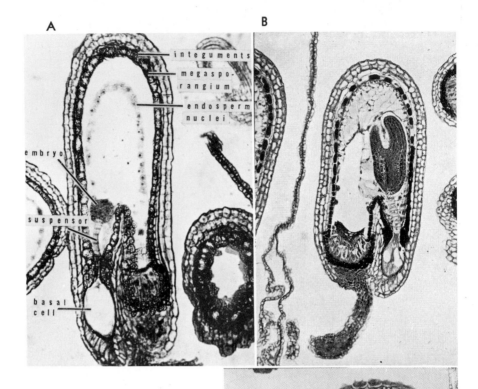

Fig. 29–23. *Capsella bursa-pastoris*
(L.) Medic. Embryogeny and development of the seed. *A,* Median longitudinal section of amphitropous ovule; note
basal cell, suspensor and embryo, ring
of endosperm nuclei, integuments, and
dark-staining cells of megasporangium.
X 120. *B,* Later stage, organization of
the cotyledons and hypocotyl. (Tissue at
funicular pole of embryo sac is antipodal in origin.) *C,* Section of an almost mature seed; note cotyledons, plumule, hypocotyl, and radicle. (The
ovule in *B* is reversed in position as
compared with those in *A* and *C.*) X
120. (*B,C,* from Whaley *et al. Principles of Biology,* Harper & Brothers,
1954.)

the terminal cell undergoes vertical division at right angles to the plane of division of the basal cell. A second vertical division in a plane perpendicular to the first results in the formation of a quartet of cells (quadrant stage) from the original terminal cell. This is followed by transverse divisions in all four cells to form an octant stage. The four cells of the octant farthest from the basal cell give rise to the cotyledons and stem apex of the embryo. The other four initiate an axis or **hypocotyl.** Periclinal divisions in each of the cells of the spherical eight-celled embryo segregate the superficial epidermal precursors from eight inner cells.

While these changes have been taking place in the descendants of the terminal (embryo-forming) cell, the products of division of the basal cell continue to divide to form a short chain that functions as a **suspensor,** the basal cell of which is attached to the wall of the embryo sac (Fig. 29–23). This cell enlarges markedly, and possibly functions in absorption. By regular sequential divisions, the lowermost of the suspensor cells give rise to the root and root cap of the embryo. In subsequent development, the original octant region becomes organized into an elongate hypocotyl bearing two large **cotyledons** (Fig. 29–23 B,C), between whose bases lies the promeristem of the stem. The embryo is curved in later development in conformity with the amphitropy of the *Capsella* ovule.

As the embryo develops, the bulk of the endosperm is digested and utilized by the developing embryo. As the latter enters a period of dormancy, histological changes in the cells of the integuments result in the formation of seed coats, the inner known as the **tegmen** and the outer as the **testa.** It should be noted that in *Capsella* the antipodal cells, having undergone several divisions, persist at the antipodal pole of the embryo sac (Fig. 29–23). It is clear that the embryos of *Capsella* are dicotyledonous.

The earlier stages in the development of monocotyledonous embryos are similar to those of dicotyledonous types (Fig. 29–22). The later stages differ in the organization of a single large cotyledon on the axis (Fig. 29–24). In a number of flowering plants––many orchids, for example––the embryo remains minute and undifferentiated. In such seeds, further development is delayed until after the seeds have been shed.

Although endosperm is produced in the development of almost all angiosperm seeds, the orchids being a notable exception, whether or not endosperm is present in the mature seed depends on the degree to which it has been absorbed by the developing embryo. In seeds that lack endosperm at maturity, such as bean, peanut, and garden pea, the embryo is massive and its cotyledons are rich in stored metabolites. In seeds with endosperm, the embryo is more delicate and the cotyledons are more like foliage leaves, as in the castor bean (*Ricinus*) and basswood

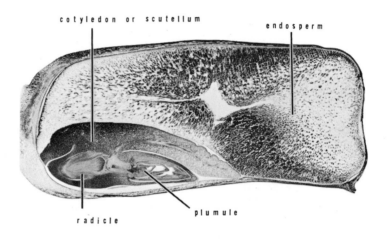

cotyledon or scutellum   endosperm

radicle   plumule

Fig. 29–24. *Zea mays.* Corn. Longitudinal section of immature grain; note embryo at the right, with single lateral cotyledon (scutellum) adjacent to endosperm. X 25. (Courtesy of Professor J. E. Sass and the Iowa State University Press.)

(*Tilia*). The **seed** of the angiosperms, therefore, may be defined as an embryonic sporophyte in a dormant condition, either surrounded by endosperm or gorged with food (Fig. 29–23C). Furthermore, the embryo is enclosed also by the remains of the megasporangium and by the matured integuments, the seed coats. The angiosperm seed differs fundamentally from that of gymnosperms in the origin of the tissue which nourishes the developing embryo. In the gymnosperms, the haploid vegetative tissue of the female gametophyte serves this purpose, whereas in the angiosperms, the food tissue or endosperm is a postfertilization development initiated and stimulated by the union of the sperm nucleus and the polar nuclei or secondary nucleus.

Soon after pollination and fertilization, the stamens and petals of most flowers wither and may be abscised from the receptacle. The ovary of the pistil which contains the ovule or ovules with developing embryos enlarges rapidly by cell division after pollination and fertilization (Fig. 29–25). The pistil, and in some cases the receptacle and other floral organs as well, mature into the structure known as the **fruit.** The structure

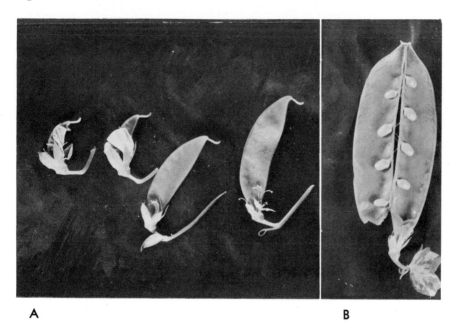

A   B

Fig. 29–25. *Pisum sativum* L. Five stages in the development of the fruit after pollination. X ⅔.

of the mature fruit varies in the families of angiosperms with respect to form, texture, and dehiscence, if any. These variations serve, in part, as criteria for the delimitation of various taxonomic categories.

In bringing to a close this brief account of reproduction in angiosperms, it should be emphasized, as would be expected in such a large and diversified assemblage of plants, that there are many deviations in detail from the general account presented above. Furthermore, as was indicated previously both in the Bryophyta and in certain vascular cryptogams, deviations from normal sexual reproduction also occur in angiosperms, both spontaneously and as a result of artificial stimulation. These deviations in angiosperms also may be grouped under the phenomenon of apogamy. Among them may be mentioned the development of haploid embryos from unfertilized egg cells, development of haploid embryos from cells of the female gametophyte other than the egg, development of diploid embryos because of parthenogenetic development of diploid eggs in aposporously produced female gametophytes, and development of diploid embryos from the megasporangium or integument. Details of these deviations are beyond the scope of this account, but they are mentioned as examples of similar phenomena seen in the lower groups.

SUMMARY

Because of the tremendous range in their diversity, consideration of the vegetative organs of the angiosperms is not presented in the present chapter. Instead, the chapter contains a brief discussion of the gross morphology of the flower and the details of the reproductive process. The latter may be considered to consist of microsporogenesis and megasporogenesis, maturation of the male and female gametophytes, double fertilization, embryogeny, and development of the seed and fruit. Brief reference to deviations from the normal reproductive cycle has been made. The flowering plants differ from other seed plants in having the seeds enclosed in the megasporophylls (angiospermy), in their double fertilization and postfertilization endosperm. Embryogeny does not involve free-nuclear stages which characterize the process in gymnosperms. The widespread occurrence of vessels (tracheae) in their xylem is a characteristic they share with the Gnetophyta.

DISCUSSION QUESTIONS

1. What reasons can you suggest to explain the fact that the flowering plants exceed any other group of plants in number of species?
2. In what respects are flowers and strobili similar? In what respects do they differ?
3. What attributes do angiosperms and gymnosperms have in common?
4. In what respects do they differ?
5. How do the seeds of gymnosperms and angiosperms differ?
6. Some botanists group all the seed plants in a single division, Spermatophyta. Give reasons for and against such a disposition of these plants.

7. On what basis are the spores of angiosperms called microspores and mega-spores? Express your opinion regarding the propriety of this practice.

8. What evidence can you cite that sepals and petals differ in origin?

9. What evidence can you cite that a carpel (simple pistil) is foliar in origin?

10. Summarize the terms used to describe the gross morphology of the flower and explain each in a single sentence.

11. Explain the proper use of the terms perfect and imperfect, monoecious and dioecious, homothallic and heterothallic.

12. Distinguish between hypogynous, perigynous, and epigynous flowers, cit-ing familiar examples of each.

13. What is meant by the term fruit?

14. What effect does epigyny have on the fruit?

15. Explain the term seed as it applies to angiosperms, and describe types of seed structure and variations in their germination.

16. Obtain seeds of corn, pea, garden bean, and castor bean and follow their germination in moist peat moss or sand.

17. Outline the major phenomena in the reproduction of the flowering plant and then prepare an account of the process, using this outline and making appropriate drawings.

18. What is an ovule? What variations in ovule form occur? Give an example of a plant with each type.

19. Are the Anthophyta unique, among seed plants, in lacking archegonia? Explain.

20. How are the gametophytes of flowering plants nourished?

21. What interval may elapse between pollination and fertilization in Antho-phyta? How does this compare with gymnosperms?

22. Distinguish between pollination and fertilization in both angiosperms and gymnosperms.

23. How does the reproductive cycle of *Lilium* deviate from the "normal" type?

24. Compare the mature male and female gametophytes of the flowering plants with those of the several genera of gymnosperms described in ear-lier chapters.

25. What is meant by cleistogamy? Give examples. Of what genetic signifi-cance is this phenomenon?

26. Comment on the possible benefits which accrue to plants through cross-pollination.

27. What is meant by xenia? Give an example.

28. With the aid of labeled diagrams, describe the embryogeny of *Capsella*.

29. In what area of plant science is the structure of the vegetative organs of the flowering plants considered in great detail?

30. What criteria are employed in the classification of flowering plants?
31. What book (manual) summarizes the flora (vascular plants) of the region in which you live? Consult its keys.
32. What branch of plant science involves detailed consideration of the characteristics of the orders and families of flowering plants?
33. How would you demonstrate the germination of angiosperm pollen?

CHAPTER 30

Plants of the Past

INTRODUCTION

In the first chapter of this book, in the discussion of the scope of plant morphology, it was stated that "the real significance of plants of the present must be sought, in part, in plants of the past which have been preserved as fossils." Discussion of the paleobotanical record has been deferred until this point, because appreciation of the significance of the fossil record is directly proportional to one's grasp of the morphology of extant plants.

Although most people are informed regarding the existence of fossilized animal remains through anthropocentric interests and by articles regarding their significance which appear in the popular press, awareness of the occurrence of fossilized plants often is restricted to those who live near coal mines or certain clay pits. This is correlated, of course, with the circumstance that most coal fields in this country are in Mississippian and Pennsylvanian strata (Fig. 30–1), in rocks that were formed during periods of lush vegetation.

Plants have been preserved in sedimentary rocks as petrifactions, casts, or impressions. Of these types of fossils, petrifactions are the most instructive, because the internal structure of the plant parts has been preserved in great detail (Fig. 30–43). Detailed structure is absent in other types of fossilized remains. Petrifactions are prepared for microscopic study either by grinding sections until they are transparent or by removing thin sections of the fossil by the peel method. In the latter, one surface of the fossil-bearing rock is made smooth, and a chemical agent such as hydrochloric acid is poured over it and permitted to remain for periods which vary with the chemical nature of the rock and of the contained fossil tissues. During this treatment, the mineral matrix is dissolved from the organic material, which remains in delicate relief on the surface. After the treated surface has dried, a liquid mixture containing collodion is poured over it as a thin film and allowed to harden through evaporation of the solvent. When the hardening and drying have been completed, it is possible to remove a thin transparent layer of collodion in which the plant tissues are more or less well preserved in thin section. This may then be mounted for microscopic study. The labor saved by the peel method obviously is enormous.

Extensive discussion of the methods of fossilization and of the physical and chemical factors involved is beyond the scope of the present book. The interested reader should consult one or more of the reference works

Era	Rock System or Series Period or Epoch	Age in Years
Cenozoic	Pleistocene	1,000,000
	Pliocene	12,000,000
	Miocene	(17,000,000)[a]
		25,000,000
	Oligocene	35,000,000
	Eocene	(58,000,000)[a]
		60,000,000
	Paleocene	70,000,000
Mesozoic	Cretaceous	130,000,000
	Jurassic	165,000,000
	Triassic	200,000,000
Paleozoic	Permian	(230,000,000)[a]
		235,000,000
	Carboniferous { Pennsylvanian	260,000,000
	{ Mississippian	285,000,000
	Devonian	325,000,000
	Silurian	350,000,000
	Ordovician	410,000,000
	Cambrian	(440,000,000)[a]
		500,000,000
Proterozoic Archaeozoic	"Pre-Cambrian"	(620,000,000)[a] to (2,200,000,000)[a]

[a] Figures in parentheses are based on determinations from radioactive minerals in rocks known to belong in the time division indicated; other figures are estimates.

Fig. 30–1. Geologic time. (Modified from C. R. Longwell and R. F. Flint, *Introduction to Physical Geology*, John Wiley & Sons, Inc., 1955.)

listed at the end of this chapter, and standard texts in geology and paleontology in addition. As a basis for understanding the discussion of the fossil floras, however, the student should refer to Fig. 30–1, a summary of the history of the earth's crust as it is understood by geologists. Examination of this figure indicates that geologic time is divided into categories of decreasing magnitude, namely, **eras** and **periods** or **epochs.** The approximate time extent of these divisions is indicated in each case. The strata of sedimentary rocks deposited during these successive periods contain a record of the plants and animals that were flourishing at the time of sedimentation. Study of these fossil plant remains belongs to the field of **paleobotany.**

Although the most ancient fossil remains are those of bacteria, algae, and fungi, living genera of which are therefore considered to be primitive, the fossil plants of successively more recent strata do not always form an orderly series. This may be explained in part, perhaps, by gaps in our knowledge of fossil floras and also by the fact that some plant types are not preserved as fossils. Of necessity, the following account is restricted in scope and length; it is designed to provide a brief introduction to plants of the past and their possible relation to extant types.

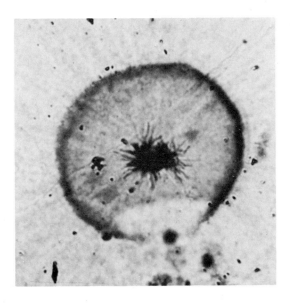

Fig. 30–2.   Fossil alga-like colonies from a Pre-Cambrian iron formation of Ontario. Note spherical gelatinous(?) sheath with central radiating filaments suggestive of certain Cyanophyta. X 725. (After Tyler and Barghoorn.)

REPRESENTATIVE TYPES

Algae and Fungi

There is both direct and indirect evidence that algae and bacteria were present on the earth in Pre-Cambrian times (Fig. 30–1). It is generally believed that algae were responsible for the precipitation of large quantities of calcium carbonate which became limestone rock. This process is continued still by algal species in coral reefs, for example. The illustrations in Figs. 30–2 to 30–4 depict several types of fossil algae from rocks of different ages. The best-preserved specimens are remarkably like modern genera. This indicates that the algae are an

Fig. 30–3. Fossil Charophyta, oogonia. X 17. (From Peck.)

ancient line of plants which have persisted with little change through long periods of geologic time. The fossil record sheds little light on the problem of relationship of extant algae, except to show that, as at present, distinct series populated ancient waters.

Among the fungi, *sensu lato,* fossil bacteria (Fig. 30–5) have been identified in such ancient strata as the Pre-Cambrian iron ores of northern Michigan and in strata of northern Minnesota. Bacteria assumed to have been parasitic have been identified within the sporangia of certain Carboniferous (Fig. 30–1) plants. In the stems and associated organic

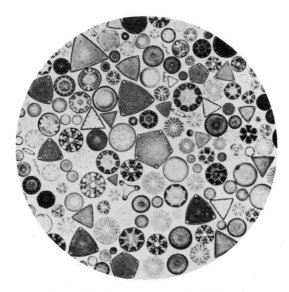

Fig. 30-4. Fossil marine diatoms from Hungary, grouped for illustration. X 45. (From Mann.)

remains of plants in an ancient bog at Rhynie, Scotland, which has been identified as Lower Devonian (Fig. 30–1), very well-preserved fossil fungi (Fig. 30–6) are present. Mycorrhizal fungi were functioning in the superficial root cells of certain Upper Carboniferous gymnosperms (Fig. 30–7). As stated in connection with the algae, the fossilized remains of ancient fungi are little different from the plant bodies of modern genera, and they have not been helpful in solving problems of fungal phylogeny.

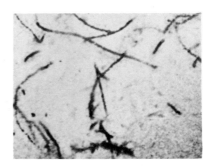

Hepatophyta and Bryophyta

Very few fossils clearly referable to the Hepatophyta and Bryophyta have been found, probably

Fig. 30–5. Fossil iron bacteria resembling *Chlamydothrix*, from Pre-Cambrian iron ores. X 300. (From Gruner.)

because of the delicate texture of these plants and the absence of calcareous precipitations on their surfaces. The best-known specimens of fossil liverworts (Fig. 30–8) have been described from Carboniferous

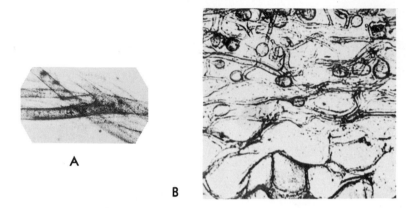

Fig. 30–6. Devonian fungi. *A*, Mycelium in decayed stem of *Asteroxylon*. X 125. *B, Palaeomyces asteroxyli* Kidston and Lang. Fungus hyphae and vesicles in the cortex of *Asteroxylon*. X 80. (From Kidston and Lang.)

rocks, although there is every reason to believe that they must have been present earlier. A few fossilized mosses and liverworts have been obtained from Mesozoic rocks (Fig. 30–1); those of Cenozoic strata are

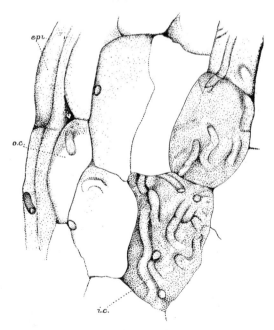

Fig. 30–7. Fungus in rootlet of *Amyelon radicans* Will., Lower Carboniferous—epi., epidermis; i.c. inner cortex; o.c., outer cortex. X 200. (From Osborn.)

similar to living genera (Fig. 30–9). The fossil record of Hepatophyta and Bryophyta, like that of the algae and fungi, has shed little light on the course of evolution in these plants.

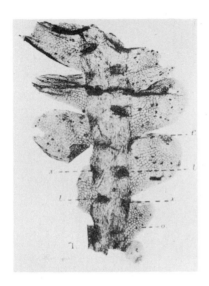

Fig. 30–8. *Hepaticites kidstoni* Walton. A fossil leafy liverwort of the Carboniferous. X 30. (From Walton.)

Fig. 30–9. *Palaeohypnum arnoldianum* Steere. A Miocene moss. X 1½. (From Steere.)

Psilophytan Fossils

The resistant nature of the xylem and sclerenchyma tissues in vascular plants has resulted in their more widespread preservation in a form suitable for microscopic study. The earliest record[1] of a vascular plant, that of *Baragwanathia* (after W. Baragwanath) (Fig. 30–10), a member of the Microphyllophyta, is from Silurian rocks in Australia (Fig. 30–1). A far richer flora is known from early Devonian strata. Our knowledge of the latter is based largely on a remarkably well-preserved bog in the vicinity of Rhynie in Scotland, the vegetation of which is sometimes called the Rhynie flora. These fossils were described by British paleobotanists about forty years ago, and Devonian rocks in other parts of the world have yielded similar plants. It should be emphasized, however, that an earlier discovery of vascular plants in

---

[1] There have been several reports of the occurrence of spores, pollen, and vascular tissues in certain Asiatic Cambrian strata.

the Devonian was made by Dawson, who described the genus *Psilophyton* (Fig. 30–11) from eastern Canada in 1859.

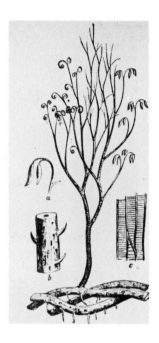

Fig. 30–10. *Baragwanathia longifolia* Lang and Cookson. Axis and leaves. Silurian of Australia. X ⅞. (From Lang and Cookson.)

Fig. 30–11. *Psilophyton princeps* Dawson. A Devonian fossil. Portion of rhizome and aerial branches, center, those at the right fertile (reconstruction); *a*, detail of pendulous sporangia, X 1; *b*, detail of stem and spiny appendage, X 1; *c*, tracheids from stele, much enlarged. (From Dawson.)

Knowledge of the Devonian flora has profoundly influenced current ideas regarding the relationship of vascular plants, largely because these extinct plants furnish us morphological features and potentialities which are developed more highly in extant genera.

Although *Psilophyton* (Gr. *psiloun*, to bare + Gr. *phyton*) (Fig. 30–11) had been described as early as 1859, its structure was so anomalous, in comparison with that of other vascular cryptogams, that it received little attention until later, when paleobotanists began to describe genera with similar attributes from the Devonian rocks at Rhynie and elsewhere. The Carboniferous had long been known as the age of ferns; but this later discovery, that the Devonian strata contain a rather diverse cryptogamic flora, has stimulated anew interest in the origin of vascular plants.

One of the best-known Devonian genera other than *Psilophyton* is *Rhynia* (after Rhynie, Scotland). *Rhynia* (Fig. 30–12) probably was a marsh plant, perhaps not unlike our modern sedges or rushes in gross appearance and stature. Its most striking feature is its lack of leaves and roots, for the plant bodies consisted entirely of dichotomously branching aerial stems attached to rhizomes on which tufts of unicellular rhizoids served as organs of absorption. As in certain modern xerophytes, these plants had stems as the chief photosynthetic organs. Stomata in the epidermis of the aerial axes are well preserved in fossil specimens. The Rhynie plants show internal structure particularly well (Fig. 30–13). The stem of species of *Rhynia* ranges from 2 to 5 mm. in diameter. Plant anatomists had earlier postulated that stems having a solid core of xylem surrounded by phloem (a protostele) represented the most primitive type of stele. The occurrence of such an anatomical pattern in the stems of many Devonian plants is striking confirmation of this theory. That these plants were

Fig. 30–12. *Rhynia gwynne-vaughani* Kidston and Lang. Reconstruction of a Devonian vascular plant; note vegetative and fertile axes with terminal sporangia. (Courtesy Chicago Natural History Museum.)

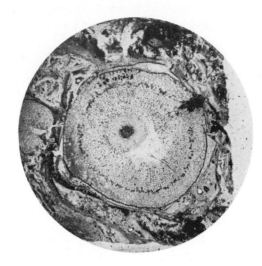

Fig. 30–13. *Rhynia* sp. Transverse section of axis; note epidermis, cortex differentiated into three zones, and central stele. X 12½.

sporophytes is evidenced by the abundant occurrence of spores in association with the stems. Specimens have been found with the spores united in tetrads (Fig. 30–14), evidence of their origin by meiosis. This occurred in elongate sporangia (Fig. 30–12) borne at the stem apices. The sporangia here are sporogenous stem apices. No special provision for sporangial dehiscence has been described, and no germinating spores or mature gametophytes are known.

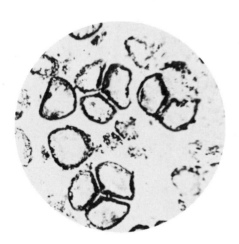

Fig. 30–14. *Rhynia* sp. Spore tetrad. X 250. (Preparation by Dr. Richard Stearns.)

In summary, it may be stated that *Rhynia* and *Psilophyton* represent a type of Devonian cryptogam in which the sporophyte consisted exclusively of branched aerial and subterranean axes. Leaves and roots were absent. Furthermore, these primitive plants had protostelic organization and cauline sporangia borne at the branch tips.

When one reviews the living vascular cryptogams in search of genera with attributes similar to those of the Devonian genera just described, it becomes apparent that *Psilotum* alone (Chapter 17), of the extant genera described in this text, seems to qualify. Here too, one finds leaves and roots absent, as well as protostelic stems and terminal cauline sporangia.

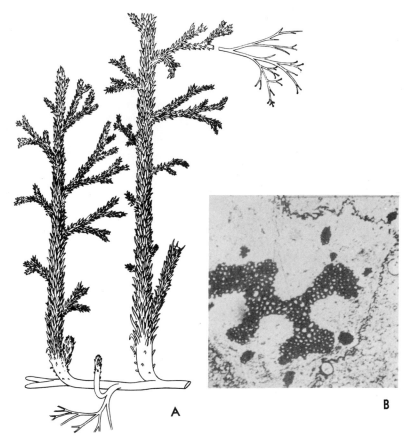

Fig. 30–15. *Asteroxylon mackeyi* Kidston and Lang, from the Devonian of Scotland. A, Rhizome and aerial branches, a fertile system upper right (reconstruction). B, Endodermis and stele. X 22. (From Kidston and Lang.)

No fossil record of *Psilotum* has been discovered, however, so classification of that genus with *Rhynia* and *Psilophyton* in the same division, namely, the Psilophyta, is based entirely on speculation. But it is quite apparent that *Psilotum* stands almost alone among other extant vascular cryptogams.

Microphyllous Fossils

The Devonian flora also contained genera which in certain respects suggest that there were precursors to other divisions of the vascular cryptogams, namely, the Microphyllophyta, Arthrophyta, and Pterophyta. It will be recalled that the division Microphyllophyta (Chapter 18) includes the vascular plants with microphyllous leaves whose sporangia are borne singly on the adaxial surface of leaves (sporophylls) or in their axils. Speculation regarding the origin of these plants is made best on the basis of the comparative morphology of the extant representatives already described and certain fossil forms, several of which are known as early as the Silurian and Devonian (Fig. 30–1), with others occurring in later strata. The fossil genera comprise two series: (1) herbaceous, eligulate, homosporous genera, and (2) ligulate, heterosporous plants.

Fig. 30–16. *Protolepidodendron scharyanum* Krejci, Devonian. Rhizome and aerial branches (reconstruction.) (From Kräusel and Weyland.)

HERBACEOUS, ELIGULATE, HOMOSPOROUS GENERA

Study of the fossil record has revealed that there existed a number of genera, some contemporary with and at least one older than the Devonian *Rhynia* and *Psilophyton*, which are of interest in providing evidence concerning the possible origin of microphyllous leaves and axillary or foliar sporangia. Both the latter, it will be recalled, are attributes of living Microphyllophyta. In this connection, the genera *Psilophyton, Asteroxylon, Baragwanathia, Drepanophycus, Protolepidodendron,* and *Lycopodites* form an instructive if somewhat artificial and unchronological series. In *Psilophyton* (Fig. 30–11) the spine-like emergences superficially suggest microphyllous leaves. However, these emergences are not connected to the stele by a vascular trace. *Asteroxylon* (Fig. 30–15), a Middle Devonian plant, was densely clothed with small *Lycopodium*-like leaves which lacked a mid-vein. A vascular trace departed from the stele but ended at the base of the leaf without entering it. The name *Asteroxylon* was suggested by the plant's actinostele (Fig. 30–15B). *Baragwanathia* (Fig. 30–10), from the Upper Silurian and therefore older than the other genera of the series, was a somewhat larger plant whose stems were clothed with longer, narrower leaves. The latter contained a central unbranched mid-vein connected to the stele by a

Fig. 30–17. *Lycopodites gutbieri* Göppert, Carboniferous. (From Geinitz.)

leaf trace. This series suggests morphological transformations leading from the nonvascular spiny emergence of *Psilophyton* to the true vascularized leaves of *Baragwanathia, Protolepidodendron* (Fig. 30–16), *Lycopodites* (Fig. 30–17), and the extant *Lycopodium.*

The same series is interesting with respect to sporangial position. In *Psilophyton,* and probably in *Asteroxylon,* the sporangia were borne at the tips of branches and therefore were terminal and cauline as in *Rhynia.*

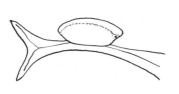

In *Baragwanathia,* the sporangia developed at the bases of certain zones of fertile leaves, much as in *Lycopodium lucidulum.* The exact point of their attachment, whether foliar or axillary and cauline, is not certain. In the Lower Devonian genus *Drepanophycus,* however, the spiny vascularized leaves bore stalked sporangia on their adaxial surface in a fashion identical to that of certain species of *Lycopodium.* Finally, in *Protolepidodendron* (Fig. 30–18), from the Middle Devonian, a plant strikingly similar

Fig. 30–18. *Protolepidodendron scharya-num.* Sporophyll. X 6. (From Kräusel and Weyland.)

in appearance to *Lycopodium,* the sporangia also were borne singly on the adaxial surface of the forked microphyllous sporophylls. *Lycopodites* (Fig. 30–17) is the name that has been assigned by paleobotanists to homosporous, *Lycopodium*-like Middle Devonian and Pennsylvanian fossils which seem to be entirely similar to living species of *Lycopodium.* A comparison of sporangial position in these fossil genera thus indicates a possible shift of the terminal cauline sporangium to an axillary and finally to an adaxial position on the sporophyll. In the ontogeny of the fertile branches and strobili of extant species of *Lycopodium,* the changes from axillary to a foliar position may be observed in some cases. The genera described in the above series possibly illustrate variations in foliar and sporangial morphology which culminated in the lycopods.

LIGULATE, HETEROSPOROUS GENERA

While the extant genera *Lycopodium* and *Selaginella* and the extinct eligulate genera just described are mostly herbaceous plants that lack extensive secondary thickening in their stems, the ligulate, heterosporous fossil lycopods are represented by both woody and herbaceous forms.

A

Fig. 30–19. *A,* A Carboniferous swamp forest as reconstructed at the Chicago Natural History Museum. *B,* Key to some of the organisms in *A:* 4, *Lepidodendron obovatum* Sternberg; 5, *Sigillaria rugosa* Brongniart; 6, *Sigillaria saulli* Brongniart; 8, *Sigillaria lacoei* Lesquereaux; 10, *Sigillaria* trunk; 12, *Lepidophloios laricinus* Sternberg; 13, *Selaginellites* sp. (4–13, lycopods); 14, *Neuropteris heterophylla* Brongniart; 15, *Neuropteris decipiens* Lesquereaux; 16, *Lyginopteris oldhamnium* Willlamson (seed ferns); 17, *Caulopteris giffordi* Lesquereaux (fern); 20, *Sphenophyllum emarginatum* (Brongniart) Koenig; 21, *Calamites* sp. (20, 21, Arthrophyta); 22, *Cordaites borassifolium* (Sternberg) Unger (gymnosperm); 26, *Archeoblattina beecheri* Sellards, a roach. (Courtesy of the Chicago Natural History Museum.)

B

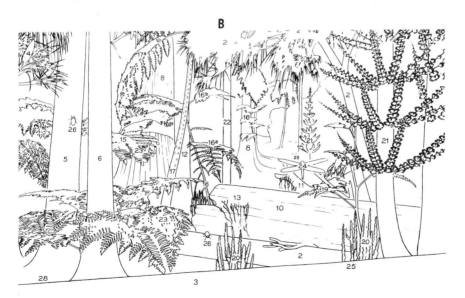

Among the woody genera, *Lepidodendron* and *Sigillaria* attained tree-like stature (Figs. 30–19, 30–20) and, from the evidence of the fossil record, apparently formed extensive forests from Late Devonian through Pennsylvanian times. Remains of these plants are distributed widely in those strata.

Fig. 30–20. *Lepidodendron* sp. Reconstruction of leafy branches and branches from apex of tree. (Courtesy of Chicago Natural History Museum.)

The trunks were unbranched in most cases, except near the top of the mature specimens. Branches, if present, were dichotomous. Although the stems achieved tree-like diameters, only a small portion of the stem was composed of xylem (Fig. 30–21). Secondary growth by cambial activity apparently took place in some species but was limited in extent. The bulk of the stem was composed of a thick cortical layer in which certain meristematic cells added extensive sclerotic, periderm-like layers that functioned in support. The primary stele itself was a simple exarch protostele (Fig. 30–21).

The upper branches in *Lepidodendron* were clothed with elongate, ligulate, linear leaves (Fig. 30–20) which in different species varied in length from 1 cm. to a meter. The leaves were closely and spirally arranged and microphyllous, their traces leaving no gaps in the vascular

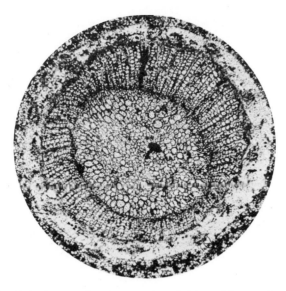

Fig. 30–21. *Lepidodendron* sp. Transverse section of stele and innermost cortex; note central exarch protostele surrounded by secondary xylem. X 25.

cylinder. Abscised leaves left characteristic rhomboidal leaf scars which persisted in older portions of the stem. A single bundle scar is present in the center of each leaf scar.

Probably in all these genera, the tree rested upon what has come to be called a "Stigmarian base" (Fig. 30–22). The name *Stigmaria* was applied originally as a generic name to bases of fossil plants whose other organs

Fig. 30–22. Stumps of *Lepidodendron* trees resting on Stigmarian bases; sandstone casts at Victoria Park, Glasgow. (Geological Survey.)

were unknown. These bases consist of thick, lobed or branched horizontal axes which were sometimes attenuated and branched repeatedly in a horizontal direction. On their surface there are scars of numerous adventitious roots. The occurrence of a large cortical air chamber in both stigmarian roots and those of *Isoetes* and the lobed rhizophore of the latter sometimes are cited as evidences of relationship. The rhizophore of *Selaginella* also has been compared to a stigmarian base.

Lepidodendron probably bore heterosporous strobili in which the microsporangia were higher up on the axis than the megasporangia. The microsporangia produced large numbers of microspores, and the megasporangia contained approximately sixteen megaspores. Sections of some megaspores indicate that they produced a female gametophyte much like that of *Selaginella*. Further details of reproduction are unknown.

Fig. 30–23. *Pleuromeia* sp. (reconstruction). (From Hirmer.)

Finally, mention must be made of the genus *Pleuromeia* (Fig. 30–23), a fossil of the Middle Triassic period. This plant consisted of an unbranched axis several meters in length, borne on a four-lobed base. The base was covered with small rootlets whose internal structure was similar to that of *Isoetes* rootlets and stigmarian bases. The upper portion of the stem bore elongate, spirally arranged leaves. The apex was surmounted by a large strobilus whose sporophylls were peltate. *Pleuromeia* was heterosporous. Further details of its reproduction are unknown.

This brief account of certain extinct vascular cryptogams from Silurian, Devonian, Mississippian, and Pennsylvanian strata of the Paleozoic (Fig. 30–1) and from the Triassic of the Mesozoic will perhaps be adequate to serve as a basis for a brief discussion of the possible relationships and origin of the living Microphyllophyta, *Lycopodium, Selaginella,* and *Isoetes.* Although these extant genera all are herbaceous, plants with similar characters were represented in the Devonian and later periods of the Paleozoic by both herbs and large trees. Extensive secondary growth occurred in some of the Paleozoic tree-like lycopods. This was effected through the activity of a vascular cambium and a phellogen-like cambium which added a thick periderm. Secondary growth is absent from living Microphyllophyta except for the limited amount in *Isoetes*. The factors responsible for the extinction of the tree-like lycopods have not been explained adequately.

The series of eligulate, homosporous genera discussed above indicates a possible transition from the completely cauline, leafless habit of such Psilophyta as *Rhynia* and *Psilophyton* to the type of leaves characteristic of the Microphyllophyta. However, the discovery of the microphyllous *Baragwanathia* in the Silurian, earlier than the leafless Psilophyta, indicates that leafy vascular cryptogams may have originated simultaneously with leafless ones. Furthermore, the possibility of secondary loss of leaves, which has occurred presumably in a number of modern flowering plants, must not be overlooked in these speculations.

While one might conclude, from studying only living genera of lycopods as they are discussed in many elementary treatments, that heterospory is a relatively late innovation, as exemplified in *Selaginella*, the fossil record indicates that it is an ancient character, extending back as far as homospory in the lycopod series. The fossil genera offer no clear comparative data regarding the origin of heterospory. The most impressive evidence in this connection is revealed by study of the ontogeny of sporangia in living heterosporous genera.

The woody members of the lycopod line share in common the attribute of having stems and roots borne on stigmarian bases. With the possible exception of the lower portion of the corm of *Isoetes*, living genera do not have this characteristic. The fossil record is likewise not enlightening with reference to the origin and function of the ligule. Both ligulate and eligulate genera occurred contemporaneously far back in the Paleozoic.

The similarities between the Triassic *Pleuromeia* and *Isoetes* are rather striking. Although the axis of the former is elongate while that of the latter is short, both plants have elongate, spirally arranged, microphyllous leaves. Furthermore, the plant base in both cases consists of a lobed rhizophore. Root structure also is highly similar in both cases. In *Pleuromeia*, however, the sporophylls were much modified from sterile leaves, and the sporangia are thought to have been abaxial, although the evidence for the latter is not conclusive.

It will be seen from this brief account that the Paleozoic flora contained vascular cryptogams that had attributes many of which are common to living Microphyllophyta. Furthermore, there were plants which

were somewhat transitional in habit between the entirely cauline Psilophyta and the leafy Microphyllophyta, although extant representatives of these groups appear markedly divergent at present. Finally, this somewhat fragmentary examination of representatives of the Paleozoic flora indicates that heterospory, frequently cited as the prerequisite of the seed habit, was already well developed in that era.

Arthrophytan Fossils

The Devonian and Later Paleozoic strata also contain remains of plants which are clearly arthrophytan in organization and morphologically similar in many respects to the sole extant genus *Equisetum*. The latter is probably but a remnant of a more extensive alliance of similarly jointed, whorled, and ribbed plants which flourished during the Paleozoic era (Figs. 30–1, 30–19). The factors which resulted in its survival and the disappearance of similarly constructed

Fig. 30–24. *Calamophyton primaevum* Kräusel and Weyland. Reconstruction of shoot bearing wedge-like leaves and paired pendulous sporangia (left). (From Kräusel and Weyland.)

plants are not understood.

On *a priori* considerations, one would expect that jointed plants with ribbed stems and whorled branching would be recognizable readily in fossiliferous rocks. That this expectation has been realized fully is indicated by the numerous descriptions of fossil genera with such attributes. One of the earliest forms with at least some arthrophytan attributes has been described under the name of *Calamophyton* (Gr. *kalamos,* reed + Gr. *phyton*) *primaevum* Kräusel and Weyland. This plant from the Middle Devonian was contemporaneous with certain psilophytan and microphyllophytan forms.

In *Calamophyton* (Fig. 30–24), the stem, the lower portion of which attained a thickness of 2 cm., was irregularly branched but clearly jointed. The upper branches bore whorled, wedge-shaped leaves 8 to 10 mm. long (Fig. 30–24). The type of leaf venation is unknown. Certain of the stouter distal branches bore whorled fertile appendages which consisted of short, slender extensions of the stem, with recurved dichotomous tips. Each of these terminated in an elongate-ovoidal sporangium (Fig. 30–24). The nature of the spores is unknown. Although the jointed stems and whorled arrangement of the leaves and fertile appendages are typically arthrophytan, the small lateral fertile branches, the sporangiophores, suggest the terminal cauline sporangia of the Psilophyta.

Fig. 30–25. *Sphenophyllum speciosum* Royle. Leafy axis and single leaf (upper right). X ½. (From Hirmer, after Arber.)

The genus *Sphenophyllum* (Gr. *sphen*, wedge + Gr. *phyllon*, leaf), which is found in rocks extending from the Upper Devonian through the Triassic (Fig. 30–1), represents a second type of arthrophytan fossil (Fig. 30–25). The plants were small, probably herbaceous, and possibly climbers. The axes were composed of clearly delimited nodes and ribbed internodes, the ribs, however, not alternating in successive internodes as they do in *Equisetum*. Each node bore a whorl of wedge-shaped leaves which in some species were traversed by dichotomously branching veins. Successive whorls of leaves and the internodal ribs were not alternately arranged. Internally the slender stems contained a protostele with exarch xylem. Older stems of certain species had considerable secondary xylem, a cambium, and secondary phloem (Fig. 30–26).

The distal portions of certain branches of *Sphenophyllum* species were fertile (Fig. 30–27); they were composed of an axis bearing whorled, leaf-like bracts which subtended a whorl of sporangiophores (Fig. 30–27). In some species the sporangiophores arose from the adaxial face of the bracts. Each sporangiophore bore three sporangia in *S. dawsoni* Williamson. The spores in some species were only slightly heterosporous.

A third type of fossil arthrophytan plant is represented by the genus

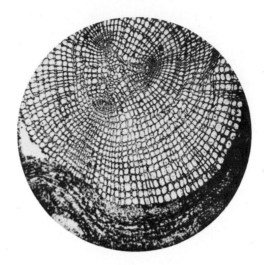

Fig. 30–26. *Sphenophyllum* sp. Transverse section of stele; note triarch protostele enclosed by secondary xylem. X 25.

Calamites (Gr. *kalamos*, reed), the giant horsetail, which is found mostly in rocks of the Mississippian and Pennsylvanian series (Fig. 30–28). The plant was tree-like in habit, in some cases perhaps extending up to 90 feet in height, with a trunk up to one foot in diameter. The aerial portion of the plant arose from a large underground rhizome, as in *Equisetum*. The great diameter of the stems was the result of cambial activity which covered the primary, *Equisetum*-like stele with successive layers of secondary xylem. The wood, however, gives no indication of annual zonation. As in *Equisetum*, the stem contained a large central canal and canals associated with the vascular tissues. Both rhizomes and aerial

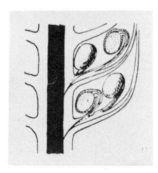

Fig. 30–27. *Sphenophyllum* sp. Median longitudinal section of portion of strobilus; note axis, bracts, and sporangia. (From Hirmer.)

branches departed from the main axis in a series of whorls. The ultimate branches were clothed with circles of slender leaves whose internal structure indicates that they were photosynthetic organs. The adventitious roots arose in whorls from the nodes of the rhizome.

The fertile appendages of *Calamites* were borne in compact strobili.

These were composed of a central axis which had alternating cycles of bracts and sporangiophores (Fig. 30–29). The sporangiophores and bracts were supplied by separate traces from the stele. In some cases, the sporangiophores were peltate and had two sporangia on their adaxial surface. Sections of the sporangia indicate that they were much like those of *Equisetum* and that the sporangial wall was composed of a single layer

Fig. 30–28. *Calamites* sp. Lower portion of trunk at left, upper portion with whorled branches at right (reconstruction). (Courtesy of the Chicago Natural History Museum.)

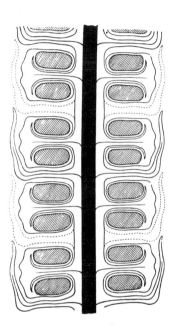

Fig. 30–29. *Càlamostachys* sp. Median longitudinal section of portion of strobilus associated with *Calamites;* note bracts, sporangiophores, and sporangia. (From Hirmer.)

of annularly thickened cells at maturity. There is evidence that some species of *Calamites* were heterosporous.

The three types of fossil genera described above—namely, *Calamophyton, Sphenophyllum,* and *Calamites*—all had become extinct by the end of the Paleozoic (Fig. 30–1) era. From the brief descriptions of these genera it is obvious that whorled branching, whorled insertion of sterile and fertile appendages, ribbed stems, and the presence of sporangiophores are the characteristics possessed in common by these fossil plants and the extant *Equisetum*. The latter, in fact, in its vegetative structure, is a miniature *Calamites*, miniature because of the absence of secondary growth. Whether *Equisetum* may have arisen from a *Calamites*-like ancestor by suppression of cambial activity has been a matter of frequent speculation. However, our knowledge of the vegetative structure of *Sphenophyllum* indicates that herbaceous Arthrophyta also existed in Paleozoic times simultaneously with *Calamites*.

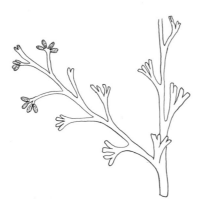

Fig. 30–30. *Protopteridium minutum* Halle. Branch with sporangia at the left, vegetative segments at the right. (Reconstruction.) (From Halle.)

The sporogenous structures of *Calamophyton* and of some species of *Sphenophyllum, Calamites* and *Equisetum* are instructive when they are compared. That sporangiophores are fundamentally cauline is suggested by a comparison of the sporangial position in the Psilophyta, *Calamophyton, Calamites,* and *Equisetum.* Their intimate association with the whorled bracts in *Sphenophyllum* suggests a secondary condition which perhaps is represented in *Equisetum* only by the annulus, a whorl of bracts at the base of the strobilus.

Pterophytan Fossils

Possible precursors of the macrophyllous Pterophyta also have been sought in the Devonian floras, although clearly fern-like genera are not abundant earlier than in Mississippian and Pennsylvanian strata (Fig. 30–1). As a matter of fact, these periods often are called the "age of ferns," although the discovery of seed-bearing plants with fern-like foliage suggests that this phrase may be misleading.

Comparative study of the axes of certain Devonian genera and of early distinctly fern-like plants provides some indication of possible precursors of the Pterophyta and affords insight into the possible origin of macrophyllous leaves. In the first place, the Devonian genus *Psilophyton* itself (Fig. 30–11) possessed stem apices which were slightly circinate in early development, an attribute characteristic of most fern leaves. The genus *Protopteridium* (Fig. 30–30), discovered in Middle Devonian strata, is often suggested as a possible precursor of ferns. Its plant body consisted of branching axes whose ultimate divisions were repeatedly dichotomous, some of them being flattened and almost blade-like, while others were fertile.

The Devonian and Mississippian genus *Cladoxylon* (Fig. 30–31) is

Fig. 30–31. *Cladoxylon scoparium* Kräusel and Weyland. Portion of axis with vegetative and sporangium-bearing branches, one of the latter enlarged, lower right. (From Kräusel and Weyland.)

instructive in two respects. The plants exhibit leaf dimorphism in bearing somewhat flattened, dichotomously lobed sterile leaves and rather plane, almost fan-like fertile leaves at the tips of whose dichotomous lobes oval sporangia were borne. *Cladoxylon* not only gives evidence of flattening and webbing of axes, but also is of interest because of its terminal sporangia which suggest those of the Psilophyta, as noted previously.

A number of genera which occur in Mississippian, Pennsylvanian, and Permian strata were homosporous and fern-like in habit. However, the leaf axis or rachis, the organ of the plant most abundantly fossilized, seems to have been almost stem-like in its prominence and in the complexity of its vascular pattern. This is illustrated in *Stauropteris* (Fig.

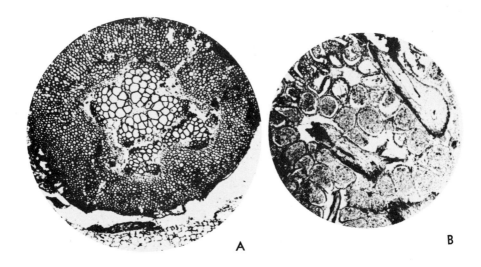

Fig. 30–32.   A, *Stauropteris* sp. Transverse section of leaf axis. X 60. B, *Botryopteris* sp. Sections of sporangia. X 30.

30–32*A*). The stalked sporangia of these plants were borne in groups on certain segments of the leaves, as shown in the photomicrographs of *Botryopteris* (Figs. 30–32*B*). The various ranks of pinnae of these ferns were arranged in successively perpendicular planes rather than in a single plane as they are in modern genera. There is an indication that the sporangia of these ferns approached the leptosporangiate condition.

Pennsylvanian strata contain a number of genera referable to modern families of ferns, among them the Osmundaceae and Marattiaceae. Cenozoic (Fig. 30–1) fossil ferns include many species of modern genera from extant species of which they differ only in minor features.

In summary, the fossil record includes forms which shed possible light on the origin of circinate, macrophyllous leaves from branch systems. In progressively more recent fossils, there can be traced a shift in sporangial position from the terminal cauline arrangement which parallels that of the Psilophyta, through marginal and, finally, superficial types. At the same time, comparison reveals a decrease in sporangial size and spore number and also the association of the sporangia into sori.

Gymnospermous Types

In general, three diverse series of plants with gymnospermous seeds are known among fossil floras. These include (1) fern-like plants,

Fig. 30–33.   *Lyginopteris* sp.   A seed fern (reconstruction).

the seed ferns, called either Cycadofilicales or Pteridospermae; (2) cycad-like plants, the Cycadeoidales or Bennettitales; (3) tree-like or arborescent forms, the Cordaitales.

THE SEED FERNS

The convincing demonstration early in the present century that certain Carboniferous (Fig. 30–1) seeds were related to fern-like vegetative organs, and the subsequent discoveries of such seeds attached to fern-like foliage, firmly established the existence of a group of fossil plants currently known as the seed ferns. These organisms were well represented in the Carboniferous; none has survived to the present. Although a number of pteridosperm genera have been described, our knowledge of only a few, like *Neuropteris* (Fig. 30–19) and *Lyginopteris* (Fig. 30–33), approaches completeness.

Lyginopteris, as reconstructed from fragments of leaves, stems, and roots as well as of reproductive structures, was somewhat like a modern

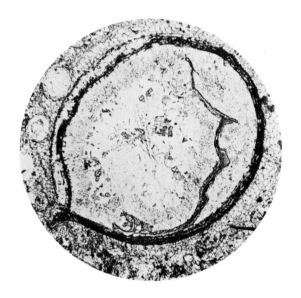

Fig. 30–34. *Lagenstoma* sp. Transverse section of seed of *Lyginopteris.* X 25.

tree fern in possessing an aerial stem. The latter, however, was more slender than those of tree ferns and probably was supported by other vegetation. The stems contained mesarch siphonosteles which were augmented by limited secondary growth. The leaves were large, much divided, and fern-like and were scattered at considerable intervals along the stems. Their blades were differentiated internally into palisade and spongy layers. The roots were adventitious, some of them arising from the stems above the soil and in association with leaf bases. Secondary growth occurred also in the root. The reproductive structures of *Lyginopteris* are represented by fossil branches bearing microsporangia and by seeds (Figs. 30–34, 30–35). The seeds were borne in cupule-like bracts (Fig. 30–36), a characteristic of many seed ferns.

Approximately eight to ten genera of seed ferns have been found with seeds attached to their fern-like foliage. The seeds may be terminal on bladeless branches of the frond, as in *Lyginopteris*, or they may replace the terminal leaflet on a pinnate branch of the frond, as in *Neuropteris*.

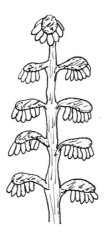

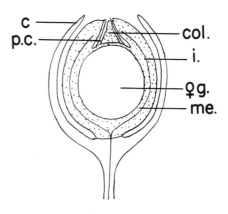

Fig. 30–35. *Crossotheca* sp. Microsporangiate branch of a species of *Lygninopteris*-like seed fern. (From Arnold.)

Fig. 30–36. *Lyginopteris lomaxi*. Median longitudinal section of cupule and seed (diagrammatic): c, cupule; col., central column of pollen chamber; i, integument; me., megasporangium; p.c., pollen chamber; ♀g., ♀ gametophyte (with embryo) (From Arnold, after Oliver.)

No account of the seed ferns, however brief, should fail to mention a group of remarkable fossil fructifications from the Yorkshire coast of England, namely, the Caytoniales, from Middle Jurassic (Fig. 30–1) strata. The fruiting stalks of these plants consist of an axis bearing two rows of small fruit-like organs (Fig. 30–37A). These enclose a number of ovules, the entire structure suggesting an angiosperm fruit (Fig. 30–37B,C). However, the presence of pollen grains in the micropyles of the ovules indicates that pollen was borne directly to the ovule rather than to the surface of the structure that enclosed them, as in the angiosperms.

As a group, the seed ferns are distinguishable from other gymnospermous plants by their fern-like foliage which bore seeds directly among the blade-like branches or on modified branches of the leaves. Neither the microspores nor ovules were associated in strobili. The

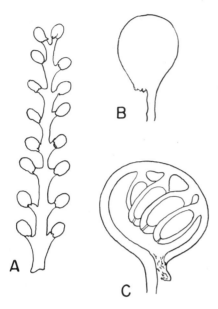

Fig. 30–37. A, *Caytonia nathorstii* (Thomas) Harris. Axis with "fruits." X ⅔. B, G. *nathorsti*. Young "fruit." X 5. C, *Caytonia sewardi* Thomas. Section of "fruit" with orthotropous ovules; note opening in "fruit" for pollination. X 4. (From Thomas.)

pteridosperms appeared possibly in the Late Devonian, reached a degree of prominence in the Carboniferous, and then declined, only a few persisting into the Mesozoic (Fig. 30–1).

CYCAD-LIKE PLANTS

A second group of gymnosperms became prominent in the Mesozoic. These plants were cycad-like in a number of respects but differed from living cycads in others. They are described in paleobotanical literature under the ordinal names Bennettitales or Cycadeoidales and are known as cycadeoids. Like the ferns, pteridosperms, and cycads, the cycadeoids had fern-like compound leaves that arose from short, rarely branched columnar trunks which were covered with the tough bases of leaves of earlier seasons (Fig. 30–38). In several genera, the trunks were more slender and were sparingly branched. As in modern cycads, the trunks contained a massive central pith surrounded by groups of endarch primary xylem which were buried by secondary growth. Extensions of the pith interrupted the woody cylinders. Unlike modern cycads, which have slowly ascending, girdling leaf traces, those of the cycadeoids passed directly into the leaf bases. The pinnately compound leaves were of firm texture and probably reached a length of ten feet in some individuals.

The cycadeoids were monoecious plants, unlike modern cycads. The microsporangia and ovules were associated on compound lateral branches that arose among the leaf bases (Fig. 30–39). The central portion of the reproductive axis was occupied by a massive conical receptacle in which the ovules were borne in surface chambers (Fig. 30–39). A rather long, micropyle-like tube projected outward between the interseminal scales which developed from the sterile tissue between successive ovules. Sur-

Fig. 30–38. *Cycadeoidea marylandica* Fontaine. The earliest described American fossil cycad; collected between Baltimore and Washington, D.C. (From Wieland.)

rounding the ovule-bearing axis were a number of fern-like leaves that bore the microsporangia (Fig. 30–39). The entire structure was surrounded in the bud by hairy, bract-like appendages. Seeds of certain cycadeoids have been found to contain dicotyledonous embryos. The two best-known genera are *Cycadeoidea* (*Bennettites* of some authors) (Fig. 30–39), whose cycad-like stems were robust and rarely branched, and *Wielandiella* (Fig. 30–40), in which the stem was slender, elongate, and branched. The cycadeoids probably arose late in the Paleozoic but attained no prominence until the Triassic (Fig. 30–1). They achieved a dominant position in the Jurassic and persisted through Cretaceous times.

ARBORESCENT FORMS

A third group of extinct gymnosperms may be illustrated by the genera *Cordaites* (Fig. 30–41) and *Callixylon* (Fig. 30–42). These plants, unlike the pteridosperms and cycadeoids, were huge, much-branched trees which formed extensive forests in the Paleozoic. Remains of *Cordaites*

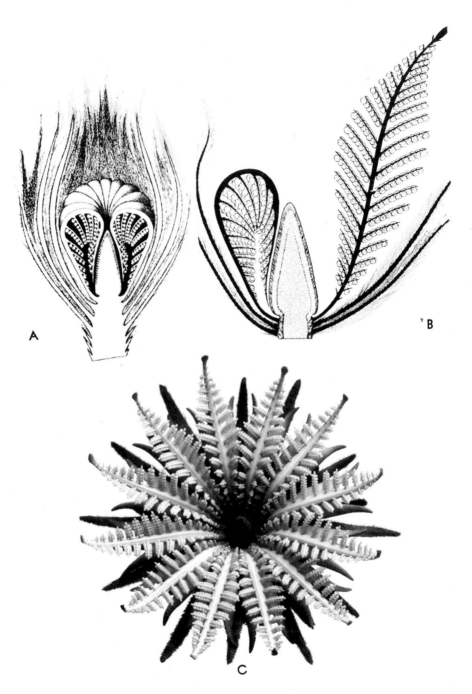

Fig. 30–39. Reproductive structures of cycadeoids. *A,* Unexpanded fertile axis of *Cycadeoidea* showing central conical axis with ovules and surrounding fronds with microsporangia. *B, C. dacotensis* Wieland. Fertile axis, one microsporangium-bearing frond expanded. *C, Cycadeoidea ingens.* Reproductive axis from above; note conical central ovule-bearing strobilus surrounded by microsporangiate fronds. (All reconstructions.) (*A,B.,* from Wieland; *C,* courtesy of Chicago Natural History Museum.)

are widely scattered in Carboniferous strata. The leaves of *Cordaites* were strap-like (Fig. 30–41) and simple and attained a meter in length in some species. Venation was parallel from the base to the apex of the leaves. The latter were restricted to the tips of the youngest branches, the older axes being leafless. The central portion of the *Cordaites* stem was occupied by an extensive pith which was broken up into disc-like

Fig. 30–40. *Wielandiella* sp. Portion of branching axes with leaves and strobili (reconstruction). (Courtesy of Chicago Natural History Museum.)

portions by a number of gaps. The primary xylem groups were endarch or sometimes mesarch and were augmented through cambial activity by a complete cylinder of secondary xylem.

Both the microsporangia and ovules of *Cordaites* were borne in strobilate axes (Fig. 30–41*B*) sometimes associated closely on the same individuals. The strobili were borne among the leaves on young branches. In the axil of each appendage of the microstrobilus there were several candelabra-like stalks with cylindrical microsporangia. The ovules terminated in short shoots subtended by bracts in the ovulate strobilus and were compound. Pollen grains containing cellular male gametophytes have been found within the micropyles of the ovules, but the embryos of *Cordaites* are unknown. The pollen grains contained a large air sac between the intine and the exine. Cordaitan seeds are difficult to distin-

A   **B**

Fig. 30–41. A, Cordaites sp. (reconstruction). B, Cordaites sp. Fertile branch. (A, Courtesy of Chicago Natural History Museum; B, from Grand 'Eury.)

guish from those of pteridosperms unless they are attached to the leafy axes. The cordaitan alliance was important in the Carboniferous but declined later.

Callixylon (Fig. 30–42) is a widely distributed fossil gymnosperm which also was arborescent. Fig. 30–43 shows the microscopic structure of the secondary xylem which has been remarkably well preserved.

In addition to the extinct genera described above, a number of fossil gymnosperms more obviously related to living genera have been described. Among these are Mesozoic cycads, Mesozoic species of *Ginkgo*, and remains of conifers extending from the Paleozoic through Cretaceous and Tertiary (Fig. 30–1) rocks. In the more recent strata—Lower Cretaceous and later, for example—certain pine-like remains have been referred to the genus *Pinites*.

One of the most remarkable fossil conifers is the genus *Metasequoia* which was described in 1941 from Pleiocene (Fig. 30–1) strata by a Japanese botanist. The fossil, as the name implies, has attributes which suggest *Sequoia*. Four years after its description as a fossil, living trees of *Metasequoia* were found growing in central China, and seeds and seedlings have been distributed since all over the world. Although many plants have been designated "living fossils," no other has been described in the fossil state and later discovered in the extant flora.

In spite of the brevity of this account of fossil gymnosperms, it should be clear that the diversity of living forms (cycads, *Ginkgo*, conifers, and

Fig. 30–42. *Callixylon newberryi.* Portion of trunk. X 1/18.

Ephedra) is paralleled by that of the types in the fossil flora. To many botanists there appear to be two distinct series of gymnospermous plants. To the first group, the cycadophytes, in which the leaves are pinnate and fern-like, the stems trunk-like, sparingly branched, armored, and poor in secondary wood, belong the pteridosperms, cycadeoids and living cycads (Cycadophyta). To the coniferophytes, the second series, in which the habit is tree-like with abundant secondary xylem, richly branching armored stems with simple leaves, belong the Cordaitales, Coniferales, and *Ginkgo* group. The Gnetophyta are considered by most authorities to represent an entirely different line of seed plants whose fossil record is too limited to warrant conjecture regarding their origin, although a cordaitan ancestry has been suggested. The coniferophytes extend back into the Upper Devonian; the cycadophytes first appeared in the Mississippian. The two series are distinct, therefore, as far back as they can be traced in the fossil record.

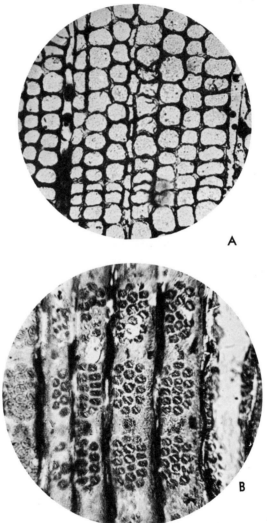

Fig. 30–43. *Callixylon* newberryi. A, Transverse section of wood. X 125. B, Radial section of wood showing multiplicity of pits. X 250.

Origin of the Angiosperms

Long ago, Charles Darwin wrote that the sudden appearance of the flowering plants in relatively recent rock strata was an "abominable mystery"; and in spite of advances in our knowledge of comparative floral morphology and of fossil angiosperms, these words still eloquently symbolize the current state of our knowledge. Remains of angiospermous

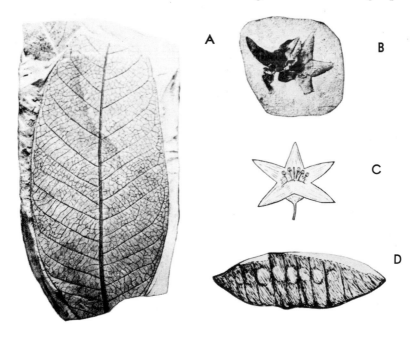

Fig. 30–44. Eocene angiosperm fossils. *A,* Leaf of *Diospyros wilcoxiana* Berry. *B,* Flowers of *Solanites saportana* Berry. *C,* Restoration of same. *D,* A leguminous fruit, *Gleditsiophyllum hilgardianum* Berry. (From Berry.)

plants (Fig. 30–44) are abundant in Late Cretaceous strata (Fig. 30–1) and continue to the present, but they appear without convincing clues as to their progenitors. Most of the remains are of vegetative organs such as leaves and stems. Flowers and fruits are not abundant, although pollen has been well preserved under certain circumstances. As far as is known, the fossil flowering plants were not markedly different from extant genera to which many of them may be assigned with confidence. Although there is evidence that flowering plants existed in the late Triassic of the

Mesozoic (Fig. 30–1), the fossil record has not contributed convincing evidence regarding their progenitors.

However, botanists have not failed to speculate on the problem of angiosperm origin and almost every one of the gymnosperm series has been suggested as a possible point of origin for the flowering plants. The seed ferns, the cycadeoids, the *Gnetum-Ephedra* alliance, and even a hypothetical group, the "Hemiangiospermae," have featured prominently in such discussions. Before proceeding, it should be emphasized that the attributes which distinguish the angiosperms from the gymnospermous seed plants usually are considered to be angiospermy, double fertilization, the development in their seeds of a special nutritive tissue (endosperm) of postfertilization origin, and the widespread presence of tracheae (vessels) in their xylem. With the exception of double fertilization and true endosperm, deviations from these attributes make absolute separation of the gymnosperms and angiosperms very difficult.

One important basis for suggesting a pteridosperm progenitor for the angiosperms is the presence of the cupule around the seed of pteridosperms, which to some indicates a possible precursor of angiospermy. The cycadeoids have been viewed with favor as a possible ancestral line of the angiosperms by those who consider the strobilus-like, dicotyledonous ranalian flowers to be the most primitive type among the flowering plants. The aggregation of ovule-bearing appendages on a central axis surrounded by microspore-bearing appendages in cycadeoids has suggested the organization of a primitive flower, in spite of the absence of true angiospermy and the frond-like structure of the microsporophylls. In the complete absence of a fossil record in support, the Gnetophyta have been suggested as angiosperm precursors for a number of reasons, especially by those who consider the inconspicuous, imperfect type of flower to represent the primitive condition in angiosperms. The bracted ovulate and microsporangiate sporophylls of the Gnetophyta, their aggregation into "inflorescences," the presence of vessels in the secondary xylem, and the absence of archegonia and the free-nuclear female gametophyte of two of the genera (*Gnetum* and *Welwitschia*) all are cited in support of this suggestion.

Because of the lack of strong evidence from paleobotany, clues to the origin of the angiosperms have been sought in the ontogeny and morphology of their flowers, especially those of supposed primitive types in the order Ranales. In this order, long considered to be primitive on the basis of the gross structure of the flower (elongate floral axis, spirally arranged appendages, and indefinite number and separate attachment of the latter) and also because of their presence in early strata, there occur a number of genera with vessel-less xylem, a gymnosperm attribute, and others with a primitive type of carpel (Fig. 30–45). The latter is clearly a folded, three-veined leaf blade that is not firmly sealed along the line of union of the blade margins, which may be merely appressed. These bear interlocking glandular hairs which function as stigmatic surfaces for the reception of pollen (Fig. 30–45). There is no style or localized stigma, but the entire edge of the conduplicate carpel is stigmatic. A progressive series in modification of such primitive carpels has been traced in certain of these genera. This involves localization of the stigmatic surface to form a stigma, formation of a style, and firm closure of the carpels. In spite of such evidence from comparative morphology regarding the origin of carpels from leaves, there is no clear evidence of the derivation of this type of angiospermy from gymnospermous types.

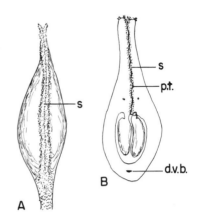

Fig. 30–45. Primitive angiosperm carpel, diagrammatic. A, Ventral view showing paired stigmatic areas, s, running the full length of the carpel. B, Transverse section showing dorsal, d.v.b., and two lateral vascular bundles, stigmatic area traversed by a pollen tube, p.t. (From Bailey and Swamy.)

Some attention has been devoted recently to the problem of explaining the absence of true "protoangiosperms" or angiosperm precursors from the fossil record. The suggestion that such forms may not have been preserved because of their herbaceous nature is vitiated by the widespread preservation of soft, hydrophytic angiosperms. The most attractive hypothesis postulates that the first angiosperms (either a monophyletic or a polyphyletic series) originally evolved in upland habitats and that therefore they were not preserved as fossils because they were so far removed from great basins of deposition (in water) and fossilization. Several lines of evidence support this view. Careful study of the whole fossil record indicates that in each successive plant formation the newer, more complex types, which gradually replace the older forms, are migrants from uplands where they first developed. Furthermore, although the first angiosperms (and other plants) may have been preserved in small, upland fossil basins, these basins would have eroded away and their fossilized remains would thus have been lost. Finally, there is evidence that more abrupt and pronounced environmental extremes of upland environments may favor "successful evolution of a new adaptive type." These lines of evidence support the hypothesis that the primitive angiosperms may have arisen in upland habitats and suggest an explanation for the gap in the fossil record.

Not only does the origin of angiosperms remain in the realm of speculation, but the true relation of the numerous orders and families of angiosperms to each other is conjectural. There are those who raise the question whether the angiosperms are truly monophyletic. Whether monophyletic or polyphyletic in origin, the relation of the monocotyledons and dicotyledons to each other is a further perplexing problem. The monocotyledons are sometimes considered to be primitive and sometimes interpreted as derived from dicotyledonous forms in the ranalian series. That woody genera in each family are primitive and that herbaceous ones have arisen from woody forms by curtailment of cambial activity has been proposed on the basis of comparative anatomy and other considerations. This point of view has found wide acceptance.

If this brief discussion of the possible origin of the angiosperms seems somewhat nebulous and unsubstantial, it will correspond quite appropriately to the state of our knowledge about the problem. Inasmuch as there are such a large number of orders and families of flowering plants, an eloquent manifestation of the great range of variation and complexity, no summary of their classification will be presented in the present text. This aspect of the flowering plants usually is treated in texts and courses in plant taxonomy.

In the preceding pages an attempt has been made to present a glimpse of plants of the past and their significance in relation to our extant flora. The data in this chapter will be drawn upon as the basis for certain conclusions presented in the next and final chapter.

DISCUSSION QUESTIONS

1. What conditions favor the preservation of plants as fossils?
2. Are any plants being so preserved at the present time? If so, suggest locations.
3. Summarize the eras of geologic time and their component epochs or periods. In which were the exposed strata in your vicinity deposited?
4. Define or explain petrifaction, cast, and impression. Which is most valuable to the morphologist? Why?

5. Briefly explain the peel method of preparing fossils for microscopic study.

6. Inasmuch as fossilized vascular cryptogams are known from Silurian and Devonian strata, whereas liverworts and mosses are unknown earlier than in Carboniferous strata, is one to conclude that the latter arose from the former? Explain.

7. What evidence does the study of Paleozoic fossils contribute to the question of origin of microphyllous leaves?

8. What evidence of possible relationship or common origin of Psilophyta and Microphyllophyta is available from our knowledge of Paleozoic plant fossils?

9. Does the fossil record shed any light on the origin of heterospory?

10. What significance do you attach to the fact that Baragwanathia occurs in Silurian strata?

11. What lines of evidence are available regarding phylogenetic relationships of plants?

12. Define the terms ontogeny, phylogeny, monophyletic, polyphyletic.

13. What is meant by the statement, "Ontogeny recapitulates phylogeny"?

14. On the basis of your present knowledge, can you suggest any genera, extant or extinct, transitional between (a) algae and fungi; (b) algae and Hepatophyta; (c) algae and Bryophyta; (d) algae and Pterophyta; (e) Hepatophyta and Bryophyta; (f) Bryophyta and Pterophyta; (g) Hepatophyta and Pterophyta; (h) Pterophyta and gymnosperms or angiosperms; (i) any two divisions?

15. Is all evidence regarding plant and animal relationship speculative? Explain.

16. Describe the genera Calamophyton, Sphenophyllum, and Calamites with respect to vegetative structure and reproduction.

17. What attributes do these genera possess in common with Equisetum?

18. To what do you ascribe the absence of annual rings in the secondary xylem of Calamites?

19. Of what significance is the evidence that certain fossil Arthrophyta were slightly heterosporous?

20. Speculate regarding the nature of the gametophytes in fossil Arthrophyta.

21. What paleobotanical evidence is available regarding the origin of macrophylly?

22. What significance do you attach to the position of sporangia at vein endings and leaf margins in living ferns, in the light of the fossil record?

23. After reflection, would you favor a return to the practice of grouping all vascular cryptogams into a single division, "Pteridophyta," or do you prefer their separation into four divisions? Give the reasons for your answer.

24. Compare the seed ferns (pteridosperms), cycadeoids, and Cordaites with respect to vegetative habit.

25. Compare these forms with respect to occurrence of the sporogenous tissues and their seeds.

26. What morphological features comprise the phenomenon known as the "seed habit"?

27. Can you suggest a reason why the cycadeoids sometimes are regarded as possible progenitors of the flowering plants?

28. Does the fossil record indicate the probability of a common ancestry for living gymnosperms?

29. What origin has been suggested for these plants?

30. What special interest attaches to the genus *Metasequoia*?

31. On what grounds have the Gnetophyta been suggested as possible progenitors of angiosperms?

32. On what grounds have the pteridosperms been suggested as possible ancestors of the angiosperms?

33. What explanation has been suggested for the absence of angiosperm precursors from the fossil record?

REFERENCE WORKS ON PLANTS OF THE PAST

Andrews, H. N. *Ancient Plants and the World They Lived In,* Comstock Publishing Company, 1947.

Arnold, C. A. *An Introduction to Paleobotany,* McGraw-Hill Book Co., Inc., 1947.

Arnold, C. A. Origin and Relationship of the Cycads, *Phytomorphology,* 3:51–65, 1953.

Campbell, D. H. *The Evolution of the Land Plants (Embryophyta),* Stanford Univ. Press, 1940.

Chamberlain, C. J. *Gymnosperms: Structure and Evolution,* Univ. of Chicago Press, 1935.

Darragh, W. C. *Principles of Paleobotany,* Chronica Botanica Co., 1939.

Eames, A. J. *Morphology of Vascular Plants,* McGraw-Hill Book Co., Inc., 1936.

Schellbach, Louis, and Locke, Justin. Grand Canyon: Nature's Story of Creation, *National Geographic Magazine,* 107:589–629, 1955.

Seward, A. C. *Plant Life Through the Ages,* Cambridge Univ. Press, 1933.

Smith, G. M. *Cryptogamic Botany,* Vol. II, *Bryophytes and Pteridophytes,* McGraw-Hill Book Co., Inc., 1955.

Walton, J. *An Introduction to the Study of Fossil Plants,* Adams and Charles Black, 1953.

CHAPTER 31

General Summary

INTRODUCTION

The preceding chapter brought to a conclusion the systematic discussion of representative types, both extant and extinct, of the various divisions of the plant kingdom. Although the treatment of these plants has not been exhaustive in scope, thoughtful reading of it, along with study of the relevant laboratory materials, will have provided a substantial basis upon which to consider some generalizations and conclusions. The purpose of this final chapter, therefore, is to emphasize some of the more important principles and phenomena that have been alluded to in earlier pages. These are discussed under three categories, namely, **vegetative phenomena, reproduction,** and **classification.** The discussion which follows presupposes that the reader is familiar with the more important attributes of the type genera described up to this point.

VEGETATIVE PHENOMENA

Form and Growth

With respect to form of the plant body, the plant kingdom includes a rather wide range of organisms. The simplest are those in which the organism exists as a single cell, the great multiplicity of vital processes taking place within an extremely minute unit of protoplasm. This concept of the **unicellular organism,** as exemplified by such an assemblage as certain bacteria, and algae like *Chlamydomonas, Chlorella,* and *Pinnularia,* among others, is here restricted in scope. It does not include such siphonaceous and coenocytic plants as *Bryopsis* and *Rhizopus,* for example, which may be interpreted more properly as **acellular** organisms in which partition into cells has not accompanied nuclear multiplication.

Increasing complexity of body form resulted when single-celled organisms remained together after division, either in the form of **colonies** in which the cells are remote from each other and separated by colloidal secretions (*Volvox*), or in the form of chains of cells, namely, **filaments.** That such colonies and filaments are relatively loosely organized assemblages of cells is attested by the ease with which fragments survive and regenerate. More highly organized colonies with contiguous cells are illustrated by *Pediastrum* and *Hydrodictyon,* among others.

It is doubtful, however, that the colonial type of organism was the precursor from which the more complex bodies of the higher plants have developed. Instead, the simple filament may well have been their origin. If ontogeny furnishes us with any clue, it is that unbranched filaments preceded both branched types as well as membranous, **parenchymatous** types of plant bodies. In the development of the germlings of such membranous plants as *Ulva* and *Laminaria,* the reproductive cells pass through the stage of an unbranched filament before forming a parenchymatous plant body. The same phenomenon also occurs in developing gametophytes of liverworts and ferns, in the protonemata of mosses, in the sporophyte of *Sphagnum,* and even in the development of the sporophyte of *Capsella.*

The fungi, of course, and many siphonaceous algae have remained permanently filamentous, although they often consist of complex pseudo-parenchymatous plant bodies which result from interweaving of their filaments. This type of construction, however, like the colonial one, probably was not involved in the ancestry of parenchymatous organisms.

By continuous cell division in more than two directions, the unbranched filament may have given rise to another type of plant body, the solid cylindrical axis, exemplified by such algae as *Chara, Nitella,* and many genera of Phaeophyceae. A parenchymatous cylindrical type of construction is represented widely in the plant kingdom, as, for example, in the Psilophyta and the axes of many other plants.

Another aspect of filamentous algae must be emphasized in discussing the origin of plant body types, namely, the phenomenon of **heterotrichy,** in which a much-branched or even disc-like prostrate system supports an erect filamentous one. There are numerous examples of algae in which the erect system has been almost entirely suppressed, so that the prostrate system expands as a membranous parenchymatous layer, as in *Cole-ochaete,* for example. It is possible that some of the early hepatophytan land plants may have arisen from such prostrate algae, and the cylindrical axes of other land plants may have been derived from the erect portions of algal ancestors.

Whatever its origin, the plant body increases in size throughout its individual existence by the process known as **growth.** The latter has been defined as increase in mass usually with accompanying differentiation. Increase in mass without differentiation occurs in the plasmodial phase of the Myxomycota. Increase in mass of multicellular organisms is expressed by increase in cell number and cell size, and these, in turn, are but expressions of synthesis of additional protoplasm. Increase in cell number and size may be entirely separate processes, as illustrated by the rapid enlargement of the fruiting bodies of fleshy fungi after a rain.

In the plant kingdom, growth may be **generalized,** as in free-floating filamentous algae and noncoenobic colonies, or **localized.** The growing region may be **apical, basal, intercalary,** or **peripheral,** the last type exemplified by the cambium of the vascular plants. Representative plants displaying one or another type of localization of growth have been referred to repeatedly in the preceding pages. Growth also may be classified as **determinate** or **indeterminate** and as **continuous** or **periodic.** Determinate growth is illustrated by the acrogynous liverworts, the differentiation of branches of algae and fungi into sporangia or gametangia, and by strobili and flowers in which the axis usually differentiates completely, thus "using up" the meristem. Indeterminate growth is manifested in vegetative apices of many plants in all divisions of the plant kingdom. **Periodic** as contrasted with **continuous growth** involves periods of inactivity. Although this may occur in all plants, it is most strikingly manifested in woody perennial plants of the temperate zone with their closed buds. Differentiation, which usually accompanies growth, will be discussed in the next paragraphs.

Differentiation

In unicellular organisms, differentiation occurs entirely within a single cell. Special portions of the protoplasm and the wall perform all the functions which support the individual and maintain the species. Similarly, in many colonial algae, the individual cells of the aggregate differ little from each other in structure or function. In other colonies, however, the cells are differentiated into so-called **vegetative** and **reproduc-**

tive cells. The implications of these terms in these and similar cases often are misunderstood. Vegetative activities are those that are involved in the maintenance of the individual; reproduction results in the maintenance of the species or race. The differentiation between vegetative and reproductive cells probably arose when cells which originally performed both types of functions lost the capacity for reproduction. All cells are vegetative in the sense that they carry on the functions essential to the life of the individual cell. Although this segregation of function seems quite absolute in such a plant as *Volvox*, because the vegetative cells survive for only one generation, segregation of vegetative from reproductive activities in other plants seems to be less complete. This is evidenced by the widespread occurrence of vegetative reproduction and regeneration from specialized tissues, a phenomenon which will be discussed below.

In addition to this primary dichotomy into vegetative and reproductive phases, further differentiation and specialization are manifest in plant bodies. Differentiation of vegetative tissues and functions in multicellular organisms is a measure of degree of advancement and complexity in the plant kingdom. As a group, the fungi offer few indications that differentiation of the vegetative system, their mycelium, has progressed to any marked degree. The algae on the other hand, include an instructive series in this connection. The colonial forms have already been cited. In the filamentous and membranous green algae, the plant bodies are histologically uniform except for the lower holdfast or rhizoidal cells. In many Rhodophyceae and Phaeophyceae, however, the plant bodies are differentiated into a medullary region composed of cells with few or no plastids, presumably a storage region, and more superficial, chlorophyllous cells which form the photosynthetic cortex. Histological simplicity, of course, characterizes algae whose plant bodies are immersed in a solution containing the elements essential for metabolism. No part of the plant body is far removed from the source of water and the inorganic salts dissolved in it. But in the larger, longer-lived rock weeds and kelps among the Phaeophyta, there has developed a specialized conducting system which transports organic materials from the site of their manufacture to more remote portions of the plant. It is of interest that no water-conducting system has been discovered in such algae. That extensive development of water-conducting tissues does not usually occur in plants with aquatic habitats is indicated also by the paucity of xylem in aquatic representatives of the vascular plants.

The differentiation of a water-conducting system and other specializations have made possible plant life on land. It is true that a number of terrestrial plants are scarcely more differentiated than membranous green algae. Such liverworts as *Sphaerocarpos* and *Pellia,* for example, are not markedly more complex internally than *Ulva.* It is noteworthy, however, that such simple terrestrial plants as the liverworts, as a group, are restricted mostly to moist habitats, although there are such conspicuous exceptions as the corticolous *Frullania* and others. The transfer from a habitat in which the plant surface is bathed in a solution containing its required raw materials to one in which at least one surface is exposed to the atmosphere was probably an important force in selecting differentiations and specializations of survival value. Special cells and tissues for absorption, cuticular mechanisms and stomata, some types of epidermal hairs, and silicification all are manifestations of adaptation to a terrestrial habitat. The development of supporting tissues and of those for the efficient conduction of water and solutes and organic substances throughout the plant body resulted in the possibility of increase in size and extension of plant habitats to less hydric surroundings.

Differentiation in the plant kingdom occurred not only at the cellular level but also in the grouping and arrangement of the cells and tissues in plant bodies as specialized organs, namely, roots, stems, and leaves. True roots, stems, and leaves are those which have vascular tissues, xylem and phloem. However, root-like organs, leaves, and stems, all lacking vascular tissues, are present in certain algae, in the liverworts, and in the mosses. Although these vascularized and nonvascularized structures differ, there is every indication of parallelism in function. The unicellular rhizoids of *Botrydium* among the algae, of the liverworts, of the *Psilotum* rhizome and gametophyte, and of the fern prothallium, the root hairs of the vascular plants, the multicellular rhizoids of mosses, and vascularized roots all perform the functions of anchorage and absorption. Similarly, the blade-like branches of *Sargassum* and the kelps, those of the leafy liverworts and mosses, the microphyllous leaves of *Lycopodium, Selaginella,* and *Isoetes,* and the macrophyllous leaves of other plants all represent expanded surfaces which function primarily in photosynthesis. The axis of *Chara,* that of the kelps, those of leafy liverworts and mosses, and the stems of vascular plants all are organs supporting photosynthetic appendages and performing translocation. The several series just cited indicate that differentiation may follow diverse paths in relation to a given function.

Nutrition and Habitat

Growth and differentiation, of course, involve syntheses of additional protoplasm and its nonliving adjuncts. The preceding chapters have referred to organisms which vary in the materials they require and the pathways by which syntheses are accomplished, and these will be reviewed briefly at this point.

Autotrophic organisms are those which synthesize their protoplasm entirely from inorganic sources. Their enzyme systems, therefore, are the most extensive and complex in the world of living things. As noted in Chapter 9, autotrophism has been interpreted both as a primitive and as a derived attribute. Autotrophic organisms obtain their primary energy either from light, as in **photoautotrophism,** or from chemical processes, as in **chemoautotrophism.** Although most organisms which have chlorophyll are assumed to be photoautotrophic, there are relatively few in which this has actually been demonstrated by cultivation in a controlled environment. On the other hand, in such organisms as *Euglena* and probably many other flagellates, in spite of the presence of chlorophyll, one or more organic substances are required. It seems probable, too, that although organisms can grow in a completely autotrophic environment in the laboratory, such conditions rarely prevail in natural habitats, and it is possible that syntheses from inorganic sources may be augmented by the organic materials of the surrounding medium.

Of the plants considered in this text, the fungi and bacteria which lack chlorophyll are largely **heterotrophic,** with the exception of certain chemosynthetic bacteria. Both **parasitism** and **saprophytism** are exemplified in the various groups of these colorless organisms. Heterotrophic nutrition is not confined exclusively to fungi and bacteria, however. Parasitism and lack of chlorophyll are found in the angiosperms in such a plant as dodder (*Cuscuta*); such saprophytic genera as Indian pipe (*Monotropa*) are widely distributed.

Finally, it should be noted that both photoautotrophic and heterotrophic nutrition may prevail in different phases of the same organism. The nutrition of the developing carpospore-producing filaments (gonimoblasts) of the red algae and the embryos of the higher cryptogams and seed plants is certainly heterotrophic during early stages of development, although the parent plants are photoautotrophic. Similarly, the gametophytes of the heterosporous plants are either saprophytic, in those in which the spores are shed, or parasitic, in those in which the spores are retained, although the mature sporophytes are presumably photo-autotrophic. Whatever the methods and pathways of syntheses, they culminate in the production of additional protoplasm and its subsequent differentiation.

The representative genera described in this text are found in a wide range of natural habitats. As a group, the algae arc predominantly aquatics, although a number occur both in the soil and in moist aerial habitats. A majority of fungi must be classified as hydrophytes, for they cannot grow actively except in the presence of abundant moisture. Most liverworts and mosses also are plants with high moisture requirements, although many are able to withstand desiccation for long periods during which they remain dormant. A few grow exclusively under xeric situations. The vascular plants, probably primarily because of the efficiency of their absorbing and conducting systems, are less restricted and occur in a wide range of habitats, insofar as available water is involved. There is every indication that morphological adaptations for absorbing, conducting, and conserving water are correlated closely with the habitats in which the various plant types can survive.

REPRODUCTION

Once generated, the plant body ultimately reaches a degree of maturity at which the phenomenon of reproduction begins. **Reproduction** is simply the reduplication of the individual and it results in increase in numbers, directly or indirectly. The various reproductive processes cited in earlier chapters have been treated as examples of two basic types, **sexual** and **asexual** reproduction. The former always involves the union of cells and nuclei, and the association of chromosomes and genes in a zygote from which a new individual sooner or later arises. In contrast to the unions involved in sexual reproduction, asexual reproduction includes methods of reduplication of individuals in which no such union takes place.

Perhaps the simplest type of asexual reproduction is that of unicellular organisms in which the **division of the cell** duplicates the individual. In colonial aggregates and multicellular organisms, however, cell division results only in the reduplication of the component cells and in growth of the plant body. In these, a variety of reproductive phenomena have been described. One of the most widespread may be designated as **fragmentation**; it occurs throughout the whole plant kingdom. It involves the separation of the original plant body into segments and their distribution and subsequent development into new individuals. It is illustrated, for example, in the breaking up of colonial algae, in hormogonium formation, in the separation of branches by posterior decay, and by the natural and artificial propagation of segments of leaves, stems, and roots. In a number of cases, special portions of the plant body are set aside as reproductive fragments. This is exemplified by the gemmae of certain fungi, liverworts, and mosses, by the soredia of lichens and the bulbils of *Lycopodium* and certain ferns, and by the formation of bulbs, rhizomes, and stolons in many vascular plants.

Asexual reproduction also is accomplished in the lower cryptogams by the formation of special bodies usually known as **spores.** These may be unicellular or few-celled; in the latter case, they are not very different from certain types of gemmae. Such structures as zoospores, aplanospores, autospores, conidiospores, and other numerous types of fungal spores all may be classified as asexual because they continue their development without prior union with other reproductive cells. According to this concept, the spermatia of rusts and the uniting basidiospores of certain smuts can scarcely be interpreted as asexual spores. Although many spores are asexual in the sense that they develop without union, they are in many cases more or less closely related to the sexual process. Examples of this are seen in the auxospores of diatoms, the zygospores and carpospores of algae, the ascospores and basidiospores of fungi, and especially the spores of the land plants.

The origin of sexual reproduction remains obscure in spite of numerous investigations of the lower algae where sexuality seems to be incipient. Sexuality in such organisms is thought to be incipient both because the individual vegetative cells themselves may function directly as gametes without special morphological differentiation, and because the gametes may develop into new individuals whether or not they undergo sexual union. There is good evidence that even in such lower organisms, in the absence of morphological differentiations, the process of sexual union is regulated by a complex series of hormones, and that disturbances in their functioning prevent the culmination of sexuality. Regarding the actual origin of sexuality, however, nothing is known with certainty.

In some organisms, although sexuality is present potentially the race is maintained through many generations by asexual means, and sexuality may be considered a purely genetic phenomenon. The plant kingdom includes organisms which exhibit a high degree of differentiation in the sexual process. Perhaps the most primitive examples are plants like

Chlamydomonas eugametos and *Spirogyra,* in which there is no morphological differentiation of vegetative cells from gametes. In other
plants, special reproductive cells are differentiated when the individual
attains maturity. These may be scattered in the plant body, as in the lower
filamentous green algae (*Ulothrix, Stigeoclonium*), or they may be
restricted to certain regions where they are borne in special structures
called **gametangia.**

The gametes may be *apparently* similar to each other, as in **isogamy,**
or differentiated, as in **heterogamy** and its advanced form, **oogamy.** The
compatible isogamous gametes, male or female sex cells, may both be
borne on the same individual (**homothallism, bisexuality, hermaphrodit-
ism**) or they may be segregated on different individuals (**heterothallism,
unisexuality**). The application of the terms "monoecious" and "dioecious"
to describe the distribution of sexes on gametophytes is unfortunate,
inasmuch as the terms were first devised to refer to the distribution of
the spore-bearing organs of the asexual generation, the sporophyte. In
this connection it is noteworthy that although stamens (microsporophylls)
and pistils (megasporophylls) of seed plants are spore-producing organs
rather than gametophores, they have long been interpreted as manifestations of sexuality. The segregation of plants into Cryptogamae and Phanerogamae was based originally on the premise that stamens and pistils are
sex organs. Allen[1] has called attention succinctly to this problem in the
following sentences: "Any genetic anaylsis of sex in Angiosperms must
deal almost exclusively with characters of the so-called asexual generation, since those of the much reduced haploid 'sexual' generation have yet
afforded little material for genetic study. To speak of sexual characters in
an asexual generation is paradoxical; but the paradox inheres in the terminology, not in the facts. The diploid sporophyte helps through various devices to effect union of gametes produced by the filial gametophytes, and
to provide for the shelter and nutrition of the embryonic grand-filial sporophyte; and such devices are sexual characters under any usable definition of the term."

The advent of the meiotic process must have been coincident with
the evolution of sexuality. As pointed out more than sixty years ago by
the German botanist Strasburger, for every act of sexuality in which two
chromosome complements (and genotypes) are brought together, there
follows meiosis in which the chromosomes and the genes they bear are

---

[1] C. E. Allen, Sex Inheritance and Sex Determination, *American Naturalist,* 66:97–
107, 1932.

again segregated. The relation between these two phenomena, in time, differs in various plants (and animals). Three fundamental types of life cycle based on these differences have been described. In the first, the vegetative phase is haploid and potentially sexual and is designated as the gametophyte. Gametic union produces a zygote, the only diploid cell in the life cycle. This zygote is interpreted by some to represent the precursor of and to be the homologue of the sporophyte of other types of life cycles. **Zygotic meiosis** restores the haploid gametophytic phase; hence alternation of generations is absent in a morphological sense, although cytological alternation is present.

At the other extreme lies a second type of life cycle, characteristic of most members of the animal kingdom, but also occurring in certain lower plants. In this type, the sexual individual is diploid and meiosis is **gametic.** The gametes alone in the life cycle are haploid, and here again morphological alternation is absent.

Many algae and fungi and all the land plants are characterized by a third type of life cycle which involves morphological as well as cyto-logical alternation of generations. In these, the gametophytic and sporo-phytic phases both exceed a single cell generation (gamete or zygote) in duration and complexity. The diploid zygote gives rise to the sporo-phyte in which meiosis occurs at sporogenesis. The products of meiosis (spores) develop into haploid gametophytes. The two alternants may be free-living (**diplobiontic cycle**) or one may be physically associated with the other. Furthermore, the alternants may be morphologically equivalent (**isomorphic alternation**) or divergent (**heteromorphic alternation**). Both generations may be propagated indefinitely either by naturally occurring reproductive cells or by artificial manipulation. That the chromosome number of itself is not responsible for the divergence of the alternants in ontogeny is clear from the phenomena of apogamy and apospory dis-cussed in Chapter 22.

Sexuality is present almost universally in the plant kingdom. Only the Cyanophyta and Euglenophyta seem to lack it entirely. The significance of sexuality, quite aside from its role in maintaining the species, is the opportunity it affords for originating new genetic combinations at meiosis and gametic union. Sexual reproduction is the mechanism on which evolution proceeds.

In bringing to a conclusion this summary of reproductive processes in the plant kingdom, brief consideration must again be given to the phenomena which culminate in the production of seeds. The initiation of seed formation has certainly changed the face of the earth, for the seed plants, especially modern flowering plants, constitute its dominant vegetation.

A number of coordinated morphological phenomena are associated in the formation of the seed. A seed consists of an embryonic sporophyte embedded within a female gametophyte which is surrounded by the delicate remains of the megasporangium tissue and covered by an integumentary layer. In angiospermous seeds, an additional nutritive tissue, the postfertilization endosperm, may persist. Among these coordinated phenomena may be cited the permanent retention of a single functional spore that produces the female gametophyte within the tissues of its sporangium and surrounding integument and the transportation of the male gametophyte to the proximity of the female gametophyte. The latter is known as **pollination.** In relation to pollination and proximity of the gametophytes, several further correlated phenomena may occur. In gymnosperms, these include the formation of a pollen chamber at the apex of the megasporangium for the reception of pollen grains and the formation of a pollen tube. The latter may be long or short, branched or unbranched. It is chiefly haustorial in the lower gymnosperms but primarily a mechanism for sperm transfer in the higher groups and the angiosperms. Pollen chambers are absent in the latter, the receptive function residing in the stigma of the megasporophyll.

In spite of the probable presence of chlorophyll in the female gametophyte of *Gingko,* the gametophytes of other seed plants are colorless, and their nutrition is based ultimately on the materials synthesized by the parent sporophyte. The nutrition of the male gametophyte of such genera as *Zamia, Ginkgo,* and *Pinus,* which involves breakdown of megasporangium tissue through enzymatic activity, probably should be classified as parasitism. In *Ephedra* and most angiosperms, however, the pollen tube is so ephemeral that there is little probability of its absorbing much nutriment, unless it be from the mucilaginous secretions present in the micropyle or style.

The origin and steps in the development of these coordinated processes associated in seed formation remain in the realm of speculation, since the most trustworthy area of evidence, the fossil record, is eloquent in its silence. As far as is known, these phenomena characterize both extinct and extant seeds and their development. A great majority of botanists and their writings cite still another morphological attribute, namely, **heterospory,** as the inevitable concomitant of the seed habit. It will be recalled that this term is applied to such plants as *Selaginella, Isoetes,* and *Marsilea,* and certain fossil genera, in which the spores that produce male gametophytes are markedly smaller than those that develop into female gametophytes. This is the reason for the terms **microspores** and **megaspores.**

Quite a different interpretation of the spores of seed plants has been suggested (Chapter 24), namely, that the spores are really homosporous in spite of their unisexual potentialities and endosporous formation of gametophytes. A number of lines of evidence have been evoked in support of this view. The most direct is that provided by comparative measurements of the so-called microspores and megaspores of seed plants. Careful measurements of the microspores and megaspores of gymnosperms and angiosperms supply no evidence that so-called megaspores are consistently larger than microspores. In fact, the contrary is true in a number of genera. This is in striking contrast to such heterosporous cryptogams as *Selaginella scandens,* for example, in which the ratio, by volume, of megaspore to microspore is in the order of 30,000 to 1. A second line of evidence in support of the homosporous nature of the spores of seed plants is that endosporous cell divisions to form the early stages of the gametophytes are not restricted to heterosporous plants, as is evident from the spores of *Pellia, Conacephalum, Andreaea,* and *Lycopodium.* A third fact that must be considered is that homosporous spores may be of two classes with respect to sex potential; this is indicated by the heterothallism of the gametophytes of the homosporous *Marchantia, Pallavicinia, Polytrichum* (and other mosses), and possibly species of *Equisetum.* Finally, it has been emphasized that the spores in true heterospory, which involves size differences, represent resting or dormant phases in the life cycle, whereas the spores of seed plants are formed from mother cells and continue development into gametophytes with little if any interruption. Their food supply and that of their gametophytes is gradual rather than simultaneous and precocious. To all these evidences in support of the homosporous nature of the spores of seed plants, proponents of their heterosporous nature rejoin that permanent retention of the megaspore within the sporangium has been responsible for the reduction in its size. As evidence of its pristine free existence, such botanists emphasize the thickness of the megaspore membrane which surrounds the female gametophyte in such genera as *Ginkgo* (8 microns thick) and *Pinus* (3 to 4 microns).

Finally, seed size and certain changes in the protective layers (integuments and/or megasporophylls) are correlated with the phenomena of pollination and fertilization in that they take place only when stimulated by these latter occurrences. The possession of the seed habit together with a wide range of adaptive vegetative features certainly explains the extensive colonization of the earth by angiosperms.

CLASSIFICATION AND RELATIONSHIP

In concluding this volume on the morphology of representative plants, reference must be made again to the problem of classifying the groups of which the type plants discussed are representatives. The problem of classification was alluded to in Chapter 1, when it was stated that fruitful discussion of systems of classification should be deferred until one has become familiar with the plants to be classified. It is assumed that the reader is now in this position, at least to some degree.

In initiating such a discussion, a word of caution from an eminent morphologist seems particularly appropriate. He writes: "Once a system of classification becomes widely adopted, it takes on many of the attributes of a creed. Not only does it constitute the framework about which the botanist does his thinking, but it rapidly becomes a substitute for it. It comes to be looked upon as having emanated from some authoritative and inspired source."[2]

The old saying, "a little knowledge is a dangerous thing," is an appropriate and chastening thought for anyone who attempts to erect a phylogenetic system of classification of plants and animals. A phylogenetic classification is one in which the organisms are arranged in categories or taxa in an order which describes their supposed relationship based on evolutionary development. As expressed by a distinguished taxonomist: "A phylogenetic system classifies organisms according to their evolutionary sequence, it reflects genetic relationships, and it enables one to determine at a glance the ancestors or derivatives (when present) of any taxon."[3] Attempts at phylogenetic classification multiplied after Darwin's *Origin of Species* was published in 1859. In spite of the paucity of paleobotanical evidence and that from the comparative morphology of living plants, faith that plants could be arranged in phylogenetic systems apparently was unbounded, and in some cases

[2] C. A. Arnold, Classification of the Gymnosperms from the Viewpoint of Paleobotany, *Bot. Gaz.*, 110:2–12, 1948.

[3] G. H. M. Lawrence, *Taxonomy of Vascular Plants*, The Macmillan Company, 1951, p. 13.

TABLE 1. A Comparative Summary of Some Classifications of the Plant Kingdom
(Arrows show fate of taxa in successively more modern schemes.)

Eichler and Modifications	Tippo (1942)	Present Text
Plant Kingdom →	Plant Kingdom →	Plant Kingdom
A. Cryptogamae →	Abandoned	
DIVISION 1. Thallophyta →	SUBKINGDOM Thallophyta →	Abandoned
Class 1. Algae →	Abandoned	
Cyanophyceae →	PHYLUM 1. Cyanophyta →	DIVISION 1. Cyanophyta
Chlorophyceae →	PHYLUM 2. Chlorophyta →	DIVISION 2. Chlorophyta
	PHYLUM 3. Euglenophyta →	DIVISION 3. Euglenophyta
		DIVISION 4. Charophyta
Phaeophyceae →	PHYLUM 4. Phaeophyta →	DIVISION 5. Phaeophyta
Rhodophyceae →	PHYLUM 5. Rhodophyta →	DIVISION 6. Rhodophyta
Diatomeae →	PHYLUM 6. Chrysophyta →	DIVISION 7. Chrysophyta
	PHYLUM 7. Pyrrophyta →	DIVISION 8. Pyrrophyta
Class 2. Fungi →	Abandoned	
Schizomycetes →	PHYLUM 8. Schizomycophyta →	DIVISION 9. Schizomycota
	PHYLUM 9. Myxomycophyta →	DIVISION 10. Myxomycota
Eumycetes →	PHYLUM 10. Eumycophyta →	Abandoned
	Class 1. Phycomycetes →	DIVISION 11. Phycomycota
	Class 2. Ascomycetes →	DIVISION 12. Ascomycota
Lichenes →	Class 3. Basidiomycetes →	DIVISION 13. Basidiomycota
	(Fungi Imperfecti) →	(Fungi Imperfecti)

SUBKINGDOM Embryophyta ⟶ Abandoned

DIVISION 2. Bryophyta ⟶ PHYLUM 11. Bryophyta

Class 1. Hepaticae ⟶ Class 1. Hepaticae ⟶ DIVISION 14. Hepatophyta
Class 2. Musci ⟶ Class 2. Musci ⟶ DIVISION 15. Bryophyta

DIVISION 3. Pteridophyta ⟶ Abandoned

PHYLUM 12. Tracheophyta ⟶ Abandoned

SUBPHYLUM 1. Psilopsida ⟶ DIVISION 16. Psilophyta
SUBPHYLUM 2. Lycopsida ⟶ DIVISION 17. Microphyllophyta
SUBPHYLUM 3. Sphenopsida ⟶ DIVISION 18. Arthrophyta
SUBPHYLUM 4. Pteropsida ⟶ Abandoned

Class 1. Lycopodinae
Class 2. Equisetinae

Class 3. Filicinae ⟶ Class 1. Filicinae ⟶ DIVISION 19. Pterophyta

B. Phanerogamae ⟶ Abandoned

DIVISION 4. Spermatophyta ⟶ Abandoned

Class 1. Gymnospermae ⟶ Class 2. Gymnospermae ⟶ Abandoned

Subclass 1. Cycadophytae ⟶ DIVISION 20. Cycadophyta
Subclass 2. Coniferophytae ⟶ DIVISION 21. Ginkgophyta
DIVISION 22. Coniferophyta
DIVISION 23. Gnetophyta

Class 2. Angiospermae ⟶ Class 3. Angiospermae ⟶ DIVISION 24. Anthophyta enthusiasm surpassed critical judgment. One might well conclude, there-fore, that, rich as the years have been in scientific inquiry, the intervening decades, almost a century, would have provided firm and convincing data on which to erect accurate phylogenetic schemes. Although many such schemes have been presented, and although incontrovertible evidence of evolution and kinship has been educed at the species level and below it, increasing knowledge has indicated caution regarding the degree of assurance with which we should postulate relationship among the higher categories. This caution is reflected in a marked increase in the number and degree of polyphyletic systems of the plant kingdom which have been suggested in the literature.

Table 1 presents in comparative fashion a summary of the widely used system of Eichler,[4] somewhat modified by others, the system of Tippo,[5] and the system proposed in the current text. The legend of the table explains the mechanics of comparison. It is clear at once that the number of divisions has increased from Eichler's four, through Tippo's fifteen, to the twenty-four of the present volume. The table shows the progressive subdivision of earlier categories. Classification of the old Eichlerian class Algae into seven or eight separate taxa, raised to divi-sional rank, was the first manifestation of a more polyphyletic viewpoint. The partition of the Eichlerian Pteridophyta, which included the ferns and their "allies" (Table 1) was later. Abandonment of the class name Gymnospermae has been proposed more recently and is accepted in the present volume. The classification here presented differs mainly in that it is still a little more polyphyletic than other systems. Its deviations in this respect will now be presented.

The Phycomycota, Ascomycota, and Basidiomycota, still included in a single division, Eumycophyta, in other systems (Table 1), here are raised to the rank of divisions for reasons already presented in Chapter 14. Similarly, the liverworts and mosses have been treated as separate divisions, the Hepatophyta and Bryophyta, in the present text, as ex-plained at the end of Chapter 16. Doubt that liverworts and mosses are closely related was expressed more than fifty years ago by Goebel. No convincing evidence to contradict Goebel's view has been educed in the interim, in the opinion of the writer.

---

[4] G. M. Smith (*Cryptogamic Botany*, vol. 1, 1955) has presented evidence that this system was used, at least in part, before Eichler.

[5] O. Tippo, A Modern Classification of the Plant Kingdom, *Chronica Botanica*, 7:203–206, 1942. (Tippo calls divisions "phyla.")

The most striking departures of the present system are apparent in the disposition of the vascular plants, now widely conceived of as a single division, namely, Tracheophyta (Table 1). As noted in Chapter 17, uniting such a large and diverse assemblage of morphological types in a single division on the basis of a single common attribute, namely, the possession of xylem and phloem, is open to question. "The result of the widespread practice of classifying plants on single sets of characters has been to encourage overemphasis on certain morphological phenomena, to the neglect or exclusion of others of equal significance, and to try to construct phylogenetic lines on them alone."[6]

Tracheophyta is subject to this same criticism, in the writer's opinion. Accordingly, the vascular plants have been broken up into a number of separate divisions. This has occasioned raising the subdivisions Psilopsida, Lycopsida, and Sphenopsida to divisional rank and has required changing the suffixes of the group names.[7] The quite meaningless name Lycopsida ("having the appearance of a wolf") has been replaced by the designation Microphyllophyta, an allusion to an important attribute of the group. Arthrophyta, an older name, here is used as divisional to replace Sphenopsida, because the latter is based on a fossil genus not as widely known to many students.

The treatment of the macrophyllous vascular plants in the present text (Table 1) also deviates from current practice. As noted previously, to unite spore-bearing plants with free-living gametophytes and seed-bearing plants with retained gametophytes in the same taxon on the basis of their single common attribute of macrophylly seems questionable. In this volume, therefore, the subdivision Pteropsida (Table 1) has been abandoned and has been replaced by six divisions, namely, the Pterophyta (now restricted to macrophyllous plants lacking seeds), Cycadophyta, Ginkgophyta, Coniferophyta, Gnetophyta, and Anthophyta. The reasons for this arrangement were stated in Chapters 28 and 30 and need not be repeated.

Although the number of divisions has been increased by these changes from four (Eichler) and fifteen (Tippo) to twenty-four, the author is strongly of the opinion that in the present state of our factual knowledge

[6] C. A. Arnold, Classification of the Gymnosperms from the Viewpoint of Paleobotany, *Bot. Gaz.*, 110:2–12, 1948.

[7] International Code of Botanical Nomenclature; adopted by the Seventh International Botanical Congress, Stockholm, 1950. *Regnum Vegetabile* 3, Chronica Botanica Co.

an extremely polphyletic view really is the more conservative one. His opinion in this connection and the system of classification used in this volume should not be considered as representing the final solution to the question of plant relationship. The author himself looks upon the suggested classification as an approximation, at best.

Certain criticisms of the classification, as herein presented, have been expressed by several colleagues. The strongest of these held that it is a negative, retrogressive system which overlooks evidences of relationship and separates subdivisions of plants grouped together in other classifications. This criticism has been directed especially against the treatment of the vascular plants and the author's abandonment of the "phylum" Tracheophyta. No doubt a similar criticism was voiced in certain circles when the Eichlerian division Thallophyta, and also its component classes, the algae and fungi, were dismembered a number of years ago. We still speak of "thallophytes," "algae," and "fungi," and one can continue to speak of "tracheophytes" or "vascular plants," "seed plants," "gymnosperms," and "angiosperms" in informal designation of groups of taxa, even if he is reluctant to use these names as proper nouns in the system of classification, thereby formalizing relationships.

In final defense of his proposals, the writer can only reiterate that the appraisal and interpretation of the evidence of evolutionary development and phylogeny vary with the appraiser and interpreter. The translation of their conclusions into a system of classification will therefore vary accordingly. Variations in and prolonged consideration of diverse systems of classification should serve as the inspiration for discussion and should not detract from the reader's understanding of the plants themselves, as they have been presented in earlier chapters.

After all, nature mocks at human categories, and our present series of classifications represent only our current, subjective appraisals of the significance of available data and their bearing on phylogeny. Plants, both living and fossil, remain on the earth despite our clumsy attempts to classify them. "No single system (of classification) can be accepted as final as long as a single fact concerning any kind of plant remains unknown."[8]

---

[8] C. A. Arnold, Classification of the Gymnosperms from the Viewpoint of Paleobotany, *Bot. Gaz.*, 110:2–12, 1948.

Appendix

INTRODUCTION

In the Preface to the Teacher, it was stated that "the author cannot emphasize sufficiently the indispensability of providing the students with living laboratory materials whenever possible." Furthermore, in those cases where nonliving materials must be substituted, the sources of such materials are frequently elusive and not widely known. During the years, the writer has gathered together a number of procedures, methods, and devices all of which have the purpose of providing good materials for the laboratory work in plant morphology. Unless the student can observe, handle, and if possible grow some of this material, the recitation period and textbook, however adequate, will fail to provide him with real familiarity with the type plants.

Some of these methods and devices are original. Others have been suggested by colleagues in various parts of this country and abroad. They are assembled in this appendix in order to inform the teacher (and students) of the sources and preparation of the various materials. The easiest path, from the instructor's point of view, is to have neatly labeled jars of preserved materials arranged in orderly fashion on the laboratory shelves. This is a deadly practice which has done incalculable harm to the best interests of plant science. The writer's interest in the subject almost died prematurely as a result of a second-year course in which the laboratory work consisted almost entirely of the study of (colorless) flowers preserved in rather strong formaldehyde solution. Memory of these dull laboratory periods has inspired a kind of obsession to supply students with living plants whenever possible. No doubt, many of the suggestions here summarized are well known to experienced teachers and to them they will seem unnecessary.

LABORATORY STUDY OF ALGAE (Chapters 2–8)

Methods of Cultivation

There is no longer any excuse for failure to provide students with a wide array of living algae for study in the laboratory. For those who are far from the coast, the marine algae may prove difficult to obtain, but even this may be overcome, in part. A great variety of living algae can be collected from moist rocks and wood, ponds, ditches, brooks, creeks, lakes, springs, lily pools and other ornamental pools, and from temporary puddles in a given vicinity. Periodic collection and microscopic examination of living materials from such sources over a period of years, with careful recording of data, will usually indicate a repeated seasonal appearance of a succession of algal forms. Coarser organisms may be collected by hand, directly into discarded mayonnaise jars filled to not more that three-quarters capacity. A plankton-type dip net is a useful adjunct for concentrating smaller algae. They can also be collected by squeezing coarser algae and aquatic vegetation and collecting the liquid in jars. The undisturbed soil and moist flower pots in parts of many greenhouses furnish numerous algae useful in teaching. For those who wish to be certain in advance of having at least some of the type plants available and for those who wish to demonstrate particular stages in the life cycle, the great improvements in algal culture techniques in recent decades will be helpful. Relevant references are listed at the end of this appendix. After obtaining the original cultures, either through purchase or by isolating the organisms with fine needles or glass capillary pipettes, a large number of fresh-water algae can be maintained with a minimum of effort by one of several methods (Bold, 1942; Pringsheim, 1946). Some of these will be described in detail.

Probably the most useful and universally applicable technique for maintaining unialgal cultures of a wide range of fresh-water algae is the "soil-water culture method" of Pringsheim (1946, 1950). This method requires a minimum of equipment, of time, and of effort. The writer uses either culture tubes (test tubes) or half-pint milk bottles. These are cleaned thoroughly with detergent, rinsed repeatedly in water, and then prepared as follows. A small quantity of calcium carbonate ($CaCO_3$) (approximately as much as the tip of a scalpel full, for a tube, correspondingly more for the milk bottle) is placed at the bottom of the culture vessel and covered with about ½ inch of garden soil. The culture vessel is filled three-quarters full by allowing a gentle stream of tap water to run down the side wall. The bottle may be stoppered *loosely* with cotton or covered with a small piece of glass. The culture vessels are then steamed (without pressure) for one hour at 100° C. on each of three successive days. Sufficient calcium carbonate should have been added so that it is visible under the soil when the steaming process has been completed. The culture vessels may be inoculated as soon as they have cooled sufficiently, but better results are usually obtained if they are stored and allowed to clear by settling before they are inoculated. This method is herein designated by the abbreviation **SW**.

Unialgal cultures of many algae also may be maintained in inorganic salt solutions both in the liquid state and when solidified with agar. The following formula has proven satisfactory: Six stock solutions, 400 ml. in volume, are employed, each containing one of the following salts in the concentration listed:

$NaNO_3$	10.0 g.	KH_2PO_4	7.0 g.
$CaCl_2$	1.0 g.	$MgSO_4 \cdot 7H_2O$	3.0 g.
K_2HPO_4	3.0 g.	NaCl	1.0 g.

For the proper dilution, 10 ml. of each stock solution are added to 940.0 ml. of pyrex-distilled water. To this are added one drop of 1.0% $FeCl_3$ solution and 2 ml. of a standard minor element solution. This diluted solution, thus prepared, is designated as **IL**. Addition of 15 g. of agar to a liter of this inorganic solution yields a satisfactory solid medium on which algae may be maintained for long periods without transfer. This solidified medium is designated **IA**. Substitution of 50 ml. of soil extract for 50 ml. of IL per liter provides a richer medium on which many algae grow more luxuriantly. This medium is designated **ISL** for the liquid form and **ISA** when solidified with agar. The soil extract may be prepared by autoclaving for one hour at 15 lb. pressure a mixture of equal volumes of garden soil and distilled water. After the mixture has cooled and settled, the supernatant liquid is decanted, filtered, and resterilized. Some investigators prefer merely to steam the soil-water mixture rather than to autoclave it. The soil extract is designated as **S** in this appendix.

An increasingly large number of marine algae are being cultivated successfully in laboratory cultures. *Callithamnion,* a rhodophycean form with a diplobiontic cycle, has been cultivated through nine complete cycles in the laboratory. Many marine diatoms, Chlorophyta, Phaeophyta, and *Callithamnion* grow well in an enriched sea water, Schreiber's (1930) solution, herein designated **SCHR,** when the solution has been fortified with soil extract, **S,** as suggested by Föyn (1934). Plants cultivated in this soil extract-enriched Schreiber's solution, **SSCHR,** in petri dishes or larger vessels, approximate in size those growing in nature. Schreiber's solution is prepared as follows:

NaNO$_3$	0.1 gr.
Na$_2$HPO$_4$	0.02 gr.
Dist. H$_2$O	50.0 ml.
Sea H$_2$O to	1000.0 ml.

In preparing the SSCHR solution, Föyn's original formula may be employed:

NaNO$_3$	0.1 gr.
Na$_2$HPO$_4$	0.02 gr.
Soil extract	50.0 ml.
Sea H$_2$O to	1000.0 ml.

It has been demonstrated also that crude cultures consisting merely of a branch of a naturally occurring marine alga, transplanted to a large test tube containing about 2½ inches of sea water filtered through paper, will survive for several months in the light from a north window. The temperature range should not exceed that of the normal habitat of the alga. Humm (1948), who described this method, reported successful maintenance of *Ulva, Enteromorpha, Cladophora, Codium, Ectocarpus, Dictyota, Agardhiella,* and *Polysiphonia harveyi* with this technique.

Although light from a north window often is adequate to maintain cultures of many types of algae, an artificial light source is useful to effect rapid development of cultures, especially during the winter months. A fluorescent fixture arranged to illuminate the culture vessels which have been placed on a white surface affords a simple and relatively inexpensive method of illumination. An intensity of 100 foot-candles is adequate to maintain active growth of most cultures. Higher intensities increase the rate of growth. The organisms are apparently variable in their light requirements; the optimum for each type will soon become apparent through experience.

In summary, the more important types of algae discussed in this text, which have been or can be cultivated easily in the laboratory, are listed below. All fresh-water species usually grow readily in soil-water cultures.

This medium is indicated, however, only for those that will not grow readily in other media. After each algal type there is appended the abbreviation for the suitable solution or solutions in which the organism may be cultivated. The abbreviations and their corresponding meanings are repeated at this point for convenience:

SW = Soil-water cultures
IL = Inorganic medium, liquid form
IA = Inorganic medium, solidified with 1.5% agar
ISL = Inorganic medium, with soil extract, **S**, liquid form
ISA = Inorganic medium, with soil extract, **S**, solidified with 1.5% agar
SCHR = Schreiber's (1930) solution
SSCHR = Schreiber's solution with soil extract, **S**, as suggested by Föyn (1934)

I. Cyanophyta
   Calothrix: IA
   Chroococcus: SW

II. Chlorophyta
   Carteria: ISL, ISA
   Chlamydomonas:
      C. chlamydogama: ISA
      C. eugametos: IA
      C. monadina: SW
   Chlorella: IL, IA
   Chlorococcum: IL, IA
   Cladophora (germlings)
      C. glomerata: SW
      C. albida: SSCHR
   Closterium: SW
   Cosmarium: SW
   Desmidium: SW
   Enteromorpha: SSCHR
   Hydrodictyon: SW
   Micrasterias: SW
   Mougeotia: SW
   Oedogonium: SW
   Pandorina: SW
   Pediastrum: SW
   Scenedesmus: IL, IA
   Spirogyra: SW (minus CaCo₃)
   Stigeoclonium: SW
   Ulothrix: SW

   Ulva: SSCHR
   Volvox: SW
   Zygnema: SW

III. Phaeophyta
   Ectocarpus: SSCHR
   Fucus (germlings): SSCHR
   Laminaria: SSCHR
   Pylaiella: SSCHR

IV. Rhodophyta
   Bangia: SSCHR
   Callithamnion: SSCHR
   Griffithsia (germling): SSCHR
   Nemalion (germling): SSCHR

V. Chrysophyta
   Botrydiopsis: IA
   Botrydium: ISA
   Ochromonas: SW
   Synura: SW (20° C. or less)
   Tribonema: SW
   Vaucheria: SW
   Marine diatoms: SSCHR
   Fresh-water diatoms: SW

Specific Methods for Selected Algae

SEXUALITY IN CHLAMYDOMONAS

In *C. chlamydogama* and *C. eugametos,* especially the latter, the most successful demonstrations of sexuality may be effected by using heavily inoculated agar cultures (petri dishes) between 10 and 21 days old. In *C. monadina,* stages in heterogamous union are observable in the phototactic ring near the surface of the culture. *C. chlamydogama* and *C. eugametos* are heterothallic. Both mating types may be obtained from the Culture Collection, Department of Botany, Indiana University, Bloomington, Indiana, and from the Culture Collection, Botany School, Cambridge, England. In demonstrating sexuality in these heterothallic species, the following procedure usually gives satisfactory results. About an hour or more before the class is to convene, the petri dish or agar slant cultures (10 to 21 days old) should be flooded with distilled water. This stimulates motility of the organisms if the dishes are illuminated. If the cultures are not agitated, the motile cells will assemble at the most brilliantly illuminated point in the culture vessel. When drops of densely swarming cells from each mating type are mixed in Pyrex spot plates or depression slides, or as hanging-drop preparations, the clumping phenomenon follows almost immediately and pairing, gametic union, and zygote formation ensue at temperatures below 25° C. Hanging-drop cultures are the most convenient for study of the details of gametic union under high magnification, especially if one restricts his observations to cells near the margin of the drop. The flooded stock cultures often yield sexually active material for several days if they are intermittently stored in darkness. For actual plasmogamy in *C. eugametos,* hanging-drop preparations should be started periodically every eight hours for several days, in order to provide a series of stages from clump formation to spiny-walled zygospores.

SEXUALITY IN PANDORINA MORUM

Heterogamous and heterothallic sexual reproduction is readily demonstrable in *Pandorina morum* Bory, both strains of which were isolated by Professor R. C. Starr and maintained by him at the Culture Collection of Algae at Indiana University. The organisms grow well in SW. For demonstration of sexuality, concentrated suspensions of the two strains should be mixed in Pyrex spot plates or small petri dishes to which fresh SW is added. Sexual fusions should be abundant between 10 and 24 hours later.

CHLOROCOCCUM AND CHLORELLA

These genera grow luxuriantly in IA cultures. The petri dish cultures for class use should be inoculated approximately 14 to 21 days before these genera are to be studied. Some species of *Chlorococcum* form zoosporangia in such agar cultures; others remain in a vegetative state. Zoosporangium formation may be induced in the latter by transferring some of the surface growth to a freshly poured agar surface 24 hours before the organism is to be studied. Material scraped from the surface of agar cultures into distilled water in ordinary mounts or into hanging-drop preparations usually shows liberation of zoospores and sexuality, in sexual strains.

Chlorella also grows well in surface-inoculated agar cultures. Actively growing cultures usually show an abundance of cells with enclosed autospores.

HYDRODICTYON AND PEDIASTRUM

Although these genera are widely distributed in nature, the former is seasonal in appearance and the latter is frequently sparingly intermingled with other algae; hence unialgal cultures are especially desirable. Huge nets, rivaling in size those developing in nature, may be grown in laboratory SW cultures, provided single nets are inoculated into large, well-illuminated vessels. The changes in cellular structure can be demonstrated by a series of cultures with nets of various ages. Although the numerous nuclei are usually visible with proper illumination at magnifications of 970X, staining in Chamberlain's iodine solution makes them more apparent. Transfer of portions of older nets into shallow petri dishes with ISL or the supernatant liquid from SW tubes 48 to 72 hours before study frequently evokes zoospore and/or gamete formation.

Similarly, mature colonies of *Pediastrum* can be induced to undergo daughter colony formation by transfer into fresh media 48 to 72 hours before class is to convene.

SEXUALITY IN SPIROGYRA

Certain strains of *Spirogyra*, isolated by Miss Ann Allen, Department of Botany, Indiana University, grow well in SW and can be induced to conjugate at will. Masses of rapidly growing filaments are placed on the surface of plain agar (1.5% in distilled water) in petri dishes and illuminated. Lateral and sometimes scalariform conjugation usually occur in 3 or 4 days at 22° C. SW without $CaCO_3$ is favorable for many species of *Spirogyra*.

SEXUALITY IN DESMIDS

Cultures of sexual strains (heterothallic) of *Cosmarium* are available at the Culture Collection, Indiana University. Two homothallic races of *Closterium* also are under cultivation. The latter form zygospores without special manipulation in SW cultures. Actively growing strains of *Cosmarium* should be mixed in shallow watch glasses, petri dishes, or spot plates 96 and 48 hours before the class is to convene. Mixtures 48 hours old illustrate pairing of gametes; actual cell unions should be visible in the 96-hour cultures.

CHARA AND NITELLA

Certain species of these genera can be maintained in the laboratory and greenhouse in large culture vessels (battery jars, cookie jars, and crocks) in the bottom of which sandy soil has been placed. Soil from the vicinity of the pond where the plants are growing and water from the same source usually produce the best results.

EUGLENA, PHACUS, AND TRACHELOMONAS

Strains of many species of *Euglena,* such as *E. gracilis* and *E. mesnili,* may be maintained indefinitely in the laboratory in SW media to which a rice grain, wheat or barley grain, or split pea has been added. *E. gracilis* strains multiply luxuriantly in very dilute supernatant from boiled split peas. Approximately 40 split peas per liter of tap water is satisfactory. The cultures should be transferred every two months, and always three or four days before they are to be used in class.

Some species of *Phacus* and many species of *Trachelomonas* thrive in well-illuminated SW cultures to which a barley grain or split pea has been added.

BACILLARIOPHYCEAE

A number of the smaller pennate diatoms grow readily on ISA or ISL, and in SW cultures. The larger species of *Navicula* and *Pinnularia* and the centric *Melosira* (fresh-water species) frequently occur on the bottom sludge of pools and springs with cold water. A number of marine diatoms grow luxuriantly in SSCHR. Fossil diatoms may be demonstrated in suspensions of silver polish. A small amount of diatomaceous earth suspended in water yields instructive and spectacular preparations. Glass slides suspended in bodies of fresh and salt water soon become covered with a flora of diatoms (and other organisms).

BOTRYDIOPSIS, BOTRYDIUM, TRIBONEMA AND VAUCHERIA

Botrydiopsis, like *Botrydium* a member of the soil flora, rarely occurs in sufficient abundance to be recognizable as such; hence it is necessary to resort to cultures. The organism grows readily on ISA medium and may be treated like *Chlorococcum* to induce zoosporogenesis and zoospore liberation.

Although *Botrydium* grows well in laboratory culture on ISA, if possible the cultures should be supplemented by field-grown material in which the sacs are usually larger and covered with calcareous granules. The plants are spectacular on soil when viewed under a wide-field binocular with proper illumination. Immersion of cultivated or natural plants in distilled water evokes gamete formation. Aplanospores are formed when the soil or cultures begin to dry.

Tribonema is widespread in the colder months of the year or in colder bodies of water. SW cultures provide material suitable for demonstrating the essential attributes of the organism.

Vaucheria occurs frequently in greenhouses on the surface of undisturbed soil. A mat of soil with the alga should be cut from the flower pot and placed in a covered petri dish. Examination of such a mass culture under low magnification with reflected light provides better insight into its habit than does the tangled mass of threads which usually results from attempting to transfer material to a slide. For details of cell structure, however, the latter expedient is necessary. Aquatic species are easier to study, and transfer of portions of the mat to small petri dishes several days before they are to be studied permits regeneration of torn segments. Terrestrial species often form zoospores when immersed in water in petri dishes. Sex organs of aquatic species frequently are most abundant in the portions of the plant stranded on the marginal soil. Similarly, the exposed threads in SW cultures are usually fruiting.

PHAEOPHYCEAE AND RHODOPHYCEAE

Because of distance from the coast, it is frequently impractical to obtain living material of all the illustrative types of Phaeophyceae and

Rhodophyceae discussed in this volume. However, *Ectocarpus, Pylaiella, Laminaria, Fucus, Sargassum,* and *Ascophyllum* have been successfully shipped to great distances from the Marine Biological Laboratory, Woods Hole, Mass., during the winter months. Dried plants of the coarser species present a fairly natural appearance when soaked in tap water some hours before use. SSCHR cultures of the more delicate types like *Ectocarpus* and *Pylaiella* will probably survive far from the seashore, especially if the temperature of the culture room is 22° C. or lower. It is probable that an increasing number of marine Rhodophyceae will be available in culture. The experiments of Humm (1948) in this connection are promising. A number of fresh-water Rhodophyceae are available for study in many localities. *Batrachospermum* is widely distributed in cold waters and is an excellent type for illustrating the sex organs and development of carposporangia. The reproductive branches are almost colorless and therefore readily distinguishable from the photosynthetic branches in crushed preparations of living material. Transverse sections or longitudinally bisected segments of the thallus of *Lemanea australis* provide instructive views of spermatia, carpogonial branches (with branching trichogynes), and carposporangium development. No diplobiontic types occur in fresh water. Well-preserved material of such marine genera as *Nemalion, Polysiphonia,* and *Griffithsia* is satisfactory for laboratory study, especially if supplemented by herbarium specimens of the plants themselves. Air-dried *Nemalion* soaked in sea water some hours before study is better in some respects than preserved material.

Miscellaneous Aids for the Study of Algae

Mounting certain algae in India ink provides a striking demonstration of their sheaths, which are sometimes almost invisible without special treatment. This technique is especially useful in planktonic species of *Anabaena* and *Polycystis* and in certain desmids, *Spirogyra, Zygnema,* and *Mougeotia.* The sheaths also stain with aqueous solutions of methylene blue.

Staining the cells of many algae with Chamberlain's iodine solution (Chamberlain, 1935) not only aids the detection of starch grains and certain other photosynthates like Floridean starch but frequently clarifies the structure of the pyrenoid, plastid, and nucleus.

Aceto-carmine stain applied directly to fresh material of a number of algae stains the nuclear material without or after gentle heating. This fixative-stain combination is especially valuable for Myxophyceae, Euglenophyceae, and Bacillariophyceae. Beautifully clear preparations of the carpogonial branches of *Nemalion* and *Griffithsia* may be made by this procedure. Most Chlorophyceae require prefixation in absolute alcohol-acetic acid 3:1, saturated with ferric acetate, prior to staining with aceto-carmine.

Finally, a few words must be said regarding the optical equipment necessary for demonstrating the gross and minute structure of algae. For such morphological features as red eyespots, contractile vacuoles, and flagella, it is usually necessary to study the cells with magnification of approximately 970X and sufficiently intense illumination. Substage lamps are not intense enough in most cases. For the gross structure and arrangement of branching in many algae, material mounted in watch glasses for study under the various magnifications provided by a wide-field binocular is especially instructive.

LABORATORY MATERIALS ON FUNGI (Chapters 9–14)

Introduction

Stock cultures of many of the organisms described in Chapters 9 through 14 are maintained in a number of university laboratories. They can also be purchased from various biological supply houses and from the American Type Culture Collection.[1] Most of them can be maintained on simple media with little effort and infrequent transfer. The media may be purchased in dehydrated form, prepared, distributed into smaller vessels (flasks and culture tubes), and sterilized in an autoclave or pressure cooker. Because of the great range of organisms treated under the title "fungi," *sensu lato*, directions are presented below under several categories.

Schizomycota

The chapter on bacteria was written on the assumption that more extensive attention will be devoted by the student to these organisms in a special course in bacteriology. Living bacteria, other than named pure cultures, are easy to obtain from an infinite variety of organic substrata. A heavy growth will appear as a surface scum in undisturbed hay infusions (made by cutting up stalks of hay or dried grass and submerging

---

[1] Address: 2029 M Street, N.W., Washington 6, D.C.

them in warm water) or in dishes containing decaying seeds submerged in water. Most satisfactory results will be obtained by studying the organisms under magnifications of at least 970X (oil immersion) at the margin of hanging-drop preparations. Bacteria from tooth pickings smeared in a small amount of saline solution are also of interest. Study of the living organisms may be supplemented with stained preparations of various pathogenic and nonpathogenic forms. Phase and dark-field demonstrations of living bacteria are especially striking.

Myxomycota

The plasmodial stage of *Physarum polycephalum* is maintained in active condition or as sclerotia in many botanical laboratories and may be purchased from biological supply houses. Several days before the class is to study slime molds, small transfers of the plasmodium should be placed on the surface of petri dishes one-third full of inorganic salt agar, IA. Several small fragments of uncooked rolled oats should then be placed directly on the transferred bit of plasmodium. The latter will engulf and digest the oatmeal, synthesize more protoplasm, and spread out in fan-shaped fashion. By continuous transfer and feeding with fragments of oatmeal, the plasmodium can be increased rapidly in amount. Its movement may be observed with low magnifications on the surface of agar. Inorganic agar is recommended because it markedly reduces the danger from contamination by fungi. When oatmeal is withheld from the plasmodia, they migrate to the sides and covers of the petri dishes and form their many-headed fruiting bodies. Spore germination to form motile cells occurs rapidly when spores of many slime molds are planted in water in hanging-drop preparations. Many genera occur in the sporangial stages on decaying leaves, stumps, and wood. They may be preserved by drying and mounted in shallow cardboard boxes suitable for study under the wide-field binocular microscope. Plasmodia may also be induced to migrate from decaying wood fragments by placing them in moist chambers with moist filter paper.

Phycomycota

CHYTRIDS

Cultures of *Polychytrium aggregatum* are available in several university laboratories or they may be obtained from the American Type Culture Collection. This organism grows readily on a medium of the following composition:

Peptone	0.1%
Dextrose	1.0%
Yeast extract	0.1%
Dist. H_2O	100.0 ml.

This liquid may be solidified with 1.5% agar to produce a satisfactory solid medium. Large numbers of thalli with sporangia may be obtained by diluting the above solution with 6 parts of water to 4 of solution.[2]

A good many other types of chytrids may be collected in advance of class study by using various types of substrata as "bait" in samples of pond and ditch water and in soil-water suspensions. Water containing bottom sludge and soil usually yields a rich chytrid flora. *Elodea* leaves, young corn and wheat leaves, all previously bleached in 70% alcohol, are rinsed in water and introduced into petri dishes or finger bowls of pond water, etc.; they are examined microscopically at intervals of several days for the presence of chytrids. The mature zoosporangia of chytrids frequently liberate their zoospores when the "bait" is transferred to a slide with fresh water. Untreated cellophane, onion scale epidermis, skin scrapings, and hair may also be used as "bait."

ALLOMYCES

Allomyces may be isolated from soil by introducing some soil into finger bowls of charcoaled water (water shaken vigorously with charcoal and subsequently filtered). After the soil has settled, the suspension is baited with boiled split hemp seed (obtainable from Eimer and Amend or from pet shops as bird seed). A number of laboratories maintain stocks of races of *Allomyces* stored on dried hemp seeds removed from the above cultures. The resistant sporangia stand desiccation well. In addition, agar cultures of both the sexual gametophyte stage and the asexual sporophytic phase may be maintained on agar of the following composition (Emerson, 1941):

K_2HPO_4	1.0 g.
$MgSO_4 \cdot 7H_2O$	0.5 g.
Difco Yeast Extract	4.0 g.
Soluble starch	15.0 g.
Agar	20.0 g.
Dist. H_2O	1000.0 ml.

---

[2] Personal communication from Dr. Libero Ajello.

The writer has grown them also on ordinary Difco Potato Dextrose agar (PDA). In inoculating the two strains, care must be exercised not to use freshly prepared moist agar. This will effect liberation of either zoospores from the sporophytic strain or gametes from the gametophytic strain, so that the original phases will become lost or mixed. Material should be transferred into the drier region of agar slants or drier petri dishes which have been prepared some days in advance of transfer. For class study, portions of the agar culture may be removed from the petri dish with the fungus intact, mounted in water, flooded with a little water (to prevent accumulation of an air film), covered with a cover glass, and gently compressed by using a blunt eraser. Aquatic cultures may be grown on boiled split hemp seed in charcoal water. Thalli suitable for class study develop on hemp seed within 40 to 72 hours after inoculation. For microscopic study, the writer lifts the half hemp seed with the fungus to the surface of a slide in a drop of charcoal water and then cuts off the hemp seed, leaving the mycelium undisturbed and intact. This prevents the tangling that results when the mycelia are handled with needles and forceps. Hemp seed with mycelium bearing resistant sporangia may be removed from the culture dish to filter paper, allowed to air-dry, and be stored for months and used again as inoculum.

SAPROLEGNIA AND ACHLYA

These organisms and related genera are of widespread occurrence in fresh water and may be obtained by using boiled hemp seed or small insects (*Drosophila*) as bait. They may be isolated also from soil suspensions in water. Petri dishes half-filled with pond water or a suspension of soil in charcoal water are baited with the hemp seed. Within 72 hours to a week, a mycelial halo will be visible macroscopically on some of the hemp seed. These seeds may be lifted from the culture dish and examined microscopically at low magnification. Desired species may then be transferred to separate dishes and baited with fresh hemp seed in charcoal water. In preparing material for class study, the hemp seed which bears the desired water mold is transferred to a petri dish to which about six half hemp seeds have been added. The stimulus of the transfer of the inoculum to the fresh medium usually effects liberation of the zoospores which assemble chemotactically on the uninoculated seed. At 22° C. under these conditions, zoosporangia appear on the new mycelium within 48 to 72 hours. The asexual stages may be maintained by transfer every three or four days. For demonstrating zoospore discharge, the hemp seed fragment should be lifted into a drop of fresh charcoal water on a slide. Zoospore liberation usually follows in a short time. Cultures containing strains which are potentially sexual will produce sexual stages if the cultures are not transferred too often. This usually occurs in cultures 4 to 8 days old. Gemmae are produced abundantly in charcoal water cultures.

RHIZOPUS AND RELATED MOLDS

Living material of *Rhizopus, Mucor,* and related genera frequently appear on a variety of substrata such as bread, oatmeal, and fruit if these are stored in a warm moist atmosphere. They also grow as contaminants on agar plates being used for the cultivation of other organisms. However, named cultures are maintained in a number of laboratories and may be purchased from the American Type Culture Collection and several biological supply houses. Once obtained, the cultures are easy to maintain and may be stored in the refrigerator and transferred several times a year. Most forms make adequate growth on PDA. The heterothallic races of *Rhizopus nigricans* are favorable for study of both the asexual and sexual phases. A common error in preparing material of this fungus for laboratory study is to provide cultures that are too old. At temperatures between 22° and 25° C., petri dish cultures on potato dextrose agar three to four days old are best for demonstrating stages in sporangium development. To demonstrate topography, one sealed petri dish should be available for study with a wide-field binocular microscope. The stolon-like hyphae, rhizoidal branches, erect sporangiophores, and sporangia are strikingly revealed in this way, whereas they are disturbed and torn when the petri dishes are opened. Because of the tendency of the living spores and mycelium to hold adherent films of air, the cultures should be flooded with 70% alcohol immediately before study. Blocks of agar may then be cut out of the petri dish cultures and mounted on slides and covered. The diluted 70% alcohol from the petri dish should be used as the mounting fluid. In preparing material for studying the sexual stages, the "plus" and "minus" mating types should be inoculated on opposite sides of petri dishes of sterile agar about 5 to 7 days before they are to be studied. Cultures should be flooded with 70% alcohol for study. Abundant sexual stages should be present along the region where the compatible mycelia have intermingled. *Phycomyces nitens* produces more spectacular lines of zygospores between the "plus" and "minus" mycelia because of the dark appendages of the suspensors, which make the line of zygospores macroscopically visible.

Pilobolus usually develops when fresh horse dung (24 to 48 hours old) is incubated in covered glass dishes. When these are illuminated with unilateral light, the sporangia are ejected toward the light source.

ALBUGO

Material of *Albugo* on such hosts as *Amaranthus* and *Ipomoea* usually is abundant in the autumn. Dried and pressed leaves of these hosts infected with the fungus represent adequate habit material. Scraping some of the infected area into drops of water provides conidiosporangia for microscopic study.

Ascomycota

YEASTS

Pure cultures of several species of *Schizosaccharomyces* and *Saccharomyces* grown on PDA or other organic media are excellent for study of these organisms. Week-old cultures of *Schizosaccharomyces octosporus* on agar in petri dishes usually provide good material to show uniting cells and ascospore formation. Tube slant cultures of *Saccharomyces cerevisiae* flooded with a 5% cane sugar solution to which a few drops of fresh orange juice have been added yield excellent budding material if the cultures are incubated at 30° to 37° C. Staining the cells of *S. octosporus* with aceto-carmine is a rapid method for demonstrating the residual cytoplasm among the ascospores.

ASPERGILLUS, PENICILLIUM, AND NEUROSPORA

Cultures of *Aspergillus* and *Penicillium* may be readily started on bread and cooked fruits and jellies exposed to the air and kept moist. These fungi are frequent contaminants of petri dish cultures of bacteria. Various species of *Penicillium* may be demonstrated readily on moldy fruits and in several kinds of cheese as well as on mildewed cloth. These fungi, when grown on PDA in petri dishes, are especially favorable for laboratory study. *Penicillium* cultures should be inoculated about a week in advance of study. When colonies of adequate size have developed, in each of which a whitish peripheral mycelium (the nonfruiting portion) remains, the cultures should be flooded with 70% alcohol. Cultures may be retained for several days in this condition. Inasmuch as the flooded cultures no longer show the characteristic color, one or more sealed dishes should be retained unflooded, for demonstration. *Aspergillus* also is studied most satisfactorily from flooded cultures. With a sharp scalpel, remove a small portion of the agar surface with the adherent mycelium, place it on a slide and immerse in 70% alcohol, cover, and squash gently with an eraser. At least some of the conidiospores will remain on the conidiophores with this treatment.

A number of species of *Aspergillus* and *Penicillium* which form cleistothecia and ascospores in culture are available in culture collections. *Aspergillus chevalieri* (Mangin) Thom and Church, inoculated on potato dextrose agar in petri dishes, forms abundant ascogonial coils within 10 days after inoculation at 25° C. Cleistothecia with mature asci and ascospores develop luxuriantly in cultures about a month old.

Neurospora sitophila, an eight-spored species, is widely cultivated in university laboratories and grows well on PDA. A number of compatible mating types are known. One race produces few conidiospores but abundant protoperithecia which, however, will not develop mature ascospores unless they are "diploidized" by compatible nuclei of another strain. The proper strains are inoculated on opposite sides of PDA agar plates. The ascospores are rather slow in maturing; they may be observed by crushing perithecia removed to microscope slides. Satisfactory views of ripe perithecia are obtained using the wide-field binocular microscope. Fixation of portions of the culture, at various periods in its development, in a mixture of 3 parts of absolute alcohol to 1 of glacial acetic acid after the mixture has been saturated with ferric acetate, provides good material for study when the perithecia are opened and the asci squashed in aceto-carmine stain (saturated solution in 45% acetic acid). The perithecial wall remnants should be removed from the preparation before squashing. Heating the preparation darkens the nuclear stain.

THE POWDERY MILDEWS

Material of powdery mildews is abundant on a variety of hosts during the late summer and early fall. The rose mildew, *Sphaerotheca pannosum,* usually is available in the garden or in greenhouses where roses are cultivated. Cleistothecial stages of a number of mildews occur in the autumn on such hosts as Virginia creeper, lilac, plantain, etc. The leaves may be dried and used subsequently for habit material. Infected portions of the leaves, when studied under 100X magnification without water or a cover glass and with reflected light, are satisfactory for general features. Crushed preparations of the cleistothecia show the asci and spores.

THE CUP FUNGI

The cup fungi present a challenge to the preparateur of botanical materials for a number of reasons. Apothecia preserved in liquid lose their color and may become soft and fragile. Sexual stages are known for only a few of these genera and often are not available at the proper time. Although its apothecia are small, *Pyronema* is a desirable type because the reproductive process in it has been investigated so thoroughly. It may be collected from burned-over soil and charcoal and appears on steam-sterilized soil in greenhouses. Dried substrata and apothecia have a remarkably natural appearance after they have been moistened. Cultures of *Pyronema* may be isolated by starting with germinating ascospores. Professor Richard C. Starr[3] has developed a simple method for inducing production of sex organs and apothecia in agar cultures, and these have been repeated a number of times by the author. The *Pyronema* mycelium, which does not form conidia, may be maintained in tubes or flasks of potato dextrose agar (Difco) or bacteriological "nutrient agar" (Difco). To induce formation of sex organs and apothecia, half-inch squares of agar and mycelium from a recently transferred culture on potato dextrose or "nutrient" agar should be placed, mycelium side down, in the center of a petri dish containing solidified IA or ISA. The petri dishes should be stored in an illuminated spot. The sex organs appear on the mycelium at the periphery of the dishes within three or four days. This occurred repeatedly for Dr. Starr and the author at a temperature of 22° C. with an illumination of 300 to 400 foot-candles. Apothecia and mature ascospores are produced under such conditions. Furthermore, the ascospores may be ejected and may germinate in these cultures. The apothecia are readily prepared for study in the living condition by crushing them gently. Apothecia of *Pyronema* and other cup fungi, when fixed in 3:1 absolute alcohol-glacial acetic acid (the acetic acid saturated with ferric acetate), softened for a few minutes in 80% alcohol, and then crushed and stained in aceto-carmine, yield instructive preparations of ascospore development, including nuclear divisions in the ascus and free-cell formation.

Patella and *Bulgaria* apothecia are often encountered in moist situations and may be preserved in 70% alcohol or dried and moistened several hours before they are to be studied. Sections and crushed prepara-

---

[3] Personal communication.

tions of these provide material adequate for the study of asci, ascospores, and paraphyses.

Basidiomycota

RUSTS

The telial and uredinial stages of a number of races of *Puccinia* are widespread on grasses and cereal grains. The leaves and stems may be dried or preserved in formalin solution. The aecial stage on *Berberis* is usually available only by purchase from biological supply houses, although the aecial stages of other rusts may be substituted. Instructive views of the telia, uredinia, and aecia may be observed with the wide-field binocular microscope. Buller's treatise (1909–1950) on the fungi describes methods of germinating teliospores of rusts. Those of the cedar-apple rust, *Gymnosporangium*, germinate readily in drops of distilled water on slides stored in moist chambers. Experience will reveal the time factor in relation to the formation of the basidium, its segmentation, and the production and ejection of basidiospores. Teliospores remain viable for long periods when stored in the refrigerator.

THE SMUTS

Germination of mature smut spores of a number of types is readily effected in distilled water on slides in moist chambers. They may also be germinated in dilute bacterial beef broth or on PDA agar. Fruiting material of wheat smut, corn smut, and oat smut is usually abundant at the time of harvest of these cereal grains.

THE MUSHROOMS

Mycelium of mushrooms, the vegetative stage of the fungus, grows readily on potato dextrose agar. Cultures are available in a number of laboratories and in the American Type Culture Collection. Spore prints of mushrooms may be prepared by placing the pilei of several species on appropriately colored paper and covering them with bell jars. Spore germination usually occurs readily in tap water or on potato dextrose agar. Crushed preparations of the gills of fresh mushrooms provide excellent views of the basidia and spores.

PORE FUNGI

Basidiocarps of wood-destroying pore fungi usually are abundant in forested areas and may be dried for future study. Sections of the fleshy

Boletus furnish instructive preparations of the fruiting system of pore fungi. Cultures of the mycelia of a number of species of *Polyporus* grow readily on PDA.

Lichens

Living material of lichens is usually available locally. Freshly gathered thalli may be dissected into small fragments which reveal the dual nature of the plants. Apothecial material is seasonally abundant. Introduction of portions of the lichen thallus, previously washed in sterile water, into flasks containing such an inorganic solution as IL may initiate cultures of the algal component.

LABORATORY MATERIALS ON LIVERWORTS, HEPATOPHYTA (Chapter 15)

Other than the leafy liverworts—*Porella* and *Frullania*, for example —dried specimens of Hepatophyta rarely are satisfactory for class study. The ease with which most liverworts can be maintained in culture for relatively long periods is a boon to those who seek to stimulate interest through the use of living materials. Few groups of plants are less inspiring when preserved or dried than thallose liverworts, including *Anthoceros*. Almost all the type genera discussed in this text may be collected in the field or purchased alive from biological supply houses.

Mature spores of many liverworts (except those with a dormant period, like *Fossombronia* and *Sphaerocarpos*) germinate readily on ISA medium. Mature phases of a number of liverworts can be grown from these spores if the plants are transferred with sufficient frequency. For merely the early stages of germination, IA medium is adequate in many cases, and it averts some of the danger of fungus contamination of the germlings.

A number of liverworts undergo fertilization in the late summer and autumn, but their sporophytes do not mature until the following spring. *Pallavicinia, Pellia* and *Porella,* and *Frullania* are in this category. Specimens of these species collected in the winter may be forced in the greenhouse with little trouble. The plants may be stored in moist chambers that are suitably ventilated, and watered only when really necessary. In this way the meiotic phases in sporogenesis, elongation of the setae, dehiscence of the capsule, and liberation of the spores may be demonstrated in the living material.

In addition to species which may thus be forced each season, a number grow well under continuous greenhouse cultivation. These include

Riccia fluitans (on sandy soil and in aquaria), *Ricciocarpus natans* (on sand and floating in aquaria), and *Marchantia* species. *M. polymorpha* grows well in rather full light, on sandy soil to which charcoal and/or wood ashes are added in powdered form. There is some evidence that prolonged greenhouse cultivation, without intermittent freezing, cuts down the abundance of antheridiophore and archegoniophore formation. Gemmae of *Marchantia* planted on IA in petri dishes provide instructive preparations of the development of the plant body. Segments of thalli with gemmae cups, placed on the same medium, continue to grow and produce gemmae which emerge from the cups without benefit of splashing water.

Pellia, Pallavicinia, Sphaerocarpos, and *Anthoceros* all flourish in the greenhouse under suitable conditions. Although the instructor usually is obliged to serve as caretaker for these plants in spite of the presence of a regular gardener, a great deal of knowledge accrues from such pursuits.

While microtomed stained sections of liverworts and other plants are now indispensable adjuncts to understanding their structure and development, study of sections of living material, cut free-hand, with and without the use of elder pith, goes far toward enhancing the student's real understanding of and familiarity with plants. The "cactus" cells of *Marchantia* and surface views of the air pores are striking structures in sections of living material. The presence of chlorophyll in the developing liverwort sporophyte escaped detection for a hundred years because the art of free-hand sectioning of living materials was abandoned in favor of microtomed sections. Currently, of course, in both botany and zoology there is a great revival of study of living tissues.

The time for collecting sexual material and material with sporophytes of each of the liverwort genera must be learned by experience in one's local surroundings. *Riccia, Ricciocarpus, Pellia, Pallavicinia, Sphaerocarpos,* and the leafy liverworts are usually spring-fruiting forms, with reference to the sporophyte.

Finally, one of the most satisfactory materials for the study of living cells in division, namely, the sporophyte of *Anthoceros,* is often unappreciated and superficially examined. Sporophytes which are just beginning to turn dark at the tips provide a rather complete series in sporogenesis. The sporophytes should be cut transversely in segments short enough to fit under the cover glass; they should then be arranged in order on the slide and each segment bisected with a sharp razor blade. Half of each cylindrical segment should be mounted, outer surface up and half inner surface up. This will provide clear views of the development of the stomata and guard cells as well as of the stages in sporogenesis and elater formation. Division of the chloroplasts prior to nuclear division in the spore mother cells is demonstrated readily in such preparations.

LABORATORY MATERIALS ON MOSSES, BRYOPHYTA (Chapter 16)

Sphagnopsida

Aquatic and marshy habitats of sufficiently low pH usually harbor more or less extensive masses of one or another species of *Sphagnum*. The pale-green plants survive for long periods in well-illuminated places in the greenhouse if they are protected from desiccation. Fruiting plants with sporophytes are of frequent occurrence during the summer and early autumn. Sex organs usually develop in late autumn and persist during the winter. Young sporophytes are present very early in the spring. The male branches often are recognizable by their reddish pigment.

Mature spores of *Sphagnum* survive storage in air-dry vials for a number of months. These or freshly collected spores germinate rapidly when planted on ISA medium in petri dishes. Probably acidification of the medium by addition of a few drops of peat decoction would enhance growth. The spatulate protonemata and young leafy gametophores develop in such petri dish cultures, provided they receive adequate illumination.

Mnionopsida

An abundance of moss material may usually be collected in a given locality. *Funaria* spores are especially favorable for starting agar cultures (ISA) for protonemata. If illuminated, spores sown on the surface of agar germinate within 5 to 7 days. For study of germination stages, small bits of agar with the spores may be transferred to slides in a drop of ISL medium or other isotonic solution. At 22° C. with 12-hour daily illumination at 150 foot-candles, the protonemata spread rapidly over the agar surface; gametophore development may begin as early as 45 days after the spores were sown. For study, the leafy gametophores and subtending protonema (now rhizoidal in function) may be lifted from agar cultures and studied in individual mounts. Development of the protonema and gametophores also occurs on IA medium. Spores of *Funaria* sown on sandy soil containing charcoal have been raised to sexual maturity and to the sporophytic stage in cool greenhouses.

Funaria in mild climates appears in the vegetative stage late in the fall or early winter. The sex organs are produced abundantly while the plants are small. Protandry is marked in *Funaria*. *Funaria* plants collected in this stage may be kept in the greenhouse and forced. If watered from above, development of numerous sporophytes and their maturation follow. Mature sporophytes of *Funaria* dried at room temperatures and stored furnish material for spore germination for a number of years, although the germination rate gradually falls. Although the reproductive structures of *Funaria* have long been studied and illustrated, the moss is too small for student study, unless wide-field binocular microscopes are available.

Polytrichum and *Atrichum,* especially the former, are larger mosses which are widely distributed and suitable for class study. Both these genera are heterothallic. In *Polytrichum* and *Atrichum angustatum,* the antheridia and archegonia often mature in the summer and early fall, and fertilization and early stages in embryogeny occur duing the late autumn and winter. The sporophytes then mature in large numbers in the spring and early summer. It is probable that there is seasonal and geographical variation in this pattern. Although living material always is superior, dried plants with antheridia, archegonia, and sporophytes have a remarkably fresh appearance when moistened.

Living antheridia of such mosses as *Funaria, Physcomitrium, Mnium, Atrichum,* and *Polytrichum* are excellent for the demonstration of liberation of the sperm mass and the inception of motility of the individual sperms. Material collected several days before the class is to study it should be kept in a moist chamber, but not watered. Shortly before the class convenes, the cover of the moist chamber may be removed to effect additional drying. Antheridia squeezed from the male heads by the thumb and index finger or removed by dissection into a drop of water usually shed the sperm mass promptly. When the preparations have been covered with a cover glass, examination of the margins and surface of the sperm mass will reveal the stages in motility and liberation.

VASCULAR CRYPTOGAMS (Chapters 17–23)

In the vascular cryptogams, the type plants are fewer in number but increasingly complex. The gross features of the living plants, although quite distinctive, must be supplemented by histological and morphological microscopic preparations for thorough understanding of the several type genera.

Psilophyta

Psilotum, a plant which is native in the United States only in southern Florida, is cultivated in the greenhouses of many universities and may be purchased under the name "whisk fern" from dealers in tropical plants and from certain biological supply houses. The rhizomes seem to prefer a soil rich in organic matter such as decaying leaf mold, and the plants thrive with frequent applications of bone meal and under strong illumination. Fruiting branches are usually present continuously, but are especially numerous during the winter and early spring.

Free-hand sections of the living stem, both transverse and longitudinal, are instructive when compared with stained microtomed sections. Crushed preparations of a series of sporangia, collected in order beginning near the apex, furnish a magnificent display of stages in sporogenesis and meiosis, if stained with aceto-carmine and heated gently.

The gametophytes of *Psilotum,* up to the present, have been one of the rarest materials in the plant kingdom. However, recent papers (Bierhorst, 1953) indicate that they are occasionally abundant in greenhouses, if they are sought for in the proper location and with the proper techniques. Bierhorst has raised gametophytes to maturity by planting spores in the soil of potted greenhouse plants.

Microphyllophyta

LYCOPODIUM

Apparently, few people have successfully cultivated *Lycopodium* unless there are available the soil and proximity to natural habitat demanded by members of this genus. Here as in the mosses, however, dried plants when moistened are sufficiently lifelike to afford a good concept of the habit of growth. For study of the strobili, preserved material usually is necessary for those far from *Lycopodium* habitats.

Gametophytes of *Lycopodium* are available in increasingly large numbers from biological supply houses. Rather detailed directions for collecting them in nature have been published by Eames (1942). Although the spores of *Lycopodium* (and *Psilotum, Ophioglossum,* and *Botrychium*) have been germinated and carried through the early stages of gametophyte development in laboratory culture, special techniques are probably necessary. The spores of *L. cernuum,* a southern species, grow readily into mature gametophytes in laboratory culture (Wetmore and Morel, 1951). Freeburg and Wetmore recently have succeeded with other species by scarifying the spores.

SELAGINELLA

Selaginella species are widely cultivated under glass as ornamentals and are frequently encountered in ornamental terraria. Potted in sandy soil and fertilized periodically with small amounts of bone meal, many species thrive in Wardian cases and produce strobili with viable spores.

After many attempts, the writer has recently been successful in germinating the spores of *Selaginella* which later produced mature male and female gametophytes. Strobili placed in dry petri dishes (and covered) eject their spores for some distance. These spores, planted on plaster of Paris blocks whose lower surface is immersed in distilled water or IL medium, produced mature female gametophytes in about 90 days. The male gametophytes matured more rapidly. However, more retarded spores in the same cultures continued to develop gametophytes for the next 60 days. The plaster blocks were soaked for some time before they were used in changes of distilled water. The inoculated blocks were placed in finger bowls, covered, and stored in the greenhouse.

ISOETES

Aquatic species of *Isoetes* planted in shallow pots and submerged in aquaria and shallow tanks grow under greenhouse conditions. Terrestrial species, like *I. butleri*, may be transplanted from their natural habitat to pots which may be "forced" from a dormant condition when required for study. Few investigators have succeeded in germinating the spores of *Isoetes* in any great numbers. At least in terrestrial species, there are indications that dormancy and desiccation are prerequisite to germination.

Arthrophyta

Although *Equisetum arvense* is a widely distributed and abundant plant in many parts of the country, where it occurs in sandy fields and on railroad embankments, it is less abundant in others. However, it thrives after it is transplanted either to large pots or to specially prepared beds. Pots left out-of-doors during the winter months may be forced by bringing them into the greenhouse. *Equisetum hyemale* grows readily inside and outside the greenhouse and fruits abundantly in sunny locations. Although meiosis occurs in *E. arvense* when the strobili are still below the soil, *E. hyemale* furnishes convenient material for the study of sporogenesis when squashes are prepared by the aceto-carmine method, as for *Psilotum*. Transverse sections of living stems should be compared with fixed and stained sections. Study of the stem surfaces and stomatal arrangement with the aid of the wide-field binocular is very instructive.

The autotrophic gametophytes of *Equisetum arvense* and *E. hyemale* develop readily in suitable laboratory cultures. Strobili, surface-sterilized by rapidly passing them through a flame, or by other methods, and then crushed over the surface of ISA medium in petri dishes, liberate large numbers of spores. Surface sterilization cuts down on contamination by fungi, which, however, are usually not injurious. In cultures in which the spores are not too closely aggregated, typical mound-like gametophytes with photosynthetic lobes arise in culture. On ISA medium, at 22° C., with 12-hour periods of illumination of an intensity of 150 foot-candles each day, the cultures grow luxuriantly and may produce antheridia in abundance within 30 days. Archegonia appear with less regularity, but occasional young sporophytes arising in the cultures testify to their presence. Spore germination itself is extremely rapid in *Equisetum*. Like all spores which are thin-walled and green at maturity, the spores of *Equisetum* do not remain viable long after they are shed. Gametophytes may be maintained for long periods on agar provided they are transferred with sufficient frequency.

Pterophyta

OPHIOGLOSSUM AND BOTRYCHIUM

Other than the widely distributed *O. engelmanni* of limestone regions, species of *Ophioglossum* are usually not strikingly abundant members of the flora. *O. engelmanni* is readily transplanted and may be maintained in pots or out-of-doors near the greenhouse. Pots overwintered outside respond well to forcing. In some parts of the country, two crops of leaves emerge each year, one in the spring and a second during the early autumn rains. The writer and his students have searched assiduously in the soil under and near large beds of *O. engelmanni* but have never succeeded in finding gametophytes. However, large colonies of *Ophioglossum* usually result from vegetative reproduction.

Species of *Botrychium* are more widely distributed. Their gametophytes are long-persistent, and very young plants, when carefully dug up, often have gametophytes at their bases.

Aceto-carmine squashes of small portions of the fertile spikes of these genera, previously fixed in 3:1 absolute alcohol-glacial acetic acid mixture saturated with ferric acetate (3:1 FA), yield magnificent preparations of sporogenesis and the meiotic process. The metaphase plates of

Ophioglossum spore mother cells contain approximately 256 chromosomes.

OSMUNDA

The three common species of *Osmunda* are abundant in the wild in many parts of the country and survive well upon transplanting. The spore mother cells of these ferns, with their relatively low chromosome numbers, yield striking preparations of meiosis which may be prepared in a matter of minutes from previously fixed material (3:1 FA) undergoing sporogenesis. (Such material may be stored after fixation in 70% alcohol.) The spores of *Osmunda* species, like those of *Equisetum*, must be planted soon after they mature. ISA medium is especially satisfactory, as are also flower pots of sterile sand watered with 1L solution. The rather massive gametophytes may be retained for long periods under cultivation. Antheridia and archegonia often develop within 60 days after the spores are planted.

POLYPODIACEOUS FERNS

The choice of ferns to be studied in the laboratory will vary with their availability in the greenhouse and in local natural environments. Leaves showing both immature sori and those whose sporangia are dehiscing should be provided. Until they are to be studied, the leaves should be stored in water under a bell jar to prevent wilting. Although spore dissemination and sporangial dehiscence occur rapidly in material scraped into drops of glycerin, another method is perhaps more striking. A portion of a pinna bearing sori with mature sporangia is placed, with the sorus surface up, on a dry slide without a cover glass. The preparation should then be examined under the 100X magnification of the microscope or with the several magnifications supplied by a wide-field binocular, in either case with reflected light. The forceful and continuous ejection of spores is very striking when observed in this manner.

Fern gametophytes may be sought for and found in nature or in the moist soil and cinders of greenhouse benches, but a far more reliable expedient is to grow them from spores. This may be done in a number of ways with a minimum of effort and equipment. Just-mature sori should be allowed to discharge their spores upon white paper by placing a frond sorus side down. The spores may be blown or dusted over the surface where they are to be germinated. Care should be taken not to sow them too thickly. Various substrata are satisfactory, among them the plaster blocks alluded to with reference to *Selaginella,* fresh *Sphagnum* moss in finger bowls, peat moss, sand, soil, and clean flower pots filled with *Sphagnum* or peat and inverted under a bell jar. All these substrata may be watered with one or another solution of inorganic salts. IL is satisfactory for this purpose. The writer prefers to grow the gametophytes of such ferns as cultivated species of *Pteris, Adiantum,* and *Dryopteris* on IA medium in petri dishes. Spore germination of *Dryopteris* reaches a stage suitable for study in about 8 to 10 days. Sex organs often begin to appear on the gametophytes as early as 45 days after the spores have been sown. If liquid water is withheld, they continue to be produced for some months, provided the agar substratum remains moist enough. Formation of young sporophytes may be evoked by watering the sexually mature gametophytes with IL solution several times.

Dehiscence of the antheridia and spreading of the cover cells of the archegonia, as well as liberation of the sperms and their entry into the archegonial necks, are not difficult to demonstrate with laboratory-grown prothallia immersed in distilled water or IL solution and studied microscopically. Prothallia with young sporophytes may be transplanted to well-spaced positions on fresh petri dishes of IA or ISA agar and their further development may be followed. Such embryonic sporophytes of *Dryopteris,* ultimately transferred to pots of soil, produced spores after three years in the writer's greenhouse.

MARSILEA

Although *Marsilea* is not widely distributed in this country, several species are under cultivation in greenhouses and may be obtained from biological supply houses. *Marsilea* grows especially well under greenhouse treatment. The plants flourish in ordinary pots of soil if watered sufficiently and maintained in a sunny location. Extensive stolon development occurs in shallow trays filled with sand and submerged in water. Pots sunken in indoor and outside pools produce floating leaves if the water depth is sufficient. Three species of *Marsilea* have overwintered in a pool when the temperature fell to 15° below zero for three consecutive days.

Pot-bound plants in soil frequently form sporocarps at the surface of the soil. These may be dried and stored at maturity, and they supply a source of material for demonstration of the gametophytes. Mature sporocarps may also be purchased from biological supply companies.

Demonstration of the "germination" of the sporocarp and the megaspores and microspores, fertilization, and embryogeny are strikingly clear in *Marsilea* and are rapid and dynamic processes which should be available for study. The sporocarps should be nicked at the pole opposite their peduncle and immersed in small petri dishes with distilled water or IL solution. Emergence of the sporophore begins within a short time, and the later stages follow, as described in the text. Several plantings of two or three sporocarps, at appropriate intervals before the class is to convene, usually provide ample material to illustrate the reproductive cycle. Embryonic sporophytes of *M. vestita* initiated in April one year, grew into mature, sporocarp-producing plants by the following October when planted in pots in greenhouse soil.

OTHER PTEROPHYTA

Lygodium, Ceratopteris, Cyathea, Salvinia, and *Azolla* all grow readily even in limited greenhouse space. *Ceratopteris,* which may be purchased in many aquarium supply companies and pet shops, grows well as a floating plant in pools and aquaria. *Cyathea,* a tree fern, may be purchased from a number of nurserymen in the southern part of the country. *Cyathea* grows well in tub culture. *Salvinia* and *Azolla* are floating plants which may be maintained in aquaria in full sunlight. *Lygodium* is widely distributed in university greenhouses and may be purchased. The native *L. palmatum* does not thrive in greenhouse culture.

THE SEED PLANTS (Chapters 24–29)

Although the reproductive process in seed plants is of such a nature as to require many microtomed stained sections for its demonstration, a number of its aspects become more real if living material is examined as a supplement.

The Cycads

Zamia and *Cycas,* living plants of which are available from dealers in tropical plants, grow without special treatment in sunny greenhouses. Sufficiently mature specimens of these plants regularly develop strobili. Sporogenesis in the microsporangia in these and most seed plants may be demonstrated effectively by the aceto-carmine squash method; prior fixation with 3:1 FA may be beneficial. The same technique demonstrates with great clarity the intrasporal stages in the development of the male gametophytes. Mounting the microspores of these plants in Chamberlain's iodine solution also renders these stages readily observable. Other representative cycad genera may be present in municipal and other conservatory collections.

Ginkgo

Ginkgo biloba is extensively cultivated in many parts of this country and abroad and justifiably so. Mature microsporangiate and ovulate trees are often present on college campuses or the grounds of public institutions. The microstrobili and ovules appear among the leaves of certain spur shoots as they emerge early in the spring. The aceto-carmine and iodine techniques are useful also in *Ginkgo* in demonstrating microsporogenesis and the early stages of gametophyte development within the microspores. Examination of living ovules and their micropyles at the time of pollination is especially instructive. *Ginkgo* seeds germinate readily in the greenhouse and provide a supply of plants to illustrate the juvenile stages.

Pinus and Other Conifers

Few parts of the world are entirely lacking in some representative of the coniferous group, of which *Pinus* is the most frequently studied genus in the northern hemisphere. Dissection of living microstrobili and megastrobili at various stages of development, with the aid of the wide-field binocular microscope, provides a useful supplement to the study of stained sections. The aceto-carmine and iodine methods again are useful in demonstrating microsporogenesis and the early development of the male gametophyte. Observations of local specimens with reference to time of emergence of microstrobili and megastrobili, time of pollination and behavior of the pollen and pollination droplet, time required for maturation of the seed and its liberation all are worth-while adjuncts to the formal laboratory study of stained preparations. Dissemination of the seed and its germination may be readily demonstrated from suitable material.

Ephedra

Ephedra is native to the southwestern portions of the United States, and elsewhere it may be cultivated in greenhouses. *E. foliata,* an Indian species, may be found in a number of greenhouse collections. The seeds of *Ephedra* germinate readily in ordinary soil. Branches of the living plants, shipped in parafilm, survive remarkably well in transit and furnish excellent material for the study of microsporogenesis and the grosser aspects of reproduction. The fact that species of *Ephedra* survive out-of-doors in the Botanical Garden at Kew and at Ann Arbor, Michigan, suggests that *Ephedra* might well be cultivated more widely in the temperate zone. The aceto-carmine method, without prior fixation, yields magnificent preparations of microsporogenesis and male gametogenesis.

Flowering Plants

In spite of the almost limitless types of angiosperms available for study, lily continues to be the favorite material for the demonstration of the reproductive process in the flowering plants, regardless of its deviations from the "normal" type. Study of stained slides should be supplemented with material from a number of types of living flowers. Microsporogenesis in corn and lily and the formation of the generative and tube nuclei in these genera are readily demonstrated with the aceto-carmine squash method. *Torenia*, a widely grown annual available in greenhouse culture and gardens, is of interest in that the micropylar pole of the female gametophyte is protuberant at maturity; hence the egg apparatus may be observed readily. Germinating pollen grains may be crushed from styles and stigmas, especially the hollow types like those of *Viola*, or they may be germinated in sugar solutions with or without agar. The writer maintains a number of flasks of 1.5% agar dissolved in cane sugar concentrations of 1, 3, 5, 7, 10, and 15%. Drops of melted agar from this series, after they have congealed on clean slides, provide a suitable surface for sowing pollen grains of locally available flowers. Some grains usually germinate in one of the sugar concentrations in this series. The inoculated slides are stored in moist chambers and are examined for germination from time to time.

Seed germination and seedlings of angiosperms, often neglected in the laboratory, are topics which stimulate student interest. Seeds of garden bean, pea, corn, and castor bean germinated in moist peat provide a fairly representative series.

PLANT FOSSILS (Chapter 30)

The availability of fossil plant material in one's locality depends, of course, on location and the strata exposed. Members of the geology department are helpful in this connection. Paleobotanical materials often are available in the collections of geology departments. Conveniently located museums also provide material for this aspect of plant morphology.

A number of biological supply houses and private individuals prepare and offer for sale gross specimens and peels of fossil plants. If suitable petrifactions are available, instructive preparations can be made with little effort by the peel technique. Thick peels are useful when studied under the lower magnifications of the wide-field binocular with transmitted light.

LITERATURE CITED

Bierhorst, D. Structure and Development of the Gametophyte of *Psilotum nudum, Amer. Jour. Bot.*, 40:649–658, 1953.

Bold, H. C. The Cultivation of Algae, *Bot. Rev.*, 8:69–138, 1942.

Buller, A. H. *Researches on the Fungi*, Vols. 1–6, Longmans, Green and Co.; Vol. 7, Univ. Press, Toronto, 1909–1950.

Chamberlain, C. J. *Methods in Plant Histology*, Univ. of Chicago Press, 1935.

Eames, A. J. Illustrations of Some *Lycopodium* Gametophytes, *Amer. Fern Jour.*, 32:1–12, 1942.

Emerson, R. An Experimental Study of the Life Cycles and Taxonomy of *Allomyces, Lloydia*, 4:77–144, 1941.

Föyn, B. Lebenzyklus, Cytologie und Sexualität der Chlorophycee Cladophora Suhriana Kützing, *Arch. f. Protistenk.*, 83:1–56, 1934.

Humm, H. Marine Algae in Test Tubes, *Turtox News 26*, No. 1:11–12, 1948.

Pringsheim, E. G. *Pure Cultures of Algae, Their Preparation and Maintenance*, Cambridge Univ. Press, 1946.

Pringsheim, E. G. The Soil-water Culture Technique for Growing Algae, in *The Culturing of Algae, a Symposium*, Kettering Foundation, 1950.

Schreiber, E. Untersuchungen über Parthenogenesis, Geschlechtsbestimmung und Bastardierungsvermögen bei Laminarien, *Planta*, 12:331–353, 1930.

Wetmore, R. H., and Morel, Georges. Sur la Culture in vitro de prothalles de *Lyocopodium cernuum, Comp. Rend. d. l'Academ. Sci. Paris*, 233:323–324, 1951.

INDEX

653

Format by D. F. Bradley
Composition by Kingsport Press, Inc.
Set in Linotype Caledonia
Lithography by The Murray Printing Company
Binding by The Haddon Craftsmen, Inc.